MATHEMATICAL TABLES

OF ELEMENTARY *AND* SOME HIGHER MATHEMATICAL FUNCTIONS

By

HERBERT BRISTOL DWIGHT

THIRD REVISED AND ENLARGED EDITION

DOVER PUBLICATIONS, INC.
NEW YORK

Published in Canada by General Publishing Company, Ltd., 30 Lesmill Road, Don Mills, Toronto, Ontario.

Published in the United Kingdom by Constable and Company, Ltd., 10 Orange Street, London WC 2.

This Dover edition, first published in 1961, is an enlarged and revised version of the work originally published by the McGraw-Hill Book Company, Inc., in 1941.

Library of Congress Catalog Card Number: 58-8523

Manufactured in the United States of America
Dover Publications, Inc.
180 Varick Street
New York, N. Y. 10014

CONTENTS

Contents

Contents

MATHEMATICAL TABLES

INTRODUCTION

This edition is an unabridged republication of the first edition, published by the McGraw-Hill Book Company, Inc. in 1941, to which has been added a considerable number of tables, including those of a number of types of Bessel functions.

In the use of tables, a good number of significant figures are needed not only in the value of the function but also in that of the argument. To obtain the latter, interpolation is used, and this can be done much more conveniently if differences are given.

Differences are shown at the right-hand side of most of the tables in this book. For the greater part the differences are small and interpolation can be done with a slide rule or, in most cases, mentally.

In the trigonometric tables in this book, decimals of degrees to 1/100 degree are used instead of degrees, minutes and seconds which are in many ways less convenient than decimals. The same advantages of a decimal system that are experienced in the use of meters and centimeters in place of feet and inches are found in these tables.

A growing number of mathematical results are now expressed in decimals of degrees and to use these it is almost necessary to employ tables of sines and tangents, etc., of decimals of degrees such as those here given. Where calculating machines are used, a decimal system is usually employed.

Although the numbers in this book have been carefully checked, some errors doubtless occur, and the author would consider it a favor to be informed of any of them.

Acknowledgment is made of valued help and suggestions from Professor Philip Franklin of the Department of Mathematics, Massachusetts Institute of Technology.

Useful and very complete lists of numerical tables, with many descriptive details, may be found in "An Index of Mathematical Tables" by A. Fletcher, J. C. P. Miller, and L. Rosenhead (McGraw-Hill Book Co., New York, 1946), and in "A Guide to Mathematical Tables, and Supplement No. 1" by A. V. Lebedev and R. M. Fedorova, translated into English by D. G. Fry (Pergamon Press, New York, 1960).

1961

HERBERT B. DWIGHT.

SQUARES n^2

n	0	1	2	3	4	5	6	7	8	9	Diff.
.10	.01 000	020	040	061	082	102	124	145	166	188	20-22
.11	210	232	254	277	300	322	346	369	392	416	22-24
.12	440	464	488	513	538	562	588	613	638	664	24-26
.13	690	716	742	769	796	822	850	877	904	932	26-28
.14	960	988	$\overline{016}$	$\overline{045}$	$\overline{074}$	$\overline{102}$	$\overline{132}$	$\overline{161}$	$\overline{190}$	$\overline{220}$	28-30
.15	.02 250	280	310	341	372	402	434	465	496	528	30-32
.16	560	592	624	657	690	722	756	789	822	856	32-34
.17	890	924	958	993	$\overline{028}$	$\overline{062}$	$\overline{098}$	$\overline{133}$	$\overline{168}$	$\overline{204}$	34-36
.18	.03 240	276	312	349	386	422	460	497	534	572	36-38
.19	610	648	686	725	764	802	842	881	920	960	38-40
.20	.04 000	040	080	121	162	202	244	285	326	368	40-42
.21	410	452	494	537	580	622	666	709	752	796	42-44
.22	840	884	928	973	$\overline{018}$	$\overline{062}$	$\overline{108}$	$\overline{153}$	$\overline{198}$	$\overline{244}$	44-46
.23	.05 290	336	382	429	476	522	570	617	664	712	46-48
.24	760	808	856	905	954	$\overline{002}$	$\overline{052}$	$\overline{101}$	$\overline{150}$	$\overline{200}$	48-50
.25	.06 250	300	350	401	452	502	554	605	656	708	50-52
.26	760	812	864	917	970	$\overline{022}$	$\overline{076}$	$\overline{129}$	$\overline{182}$	$\overline{236}$	52-54
.27	.07 290	344	398	$\overline{453}$	508	562	618	673	728	784	54-56
.28	840	896	952	$\overline{009}$	$\overline{066}$	$\overline{122}$	$\overline{180}$	$\overline{237}$	$\overline{294}$	$\overline{352}$	56-58
.29	.08 410	468	526	585	644	702	762	821	880	940	58-60
.30	.09 000	060	120	181	242	302	364	425	486	548	60-62
.31	610	672	734	797	860	922	986				62-64
.1								005	011	018	
.32	024	030	037	043	050	056	063	069	076	082	6-7
.33	089	096	102	109	116	122	129	136	142	149	
.34	156	163	170	176	183	190	197	204	211	218	
.35	225	232	239	246	253	260	267	274	282	289	7
.36	296	303	310	318	325	332	340	347	354	362	
.37	369	376	384	391	399	406	414	421	429	436	
.38	444	452	459	467	475	482	490	498	505	513	
.39	521	529	537	544	552	560	568	576	584	592	
.40	600	608	616	624	632	640	648	656	665	673	8
.41	681	689	697	706	714	722	731	739	747	756	
.42	764	772	781	789	798	806	815	823	832	840	
.43	849	858	866	875	884	892	901	910	918	927	
.44	936	945	954	962	971	980	989	998	$\overline{007}$	$\overline{016}$	
.45	.2 025	034	043	052	061	070	079	088	098	107	9
.46	116	125	134	144	153	162	172	181	190	200	
.47	209	218	228	237	247	256	266	275	285	294	
.48	304	314	323	333	343	352	362	372	381	391	
.49	401	411	421	430	440	450	460	470	480	490	
.50	500	510	520	530	540	550	560	570	581	591	10
.51	601	611	621	632	642	652	663	673	683	694	
.52	704	714	725	735	746	756	767	777	788	798	
.53	809	820	830	841	852	862	873	884	894	905	
.54	916	927	938	948	959	970	981	992	$\overline{003}$	$\overline{014}$	
.55	.3 025	036	047	058	069	080	091	102	114	125	11
.56	136	147	158	170	181	192	204	215	226	238	
.57	249	260	272	283	295	306	318	329	341	352	
.58	364	376	387	399	411	422	434	446	457	469	
.59	481	493	505	516	528	540	552	564	576	588	12

n	0	1	2	3	4	5	6	7	8	9	Diff.
.60	.3 600	612	624	636	648	660	672	684	697	709	12
.61	721	733	745	758	770	782	795	807	819	832	
.62	844	856	869	881	894	906	919	931	944	956	
.63	969	982	994	007	020	032	045	058	070	083	
.64	.4 096	109	122	134	147	160	173	186	199	212	
.65	225	238	251	264	277	290	303	316	330	343	13
.66	356	369	382	396	409	422	436	449	462	476	
.67	489	502	516	529	543	556	570	583	597	610	
.68	624	638	651	665	679	692	706	720	733	747	
.69	761	775	789	802	816	830	844	858	872	886	
.70	900	914	928	942	956	970	984	998	013	027	14
.71	.5 041	055	069	084	098	112	127	141	155	170	
.72	184	198	213	227	242	256	271	285	300	314	
.73	329	344	358	373	388	402	417	432	446	461	
.74	476	491	506	520	535	550	565	580	595	610	
.75	625	640	655	670	685	700	715	730	746	761	15
.76	776	791	806	822	837	852	868	883	898	914	
.77	929	944	960	975	991	006	022	037	053	068	
.78	.6 084	100	115	131	147	162	178	194	209	225	
.79	241	257	273	288	304	320	336	352	368	384	
.80	400	416	432	448	464	480	496	512	529	545	16
.81	561	577	593	610	626	642	659	675	691	708	
.82	724	740	757	773	790	806	823	839	856	872	
.83	889	906	922	939	956	972	989	006	022	039	
.84	.7 056	073	090	106	123	140	157	174	191	208	
.85	225	242	259	276	293	310	327	344	362	379	17
.86	396	413	430	448	465	482	500	517	534	552	
.87	569	586	604	621	639	656	674	691	709	726	
.88	744	762	779	797	815	832	850	868	885	903	
.89	921	939	957	974	992	010	028	046	064	082	
.90	.8 100	118	136	154	172	190	208	226	245	263	18
.91	281	299	317	336	354	372	391	409	427	446	
.92	464	482	501	519	538	556	575	593	612	630	
.93	649	668	686	705	724	742	761	780	798	817	
.94	836	855	874	892	911	930	949	968	987	006	
.95	.9 025	044	063	082	101	120	139	158	178	197	19
.96	216	235	254	274	293	312	332	351	370	390	
.97	409	428	448	467	487	506	526	545	565	584	
.98	604	624	643	663	683	702	722	742	761	781	
.99	801	821	841	860	880	900	920	940	960	980	20
1.00	1.0 000										

CUBES n^3

n	0	1	2	3	4	5	6	7	8	9	Diff.
.10	.001 000	030	061	093	125	158	191	225	260	295	30-36
.11	331	368	405	443	482	521	561	602	643	685	37-43
.12	728	772	816	861	907	953	000	048	097	147	44-50
.13	.002 197	248	300	353	406	460	515	571	628	686	51-58
.14	744	803	863	924	986	049	112	177	242	308	59-66
.15	.003 375	443	512	582	652	724	796	870	944	020	68-76
.16	.004 096	173	252	331	411	492	574	657	742	827	77-86
.17	913	000	088	178	268	359	452	545	640	735	87-97
.18	.005 832	930	029	128	230	332	435	539	645	751	98-108
.19	.006 859	968	.007 078	189	301	415	530	645	762	881	109-119
.20	.008 000	121	242	365	490	615	742	870	999	129	121-132
.21	.009 261	394	528	664	800	938	.01 008	022	036	050	133-138 / 14-15
.22	065	079	094	109	124	139	154	170	185	201	14-16
.23	217	233	249	265	281	298	314	331	348	365	14-16
.24	382	400	417	435	453	471	489	507	525	544	17-19
.25	562	581	600	619	639	658	678	697	717	737	19-21
.26	758	778	798	819	840	861	882	903	925	947	20-22
.27	968	990	012	035	057	080	102	125	148	172	22-24
.28	.02 195	219	243	267	291	315	339	364	389	414	24-25
.29	439	464	490	515	541	567	593	620	646	673	25-27
.30	700	727	754	782	809	837	865	893	922	950	27-29
.31	979	008	037	066	096	126	155	186	216	246	29-31
.32	.03 277	308	339	370	401	433	465	497	529	561	31-33
.33	594	626	659	693	726	760	793	827	861	896	32-35
.34	930	965	000	035	071	106	142	178	214	251	35-37
.35	.04 287	324	361	399	436	474	512	550	588	627	37-39
.36	666	705	744	783	823	863	903	943	984	024	39-41
.37	.05 065	106	148	190	231	273	316	358	401	444	41-43
.38	487	531	574	618	662	707	751	796	841	886	43-46
.39	932	978	024	070	116	163	210	257	304	352	46-48
.40	.06 400	448	496	545	594	643	692	742	792	842	48-50
.41	892	943	993	044	096	147	199	251	303	356	50-53
.42	.07 409	462	515	569	623	677	731	785	840	895	53-56
.43	951	006	062	118	175	231	288	345	403	460	55-58
.44	.08 518	577	635	694	753	812	872	931	992	052	58-61
.45	.09 112	173	235	296	358	420	482	544	607	670	61-64
.46	734	797	861	925	990	.1 005	012	018	025	032	63-65 / 6-7
.47	038	045	052	058	065	072	079	085	092	099	
.48	106	113	120	127	134	141	148	155	162	169	7
.49	176	184	191	198	206	213	220	228	235	243	
.50	250	258	265	273	280	288	296	303	311	319	
.51	327	334	342	350	358	366	374	382	390	398	8
.52	406	414	422	431	439	447	455	464	472	480	
.53	489	497	506	514	523	531	540	549	557	566	
.54	575	583	592	601	610	619	628	637	646	655	9
.55	664	673	682	691	700	710	719	728	737	747	
.56	756	766	775	785	794	804	813	823	833	842	
.57	852	862	871	881	891	901	911	921	931	941	10
.58	951	961	971	982	992	002	012	023	033	043	
.59	.2 054	064	075	085	096	106	117	128	138	149	10-11

n	0	1	2	3	4	5	6	7	8	9	Diff.
.60	.2 160	171	182	193	203	214	225	236	248	259	11
.61	270	281	292	303	315	326	337	349	360	372	
.62	383	395	406	418	430	441	453	465	477	489	
.63	500	512	524	536	548	560	573	585	597	609	12
.64	621	634	646	658	671	683	696	708	721	734	
.65	746	759	772	784	797	810	823	836	849	862	13
.66	875	888	901	914	928	941	954	967	981	994	
.67	.3 008	021	035	048	062	075	089	103	117	130	
.68	144	158	172	186	200	214	228	242	257	271	14
.69	285	299	314	328	343	357	372	386	401	415	
.70	430	445	459	474	489	504	519	534	549	564	15
.71	579	594	609	625	640	655	671	686	701	717	
.72	732	748	764	779	795	811	827	842	858	874	16
.73	890	906	922	938	954	971	987	003	019	036	
.74	.4 052	069	085	102	118	135	152	168	185	202	
.75	219	236	253	270	287	304	321	338	355	372	17
.76	390	407	425	442	459	477	495	512	530	548	
.77	565	583	601	619	637	655	673	691	709	727	18
.78	746	764	782	800	819	837	856	874	893	912	
.79	930	949	968	987	006	025	044	063	082	101	19
.80	.5 120	139	158	178	197	217	236	256	275	295	
.81	314	334	354	374	394	413	433	453	473	494	20
.82	514	534	554	574	595	615	636	656	677	697	
.83	718	739	759	780	801	822	843	864	885	906	21
.84	927	948	969	991	012	034	055	076	098	120	
.85	.6 141	163	185	207	228	250	272	294	316	338	22
.86	361	383	405	427	450	472	495	517	540	562	
.87	585	608	631	653	676	699	722	745	768	792	23
.88	815	838	861	885	908	932	955	979	002	026	
.89	.7 050	073	097	121	145	169	193	217	242	266	24
.90	290	314	339	363	388	412	437	461	486	511	
.91	536	561	586	610	636	661	686	711	736	762	25
.92	787	812	838	863	889	915	940	966	992	018	
.93	.8 044	070	096	122	148	174	200	227	253	279	26
.94	306	332	359	386	412	439	466	493	520	547	27
.95	574	601	628	655	683	710	737	765	792	820	
.96	847	875	903	931	958	986	014	042	070	099	28
.97	.9 127	155	183	212	240	269	297	326	354	383	
.98	412	441	470	499	528	557	586	615	644	674	29
.99	703	732	762	791	821	851	880	910	940	970	30
1.00	1.0 000										

SQUARE ROOTS $\sqrt{n} = n^{1/2}$

n	0	1	2	3	4	5	6	7	8	9	Diff.
.010	.10 000	050	100	149	198	247	296	344	392	440	50-48
.011	488	536	583	630	677	724	770	817	863	909	48-45
.012	954	000	045	091	136	180	225	269	314	358	46-44
.013	.11 402	446	489	533	576	619	662	705	747	790	44-42
.014	832	874	916	958	000	042	083	124	166	207	42-40
.015	.12 247	288	329	369	410	450	490	530	570	610	41-39
.016	649	689	728	767	806	845	884	923	961	000	40-38
.017	.13 038	077	115	153	191	229	266	304	342	379	39-37
.018	416	454	491	528	565	601	638	675	711	748	38-36
.019	784	820	856	892	928	964	000	036	071	107	36-35
.020	.14 142	177	213	248	283	318	353	387	422	457	36-34
.021	491	526	560	595	629	663	697	731	765	799	35-33
.022	832	866	900	933	967	000	033	067	100	133	34-33
.023	.15 166	199	232	264	297	330	362	395	427	460	33-32
.024	492	524	556	588	620	652	684	716	748	780	32-31
.025	811	843	875	906	937	969	000	031	062	093	32-31
.026	.16 125	155	186	217	248	279	310	340	371	401	31-30
.027	432	462	492	523	553	583	613	643	673	703	31-30
.028	733	763	793	823	852	882	912	941	971	000	30-29
.029	.17 029	059	088	117	146	176	205	234	263	292	30-29
.03	.1 732	761	789	817	844	871	897	924	949	975	29-25
.04	.2 000	025	049	074	098	121	145	168	191	214	25-22
.05	236	258	280	302	324	345	366	387	408	429	22-20
.06	449	470	490	510	530	550	569	588	608	627	21-19
.07	646	665	683	702	720	739	757	775	793	811	19-17
.08	828	846	864	881	898	915	933	950	966	983	18-16
.09	.3 000	017	033	050	066	082	098	114	130	146	17-16
.10	162	178	194	209	225	240	256	271	286	302	
.11	317	332	347	362	376	391	406	421	435	450	15
.12	464	479	493	507	521	536	550	564	578	592	14
.13	606	619	633	647	661	674	688	701	715	728	
.14	742	755	768	782	795	808	821	834	847	860	13
.15	873	886	899	912	924	937	950	962	975	987	
.16	.4 000	012	025	037	050	062	074	087	099	111	
.17	123	135	147	159	171	183	195	207	219	231	12
.18	243	254	266	278	290	301	313	324	336	347	
.19	359	370	382	393	405	416	427	438	450	461	
.20	472	483	494	506	517	528	539	550	561	572	11
.21	583	593	604	615	626	637	648	658	669	680	
.22	690	701	712	722	733	743	754	764	775	785	
.23	796	806	817	827	837	848	858	868	879	889	
.24	899	909	919	930	940	950	960	970	980	990	
.25	.5 000	010	020	030	040	050	060	070	079	089	10
.26	099	109	119	128	138	148	158	167	177	187	
.27	196	206	215	225	235	244	254	263	273	282	
.28	292	301	310	320	329	339	348	357	367	376	
.29	385	394	404	413	422	431	441	450	459	468	9

SQUARE ROOTS $\sqrt{n} = n^{1/2}$

n	0	1	2	3	4	5	6	7	8	9	Diff.
.30	.5 477	486	495	505	514	523	532	541	550	559	
.31	568	577	586	595	604	612	621	630	639	648	9
.32	657	666	675	683	692	701	710	718	727	736	
.33	745	753	762	771	779	788	797	805	814	822	
.34	831	840	848	857	865	874	882	891	899	908	
.35	916	925	933	941	950	958	967	975	983	992	
.36	.6 000	008	017	025	033	042	050	058	066	075	
.37	083	091	099	107	116	124	132	140	148	156	
.38	164	173	181	189	197	205	213	221	229	237	
.39	245	253	261	269	277	285	293	301	309	317	8
.40	325	332	340	348	356	364	372	380	387	395	
.41	403	411	419	427	434	442	450	458	465	473	
.42	481	488	496	504	512	519	527	535	542	550	
.43	557	565	573	580	588	595	603	611	618	626	
.44	633	641	648	656	663	671	678	686	693	701	
.45	708	716	723	731	738	745	753	760	768	775	
.46	782	790	797	804	812	819	826	834	841	848	
.47	856	863	870	877	885	892	899	907	914	921	
.48	928	935	943	950	957	964	971	979	986	993	
.49	.7 000	007	014	021	029	036	043	050	057	064	
.50	071	078	085	092	099	106	113	120	127	134	
.51	141	148	155	162	169	176	183	190	197	204	7
.52	211	218	225	232	239	246	253	259	266	273	
.53	280	287	294	301	308	314	321	328	335	342	
.54	348	355	362	369	376	382	389	396	403	409	
.55	416	423	430	436	443	450	457	463	470	477	
.56	483	490	497	503	510	517	523	530	537	543	
.57	550	556	563	570	576	583	589	596	603	609	
.58	616	622	629	635	642	649	655	662	668	675	
.59	681	688	694	701	707	714	720	727	733	740	7-6
.60	746	752	759	765	772	778	785	791	797	804	
.61	810	817	823	829	836	842	849	855	861	868	
.62	874	880	887	893	899	906	912	918	925	931	
.63	937	944	950	956	962	969	975	981	987	994	
.64	.8 000	006	012	019	025	031	037	044	050	056	
.65	062	068	075	081	087	093	099	106	112	118	
.66	124	130	136	142	149	155	161	167	173	179	
.67	185	191	198	204	210	216	222	228	234	240	
.68	246	252	258	264	270	276	283	289	295	301	
.69	307	313	319	325	331	337	343	349	355	361	6
.7	367	426	485	544	602	660	718	775	832	888	59-56
.8	944	000	055	110	165	220	274	327	381	434	56-53
.9	.9 487	539	592	644	695	747	798	849	899	950	53-50
1.0	1.0 000										

CUBE ROOTS $n^{1/3}$

n	0	1	2	3	4	5	6	7	8	9	Diff.
.0010	.10 000	033	066	099	132	164	196	228	260	291	33-31
.0011	323	354	385	416	446	477	507	537	567	597	31-30
.0012	627	656	685	714	743	772	801	829	858	886	29-28
.0013	914	942	970	997	025	052	079	106	133	160	28-27
.0014	.11 187	213	240	266	292	319	344	370	396	422	27-25
.0015	447	473	498	523	548	573	598	623	647	672	26-24
.0016	696	720	745	769	793	817	840	864	888	911	25-23
.0017	935	958	981	005	028	051	074	096	119	142	24-22
.0018	.12 164	187	209	232	254	276	298	320	342	364	23-22
.0019	386	407	429	450	472	493	515	536	557	578	22-21
.0020	599	620	641	662	683	703	724	745	765	785	21-20
.0021	806	826	846	866	887	907	927	947	966	986	21-19
.0022	.13 006	026	045	065	084	104	123	142	162	181	20-19
.0023	200	219	238	257	276	295	314	333	351	370	19-18
.0024	389	407	426	444	463	481	499	518	536	554	19-18
.0025	572	590	608	626	644	662	680	698	715	733	18-17
.0026	751	768	786	803	821	838	856	873	890	908	18-17
.0027	925	942	959	976	993	010	027	044	061	078	17
.0028	.14 095	111	128	145	161	178	195	211	228	244	17-16
.0029	260	276	293	309	326	342	358	374	390	406	17-16
.003	.1 442	458	474	489	504	518	533	547	560	574	16-13
.004	587	601	613	626	639	651	663	675	687	698	14-11
.005	710	721	732	744	754	765	776	786	797	807	12-10
.006	817	827	837	847	857	866	876	885	895	904	10-9
.007	913	922	931	940	949	957	966	975	983	992	9-8
.008	.2 000	008	017	025	033	041	049	057	065	072	
.009	080	088	095	103	110	118	125	133	140	147	
.010	154	162	169	176	183	190	197	204	210	217	7
.011	224	231	237	244	251	257	264	270	277	283	
.012	289	296	302	308	315	321	327	333	339	345	
.013	351	357	363	369	375	381	387	393	399	404	6
.014	410	416	422	427	433	438	444	450	455	461	
.015	466	472	477	483	488	493	499	504	509	515	
.016	520	525	530	535	541	546	551	556	561	566	
.017	571	576	581	586	591	596	601	606	611	616	5
.018	621	626	630	635	640	645	650	654	659	664	
.019	668	673	678	682	687	692	696	701	705	710	
.020	.2 714	719	723	728	732	737	741	746	750	755	
.021	759	763	768	772	776	781	785	789	794	798	
.022	802	806	811	815	819	823	827	831	836	840	
.023	844	848	852	856	860	864	868	872	876	880	4
.024	884	888	892	896	900	904	908	912	916	920	
.025	924	928	932	936	940	943	947	951	955	959	
.026	962	966	970	974	978	981	985	989	993	996	
.027	.3 000	004	007	011	015	018	022	026	029	033	
.028	037	040	044	047	051	055	058	062	065	069	
.029	072	076	079	083	086	090	093	097	100	104	4-3

n	0	1	2	3	4	5	6	7	8	9	Diff.
.03	.3 107	141	175	208	240	271	302	332	362	391	34-29
.04	420	448	476	503	530	557	583	609	634	659	28-25
.05	684	708	733	756	780	803	826	849	871	893	25-22
.06	915	936	958	979	$\overline{000}$	$\overline{021}$	$\overline{041}$	$\overline{062}$	$\overline{082}$	$\overline{102}$	22-19
.07	.4 121	141	160	179	198	217	236	254	273	291	20-18
.08	309	327	344	362	380	397	414	431	448	465	18-16
.09	481	498	514	531	547	563	579	595	610	626	17-15
.10	642	657	672	688	703	718	733	747	762	777	
.11	791	806	820	835	849	863	877	891	905	919	14
.12	932	946	960	973	987	$\overline{000}$	$\overline{013}$	$\overline{027}$	$\overline{040}$	$\overline{053}$	
.13	.5 066	079	092	104	117	130	143	155	168	180	13
.14	192	205	217	229	241	254	266	278	290	301	12
.15	313	325	337	348	360	372	383	395	406	418	
.16	429	440	451	463	474	485	496	507	518	529	11
.17	540	550	561	572	583	593	604	615	625	636	
.18	646	657	667	677	688	698	708	718	729	739	
.19	749	759	769	779	789	799	809	819	828	838	10
.20	848	858	867	877	887	896	906	915	925	934	
.21	944	953	963	972	981	991	$\overline{000}$	$\overline{009}$	$\overline{018}$	$\overline{028}$	
.22	.6 037	046	055	064	073	082	091	100	109	118	9
.23	127	136	145	153	162	171	180	188	197	206	
.24	214	223	232	240	249	257	266	274	283	291	
.25	300	308	316	325	333	341	350	358	366	374	
.26	383	391	399	407	415	423	431	439	447	455	
.27	463	471	479	487	495	503	511	519	527	534	8
.28	542	550	558	565	573	581	589	596	604	611	
.29	619	627	634	642	649	657	664	672	679	687	
.30	694	702	709	717	724	731	739	746	753	761	
.31	768	775	782	790	797	804	811	818	826	833	
.32	840	847	854	861	868	875	882	889	896	903	7
.33	910	917	924	931	938	945	952	959	966	973	
.34	980	986	993	$\overline{000}$	$\overline{007}$	$\overline{014}$	$\overline{020}$	$\overline{027}$	$\overline{034}$	$\overline{041}$	
.35	.7 047	054	061	067	074	081	087	094	101	107	
.36	114	120	127	133	140	147	153	160	166	173	7-6
.37	179	186	192	198	205	211	218	224	230	237	
.38	243	250	256	262	268	275	281	287	294	300	
.39	306	312	319	325	331	337	343	350	356	362	
.4	368	429	489	548	606	663	719	775	830	884	61-53
.5	937	990	$\overline{041}$	$\overline{093}$	$\overline{143}$	$\overline{193}$	$\overline{243}$	$\overline{291}$	$\overline{340}$	$\overline{387}$	53-47
.6	.8 434	481	527	573	618	662	707	750	794	837	47-42
.7	879	921	963	$\overline{004}$	$\overline{045}$	$\overline{086}$	$\overline{126}$	$\overline{166}$	$\overline{205}$	$\overline{244}$	42-39
.8	.9 283	322	360	398	435	473	510	546	583	619	39-36
.9	655	691	726	761	796	830	865	899	933	967	36-33
1.0	1.0 000										

n	0	1	2	3	4	5	6	7	8	9	Diff. (Subtract)
1.0	1.0 000	901	804	709	615	524	434	346	259	174	99-83
1.1	.9 091	009	929	850	772	696	621	547	475	403	82-70
1.2	.8 333	264	197	130	065	000	937	874	812	752	69-60
1.3	.7 692	634	576	519	463	407	353	299	246	194	58-51
1.4	143	092	042	993	944	897	849	803	757	711	51-44
1.5	.6 667	623	579	536	494	452	410	369	329	289	44-39
1.6	250	211	173	135	098	061	024	988	952	917	39-35
1.7	.5 882	848	814	780	747	714	682	650	618	587	34-31
1.8	556	525	495	464	435	405	376	348	319	291	31-28
1.9	263	236	208	181	155	128	102	076	051	025	28-25
2.0	000	975	950	926	902	878	854	831	808	785	25-23
2.1	.4 762	739	717	695	673	651	630	608	587	566	23-21
2.2	545	525	505	484	464	444	425	405	386	367	21-19
2.3	348	329	310	292	274	255	237	219	202	184	19-17
2.4	167	149	132	115	098	082	065	049	032	016	18-16
2.5	000	984	968	953	937	922	906	891	876	861	16-15
2.6	.3 846	831	817	802	788	774	759	745	731	717	15-13
2.7	704	690	676	663	650	636	623	610	597	584	14-13
2.8	571	559	546	534	521	509	497	484	472	460	13-12
2.9	448	436	425	413	401	390	378	367	356	344	12-11
3.0	333	322	311	300	289	279	268	257	247	236	11-10
3.1	226	215	205	195	185	175	165	155	145	135	11-10
3.2	125	115	106	096	086	077	067	058	049	040	10-9
3.3	030	021	012	003	994	985	976	967	959	950	9-8
3.4	.2 941	933	924	915	907	899	890	882	874	865	9-8
3.5	857	849	841	833	825	817	809	801	793	786	8-7
3.6	778	770	762	755	747	740	732	725	717	710	8-7
3.7	703	695	688	681	674	667	660	653	646	639	8-7
3.8	632	625	618	611	604	597	591	584	577	571	7-6
3.9	564	558	551	545	538	532	525	519	513	506	7-6
4.0	500	494	488	481	475	469	463	457	451	445	7-6
4.1	439	433	427	421	415	410	404	398	392	387	6-5
4.2	381	375	370	364	358	353	347	342	336	331	6-5
4.3	326	320	315	309	304	299	294	288	283	278	6-5
4.4	273	268	262	257	252	247	242	237	232	227	6-5
4.5	222	217	212	208	203	198	193	188	183	179	5-4
4.6	174	169	165	160	155	151	146	141	137	132	5-4
4.7	128	123	119	114	110	105	101	096	092	088	5-4
4.8	083	079	075	070	066	062	058	053	049	045	5-4
4.9	041	037	033	028	024	020	016	012	008	004	5-4
5.0	000	996	992	988	984	980	976	972	969	965	4-3
5.1	.1 961	957	953	949	946	942	938	934	931	927	4-3
5.2	923	919	916	912	908	905	901	898	894	890	4-3
5.3	887	883	880	876	873	869	866	862	859	855	4-3
5.4	852	848	845	842	838	835	832	828	825	821	4-3
5.5	818	815	812	808	805	802	799	795	792	789	4-3
5.6	786	783	779	776	773	770	767	764	761	757	4-3
5.7	754	751	748	745	742	739	736	733	730	727	3
5.8	724	721	718	715	712	709	706	704	701	698	3-2
5.9	695	692	689	686	684	681	678	675	672	669	3-2

n	0	1	2	3	4	5	6	7	8	9	Diff. (Subtract)
6.0	.16 667	639	611	584	556	529	502	474	447	420	28-27
6.1	393	367	340	313	287	260	234	207	181	155	27-26
6.2	129	103	077	051	026	000	974	949	924	898	26-25
6.3	.15 873	848	823	798	773	748	723	699	674	649	25-24
6.4	625	601	576	552	528	504	480	456	432	408	25-23
6.5	385	361	337	314	291	267	244	221	198	175	24-23
6.6	152	129	106	083	060	038	015	993	970	948	23-22
6.7	.14 925	903	881	859	837	815	793	771	749	728	22-21
6.8	706	684	663	641	620	599	577	556	535	514	22-21
6.9	493	472	451	430	409	388	368	347	327	306	21-20
7.0	286	265	245	225	205	184	164	144	124	104	21-19
7.1	085	065	045	025	006	986	966	947	928	908	20-19
7.2	.13 889	870	850	831	812	793	774	755	736	717	20-18
7.3	699	680	661	643	624	605	587	569	550	532	19-18
7.4	514	495	477	459	441	423	405	387	369	351	19-18
7.5	333	316	298	280	263	245	228	210	193	175	18-17
7.6	158	141	123	106	089	072	055	038	021	004	18-17
7.7	.12 987	970	953	937	920	903	887	870	853	837	17-16
7.8	821	804	788	771	755	739	723	706	690	674	17-16
7.9	658	642	626	610	594	579	563	547	531	516	16-15
8.0	500	484	469	453	438	422	407	392	376	361	16-15
8.1	346	330	315	300	285	270	255	240	225	210	16-15
8.2	195	180	165	151	136	121	107	092	077	063	15-14
8.3	048	034	019	005	990	976	962	947	933	919	15-14
8.4	.11 905	891	876	862	848	834	820	806	792	779	15-13
8.5	765	751	737	723	710	696	682	669	655	641	14-13
8.6	628	614	601	587	574	561	547	534	521	507	14-13
8.7	494	481	468	455	442	429	416	403	390	377	13
8.8	364	351	338	325	312	299	287	274	261	249	13-12
8.9	236	223	211	198	186	173	161	148	136	123	13-12
9.0	111	099	086	074	062	050	038	025	013	001	13-12
9.1	.10 989	977	965	953	941	929	917	905	893	881	12-11
9.2	870	858	846	834	823	811	799	787	776	764	12-11
9.3	753	741	730	718	707	695	684	672	661	650	12-11
9.4	638	627	616	604	593	582	571	560	549	537	12-11
9.5	526	515	504	493	482	471	460	449	438	428	11-10
9.6	417	406	395	384	373	363	352	341	331	320	11-10
9.7	309	299	288	277	267	256	246	235	225	215	11-10
9.8	204	194	183	173	163	152	142	132	121	111	11-10
9.9	101	091	081	070	060	050	040	030	020	010	11-10

If $e^y = x$, then ln x = y.   e = 2.718282

x	0	1	2	3	4	5	6	7	8	9	Diff.
1.00	.0 000	010	020	030	040	050	060	070	080	090	10
.01	100	109	119	129	139	149	159	169	178	188	9 - 10
.02	198	208	218	227	237	247	257	266	276	286	9 - 10
.03	296	305	315	325	334	344	354	363	373	383	9 - 10
.04	392	402	411	421	431	440	450	459	469	478	9 - 10
.05	488	497	507	516	526	535	545	554	564	573	9 - 10
.06	583	592	602	611	620	630	639	649	658	667	9 - 10
.07	677	686	695	705	714	723	733	742	751	760	9 - 10
.08	770	779	788	797	807	816	825	834	843	853	9 - 10
.09	862	871	880	889	898	908	917	926	935	944	9 - 10
1.10	953	962	971	980	989	998	007	017	026	035	9 - 10
.11	.1 044	053	062	071	080	089	098	106	115	124	8 - 9
.12	133	142	151	160	169	178	187	196	204	213	8 - 9
.13	222	231	240	249	258	266	275	284	293	302	8 - 9
.14	310	319	328	337	345	354	363	371	380	389	8 - 9
.15	398	406	415	424	432	441	450	458	467	476	8 - 9
.16	484	493	501	510	519	527	536	544	553	561	8 - 9
.17	570	579	587	596	604	613	621	630	638	647	8 - 9
.18	655	664	672	681	689	697	706	714	723	731	8 - 9
.19	740	748	756	765	773	781	790	798	807	815	8 - 9
1.20	823	832	840	848	856	865	873	881	890	898	8 - 9
.21	906	914	923	931	939	947	956	964	972	980	8 - 9
.22	989	997	005	013	021	029	038	046	054	062	8 - 9
.23	.2 070	078	086	095	103	111	119	127	135	143	8 - 9
.24	151	159	167	175	183	191	199	207	215	223	8
.25	231	239	247	255	263	271	279	287	295	303	8
.26	311	319	327	335	343	351	359	367	374	382	7 - 8
.27	390	398	406	414	422	429	437	445	453	461	7 - 8
.28	469	476	484	492	500	508	515	523	531	539	7 - 8
.29	546	554	562	570	577	585	593	601	608	616	7 - 8
1.30	624	631	639	647	654	662	670	677	685	693	7 - 8
.31	700	708	716	723	731	738	746	754	761	769	7 - 8
.32	776	784	791	799	807	814	822	829	837	844	7 - 8
.33	852	859	867	874	882	889	897	904	912	919	7 - 8
.34	927	934	942	949	957	964	971	979	986	994	7 - 8
.35	.3 001	008	016	023	031	038	045	053	060	067	7 - 8
.36	075	082	090	097	104	112	119	126	133	141	7 - 8
.37	148	155	163	170	177	185	192	199	206	214	7 - 8
.38	221	228	235	243	250	257	264	271	279	286	7 - 8
.39	293	300	307	315	322	329	336	343	350	358	7 - 8
1.40	365	372	379	386	393	400	407	415	422	429	7 - 8
.41	436	443	450	457	464	471	478	485	492	500	7 - 8
.42	507	514	521	528	535	542	549	556	563	570	7
.43	577	584	591	598	605	612	619	626	633	639	6 - 7
.44	646	653	660	667	674	681	688	695	702	709	7
.45	716	723	729	736	743	750	757	764	771	778	6 - 7
.46	784	791	798	805	812	819	825	832	839	846	6 - 7
.47	853	859	866	873	880	887	893	900	907	914	6 - 7
.48	920	927	934	941	947	954	961	968	974	981	6 - 7
.49	988	994	001	008	015	021	028	035	041	048	6 - 7
	.4										

$$Ln\ x = 2.302585 \log_{10} x$$

x	0	1	2	3	4	5	6	7	8	9	Diff.
1.50	.4 055	061	068	075	081	088	095	101	108	114	6 - 7
.51	121	128	134	141	148	154	161	167	174	181	6 - 7
.52	187	194	200	207	213	220	226	233	240	246	6 - 7
.53	253	259	266	272	279	285	292	298	305	311	6 - 7
.54	318	324	331	337	344	350	357	363	370	376	6 - 7
.55	383	389	395	402	408	415	421	428	434	440	6 - 7
.56	447	453	460	466	472	479	485	492	498	504	6 - 7
.57	511	517	523	530	536	543	549	555	562	568	6 - 7
.58	574	581	587	593	600	606	612	618	625	631	6 - 7
.59	637	644	650	656	662	669	675	681	688	694	6 - 7
1.60	700	706	713	719	725	731	737	744	750	756	6 - 7
.61	762	769	775	781	787	793	800	806	812	818	6 - 7
.62	824	830	837	843	849	855	861	867	874	880	6 - 7
.63	886	892	898	904	910	916	923	929	935	941	6 - 7
.64	947	953	959	965	971	977	983	990	996	$\overline{002}$	6 - 7
.65	.5 008	014	020	026	032	038	044	050	056	062	6
.66	068	074	080	086	092	098	104	110	116	122	6
.67	128	134	140	146	152	158	164	170	176	182	6
.68	188	194	200	206	212	218	224	230	235	241	5 - 6
.69	247	253	259	265	271	277	283	289	295	300	5 - 6
1.70	306	312	318	324	330	336	342	347	353	359	5 - 6
.71	365	371	377	382	388	394	400	406	412	417	5 - 6
.72	423	429	435	441	446	452	458	464	470	475	5 - 6
.73	481	487	493	499	504	510	516	522	527	533	5 - 6
.74	539	545	550	556	562	568	573	579	585	590	5 - 6
.75	596	602	608	613	619	625	630	636	642	647	5 - 6
.76	653	659	664	670	676	682	687	693	698	704	5 - 6
.77	710	715	721	727	732	738	744	749	755	761	5 - 6
.78	766	772	777	783	789	794	800	805	811	817	5 - 6
.79	822	828	833	839	844	850	856	861	867	872	5 - 6
1.80	878	883	889	895	900	906	911	917	922	928	5 - 6
.81	933	939	944	$\underline{950}$	$\underline{955}$	$\underline{961}$	$\underline{966}$	$\underline{972}$	$\underline{977}$	$\underline{983}$	5 - 6
.82	988	994	999	$\overline{005}$	$\overline{010}$	$\overline{016}$	$\overline{021}$	$\overline{027}$	$\overline{032}$	$\overline{038}$	5 - 6
.83	.6 043	049	054	060	065	070	076	081	087	092	5 - 6
.84	098	103	109	114	119	125	130	136	141	146	5 - 6
.85	152	157	163	168	173	179	184	190	195	200	5 - 6
.86	206	211	217	222	227	233	238	243	249	254	5 - 6
.87	259	265	270	275	281	286	291	297	302	307	5 - 6
.88	313	318	323	329	334	339	345	350	355	360	5 - 6
.89	366	371	376	382	387	392	397	403	408	413	5 - 6
1.90	419	424	429	434	440	445	450	455	461	466	5 - 6
.91	471	476	481	487	492	497	502	508	513	518	5 - 6
.92	523	528	534	539	544	549	554	560	565	570	5 - 6
.93	575	580	586	591	596	601	606	611	617	622	5 - 6
.94	627	632	637	642	647	653	658	663	668	673	5 - 6
.95	678	683	689	694	699	704	709	714	719	724	5 - 6
.96	729	735	740	745	750	755	760	765	770	775	5 - 6
.97	780	785	790	796	801	806	811	816	821	826	5 - 6
.98	831	836	841	846	851	856	861	866	871	876	5
.99	881	886	891	896	901	906	911	916	921	926	5

NATURAL LOGARITHMS   LN X

x	0	1	2	3	4	5	6	7	8	9	Diff.
2.00	.6 931	936	941	946	951	956	961	966	971	976	5
.01	981	986	991	996	0̅0̅1̅	0̅0̅6̅	0̅1̅1̅	0̅1̅6̅	0̅2̅1̅	0̅2̅6̅	5
.02	.7 031	036	041	046	051	056	061	066	071	075	4 - 5
.03	080	085	090	095	100	105	110	115	120	125	4 - 5
.04	129	134	139	144	149	154	159	164	169	174	4 - 5
.05	178	183	188	193	198	203	208	212	217	222	4 - 5
.06	227	232	237	242	246	251	256	261	266	271	4 - 5
.07	275	280	285	290	295	300	304	309	314	319	4 - 5
.08	324	328	333	338	343	348	352	357	362	367	4 - 5
.09	372	376	381	386	391	396	400	405	410	415	4 - 5
2.10	419	424	429	434	438	443	448	453	457	462	4 - 5
.11	467	472	476	481	486	491	495	500	505	509	4 - 5
.12	514	519	524	528	533	538	542	547	552	557	4 - 5
.13	561	566	571	575	580	585	589	594	599	603	4 - 5
.14	608	613	617	622	627	631	636	641	645	650	4 - 5
.15	655	659	664	669	673	678	683	687	692	696	4 - 5
.16	701	706	710	715	720	724	729	733	738	743	4 - 5
.17	747	752	756	761	766	770	775	779	784	789	4 - 5
.18	793	798	802	807	812	816	821	825	830	834	4 - 5
.19	839	844	848	853	857	862	866	871	875	880	4 - 5
2.20	885	889	894	898	903	907	912	916	921	925	4 - 5
.21	930	934	939	943	948	953	9̅5̅7̅	9̅6̅2̅	9̅6̅6̅	9̅7̅1̅	4 - 5
.22	975	980	984	989	993	998	0̅0̅2̅	0̅0̅7̅	0̅1̅1̅	0̅1̅6̅	4 - 5
.23	.8 020	024	029	033	038	042	047	051	056	060	4 - 5
.24	065	069	074	078	083	087	092	096	100	105	4 - 5
.25	109	114	118	123	127	131	136	140	145	149	4 - 5
.26	154	158	162	167	171	176	180	185	189	193	4 - 5
.27	198	202	207	211	215	220	224	229	233	237	4 - 5
.28	242	246	251	255	259	264	268	272	277	281	4 - 5
.29	286	290	294	299	303	307	312	316	320	325	4 - 5
2.30	329	333	338	342	346	351	355	359	364	368	4 - 5
.31	372	377	381	385	390	394	398	403	407	411	4 - 5
.32	416	420	424	429	433	437	442	446	450	454	4 - 5
.33	459	463	467	472	476	480	484	489	493	497	4 - 5
.34	502	506	510	514	519	523	527	531	536	540	4 - 5
.35	544	548	553	557	561	565	570	574	578	582	4 - 5
.36	587	591	595	599	604	608	612	616	620	625	4 - 5
.37	629	633	637	642	646	650	654	658	663	667	4 - 5
.38	671	675	679	684	688	692	696	700	705	709	4 - 5
.39	713	717	721	725	730	734	738	742	746	751	4 - 5
2.40	755	759	763	767	771	775	780	784	788	792	4 - 5
.41	796	800	805	809	813	817	821	825	829	834	4 - 5
.42	838	842	846	850	854	858	862	867	871	875	4 - 5
.43	879	883	887	891	895	899	904	908	912	916	4 - 5
.44	920	924	928	932	936	940	945	949	953	957	4 - 5
.45	961	965	969	973	977	981	985	989	993	998	4 - 5
.46	.9 002	006	010	014	018	022	026	030	034	038	4
.47	042	046	050	054	058	062	066	070	075	079	4 - 5
.48	083	087	091	095	099	103	107	111	115	119	4
.49	123	127	131	135	139	143	147	151	155	159	4

x	0	1	2	3	4	5	6	7	8	9	Diff.
2.50	.9 163	167	171	175	179	183	187	191	195	199	4
.51	203	207	211	215	219	223	227	231	235	239	4
.52	243	247	251	254	258	262	266	270	274	278	3 – 4
.53	282	286	290	294	298	302	306	310	314	318	4
.54	322	326	330	333	337	341	345	349	353	357	3 – 4
.55	361	365	369	373	377	381	384	388	392	396	3 – 4
.56	400	404	408	412	416	420	423	427	431	435	3 – 4
.57	439	443	447	451	455	458	462	466	470	474	3 – 4
.58	478	482	486	490	493	497	501	505	509	513	3 – 4
.59	517	520	524	528	532	536	540	544	547	551	3 – 4
2.60	555	559	563	567	570	574	578	582	586	590	3 – 4
.61	594	597	601	605	609	613	616	620	624	628	3 – 4
.62	632	636	639	643	647	651	655	658	662	666	3 – 4
.63	670	674	677	681	685	689	693	696	700	704	3 – 4
.64	708	712	715	719	723	727	730	734	738	742	3 – 4
.65	746	749	753	757	761	764	768	772	776	780	3 – 4
.66	783	787	791	795	798	802	806	810	813	817	3 – 4
.67	821	825	828	832	836	839	843	847	851	854	3 – 4
.68	858	862	866	869	873	877	881	884	888	892	3 – 4
.69	895	899	903	907	910	914	918	921	925	929	3 – 4
2.70	933	936	940	944	947	951	955	958	962	966	3 – 4
.71	969	973	977	981	984	988	992	995	999	$\overline{003}$	3 – 4
.72	1.0 006	010	014	017	021	025	028	032	036	039	3 – 4
.73	043	047	050	054	058	061	065	069	072	076	3 – 4
.74	080	083	087	091	094	098	101	105	109	112	3 – 4
.75	116	120	123	127	131	134	138	141	145	149	3 – 4
.76	152	156	160	163	167	170	174	178	181	185	3 – 4
.77	188	192	196	199	203	207	210	214	217	221	3 – 4
.78	225	228	232	235	239	242	246	250	253	257	3 – 4
.79	260	264	268	271	275	278	282	285	289	293	3 – 4
2.80	296	300	303	307	310	314	318	321	325	328	3 – 4
.81	332	335	339	343	346	350	353	357	360	364	3 – 4
.82	367	371	374	378	382	385	389	392	396	399	3 – 4
.83	403	406	410	413	417	420	424	427	431	435	3 – 4
.84	438	442	445	449	452	456	459	463	466	470	3 – 4
.85	473	477	480	484	487	491	494	498	501	505	3 – 4
.86	508	512	515	519	522	526	529	533	536	540	3 – 4
.87	543	547	550	554	557	561	564	567	571	574	3 – 4
.88	578	581	585	588	592	595	599	602	606	609	3 – 4
.89	613	616	619	623	626	630	633	637	640	644	3 – 4
2.90	647	651	654	657	661	664	668	671	675	678	3 – 4
.91	682	685	688	692	695	699	702	706	709	712	3 – 4
.92	716	719	723	726	730	733	736	740	743	747	3 – 4
.93	750	753	757	760	764	767	770	774	777	781	3 – 4
.94	784	787	791	794	798	801	804	808	811	815	3 – 4
.95	818	821	825	828	832	835	838	842	845	849	3 – 4
.96	852	855	859	862	865	869	872	876	879	882	3 – 4
.97	886	889	892	896	899	902	906	909	913	916	3 – 4
.98	919	923	926	929	933	936	939	943	946	949	3 – 4
.99	953	956	959	963	966	969	973	976	979	983	3 – 4

NATURAL LOGARITHMS   LN X

x	0	1	2	3	4	5	6	7	8	9	Diff.
3.0	1.0 986	019	053	086	119	151	184	217	249	282	32 - 34
.1	1.1 314	346	378	410	442	474	506	537	569	600	31 - 32
.2	632	663	694	725	756	787	817	848	878	909	30 - 31
.3	939	969	000	030	060	090	119	149	179	208	29 - 31
.4	1.2 238	267	296	326	355	384	413	442	470	499	28 - 30
.5	528	556	585	613	641	669	698	726	754	782	28 - 29
.6	809	837	865	892	920	947	975	002	029	056	27 - 28
.7	1.3 083	110	137	164	191	218	244	271	297	324	26 - 27
.8	350	376	403	429	455	481	507	533	558	584	25 - 27
.9	610	635	661	686	712	737	762	788	813	838	25 - 26
4.0	863	888	913	938	962	987	012	036	061	085	24 - 25
.1	1.4 110	134	159	183	207	231	255	279	303	327	24 - 25
.2	351	375	398	422	446	469	493	516	540	563	23 - 24
.3	586	609	633	656	679	702	725	748	770	793	22 - 24
.4	816	839	861	884	907	929	951	974	996	019	22 - 23
.5	1.5 041	063	085	107	129	151	173	195	217	239	22
.6	261	282	304	326	347	369	390	412	433	454	21 - 22
.7	476	497	518	539	560	581	602	623	644	665	21 - 22
.8	686	707	728	748	769	790	810	831	851	872	20 - 21
.9	892	913	933	953	974	994	014	034	054	074	20 - 21
5.0	1.6 094	114	134	154	174	194	214	233	253	273	19 - 20
.1	292	312	332	351	371	390	409	429	448	467	19 - 20
.2	487	506	525	544	563	582	601	620	639	658	19
.3	677	696	715	734	752	771	790	808	827	845	18 - 19
.4	864	882	901	919	938	956	974	993	011	029	18 - 19
.5	1.7 047	066	084	102	120	138	156	174	192	210	18 - 19
.6	228	246	263	281	299	317	334	352	370	387	17 - 18
.7	405	422	440	457	475	492	509	527	544	561	17 - 18
.8	579	596	613	630	647	664	681	699	716	733	17 - 18
.9	750	766	783	800	817	834	851	867	884	901	16 - 17
6.0	918	934	951	967	984	001	017	034	050	066	16 - 17
.1	1.8 083	099	116	132	148	165	181	197	213	229	16 - 17
.2	245	262	278	294	310	326	342	358	374	390	15 - 17
.3	405	421	437	453	469	485	500	516	532	547	15 - 16
.4	563	579	594	610	625	641	656	672	687	703	15 - 16
.5	718	733	749	764	779	795	810	825	840	856	15 - 16
.6	871	886	901	916	931	946	961	976	991	006	15
.7	1.9 021	036	051	066	081	095	110	125	140	155	14 - 15
.8	169	184	199	213	228	242	257	272	286	301	14 - 15
.9	315	330	344	359	373	387	402	416	430	445	14 - 15
7.0	459	473	488	502	516	530	544	559	573	587	14 - 15
.1	601	615	629	643	657	671	685	699	713	727	14
.2	741	755	769	782	796	810	824	838	851	865	13 - 14
.3	879	892	906	920	933	947	961	974	988	001	13 - 14
.4	2.0 015	028	042	055	069	082	096	109	122	136	13 - 14
.5	149	162	176	189	202	215	229	242	255	268	13 - 14
.6	281	295	308	321	334	347	360	373	386	399	13 - 14
.7	412	425	438	451	464	477	490	503	516	528	12 - 13
.8	541	554	567	580	592	605	618	631	643	656	12 - 13
.9	669	681	694	707	719	732	744	757	769	782	12 - 13

x	0	1	2	3	4	5	6	7	8	9	Diff.
8.0	2.0 794	807	819	832	844	857	869	882	894	906	12 - 13
.1	919	931	943	956	968	980	992	005	017	029	12 - 13
.2	2.1 041	054	066	078	090	102	114	126	138	150	12 - 13
.3	163	175	187	199	211	223	235	247	258	270	11 - 12
.4	282	294	306	318	330	342	353	365	377	389	11 - 12
.5	401	412	424	436	448	459	471	483	494	506	11 - 12
.6	518	529	541	552	564	576	587	599	610	622	11 - 12
.7	633	645	656	668	679	691	702	713	725	736	11 - 12
.8	748	759	770	782	793	804	815	827	838	849	11 - 12
.9	861	872	883	894	905	917	928	939	950	961	11 - 12
9.0	972	983	994	006	017	028	039	050	061	072	11 - 12
.1	2.2 083	094	105	116	127	138	148	159	170	181	10 - 11
.2	192	203	214	225	235	246	257	268	279	289	10 - 11
.3	300	311	322	332	343	354	364	375	386	396	10 - 11
.4	407	418	428	439	450	460	471	481	492	502	10 - 11
.5	513	523	534	544	555	565	576	586	597	607	10 - 11
.6	618	628	638	649	659	670	680	690	701	711	10 - 11
.7	721	732	742	752	762	773	783	793	803	814	10 - 11
.8	824	834	844	854	865	875	885	895	905	915	10 - 11
.9	925	935	946	956	966	976	986	996	006	016	10 - 11
10.0	2.3 026										

X	LN X		X	LN X
10^2	2.3026		10^{21}	48.3543
10^3	4.6052		10^{22}	50.6569
	6.9078		10^{23}	52.9595
10^4	9.2103		10^{24}	55.2620
10^5	11.5129		10^{25}	57.5646
10^6	13.8155		10^{26}	59.8672
10^7	16.1181		10^{27}	62.1698
10^8	18.4207		10^{28}	64.4724
10^9	20.7233		10^{29}	66.7750
10^{10}	23.0259		10^{30}	69.0776
10^{11}	25.3284		10^{31}	71.3801
10^{12}	27.6310		10^{32}	73.6827
10^{13}	29.9336		10^{33}	75.9853
10^{14}	32.2362		10^{34}	78.2879
10^{15}	34.5388		10^{35}	80.5905
10^{16}	36.8414		10^{36}	82.8931
10^{17}	39.1439		10^{37}	85.1956
10^{18}	41.4465		10^{38}	87.4982
10^{19}	43.7491		10^{39}	89.8008
10^{20}	46.0517		10^{40}	92.1034

For a large table, see "Table of Natural Logarithms,"
National Bureau of Standards, Washington, D.C.

SIN X

x radians	0	1	2	3	4	5	6	7	8	9	Diff.
.00	.0 000	010	020	030	040	050	060	070	080	090	10
.01	100	110	120	130	140	150	160	170	180·	190	10
.02	200	210	220	230	240	250	260	270	280	290	10
.03	300	310	320	330	340	350	360	370	380	390	10
.04	400	410	420	430	440	450	460	470	480	490	10
.05	500	510	520	530	540	550	560	570	580	590	10
.06	600	610	620	630	640	650	660	669	679	689	9 - 10
.07	699	709	719	729	739	749	759	769	779	789	10
.08	799	809	819	829	839	849	859	869	879	889	10
.09	899	909	919	929	939	949	959	968	978	988	9 - 10
.10	998	008	018	028	038	048	058	068	078	088	10
.11	.1 098	108	118	128	138	147	157	167	177	187	9 - 10
.12	197	207	217	227	237	247	257	267	277	286	9 - 10
.13	296	306	316	326	336	346	356	366	376	386	10
.14	395	405	415	425	435	445	455	465	475	484	9 - 10
.15	494	504	514	524	534	544	554	564	573	583	9 - 10
.16	593	603	613	623	633	643	652	662	672	682	9 - 10
.17	692	702	712	721	731	741	751	761	771	780	9 - 10
.18	790	800	810	820	830	839	849	859	869	879	9 - 10
.19	889	898	908	918	928	938	947	957	967	977	9 - 10
.20	987	996	006	016	026	036	045	055	065	075	9 - 10
.21	.2 085	094	104	114	124	133	143	153	163	173	9 - 10
.22	182	192	202	212	221	231	241	251	260	270	9 - 10
.23	280	290	299	309	319	328	338	348	358	367	9 - 10
.24	377	387	396	406	416	426	435	445	455	464	9 - 10
.25	474	484	493	503	513	522	532	542	551	561	9 - 10
.26	571	580	590	600	609	619	629	638	648	658	9 - 10
.27	667	677	687	696	706	715	725	735	744	754	9 - 10
.28	764	773	783	792	802	812	821	831	840	850	9 - 10
.29	860	869	879	888	898	907	917	927	936	946	9 - 10
.30	955	965	974	984	993	003	012	022	032	041	9 - 10
.31	.3 051	060	070	079	089	098	108	117	127	136	9 - 10
.32	146	155	165	174	184	193	203	212	222	231	9 - 10
.33	240	250	259	269	278	288	297	307	316	325	9 - 10
.34	335	344	354	363	373	382	391	401	410	420	9 - 10
.35	429	438	448	457	467	476	485	495	504	513	9 - 10
.36	523	532	541	551	560	569	579	588	598	607	9 - 10
.37	616	625	635	644	653	663	672	681	691	700	9 - 10
.38	709	718	728	737	746	756	765	774	783	793	9 - 10
.39	802	811	820	830	839	848	857	867	876	885	9 - 10
.40	894	903	913	922	931	940	949	959	968	977	* 9 - 10
.41	986	995	004	014	023	032	041	050	059	068	9 - 10
.42	.4 078	087	096	105	114	123	132	141	151	160	9 - 10
.43	169	178	187	196	205	214	223	232	241	250	9
.44	259	268	277	287	296	305	314	323	332	341	9 - 10
.45	350	359	368	377	386	395	404	413	422	431	9
.46	439	448	457	466	475	484	493	502	511	520	8 - 9
.47	529	538	547	556	564	573	582	591	600	609	8 - 9
.48	618	627	636	644	653	662	671	680	689	697	8 - 9
.49	706	715	724	733	742	750	759	768	777	785	8 - 9

SIN X

x radians	0	1	2	3	4	5	6	7	8	9	Diff.
.50	.4 794	803	812	821	829	838	847	856	864	873	8 - 9
.51	882	890	899	908	917	925	934	943	951	960	8 - 9
.52	969	977	986	995	003	012	021	029	038	047	8 - 9
.53	.5 055	064	073	081	090	098	107	116	124	133	8 - 9
.54	141	150	159	167	176	184	193	201	210	218	8 - 9
.55	227	235	244	252	261	269	278	286	295	303	8 - 9
.56	312	320	329	337	346	354	363	371	379	388	8 - 9
.57	396	405	413	422	430	438	447	455	463	472	8 - 9
.58	480	489	497	505	514	522	530	53C	547	555	8 - 9
.59	564	572	580	589	597	605	613	622	630	638	8 - 9
.60	646	655	663	671	679	688	696	704	712	720	8 - 9
.61	729	737	745	753	761	770	778	786	794	802	8 - 9
.62	810	818	827	835	843	851	859	867	875	883	8 - 9
.63	891	900	908	916	924	932	940	948	956	964	8 - 9
.64	972	980	988	996	004	012	020	028	036	044	8
.65	.6 052	060	068	076	084	092	100	107	115	123	7 - 8
.66	131	139	147	155	163	171	178	186	194	202	7 - 8
.67	210	218	226	233	241	249	257	265	272	280	7 - 8
.68	288	296	303	311	319	327	334	342	350	358	7 - 8
.69	365	373	381	388	396	404	412	419	427	435	7 - 8
.70	442	450	457	465	473	480	488	496	503	511	7 - 8
.71	518	526	533	541	549	556	564	571	579	586	7 - 8
.72	594	601	609	616	624	631	639	646	654	661	7 - 8
.73	669	676	684	691	698	706	713	721	728	735	7 - 8
.74	743	750	758	765	772	780	787	794	802	809	7 - 8
.75	816	824	831	838	846	853	860	867	875	882	7 - 8
.76	889	896	904	911	918	925	933	940	947	954	7 - 8
.77	961	969	976	983	990	997	004	011	019	026	7 - 8
.78	.7 033	040	047	054	061	068	075	082	089	096	7
.79	104	111	118	125	132	139	146	153	160	167	7 - 8
.80	174	181	187	194	201	208	215	222	229	236	6 - 7
.81	243	250	257	264	270	277	284	291	298	305	6 - 7
.82	311	318	325	332	339	345	352	359	366	373	6 - 7
.83	379	386	393	400	406	413	420	426	433	440	6 - 7
.84	446	453	460	466	473	480	486	493	500	506	6 - 7
.85	513	519	526	533	539	546	552	559	565	572	6 - 7
.86	578	585	591	598	604	611	617	624	630	637	6 - 7
.87	643	650	656	663	669	675	682	688	695	701	6 - 7
.88	707	714	720	726	733	739	745	752	758	764	6 - 7
.89	771	777	783	790	796	802	808	815	821	827	6 - 7
.90	833	839	846	852	858	864	870	877	883	889	6 - 7
.91	895	901	907	913	920	926	932	938	944	950	6 - 7
.92	956	962	968	974	980	986	992	998	004	010	6
.93	.8 016	022	028	034	040	046	052	058	064	070	6
.94	076	081	087	093	099	105	111	117	123	128	5 - 6
.95	134	140	146	152	157	163	169	175	180	186	5 - 6
.96	192	198	203	209	215	220	226	232	238	243	5 - 6
.97	249	255	260	266	271	277	283	288	294	299	5 - 6
.98	305	311	316	322	327	333	338	344	349	355	5 - 6
.99	360	366	371	377	382	388	393	398	404	409	5 - 6

SIN X

x radians	0	1	2	3	4	5	6	7	8	9	Diff.
1.00	.8 415	420	425	431	436	442	447	452	458	463	5 - 5
1.01	468	474	479	484	490	495	500	505	511	516	5 - 6
1.02	521	526	532	537	542	547	552	558	563	568	5 - 6
1.03	573	578	583	588	594	599	604	609	614	619	5 - 6
1.04	624	629	634	639	644	649	654	659	664	669	5
1.05	674	679	684	689	694	699	704	709	714	719	5
1.06	724	728	733	738	743	748	753	758	762	767	4 - 5
1.07	772	777	782	786	791	796	801	805	810	815	4 - 5
1.08	820	824	829	834	838	843	848	852	857	862	4 - 5
1.09	866	871	876	880	885	889	894	898	903	908	4 - 5
1.10	912	917	921	926	930	935	939	944	948	953	4 - 5
1.11	957	961	966	970	975	979	984	988	992	997	4 - 5
1.12	.9 001	005	010	014	018	023	027	031	036	040	4 - 5
1.13	044	048	053	057	061	065	070	074	078	082	4 - 5
1.14	086	091	095	099	103	107	111	115	119	124	4 - 5
1.15	128	132	136	140	144	148	152	156	160	164	4
1.16	168	172	176	180	184	188	192	196	200	204	4
1.17	208	211	215	219	223	227	231	235	238	242	3 - 4
1.18	246	250	254	257	261	265	269	272	276	280	3 - 4
1.19	284	287	291	295	298	302	306	309	313	317	3 - 4
1.20	320	324	328	331	335	338	342	346	349	353	3 - 4
1.21	356	360	363	367	370	374	377	381	384	388	3 - 4
1.22	391	394	398	401	405	408	411	415	418	422	3 - 4
1.23	425	428	432	435	438	441	445	448	451	455	3 - 4
1.24	458	461	464	468	471	474	477	480	484	487	3 - 4
1.25	490	493	496	499	502	505	509	512	515	518	3 - 4
1.26	521	524	527	530	533	536	539	542	545	548	3
1.27	551	554	557	560	563	566	569	572	574	577	2 - 3
1.28	580	583	586	589	592	594	597	600	603	606	2 - 3
1.29	608	611	614	617	619	622	625	628	630	633	2 - 3
1.30	636	638	641	644	646	649	651	654	657	659	2 - 3
1.31	662	664	667	670	672	675	677	680	682	685	2 - 3
1.32	687	690	692	695	697	699	702	704	707	709	2 - 3
1.33	711	714	716	719	721	723	726	728	730	733	2 - 3
1.34	735	737	739	742	744	746	748	751	753	755	2 - 3
1.35	757	759	762	764	766	768	770	772	774	777	2 - 3
1.36	779	781	783	785	787	789	791	793	795	797	2
1.37	799	801	803	805	807	809	811	813	815	817	2
1.38	819	820	822	824	826	828	830	832	833	835	1 - 2
1.39	837	839	841	842	844	846	848	849	851	853	1 - 2
1.40	854	856	858	860	861	863	865	866	868	869	1 - 2
1.41	871	873	874	876	877	879	880	882	883	885	1 - 2
1.42	887	888	890	891	892	894	895	897	898	900	1 - 2
1.43	901	902	904	905	907	908	909	911	912	913	1 - 2
1.44	915	916	917	918	920	921	922	923	925	926	1 - 2
1.45	927	928	930	931	932	933	934	935	936	938	1 - 2
1.46	939	940	941	942	943	944	945	946	947	948	1
1.47	949	950	951	952	953	954	955	956	957	958	1
1.48	959	960	961	961	962	963	964	965	966	967	0 - 1
1.49	967	968	969	970	971	971	972	973	974	974	0 - 1

SIN X

x radians	0	1	2	3	4	5	6	7	8	9	Diff.
1.50	0.9 975	976	976	977	978	978	979	980	980	981	0 - 1
1.51	982	982	983	983	984	984	985	986	986	987	0 - 1
1.52	987	988	988	989	989	990	990	990	991	991	0 - 1
1.53	992	992	992	993	993	994	994	994	995	995	0 - 1
1.54	995	996	996	996	996	997	997	997	997	998	0 - 1
1.55	998	998	998	998	999	999	999	999	999	999	0 - 1
1.56	999	000	000	000	000	000	000	000	000	000	0 - 1
											(Subtract)
											0
1.57	1.0 000	000	000	000	000	000	000	000	000	000	0
1.58	000	999	999	999	999	999	999	999	999	998	0 - 1
1.59	0.9 998	998	998	998	997	997	997	997	996	996	0 - 1
1.60	0.9 996	995	995	995	994	994	994	993	993	993	0 - 1
1.61	992	992	992	991	991	990	990	989	989	988	0 - 1
1.62	988	987	987	986	986	985	985	984	984	983	0 - 1
1.63	982	982	981	981	980	979	979	978	977	977	0 - 1
1.64	976	975	975	974	973	972	972	971	970	969	0 - 1
1.65	969	968	967	966	965	965	964	963	962	961	0 - 1
1.66	960	959	958	958	957	956	955	954	953	952	0 - 1
1.67	951	950	949	948	947	946	945	944	943	942	1 - 2
1.68	940	939	938	937	936	935	934	933	931	930	1 - 2
1.69	929	928	927	925	924	923	922	920	919	918	1 - 2
1.70	0.9 917	915	914	913	911	910	909	907	906	905	1 - 2
1.71	903	902	900	899	898	896	895	893	892	890	1 - 2
1.72	889	887	886	884	883	881	880	878	877	875	1 - 2
1.73	874	872	870	869	867	865	864	862	861	859	1 - 2
1.74	857	856	854	852	850	849	847	845	843	842	1 - 2
1.75	840	838	836	834	833	831	829	827	825	823	1 - 2
1.76	822	820	818	816	814	812	810	808	806	804	2
1.77	802	800	798	796	794	792	790	788	786	784	2
1.78	782	780	778	776	774	771	769	767	765	763	2 - 3
1.79	761	759	756	754	752	750	747	745	743	741	2 - 3
1.80	0.9 738	736	734	732	729	727	725	722	720	718	2 - 3
1.81	715	713	711	708	706	703	701	698	696	694	2 - 3
1.82	691	689	686	684	681	679	676	674	671	669	2 - 3
1.83	666	663	661	658	656	653	650	648	645	642	2 - 3
1.84	640	637	634	632	629	626	624	621	618	616	2 - 3
1.85	613	610	607	604	602	599	596	593	590	588	2 - 3
1.86	585	582	579	576	573	570	567	565	562	559	2 - 3
1.87	556	553	550	547	544	541	538	535	532	529	3
1.88	526	523	520	517	514	510	507	504	501	498	3 - 4
1.89	495	492	489	485	482	479	476	473	469	466	3 - 4
1.90	0.9 463	460	457	453	450	447	443	440	437	434	3 - 4
1.91	430	427	424	420	417	413	410	407	403	400	3 - 4
1.92	396	393	390	386	383	379	376	372	369	365	3 - 4
1.93	362	358	355	351	348	344	341	337	333	330	3 - 4
1.94	326	323	319	315	312	308	304	301	297	293	3 - 4
1.95	290	286	282	278	275	271	267	263	260	256	3 - 4
1.96	252	248	245	241	237	233	229	225	221	218	3 - 4
1.97	214	210	206	202	198	194	190	186	182	178	4
1.98	174	170	166	162	158	154	150	146	142	138	4
1.99	134	130	126	122	118	114	110	105	101	097	4 - 5
2.00	0.9 093										

For larger values of x, use the method of subtracting multiples of $\pi/2 = 1.5708$

COS X

x radians	0	1	2	3	4	5	6	7	8	9	Diff. (Subtract)
.00	1.0 000	000	000	000	000	000	000	000	000	000	0
.01	000	999	999	999	999	999	999	999	998	998	0 - 1
.02	.9 998	998	998	997	997	997	997	996	996	996	0 - 1
.03	996	995	995	995	994	994	994	993	993	992	0 - 1
.04	992	992	991	991	990	990	989	989	988	988	0 - 1
.05	988	987	986	986	985	985	984	984	983	983	0 - 1
.06	982	981	981	980	980	979	978	978	977	976	0 - 1
.07	976	975	974	973	973	972	971	970	970	969	0 - 1
.08	968	967	966	966	965	964	963	962	961	960	0 - 1
.09	960	959	958	957	956	955	954	953	952	951	0 - 1
.10	950	949	948	947	946	945	944	943	942	941	1
.11	940	938	937	936	935	934	933	932	930	929	1 - 2
.12	928	927	926	924	923	922	921	919	918	917	1 - 2
.13	916	914	913	912	910	909	908	906	905	904	1 - 2
.14	902	901	899	898	896	895	894	892	891	889	1 - 2
.15	888	886	885	883	882	880	879	877	875	874	1 - 2
.16	872	871	869	867	866	864	863	861	859	858	1 - 2
.17	856	854	852	851	849	847	846	844	842	840	1 - 2
.18	838	837	835	833	831	829	828	826	824	822	1 - 2
.19	820	818	816	814	812	810	809	807	805	803	1 - 2
.20	801	799	797	795	793	791	789	787	784	782	2 - 3
.21	780	778	776	774	772	770	768	765	763	761	2 - 3
.22	759	757	755	752	750	748	746	743	741	739	2 - 3
.23	737	734	732	730	727	725	723	720	718	716	2 - 3
.24	713	711	709	706	704	701	699	697	694	692	2 - 3
.25	689	687	684	682	679	677	674	672	669	666	2 - 3
.26	664	661	659	656	654	651	648	646	643	640	2 - 3
.27	638	635	632	630	627	624	622	619	616	613	2 - 3
.28	611	608	605	602	599	597	594	591	588	585	2 - 3
.29	582	580	577	574	571	568	565	562	559	556	2 - 3
.30	553	550	547	544	541	538	535	532	529	526	3
.31	523	520	517	514	511	508	505	502	499	495	3 - 4
.32	492	489	486	483	480	477	473	470	467	464	3 - 4
.33	460	457	454	451	447	444	441	438	434	431	3 - 4
.34	428	424	421	417	414	411	407	404	401	397	3 - 4
.35	394	390	387	383	380	376	373	369	366	362	3 - 4
.36	359	355	352	348	345	341	338	334	330	327	3 - 4
.37	323	320	316	312	309	305	301	298	294	290	3 - 4
.38	287	283	279	275	272	268	264	260	257	253	3 - 4
.39	249	245	241	238	234	230	226	222	218	214	3 - 4
.40	211	207	203	199	195	191	187	183	179	175	3 - 4
.41	171	167	163	159	155	151	147	143	139	135	4
.42	131	127	123	119	115	110	106	102	098	094	4 - 5
.43	090	085	081	077	073	069	064	060	056	052	4 - 5
.44	048	043	039	035	030	026	022	017	013	009	4 - 5
.45	004	000	996	991	987	983	978	974	969	965	4 - 5
.46	.8 961	956	952	947	943	938	934	929	925	920	4 - 5
.47	916	911	907	902	897	893	888	884	879	875	4 - 5
.48	870	865	861	856	851	847	842	837	833	828	4 - 5
.49	823	819	814	809	804	800	795	790	785	781	4 - 5

COS X

x radians	0	1	2	3	4	5	6	7	8	9	Diff. (Subtract)
.50	.8 776	771	766	761	757	752	747	742	737	732	4 - 5
.51	727	723	718	713	708	703	698	693	688	683	4 - 5
.52	678	673	668	663	658	653	648	643	638	633	5
.53	628	623	618	613	608	603	598	592	587	582	5 - 6
.54	577	572	567	562	556	551	546	541	536	530	5 - 6
.55	525	520	515	510	504	499	494	488	483	478	5 - 6
.56	473	467	462	457	451	446	441	435	430	424	5 - 6
.57	419	414	408	403	397	392	386	381	376	370	5 - 6
.58	365	359	354	348	343	337	332	326	321	315	5 - 6
.59	309	304	298	293	287	281	276	270	265	259	5 - 6
.60	253	248	242	236	231	225	219	214	208	202	5 - 6
.61	196	191	185	179	173	168	162	156	150	145	5 - 6
.62	139	133	127	121	115	110	104	098	092	086	5 - 6
.63	080	074	068	063	057	051	045	039	033	027	5 - 6
.64	021	015	009	003	997	991	985	979	973	967	6
.65	.7 961	955	949	943	937	930	924	918	912	906	6 - 7
.66	900	894	888	881	875	869	863	857	851	844	6 - 7
.67	938	832	826	820	813	807	801	795	788	782	6 - 7
.68	776	769	763	757	751	744	738	732	725	719	6 - 7
.69	712	706	700	693	687	681	674	668	661	655	6 - 7
.70	648	642	636	629	623	616	610	603	597	590	6 - 7
.71	584	577	571	564	557	551	544	538	531	525	6 - 7
.72	518	511	505	498	492	485	478	472	465	458	6 - 7
.73	452	445	438	432	425	418	412	405	398	391	6 - 7
.74	385	378	371	364	358	351	344	337	331	324	6 - 7
.75	317	310	303	296	290	283	276	269	262	255	6 - 7
.76	248	241	235	228	221	214	207	200	193	186	6 - 7
.77	179	172	165	158	151	144	137	130	123	116	7
.78	109	102	095	088	081	074	067	060	053	046	7
.79	038	031	024	017	010	003	996	989	981	974	7 - 8
.80	.6 967	960	953	946	938	931	924	917	909	902	7 - 8
.81	895	888	880	873	866	859	851	844	837	830	7 - 8
.82	822	815	808	800	793	786	778	771	764	756	7 - 8
.83	749	741	734	727	719	712	704	697	690	682	7 - 8
.84	675	667	660	652	645	637	630	622	615	607	7 - 8
.85	600	592	585	577	570	562	555	547	540	532	7 - 8
.86	524	517	509	502	494	486	479	471	464	456	7 - 8
.87	448	441	433	425	418	410	402	395	387	379	7 - 8
.88	372	364	356	348	341	333	325	317	310	302	7 - 8
.89	294	286	279	271	263	255	247	240	232	224	7 - 8
.90	216	208	200	193	185	177	169	161	153	145	7 - 8
.91	137	130	122	114	106	098	090	082	074	066	7 - 8
.92	058	050	042	034	026	018	010	002	994	986	8
.93	.5 978	970	962	954	946	938	930	922	914	906	8
.94	898	890	882	874	866	857	849	841	833	825	8 - 9
.95	817	809	801	792	784	776	768	760	752	743	8 - 9
.96	735	727	719	711	702	694	686	678	669	661	8 - 9
.97	653	645	636	628	620	612	603	595	587	579	8 - 9
.98	570	562	554	545	537	529	520	512	504	495	8 - 9
.99	487	479	470	462	453	445	437	428	420	411	8 - 9

COS X

x radians	0	1	2	3	4	5	6	7	8	9	Diff. (Subtract)
1.00	.5 403	395	386	378	369	361	352	344	336	327	8 - 9
1.01	319	310	302	293	285	276	268	259	251	242	8 - 9
1.02	234	225	217	208	200	191	182	174	165	157	8 - 9
1.03.	148	140	131	122	114	105	097	088	079	071	8 - 9
1.04	062	054	045	036	028	019	010	002	993	984	8 - 9
1.05	.4 976	967	958	950	941	932	924	915	906	897	8 - 9
1.06	889	880	871	863	854	845	836	828	819	810	8 - 9
1.07	801	792	784	775	766	757	749	740	731	722	8 - 9
1.08	713	704	696	687	678	669	660	651	643	634	8 - 9
1.09	625	616	607	598	589	580	572	563	554	545	8 - 9
1.10	536	527	518	509	500	491	482	473	465	456	8 - 9
1.11	447	438	429	420	411	402	393	384	375	366	9
1.12	357	348	339	330	321	312	303	294	285	276	9
1.13	267	258	249	239	230	221	212	203	194	185	9 - 10
1.14	176	167	158	149	140	130	121	112	103	094	9 - 10
1.15	085	076	067	057	048	039	030	021	012	003	9 - 10
1.16	.3 993	984	975	966	957	948	938	929	920	911	9 - 10
1.17	902	892	883	874	865	855	846	837	828	818	9 - 10
1.18	809	800	791	781	772	763	754	744	735	726	9 - 10
1.19	717	707	698	689	679	670	661	652	642	633	9 - 10
1.20	624	614	605	596	586	577	568	558	549	540	9 - 10
1.21	550	521	511	502	493	483	474	465	455	446	9 - 10
1.22	436	427	418	408	399	389	380	371	361	352	9 - 10
1.23	342	333	324	314	305	295	286	276	267	257	9 - 10
1.24	248	239	229	220	210	201	191	182	172	163	9 - 10
1.25	153	144	134	125	115	106	096	087	077	068	9 - 10
1.26	058	049	039	030	020	011	001	991	982	972	9 - 10
1.27	.2 963	953	944	934	925	915	905	896	886	877	9 - 10
1.28	867	858	848	838	829	819	810	800	790	781	9 - 10
1.29	771	762	752	742	733	723	714	704	694	685	9 - 10
1.30	675	665	656	646	636	627	617	607	598	588	9 - 10
1.31	579	569	559	550	540	530	520	511	501	491	9 - 10
1.32	482	472	462	453	443	433	424	414	404	394	9 - 10
1.33	385	375	365	356	346	336	326	317	307	297	9 - 10
1.34	288	278	268	258	249	239	229	219	210	200	9 - 10
1.35	190	180	171	161	151	141	131	122	112	102	9 - 10
1.36	092	083	073	063	053	043	034	024	014	004	9 - 10
1.37	.1 994	985	975	965	955	945	936	926	916	906	9 - 10
1.38	896	887	877	867	857	847	837	828	818	808	9 - 10
1.39	798	788	778	769	759	749	739	729	719	710	9 - 10
1.40	700	690	680	670	660	650	641	631	621	611	9 - 10
1.41	601	591	581	571	562	552	542	532	522	512	9 - 10
1.42	502	492	482	473	463	453	443	433	423	413	9 - 10
1.43	403	393	384	374	364	354	344	334	324	314	9 - 10
1.44	304	294	284	274	265	255	245	235	225	215	9 - 10
1.45	205	195	185	175	165	155	145	136	126	116	9 - 10
1.46	106	096	086	076	066	056	046	036	026	016	10
1.47	006	996	986	976	966	956	947	937	927	917	9 - 10
1.48	.0 907	897	887	877	867	857	847	837	827	817	10
1.49	807	797	787	777	767	757	747	737	727	717	10

COS X

x radians	0	1	2	3	4	5	6	7	8	9	Diff. (Subtract)
1.50	.0 707	697	687	677	667	657	648	638	628	618	9 - 10
1.51	608	598	588	578	568	558	548	538	528	518	10
1.52	508	498	488	478	468	458	448	438	428	418	
1.53	408	398	388	378	368	358	348	338	328	318	
1.54	308	298	288	278	268	258	248	238	228	218	
1.55	208	198	188	178	168	158	148	138	128	118	
1.56	108	098	088	078	068	058	048	038	028	018	
1.57	008	002	012	022	032	042	052	062	072	082	10
1.58	-.0 092	102	112	122	132	142	152	162	172	182	
1.59	192	202	212	222	232	242	252	262	272	282	
1.60	292	302	312	322	332	342	352	362	372	382	
1.61	392	402	412	422	432	442	452	462	472	482	
1.62	492	502	512	522	532	542	552	562	572	582	
1.63	592	602	612	622	632	642	652	662	672	682	
1.64	691	701	711	721	731	741	751	761	771	781	
1.65	791	801	811	821	831	841	851	861	871	881	
1.66	891	901	911	921	931	941	951	961	971	980	
1.67	990	000	010	020	030	040	050	060	070	080	
1.68	-.1 090	100	110	120	130	140	149	159	169	179	
1.69	189	199	209	219	229	239	249	259	269	279	
1.70	288	298	308	318	328	338	348	358	368	378	
1.71	388	397	407	417	427	437	447	457	467	477	
1.72	487	496	506	516	526	536	546	556	566	575	
1.73	585	595	605	615	625	635	645	654	664	674	
1.74	684	694	704	714	723	733	743	753	763	773	
1.75	782	792	802	812	822	832	841	851	861	871	
1.76	881	891	900	910	920	930	940	949	959	969	
1.77	979	989	998	008	018	028	038	047	057	067	
1.78	-.2 077	087	096	106	116	126	135	145	155	165	
1.79	175	184	194	204	214	223	233	243	253	262	
1.80	272	282	291	301	311	321	330	340	350	360	
1.81	369	379	389	398	408	418	428	437	447	457	
1.82	466	476	486	495	505	515	524	534	544	553	
1.83	563	573	582	592	602	611	621	631	640	650	
1.84	660	669	679	689	698	708	717	727	737	746	
1.85	756	766	775	785	794	804	814	823	833	842	
1.86	852	861	871	881	890	900	909	919	928	938	
1.87	948	957	967	976	986	995	005	014	024	033	
1.88	-.3 043	053	062	072	081	091	100	110	119	129	9 - 10
1.89	138	148	157	167	176	186	195	204	214	223	
1.90	233	242	252	261	271	280	290	299	308	318	
1.91	327	337	346	356	365	374	384	393	403	412	
1.92	421	431	440	450	459	468	478	487	497	506	
1.93	515	525	534	543	553	562	571	581	590	599	
1.94	609	618	627	637	646	655	665	674	683	693	
1.95	702	711	720	730	739	748	757	767	776	785	
1.96	795	804	813	822	831	841	850	859	868	878	
1.97	887	896	905	914	924	933	942	951	960	970	
1.98	979	988	997	006	015	025	034	043	052	061	
1.99	-.4 070	079	089	098	107	116	125	134	143	152	9
2.00	161										

For larger values of x, use the method of subtracting multiples of π/2 ≡ 1.5708

TAN X

x radians	0	1	2	3	4	5	6	7	8	9	Diff.
.00	.0 000	010	020	030	040	050	060	070	080	090	10
.01	100	110	120	130	140	150	160	170	180	190	10
.02	200	210	220	230	240	250	260	270	280	290	10
.03	300	310	320	330	340	350	360	370	380	390	10
.04	400	410	420	430	440	450	460	470	480	490	10
.05	500	510	520	530	541	551	561	571	581	591	10 - 11
.06	601	611	621	631	641	651	661	671	681	691	10
.07	701	711	721	731	741	751	761	772	782	792	10 - 11
.08	802	812	822	832	842	852	862	872	882	892	10
.09	902	913	923	933	943	953	963	973	983	993	10 - 11
.10	.1 003	013	024	034	044	054	064	074	084	094	10 - 11
.11	104	115	125	135	145	155	165	175	186	196	10 - 11
.12	206	216	226	236	246	257	267	277	287	297	10 - 11
.13	307	318	328	338	348	358	368	379	389	399	10 - 11
.14	409	419	430	440	450	460	470	481	491	501	10 - 11
.15	511	522	532	542	552	563	573	583	593	604	10 - 11
.16	614	624	634	645	655	665	675	686	696	706	10 - 11
.17	717	727	737	747	758	768	778	789	799	809	10 - 11
.18	820	830	840	851	861	871	882	892	902	913	10 - 11
.19	923	934	944	954	965	975	985	996	006	017	10 - 11
.20	.2 027	038	048	058	069	079	090	100	111	121	10 - 11
.21	131	142	152	163	173	184	194	205	215	226	10 - 11
.22	236	247	257	268	278	289	299	310	320	331	10 - 11
.23	341	352	363	373	384	394	405	415	426	437	10 - 11
.24	447	458	468	479	490	500	511	521	532	543	10 - 11
.25	553	564	575	585	596	607	617	628	639	650	10 - 11
.26	660	671	682	692	703	714	725	735	746	757	10 - 11
.27	768	778	789	800	811	821	832	843	854	865	10 - 11
.28	876	886	897	908	919	930	941	951	962	973	10 - 11
.29	984	995	006	017	028	039	050	061	071	082	10 - 11
.30	.3 093	104	115	126	137	148	159	170	181	192	11
.31	203	214	225	236	247	258	270	281	292	303	11 - 12
.32	314	325	336	347	358	369	381	392	403	414	11 - 12
.33	425	436	448	459	470	481	492	504	515	526	11 - 12
.34	537	549	560	571	582	594	605	616	628	639	11 - 12
.35	650	662	673	684	696	707	718	730	741	753	11 - 12
.36	764	775	787	798	810	821	833	844	856	867	11 - 12
.37	879	890	902	913	925	936	948	959	971	983	11 - 12
.38	994	006	017	029	041	052	064	076	087	099	11 - 12
.39	111	122	134	146	157	169	181	193	204	216	11 - 12
.40	.4 228	240	252	263	275	287	299	311	323	334	11 - 12
.41	346	358	370	382	394	406	418	430	442	454	12
.42	466	478	490	502	514	526	538	550	562	574	12
.43	586	598	610	623	635	647	659	671	683	696	12 - 13
.44	708	720	732	745	757	769	781	794	806	818	12 - 13
.45	831	843	855	868	880	892	905	917	930	942	12 - 13
.46	954	967	979	992	004	017	029	042	055	067	12 - 13
.47	.5 080	092	105	117	130	143	155	168	181	193	12 - 13
.48	206	219	232	244	257	270	283	295	308	321	12 - 13
.49	334	347	360	372	385	398	411	424	437	450	12 - 13

TAN X

x radians	0	1	2	3	4	5	6	7	8	9	Diff.
.50	.5 463	476	489	502	515	528	541	554	567	580	13
.51	594	607	620	633	646	659	673	686	699	712	13 - 14
.52	726	739	752	766	779	792	806	819	832	846	13 - 14
.53	859	873	886	900	913	927	940	954	967	981	13 - 14
.54	994	008	022	035	049	062	076	090	104	117	13 - 14
.55	.6 131	145	159	172	186	200	214	228	242	256	13 - 14
.56	269	283	297	311	325	339	353	367	382	396	13 - 15
.57	410	424	438	452	466	480	495	509	523	537	14 - 15
.58	552	566	580	595	609	623	638	652	667	681	14 - 15
.59	696	710	725	739	754	768	783	797	812	827	14 - 15
.60	841	856	871	886	900	915	930	945	959	974	14 - 15
.61	989	004	019	034	049	064	079	094	109	124	15
.62	.7 139	154	169	184	200	215	230	245	261	276	15 - 16
.63	291	306	322	337	353	368	383	399	414	430	15 - 16
.64	445	461	477	492	508	523	539	555	571	586	15 - 16
.65	602	618	634	649	665	681	697	713	729	745	15 - 16
.66	761	777	793	809	825	841	858	874	890	906	16 - 17
.67	923	939	955	971	988	004	021	037	054	070	16 - 17
.68	.8 087	103	120	136	153	170	186	203	220	237	16 - 17
.69	253	270	287	304	321	338	355	372	389	406	16 - 17
.70	423	440	457	474	491	509	526	543	561	578	17 - 18
.71	595	613	630	648	665	683	700	718	735	753	17 - 18
.72	771	788	806	824	842	860	877	895	913	931	17 - 18
.73	949	967	985	003	021	040	058	076	094	113	18 - 19
.74	.9 131	149	168	186	205	223	242	260	279	297	18 - 19
.75	316	335	353	372	391	410	429	448	467	485	18 - 19
.76	505	524	543	562	581	600	619	639	658	677	19 - 20
.77	697	716	736	755	775	794	814	833	853	873	19 - 20
.78	893	912	932	952	972	992	012	032	052	072	19 - 20
.79	1.0 092	113	133	153	174	194	214	235	255	276	20 - 21
.80	296	317	338	358	379	400	421	442	463	484	20 - 21
.81	505	526	547	568	589	610	632	653	674	696	21 - 22
.82	717	739	760	782	803	825	847	869	891	912	21 - 22
.83	934	956	978	000	023	045	067	089	112	134	22 - 23
.84	1.1 156	179	201	224	247	269	292	315	338	360	22 - 23
.85	383	406	429	452	476	499	522	545	569	592	23 - 24
.86	616	639	663	686	710	734	758	781	805	829	23 - 24
.87	853	877	901	926	950	974	999	023	047	072	24 - 25
.88	1.2 097	121	146	171	196	221	246	271	296	321	24 - 25
.89	346	371	397	422	447	473	499	524	550	576	25 - 26
.90	602	627	653	680	706	732	758	784	811	837	25 - 27
.91	864	890	917	944	970	997	024	051	078	105	26 - 27
.92	1.3 133	160	187	215	242	270	297	325	353	381	27 - 28
.93	409	437	465	493	521	550	578	606	635	664	28 - 29
.94	692	721	750	779	808	837	866	896	925	954	28 - 30
.95	984	013	043	073	103	133	163	193	223	253	29 - 30
.96	1.4 284	314	345	375	406	437	468	499	530	561	30 - 31
.97	592	623	655	686	718	750	781	813	845	877	31 - 33
.98	910	942	974	007	039	072	105	138	171	204	32 - 33
.99	1.5 237	270	303	337	370	404	438	472	506	540	33 - 34

TAN X

x radians	0	1	2	3	4	5	6	7	8	9	Diff.
1.00	1.5 574	608	643	677	712	747	782	817	852	887	34 - 35
1.01	922	957	993	029	064	100	136	172	209	245	35 - 37
1.02	1.6 281	318	355	391	428	465	503	540	577	615	36 - 38
1.03	652	690	728	766	804	843	881	920	958	997	37 - 39
1.04	1.7 036	075	114	154	193	233	273	313	353	393	39 - 40
1.05	433	474	514	555	596	637	678	719	761	802	40 - 42
1.06	844	886	928	970	013	055	098	141	184	227	42 - 43
1.07	1.8 270	314	357	401	445	489	533	578	622	667	43 - 45
1.08	712	757	803	848	894	939	985	031	078	124	45 - 47
1.09	1.9 171	218	265	312	359	407	455	503	551	599	47 - 48
1.10	648	696	745	794	844	893	943	993	043	093	48 - 50
1.11	2.0 143	194	245	296	347	399	451	502	555	607	50 - 53
1.12	660	712	765	819	872	926	980	034	088	143	52 - 55
1.13	2.1 198	253	308	363	419	475	531	588	645	702	55 - 57
1.14	759	816	874	932	990	049	107	166	226	285	57 - 60
1.15	2.2 345	405	465	526	587	648	709	771	833	895	60 - 62
1.16	958	021	084	147	211	275	339	404	469	534	63 - 65
1.17	2.3 600	666	732	798	865	932	000	067	135	204	66 - 69
1.18	2.4 273	342	411	481	551	621	692	763	835	907	69 - 72
1.19	979	052	125	198	271	346	420	495	570	646	72 - 76
1.20	2.5 722	798	875	952	029	107	186	264	344	423	76 - 80
1.21	2.6 503	584	665	746	828	910	992	076	159	243	80 - 84
1.22	2.7 328	412	498	584	670	757	844	932	020	109	84 - 89
1.23	2.8 198	288	378	469	560	652	744	837	931	025	89 - 94
1.24	2.9 119	214	310	406	503	600	698	797	896	995	94 - 99
1.25	3. 010	020	030	040	050	061	071	081	092	103	10 - 11
1.26	113	124	135	146	157	168	179	190	201	212	10 - 11
1.27	224	235	247	258	270	282	293	305	317	329	11 - 12
1.28	341	354	366	378	391	403	416	429	441	454	12 - 13
1.29	467	480	493	507	520	533	547	561	574	588	13 - 14
1.30	602	616	630	644	659	673	688	702	717	732	14 - 15
1.31	747	762	777	793	808	824	839	855	871	887	15 - 16
1.32	903	920	936	953	969	986	003	020	037	055	16 - 18
1.33	4. 072	090	108	126	144	162	180	199	218	237	17 - 19
1.34	256	275	294	314	333	353	373	393	414	434	19 - 21
1.35	455	476	497	519	540	562	584	606	628	651	21 - 23
1.36	673	696	720	743	767	790	814	839	863	888	22 - 25
1.37	913	938	964	990	016	042	068	095	122	150	25 - 28
1.38	5. 177	205	234	262	291	320	350	379	410	440	27 - 31
1.39	471	502	533	565	597	630	663	696	729	763	31 - 34
1.40	798	833	868	904	940	976	013	050	088	127	35 - 39
1.41	6. 165	205	244	285	325	367	408	451	494	537	38 - 43
1.42	581	626	671	717	763	810	858	906	955	005	44 - 50
1.43	7. 055	107	158	211	264	319	374	429	486	543	50 - 57
1.44	602	661	721	782	844	907	971	036	103	170	59 - 67
1.45	8. 238	308	378	450	523	597	673	750	828	908	68 - 80
1.46	989	071	155	241	328	417	507	600	694	790	81 - 96
1.47	9. 887	987	089	193	299	407	517	630	745	863	
1.48	10. 983										
	11.	106	232	361	492	627	765	906	050	198	
1.49	12. 350	505	665	828	996						
	13.					168	345	526	713	904	

TAN X

x radians	tan x	x radians	tan x
1.500	14.101	1.540	32.461
1.501	14.304	1.541	33.551
1.502	14.513	1.542	34.717
1.503	14.727	1.543	35.967
1.504	14.949	1.544	37.310
1.505	15.176	1.545	38.757
1.506	15.411	1.546	40.320
1.507	15.654	1.547	42.015
1.508	15.904	1.548	43.859
1.509	16.162	1.549	45.872
1.510	16.428	1.550	48.078
1.511	16.703	1.551	50.508
1.512	16.988	1.552	53.196
1.513	17.283	1.553	56.185
1.514	17.588	1.554	59.531
1.515	17.904	1.555	63.301
1.516	18.231	1.556	67.579
1.517	18.571	1.557	72.478
1.518	18.923	1.558	78.143
1.519	19.289	1.559	84.768
1.520	19.670	1.560	92.620
1.521	20.065	1.561	102.08
1.522	20.477	1.562	113.68
1.523	20.906	1.563	128.26
1.524	21.354	1.564	147.14
1.525	21.821	1.565	172.52
1.526	22.308	1.566	208.49
1.527	22.818	1.567	263.41
1.528	23.352	1.568	357.61
1.529	23.912	1.569	556.69
1.530	24.498	1.570	1255.8
1.531	25.115		
1.532	25.763		
1.533	26.445		
1.534	27.164		
1.535	27.924		
1.536	28.727		
1.537	29.578		
1.538	30.480		
1.539	31.440		

For larger values of x, use the method of subtracting multiples of $\pi/2 = 1.57080$

For large tables of trigonometric functions of angles in radians, see the tables published by the National Bureau of Standards, Washington, D.C.

SIN⁻¹ X = ARC SIN X, RADIANS

x	0	1	2	3	4	5	6	7	8	9	Diff.
.00	.0 000	010	020	030	040	050	060	070	080	090	10
.01	100	110	120	130	140	150	160	170	180	190	10
.02	200	210	220	230	240	250	260	270	280	290	10
.03	300	310	320	330	340	350	360	370	380	390	10
.04	400	410	420	430	440	450	460	470	480	490	10
.05	500	510	520	530	540	550	560	570	580	590	10
.06	600	610	620	630	640	650	660	671	681	691	10 - 11
.07	701	711	721	731	741	751	761	771	781	791	10
.08	801	811	821	831	841	851	861	871	881	891	10
.09	901	911	921	931	941	951	961	972	982	992	10 - 11
.10	.1 002	012	022	032	042	052	062	072	082	092	10
.11	102	112	122	132	142	153	163	173	183	193	10 - 11
.12	203	213	223	233	243	253	263	273	284	294	10 - 11
.13	304	314	324	334	344	354	364	374	384	395	10 - 11
.14	405	415	425	435	445	455	465	475	485	496	10 - 11
.15	506	516	526	536	546	556	566	577	587	597	10 - 11
.16	607	617	627	637	647	658	668	678	688	698	10 - 11
.17	708	718	729	739	749	759	769	779	790	800	10 - 11
.18	810	820	830	840	851	861	871	881	891	901	10 - 11
.19	912	922	932	942	952	963	973	983	993	003	10 - 11
.20	.2 014	024	034	044	054	065	075	085	095	106	10 - 11
.21	116	126	136	146	157	167	177	187	198	208	10 - 11
.22	218	228	239	249	259	269	280	290	300	311	10 - 11
.23	321	331	341	352	362	372	382	393	403	413	10 - 11
.24	424	434	444	455	465	475	486	496	506	516	10 - 11
.25	527	537	547	558	568	578	589	599	610	620	10 - 11
.26	630	641	651	661	672	682	692	703	713	724	10 - 11
.27	734	744	755	765	776	786	796	807	817	828	10 - 11
.28	838	848	859	869	880	890	900	911	921	932	10 - 11
.29	942	953	963	974	984	995	005	015	026	036	10 - 11
.30	.3 047	057	068	078	089	099	110	120	131	141	10 - 11
.31	152	162	173	184	194	205	215	226	236	247	10 - 11
.32	257	268	278	289	300	310	321	331	342	352	10 - 11
.33	363	374	384	395	405	416	427	437	448	459	10 - 11
.34	469	480	490	501	512	522	533	544	554	565	10 - 11
.35	576	586	597	608	618	629	640	651	661	672	10 - 11
.36	683	693	704	715	726	736	747	758	769	779	10 - 11
.37	790	801	812	822	833	844	855	866	876	887	10 - 11
.38	898	909	920	930	941	952	963	974	985	995	10 - 11
.39	.4 006	017	028	039	050	061	072	082	093	104	10 - 11
.40	115	126	137	148	159	170	181	192	203	214	11
.41	225	236	246	257	268	279	290	301	312	323	10 - 11
.42	334	345	357	368	379	390	401	412	423	434	11 - 12
.43	445	456	467	478	489	500	511	523	534	545	11 - 12
.44	556	567	578	589	601	612	623	634	645	656	11 - 12
.45	668	679	690	701	712	724	735	746	757	769	11 - 12
.46	780	791	802	814	825	836	848	859	870	882	11 - 12
.47	893	904	916	927	938	950	961	972	984	995	11 - 12
.48	.5 007	018	029	041	052	064	075	087	098	109	11 - 12
.49	121	132	144	155	167	178	190	201	213	224	11 - 12

x	0	1	2	3	4	5	6	7	8	9	Diff.
.50	.5 236	248	259	271	282	294	305	317	329	340	11 - 12
.51	352	363	375	387	398	410	422	433	445	457	11 - 12
.52	469	480	492	504	515	527	539	551	562	574	11 - 12
.53	586	598	610	621	633	645	657	669	681	692	11 - 12
.54	704	716	728	740	752	764	776	788	800	812	12
.55	824	836	848	860	872	884	896	908	920	932	12
.56	944	956	968	980	992	004	016	029	041	053	12 - 13
.57	.6 065	077	089	102	114	126	138	151	163	175	12 - 13
.58	187	200	212	224	236	249	261	273	286	298	12 - 13
.59	311	323	335	348	360	373	385	398	410	423	12 - 13
.60	435	448	460	473	485	498	510	523	535	548	12 - 13
.61	561	573	586	599	611	624	637	649	662	675	12 - 13
.62	687	700	713	726	739	751	764	777	790	803	12 - 13
.63	816	828	841	854	867	880	893	906	919	932	12 - 13
.64	945	958	971	984	997	010	023	036	050	063	13 - 14
.65	.7 076	089	102	115	129	142	155	168	182	195	13 - 14
.66	208	222	235	248	262	275	288	302	315	329	13 - 14
.67	342	356	369	383	396	410	423	437	450	464	13 - 14
.68	478	491	505	519	532	546	560	574	587	601	13 - 14
.69	615	629	643	656	670	684	698	712	726	740	13 - 14
.70	754	768	782	796	810	824	838	852	867	881	14 - 15
.71	895	909	923	938	952	966	981	995	009	024	14 - 15
.72	.8 038	052	067	081	096	110	125	139	154	169	14 - 15
.73	183	198	213	227	242	257	271	286	301	316	14 - 15
.74	331	346	360	375	390	405	420	435	450	466	14 - 16
.75	481	496	511	526	541	557	572	587	602	618	15 - 16
.76	633	649	664	679	695	710	726	742	757	773	15 - 16
.77	788	804	820	836	851	867	883	899	915	931	15 - 16
.78	947	963	979	995	011	027	043	059	076	092	16 - 17
.79	.9 108	124	141	157	174	190	207	223	240	256	16 - 17
.80	273	290	306	323	340	357	374	391	407	424	16 - 17
.81	442	459	476	493	510	527	545	562	579	597	17 - 18
.82	614	632	649	667	684	702	720	738	755	773	17 - 18
.83	791	809	827	845	863	881	900	918	936	954	18 - 19
.84	973	991	010	028	047	066	084	103	122	141	18 - 19
.85	1.0 160	179	198	217	236	255	275	294	314	333	19 - 20
.86	353	372	392	412	432	452	471	492	512	532	19 - 21
.87	552	572	593	613	634	654	675	696	717	738	20 - 21
.88	759	780	801	822	844	865	886	908	930	952	21 - 22
.89	973	995	018	040	062	084	107	129	152	175	21 - 23
.90	1.1 198	221	244	267	290	314	337	361	385	409	23 - 24
.91	433	457	481	506	530	555	580	605	630	655	24 - 25
.92	681	706	732	758	784	810	837	863	890	917	25 - 27
.93	944	971	999	027	054	083	111	139	168	197	27 - 29
.94	1.2 226	256	285	315	346	376	407	438	469	500	29 - 31
.95	532	565	597	630	663	697	730	765	799	835	32 - 36
.96	870	906	942	979	017	054	093	132	171	212	35 - 41
.97	1.3 252	294	336	379	423	467	513	559	606	655	40 - 49
.98	705	756	808	861	917	974	033	094	157	223	50 - 66
.99	1.4 293	365	442	524	612	708	813	933	075	261	70 -186
1.00	1.5 708										

For a large inverse trigonometric table see
"Table of Arc sin x," Columbia University Press, New York.
Note that $\cos^{-1} x$ = arc cos x = $\pi/2$ − arc sin x.

x	0	1	2	3	4	5	6	7	8	9	Diff. (Subtract)
.00	1.5 708	698	688	678	668	658	648	638	628	618	10
.01	608	598	588	578	568	558	548	538	528	518	10
.02	508	498	488	478	468	458	448	438	428	418	10
.03	408	398	388	378	368	358	348	338	328	318	10
.04	308	298	288	278	268	258	248	238	228	218	10
.05	208	198	188	178	168	158	148	138	128	118	10
.06	108	098	088	078	068	058	047	037	027	017	10 - 11
.07	007	997	987	977	967	957	947	937	927	917	10
.08	1.4 907	897	887	877	867	857	847	837	827	817	10
.09	807	797	787	777	767	757	746	736	726	716	10 - 11
.10	706	696	686	676	666	656	646	636	626	616	10
.11	606	596	586	576	565	555	545	535	525	515	10 - 11
.12	505	495	485	475	465	455	445	435	424	414	10 - 11
.13	404	394	384	374	364	354	344	334	324	313	10 - 11
.14	303	293	283	273	263	253	243	233	223	212	10 - 11
.15	202	192	182	172	162	152	142	131	121	111	10 - 11
.16	101	091	081	071	061	050	040	030	020	010	10 - 11
.17	000	990	979	969	959	949	939	929	918	908	10 - 11
.18	1.3 898	888	878	868	857	847	837	827	817	807	10 - 11
.19	796	786	776	766	756	745	735	725	715	705	10 - 11
.20	694	684	674	664	654	643	633	623	613	602	10 - 11
.21	592	582	572	562	551	541	531	521	510	500	10 - 11
.22	490	480	469	459	449	439	428	418	408	397	10 - 11
.23	387	377	367	356	346	336	325	315	305	295	10 - 11
.24	284	274	264	253	243	233	222	212	202	191	10 - 11
.25	181	171	160	150	140	129	119	109	098	088	10 - 11
.26	078	067	057	047	036	026	016	005	995	984	10 - 11
.27	1.2 974	964	953	943	932	922	912	901	891	880	10 - 11
.28	870	860	849	839	828	818	807	797	787	776	10 - 11
.29	766	755	745	734	724	713	703	692	682	672	10 - 11
.30	661	651	640	630	619	609	598	588	577	567	10 - 11
.31	556	546	535	524	514	503	493	482	472	461	10 - 11
.32	451	440	430	419	408	398	387	377	366	356	10 - 11
.33	345	334	324	313	303	292	281	271	260	249	10 - 11
.34	239	228	218	207	196	186	175	164	154	143	10 - 11
.35	132	122	111	100	090	079	068	057	047	036	10 - 11
.36	025	015	004	993	982	972	961	950	939	929	10 - 11
.37	1.1 918	907	896	886	875	864	853	842	832	821	10 - 11
.38	810	799	788	778	767	756	745	734	723	713	10 - 11
.39	702	691	680	669	658	647	636	626	615	604	10 - 11
.40	593	582	571	560	549	538	527	516	505	494	11
.41	483	472	461	451	440	429	418	407	396	385	10 - 11
.42	374	362	351	340	329	318	307	296	285	274	11 - 12
.43	263	252	241	230	219	208	196	185	174	163	11 - 12
.44	152	141	130	119	107	096	085	074	063	052	11 - 12
.45	040	029	018	007	995	984	973	962	951	939	11 - 12
.46	1.0 928	917	905	894	883	872	860	849	838	826	11 - 12
.47	815	804	792	781	770	758	747	736	724	713	11 - 12
.48	701	690	679	667	656	644	633	621	610	599	11 - 12
.49	587	576	564	553	541	530	518	507	495	484	11 - 12

COS^{-1} X , RADIANS

x	0	1	2	3	4	5	6	7	8	9	Diff. (Subtract)
.50	1.0 472	460	449	437	426	414	403	391	379	368	11 - 12
.51	356	344	333	321	310	298	286	275	263	251	11 - 12
.52	239	228	216	204	193	181	169	157	146	134	11 - 12
.53	122	110	098	087	075	063	051	039	027	015	11 - 12
.54	004	992	980	968	956	944	932	920	908	896	11 - 12
.55	.9 884	872	860	848	836	824	812	800	788	776	12
.56	764	752	740	728	716	704	692	679	667	655	12 - 13
.57	643	631	619	606	594	582	570	557	545	533	12 - 13
.58	521	508	496	484	471	459	447	434	422	410	12 - 13
.59	397	385	373	360	348	335	323	310	298	285	12 - 13
.60	273	260	248	235	223	210	198	185	173	160	12 - 13
.61	147	135	122	109	097	084	071	059	046	033	12 - 13
.62	021	008	995	982	969	957	944	931	918	905	12 - 13
.63	.8 892	880	867	854	841	828	815	802	789	776	12 - 13
.64	763	750	737	724	711	698	685	672	658	645	13 - 14
.65	632	619	606	593	579	566	553	540	526	513	13 - 14
.66	500	486	473	460	446	433	420	406	393	379	13 - 14
.67	366	352	339	325	312	298	285	271	258	244	13 - 14
.68	230	217	203	189	176	162	148	134	121	107	13 - 14
.69	093	079	065	052	038	024	010	996	982	968	13 - 14
.70	.7 954	940	926	912	898	884	870	855	841	827	14 - 15
.71	813	799	785	770	756	742	727	713	699	684	14 - 15
.72	670	656	641	627	612	598	583	569	554	539	14 - 15
.73	525	510	495	481	466	451	437	422	407	392	14 - 15
.74	377	362	347	333	318	303	288	273	258	242	14 - 16
.75	227	212	197	182	167	151	136	121	106	090	15 - 16
.76	075	059	044	029	013	998	982	966	951	935	15 - 16
.77	.6 920	904	888	872	857	841	825	809	793	777	15 - 16
.78	761	745	729	713	697	681	665	649	632	616	16 - 17
.79	600	584	567	551	534	518	501	485	468	452	16 - 17
.80	435	418	402	385	368	351	334	317	300	283	16 - 17
.81	266	249	232	215	198	181	163	146	129	111	17 - 18
.82	094	076	059	041	024	006	988	970	953	935	17 - 18
.83	.5 917	899	881	863	845	827	808	790	772	754	18 - 19
.84	735	717	698	680	661	642	624	605	586	567	18 - 19
.85	548	529	510	491	472	452	433	414	394	375	19 - 20
.86	355	336	316	296	276	256	236	216	196	176	19 - 20
.87	156	136	115	095	074	054	033	012	991	970	20 - 21
.88	.4 949	928	907	886	864	843	822	800	778	756	21 - 22
.89	735	713	690	668	646	624	601	579	556	533	21 - 23
.90	510	487	464	441	418	394	371	347	323	299	23 - 24
.91	275	251	227	202	178	153	128	103	078	053	24 - 25
.92	027	002	976	950	924	898	871	845	818	791	25 - 27
.93	.3 764	737	709	681	653	625	597	569	540	511	27 - 29
.94	482	452	423	393	362	332	301	270	239	207	29 - 32
.95	176	143	111	078	045	011	977	943	909	873	31 - 36
.96	.2 838	802	766	729	691	654	615	576	537	496	35 - 41
.97	456	414	372	329	285	241	195	149	101	053	40 - 48
.98	003	952	900	847	791	734	675	614	551	485	50 - 66
.99	.1 415	343	266	184	096	000	895	775	633	447	70 -186
1.00	.0 000										

For a large table, see "Sieben- und mehrstellige
Tafeln der Kreis- und Hyperbelfunktionen," by K. Hayashi, 1926.

TAN^{-1} X , RADIANS

x	0	1	2	3	4	5	6	7	8	9	Diff.
.00	.0 000	010	020	030	040	050	060	070	080	090	10
.01	100	110	120	130	140	150	160	170	180	190	10
.02	200	210	220	230	240	250	260	270	280	290	10
.03	300	310	320	330	340	350	360	370	380	390	10
.04	400	410	420	430	440	450	460	470	480	490	10
.05	500	510	520	530	539	549	559	569	579	589	9 - 10
.06	599	609	619	629	639	649	659	669	679	689	10
.07	699	709	719	729	739	749	759	768	778	788	9 - 10
.08	798	808	818	828	838	848	858	868	878	888	10
.09	898	908	917	927	937	947	957	967	977	987	9 - 10
.10	997	0̅0̅7̅	0̅1̅6̅	0̅2̅6̅	0̅3̅6̅	0̅4̅6̅	0̅5̅6̅	0̅6̅6̅	0̅7̅6̅	0̅8̅6̅	9 - 10
.11	.1 096	105	115	125	135	145	155	165	175	184	9 - 10
.12	194	204	214	224	234	244	253	263	273	283	9 - 10
.13	293	303	312	322	332	342	352	362	371	381	9 - 10
.14	391	401	411	420	430	440	450	460	469	479	9 - 10
.15	489	499	508	518	528	538	548	557	567	577	9 - 10
.16	587	596	606	616	626	635	645	655	664	674	9 - 10
.17	684	694	703	713	723	732	742	752	762	771	9 - 10
.18	781	791	800	810	820	829	839	849	858	868	9 - 10
.19	878	887	897	907	916	926	935	945	955	964	9 - 10
.20	974	984	993	0̅0̅3̅	0̅1̅2̅	0̅2̅2̅	0̅3̅2̅	0̅4̅1̅	0̅5̅1̅	0̅6̅0̅	9 - 10
.21	.2 070	079	089	099	108	118	127	137	146	156	9 - 10
.22	166	175	185	194	204	213	223	232	242	251	9 - 10
.23	261	270	280	289	299	308	318	327	337	346	9 - 10
.24	355	365	374	384	393	403	412	422	431	440	9 - 10
.25	450	459	469	478	487	497	506	516	525	534	9 - 10
.26	544	553	562	572	581	590	600	609	618	628	9 - 10
.27	637	646	656	665	674	684	693	702	712	721	9 - 10
.28	730	739	749	758	767	776	786	795	804	813	9 - 10
.29	823	832	841	850	859	869	878	887	896	905	9 - 10
.30	915	924	933	942	951	960	970	979	988	997	9 - 10
.31	.3 006	015	024	033	043	052	061	070	079	088	9 - 10
.32	097	106	115	124	133	142	151	160	169	178	9
.33	187	196	206	215	224	232	241	250	259	268	8 - 10
.34	277	286	295	304	313	322	331	340	349	358	9
.35	367	376	385	393	402	411	420	429	438	447	8 - 9
.36	456	464	473	482	491	500	509	517	526	535	8 - 9
.37	544	553	561	570	579	588	596	605	614	623	8 - 9
.38	631	640	649	658	666	675	684	692	701	710	8 - 9
.39	719	727	736	745	753	762	771	779	788	796	8 - 9
.40	805	814	822	831	839	848	857	865	874	882	8 - 9
.41	891	900	908	917	925	934	942	951	959	968	8 - 9
.42	976	985	993	0̅0̅2̅	0̅1̅0̅	0̅1̅9̅	0̅2̅7̅	0̅3̅6̅	0̅4̅4̅	0̅5̅3̅	8 - 9
.43	.4 061	069	078	086	095	103	112	120	128	137	8 - 9
.44	145	153	162	170	179	187	195	204	212	220	8 - 9
.45	229	237	245	253	262	270	278	287	295	303	8 - 9
.46	311	320	328	336	344	353	361	369	377	385	8 - 9
.47	394	402	410	418	426	434	443	451	459	467	8 - 9
.48	475	483	491	500	508	516	524	532	540	548	8 - 9
.49	556	564	572	580	588	596	604	612	620	628	8

TAN^{-1} X , RADIANS

x	0	1	2	3	4	5	6	7	8	9	Diff.
.50	.4 636	644	652	660	668	676	684	692	700	708	8
.51	716	724	732	740	748	756	764	772	779	787	7 - 8
.52	795	803	811	819	827	834	842	850	858	866	7 - 8
.53	874	881	889	897	905	913	920	928	936	944	7 - 8
.54	951	959	967	975	982	990	998	$\overline{005}$	$\overline{013}$	$\overline{021}$	7 - 8
.55	.5 028	036	044	051	059	067	074	082	090	097	7 - 8
.56	105	112	120	128	135	143	150	158	166	173	7 - 8
.57	181	188	196	203	211	218	226	233	241	248	7 - 8
.58	256	263	271	278	286	293	301	308	315	323	7 - 8
.59	330	338	345	353	360	367	375	382	389	397	7 - 8
.60	404	412	419	426	434	441	448	456	463	470	7 - 8
.61	477	485	492	499	507	514	521	528	535	543	7 - 8
.62	550	557	564	572	579	586	593	600	608	615	7 - 8
.63	622	629	636	643	650	658	665	672	679	686	7 - 8
.64	693	700	707	714	721	729	736	743	750	757	7 - 8
.65	764	771	778	785	792	799	806	813	820	827	7
.66	834	841	848	855	862	868	875	882	889	896	6 - 7
.67	903	910	917	924	931	937	944	951	958	965	6 - 7
.68	972	979	985	992	999	$\overline{006}$	$\overline{013}$	$\overline{019}$	$\overline{026}$	$\overline{033}$	6 - 7
.69	.6 040	047	053	060	067	074	080	087	094	101	6 - 7
.70	107	114	121	127	134	141	147	154	161	167	6 - 7
.71	174	181	187	194	201	207	214	220	227	234	6 - 7
.72	240	247	253	260	267	273	280	286	293	299	6 - 7
.73	306	312	319	325	332	338	345	351	358	364	6 - 7
.74	371	377	384	390	397	403	409	416	422	429	6 - 7
.75	435	441	448	454	461	467	473	480	486	492	6 - 7
.76	499	505	511	518	524	530	537	543	549	556	6 - 7
.77	562	568	574	581	587	593	599	606	612	618	6 - 7
.78	624	630	637	643	649	655	661	668	674	680	6 - 7
.79	686	692	698	705	711	717	723	729	735	741	6 - 7
.80	747	754	760	766	772	778	784	790	796	802	6 - 7
.81	808	814	820	826	832	838	844	850	856	862	6
.82	868	874	880	886	892	898	904	910	916	922	6
.83	928	934	940	945	951	957	963	969	975	981	5 - 6
.84	987	992	998	$\overline{004}$	$\overline{010}$	$\overline{016}$	$\overline{022}$	$\overline{027}$	$\overline{033}$	$\overline{039}$	5 - 6
.85	.7 045	051	057	062	068	074	080	085	091	097	5 - 6
.86	103	108	114	120	126	131	137	143	149	154	5 - 6
.87	160	166	171	177	183	188	194	200	205	211	5 - 6
.88	217	222	228	233	239	245	250	256	261	267	5 - 6
.89	273.	278	284	289	295	300	306	312	317	323	5 - 6
.90	328	334	339	345	350	356	361	367	372	378	5 - 6
.91	383	389	394	400	405	410	416	421	427	432	5 - 6
.92	438	443	448	454	459	465	470	475	481	486	5 - 6
.93	491	497	502	508	513	518	524	529	534	539	5 - 6
.94	545	550	555	561	566	571	577	582	587	592	5 - 6
.95	598	603	608	613	619	624	629	634	640	645	5 - 6
.96	650	655	660	666	671	676	681	686	691	697	5 - 6
.97	702	707	712	717	722	727	733	738	743	748	5 - 6
.98	753	758	763	768	773	778	783	789	794	799	5 - 6
.99	804	809	814	819	824	829	834	839	844	849	5

$$\text{TAN}^{-1}\ X\ ,\ \text{RADIANS}$$

x	0	1	2	3	4	5	6	7	8	9	Diff.
1.0	.7 854	904	953	002̄	050̄	098̄	145̄	192̄	238̄	284̄	46 - 50
1.1	.8 330	375	419	464	507	551	593	636	678	719	42 - 45
1.2	761	801	842	882	921	961	999	038̄	076̄	114̄	37 - 41
1.3	.9 151	188	225	261	297	332	368	403	437	472	33 - 37
1.4	505	539	572	605	638	670	703	734	766	797	31 - 34
1.5	828	859	889	919	949	978	008̄	037̄	065̄	094̄	28 - 31
1.6	1.0 122	150	178	205	232	259	286	313	339	365	26 - 28
1.7	391	416	442	467	492	517	541	565	589	613	24 - 26
1.8	637	660	684	707	730	752	775	797	819	841	22 - 24
1.9	863	885	906	927	949	969	990	011̄	031̄	051̄	20 - 22
2.0	1.1 071	091	111	131	150	170	189	208	227	245	18 - 20
2.1	264	282	300	319	337	354	372	390	407	425	17 - 19
2.2	442	459	476	492	509	526	542	558	575	591	16 - 17
2.3	607	623	638	654	669	685	700	715	730	745	15 - 16
2.4	760	775	789	804	818	833	847	861	875	889	14 - 15
2.5	903	917	930	944	957	971	984	997	010̄	023̄	13 - 14
2.6	1.2 036	049	062	074	087	100	112	124	137	149	12 - 13
2.7	161	173	185	197	209	220	232	243	255	266	11 - 12
2.8	278	289	300	311	322	333	344	355	366	377	10 - 11
2.9	387	398	408	419	429	440	450	460	470	480	10 - 11
3.0	490	500	510	520	530	540	549	559	569	578	9 - 10
3.1	588	597	606	616	625	634	643	652	661	670	9 - 10
3.2	679	688	697	706	714	723	732	740	749	757	8 - 9
3.3	766	774	782	791	799	807	815	823	831	839	8 - 9
3.4	847	855	863	871	879	887	894	902	910	917	7 - 8
3.5	925	932	940	947	955	962	970	977	984	991	7 - 8
3.6	998	006̄	013̄	020̄	027̄	034̄	041̄	048̄	055̄	062̄	7 - 8
3.7	1.3 068	075	082	089	095	102	109	115	122	128	6 - 7
3.8	135	141	148	154	160	167	173	179	186	192	6 - 7
3.9	198	204	210	216	222	228	234	240	246	252	6
4.	258	316	371	423	473	521	567	612	654	695	39 - 58
5.	734	772	808	843	877	909	941	971	001̄	029̄	27 - 38
6.	1.4 056	083	109	134	158	181	204	226	248	269	20 - 27
7.	289	309	328	347	365	382	400	416	433	449	15 - 20
8.	464	480	494	509	523	537	550	564	576	589	12 - 16
9.	601	613	625	637	648	659	670	681	691	701	10 - 12
10.	711	721	731	740	749	758	767	776	785	793	8 - 10
11.	801	809	817	825	833	841	848	855	863	870	7 - 8
12.	877	883	890	897	903	910	916	922	928	934	6 - 7
13.	940	946	952	957	963	969	974	979	985	990	5 - 6
14.	995	000̄	005̄	010̄	015̄	019̄	024̄	029̄	033̄	038̄	4 - 5
15.	1.5 042	047	051	055	060	064	068	072	076	080	4 - 5
16.	084	088	091	095	099	103	106	110	113	117	3 - 4
17.	120	124	127	131	134	137	140	144	147	150	3 - 4
18.	153	156	159	162	165	168	171	174	177	179	2 - 3
19.	182	185	188	190	193	196	198	201	203	206	2 - 3

x	0	1	2	3	4	5	6	7	8	9	Diff.
20.	1.5 208	211	213	216	218	221	223	225	228	230	3 - 2
21.	232	234	237	239	241	243	245	247	250	252	
22.	254	256	258	260	262	264	266	268	270	272	2
23.	273	275	277	279	281	283	284	286	288	290	
24.	292	293	295	297	298	300	302	303	305	307	
25.	308	310	311	313	314	316	318	319	321	322	2 - 1
26.	324	325	326	328	329	331	332	334	335	336	
27.	338	339	340	342	343	344	346	347	348	350	
28.	351	352	354	355	356	357	358	360	361	362	
29.	363	364	366	367	368	369	370	371	373	374	

x	tan^{-1}x	Diff.	x	tan^{-1}x	Diff.	x	tan^{-1}x	Diff.
30	1.5375	10	60	1.5541	3-2	100	1.5608	9
31	1.5385		61	1.5544		110	1.5617	8
32	1.5396		62	1.5547		120	1.5625	
33	1.5405	9	63	1.5549		130	1.5631	6
34	1.5414		64	1.5552		140	1.5637	
35	1.5422	8	65	1.5554		150	1.5641	4
36	1.5430		66	1.5556		160	1.5645	
37	1.5438		67	1.5559		170	1.5649	
38	1.5445	7	68	1.5561	2	180	1.5652	3
39	1.5452		69	1.5563		190	1.5655	
40	1.5458		70	1.5565		200	1.5658	2
41	1.5464	6	71	1.5567		210	1.5660	
42	1.5470		72	1.5569		220	1.5663	
43	1.5475		73	1.5571		230	1.5664	2-1
44	1.5481	5	74	1.5573		240	1.5666	
45	1.5486		75	1.5575		250	1.5668	
46	1.5491		76	1.5576		260	1.5670	
47	1.5495		77	1.5578		270	1.5671	
48	1.5500		78	1.5580		280	1.5672	1
49	1.5504	4	79	1.5581		290	1.5673	
50	1.5508		80	1.5583		300	1.5675	8
51	1.5512		81	1.5585		400	1.5683	5
52	1.5516		82	1.5586		500	1.5688	
53	1.5519		83	1.5587		600	1.5691	3
54	1.5523		84	1.5589	2-1	700	1.5694	
55	1.5526		85	1.5590		800	1.5695	2-1
56	1.5529	3	86	1.5592		900	1.5697	
57	1.5533		87	1.5593		1000	1.5698	
58	1.5536		88	1.5594		2000	1.5703	
59	1.5538		89	1.5596		5000	1.5706	
60	1.5541		90	1.5597		Infin.	1.57080 = $\pi/2$	

For values of x larger than 30,

$$\tan^{-1}x = 1.57080 - 1/x$$

For a large table of the inverse tangent of x, see "Table of Arctan x," National Bureau of Standards, Washington, D.C., Applied Mathematics Series, No. 26.

THE EXPONENTIAL FUNCTION

$$e^x$$

x	0	1	2	3	4	5	6	7	8	9	Diff.
.00	1.0 000	010	020	030	040	050	060	070	080	090	10 - 11
.01	101	111	121	131	141	151	161	171	182	192	10 - 11
.02	202	212	222	233	243	253	263	274	284	294	10 - 11
.03	305	315	325	336	346	356	367	377	387	398	10 - 11
.04	408	419	429	439	450	460	471	481	492	502	10 - 11
.05	513	523	534	544	555	565	576	587	597	608	10 - 11
.06	618	629	640	650	661	672	682	693	704	714	10 - 11
.07	725	736	747	757	768	779	790	800	811	822	10 - 11
.08	833	844	855	865	876	887	898	909	920	931	10 - 11
.09	942	953	964	975	986	997	008	019	030	041	11
.10	1.1 052	063	074	085	096	107	118	129	140	152	11 - 12
.11	163	174	185	196	208	219	230	241	252	264	11 - 12
.12	275	286	298	309	320	331	343	354	366	377	11 - 12
.13	388	400	411	422	434	445	457	468	480	491	11 - 12
.14	503	514	526	537	549	560	572	584	595	607	11 - 12
.15	618	630	642	653	665	677	688	700	712	723	11 - 12
.16	735	747	759	770	782	794	806	818	829	841	11 - 12
.17	853	865	877	889	901	912	924	936	948	960	11 - 12
.18	972	984	996	008	020	032	044	056	068	080	12
.19	1.2 092	105	117	129	141	153	165	177	190	202	12 - 13
.20	214	226	238	251	263	275	288	300	312	324	12 - 13
.21	337	349	361	374	386	399	411	423	436	448	12 - 13
.22	461	473	486	498	511	523	536	548	561	573	12 - 13
.23	586	599	611	624	636	649	662	674	687	700	12 - 13
.24	712	725	738	751	763	776	789	802	815	827	12 - 13
.25	840	853	866	879	892	905	918	930	943	956	12 - 13
.26	969	982	995	008	021	034	047	060	073	087	13 - 14
.27	1.3 100	113	126	139	152	165	178	192	205	218	13 - 14
.28	231	245	258	271	284	298	311	324	338	351	13 - 14
.29	364	378	391	404	418	431	445	458	472	485	13 - 14
.30	499	512	526	539	553	566	580	593	607	621	13 - 14
.31	634	648	662	675	689	703	716	730	744	758	13 - 14
.32	771	785	799	813	826	840	854	868	882	896	13 - 14
.33	910	924	938	951	965	979	993	007	021	035	13 - 14
.34	1.4 049	064	078	092	106	120	134	148	162	176	14 - 15
.35	191	205	219	233	248	262	276	290	305	319	14 - 15
.36	333	348	362	376	391	405	420	434	448	463	14 - 15
.37	477	492	506	521	535	550	564	579	594	608	14 - 15
.38	623	637	652	667	681	696	711	726	740	755	14 - 15
.39	770	785	799	814	829	844	859	874	888	903	14 - 15
.40	918	933	948	963	978	993	008	023	038	053	15
.41	1.5 068	083	098	113	129	144	159	174	189	204	15 - 16
.42	220	235	250	265	281	296	311	327	342	357	15 - 16
.43	373	388	403	419	434	450	465	481	496	512	15 - 16
.44	527	543	558	574	589	605	621	636	652	667	15 - 16
.45	683	699	715	730	746	762	778	793	809	825	15 - 16
.46	841	857	872	888	904	920	936	952	968	984	15 - 16
.47	1.6 000	016	032	048	064	080	096	112	128	145	16 - 17
.48	161	177	193	209	226	242	258	274	291	307	16 - 17
.49	323	339	356	372	389	405	421	438	454	471	16 - 17

$$e^x$$

x	0	1	2	3	4	5	6	7	8	9	Diff.
.50	1.6 487	504	520	537	553	570	586	603	620	636	16 - 17
.51	653	670	686	703	720	736	753	770	787	803	16 - 17
.52	820	837	854	871	888	905	922	938	955	972	16 - 17
.53	989	006	023	040	057	074	092	109	126	143	17 - 18
.54	1.7 160	177	194	212	229	246	263	281	298	315	17 - 18
.55	333	350	367	385	402	419	437	454	472	489	17 - 18
.56	507	524	542	559	577	594	612	630	647	665	17 - 18
.57	683	700	718	736	754	771	789	807	825	843	17 - 18
.58	860	878	896	914	932	950	968	986	004	022	18
.59	1.8 040	058	076	094	112	130	148	167	185	203	18 - 19
.60	221	239	258	276	294	313	331	349	368	386	18 - 19
.61	404	423	441	460	478	497	515	534	552	571	18 - 19
.62	589	608	626	645	664	682	701	720	739	757	18 - 19
.63	776	795	814	833	851	870	889	908	927	946	18 - 19
.64	965	984	003	022	041	060	079	098	117	136	19
.65	1.9 155	175	194	213	232	251	271	290	309	329	19 - 20
.66	348	367	387	406	425	445	464	484	503	523	19 - 20
.67	542	562	581	601	621	640	660	680	699	719	19 - 20
.68	739	759	778	798	818	838	858	877	897	917	19 - 20
.69	937	957	977	997	017	037	057	077	097	117	20 - 21
.70	2.0 138	158	178	198	218	238	259	279	299	320	20 - 21
.71	340	360	381	401	421	442	462	483	503	524	20 - 21
.72	544	565	585	606	627	647	668	689	709	730	20 - 21
.73	751	772	792	813	834	855	876	897	917	938	20 - 21
.74	959	980	001	022	043	064	085	107	128	149	21 - 22
.75	2.1 170	191	212	234	255	276	297	319	340	361	21 - 22
.76	383	404	426	447	468	490	511	533	555	576	21 - 22
.77	598	619	641	663	684	706	728	749	771	793	21 - 22
.78	815	837	858	880	902	924	946	968	990	012	21 - 22
.79	2.2 034	056	078	100	122	144	167	189	211	233	22 - 23
.80	255	278	300	322	345	367	389	412	434	457	22 - 23
.81	479	502	524	547	569	592	614	637	660	682	22 - 23
.82	705	728	750	773	796	819	842	864	887	910	22 - 23
.83	933	956	979	002	025	048	071	094	117	141	23 - 24
.84	2.3 164	187	210	233	257	280	303	326	350	373	23 - 24
.85	396	420	443	467	490	514	537	561	584	608	23 - 24
.86	632	655	679	703	726	750	774	798	821	845	23 - 24
.87	869	893	917	941	965	989	013	037	061	085	24
.88	2.4 109	133	157	181	206	230	254	278	303	327	24 - 25
.89	351	376	400	424	449	473	498	522	547	571	24 - 25
.90	596	621	645	670	695	719	744	769	794	818	24 - 25
.91	843	868	893	918	943	968	993	018	043	068	25
.92	2.5 093	118	143	168	193	219	244	269	294	320	25 - 26
.93	345	370	396	421	447	472	498	523	549	574	25 - 26
.94	600	625	651	677	702	728	754	780	805	831	25 - 26
.95	857	883	909	935	961	987	013	039	065	091	26
.96	2.6 117	143	169	195	222	248	274	300	327	353	26 - 27
.97	379	406	432	459	485	512	538	565	591	618	26 - 27
.98	645	671	698	725	751	778	805	832	859	885	26 - 27
.99	912	939	966	993	020	047	074	101	129	156	27 - 28
	2.7										

e^x

x	0		1	2	3	4	5	6	7	8	9	Diff.
1.00	2.7	183	210	237	264	292	319	346	374	401	429	27 - 28
.01		456	483	511	539	566	594	621	649	677	704	27 - 28
.02		732	760	787	815	843	871	899	927	955	983	27 - 28
.03	2.8	011	039	067	095	123	151	179	207	236	264	28 - 29
.04		292	320	349	377	406	434	462	491	519	548	28 - 29
.05		577	605	634	662	691	720	748	777	806	835	28 - 29
.06		864	893	921	950	979	008	037	066	096	125	28 - 30
.07	2.9	154	183	212	241	271	300	329	359	388	417	29 - 30
.08		447	476	506	535	565	594	624	654	683	713	29 - 30
.09		743	772	802	832	862	892	922	952	982	012	29 - 30
1.10	3.0	042	072	102	132	162	192	222	253	283	313	30 - 31
.11		344	374	404	435	465	496	526	557	587	618	30 - 31
.12		649	679	710	741	771	802	833	864	895	926	30 - 31
.13		957	988	019	050	081	112	143	174	205	236	31 - 32
.14	3.1	268	299	330	362	393	424	456	487	519	550	31 - 32
.15		582	614	645	677	709	740	772	804	836	867	31 - 32
.16		899	931	963	995	027	059	091	123	156	188	32 - 33
.17	3.2	220	252	284	317	349	381	414	446	479	511	32 - 33
.18		544	576	609	642	674	707	740	772	805	838	32 - 33
.19		871	904	937	970	003	036	069	102	135	168	33
1.20	3.3	201	234	268	301	334	368	401	434	468	501	33 - 34
.21		535	568	602	636	669	703	737	770	804	838	33 - 34
.22		872	906	940	974	008	042	076	110	144	178	34
.23	3.4	212	247	281	315	349	384	418	453	487	522	34 - 35
.24		556	591	625	660	695	729	764	799	834	869	34 - 35
.25		903	938	973	008	043	078	113	149	184	219	35 - 36
.26	3.5	254	289	325	360	396	431	466	502	537	573	35 - 36
.27		609	644	680	716	751	787	823	859	895	930	35 - 36
.28		966	002	038	074	111	147	183	219	255	292	36 - 37
.29	3.6	328	364	401	437	473	510	546	583	620	656	36 - 37
1.30		693	730	766	803	840	877	914	951	988	025	36 - 37
.31	3.7	062	099	136	173	210	248	285	322	359	397	37 - 38
.32		434	472	509	547	584	622	659	697	735	773	37 - 38
.33		810	848	886	924	962	000	038	076	114	152	38
.34	3.8	190	229	267	305	344	382	420	459	497	536	38 - 39
.35		574	613	651	690	729	768	806	845	884	923	38 - 39
.36		962	001	040	079	118	157	196	236	275	314	39 - 40
.37	3.9	354	393	432	472	511	551	590	630	670	709	39 - 40
.38		749	789	829	868	908	948	988	028	068	108	39 - 40
.39	4.0	149	189	229	269	309	350	390	431	471	511	40 - 41
1.40		552	593	633	674	715	755	796	837	878	919	40 - 41
.41		960	001	042	083	124	165	206	247	289	330	41 - 42
.42	4.1	371	413	454	496	537	579	620	662	704	745	41 - 42
.43		787	829	871	913	954	996	038	081	123	165	41 - 43
.44	4.2	207	249	291	334	376	419	461	503	546	589	42 - 43
.45		631	674	716	759	802	845	888	931	974	017	42 - 43
.46	4.3	060	103	146	189	232	275	319	362	405	449	43 - 44
.47		492	536	579	623	667	710	754	798	842	886	43 - 44
.48		929	973	017	061	106	150	194	238	282	327	44 - 45
.49	4.4	371	415	460	504	549	593	638	683	727	772	44 - 45

$$e^x$$

x	0	1	2	3	4	5	6	7	8	9	Diff.
1.50	4. 482	486	491	495	500	504	509	513	518	522	4 - 5
.51	527	531	536	540	545	549	554	559	563	568	4 - 5
.52	572	577	581	586	591	595	600	604	609	614	4 - 5
.53	618	623	627	632	637	641	646	651	655	660	4 - 5
.54	665	669	674	679	683	688	693	697	702	707	4 - 5
.55	711	716	721	726	730	735	740	745	749	754	4 - 5
.56	759	764	768	773	778	783	787	792	797	802	4 - 5
.57	807	811	816	821	826	831	836	840	845	850	4 - 5
.58	855	860	865	870	874	879	884	889	894	899	4 - 5
.59	904	909	914	918	923	928	933	938	943	948	4 - 5
1.60	953	958	963	968	973	978	983	988	993	998	5
.61	5. 003	008	013	018	023	028	033	038	043	048	5
.62	053	058	063	068	073	078	083	089	094	099	5 - 6
.63	104	109	114	119	124	129	135	140	145	150	5 - 6
.64	155	160	165	171	176	181	186	191	197	202	5 - 6
.65	207	212	217	223	228	233	238	244	249	254	5 - 6
.66	259	265	270	275	280	286	291	296	302	307	5 - 6
.67	312	317	323	328	333	339	344	349	355	360	5 - 6
.68	366	371	376	382	387	392	398	403	409	414	5 - 6
.69	419	425	430	436	441	447	452	458	463	468	5 - 6
1.70	474	479	485	490	496	501	507	512	518	523	5 - 6
.71	529	534	540	546	551	557	562	568	573	579	5 - 6
.72	585	590	596	601	607	613	618	624	629	635	5 - 6
.73	641	646	652	658	663	669	675	680	686	692	5 - 6
.74	697	703	709	714	720	726	732	737	743	749	5 - 6
.75	755	760	766	772	778	783	789	795	801	807	5 - 6
.76	812	818	824	830	836	842	847	853	859	865	5 - 6
.77	871	877	883	888	894	900	906	912	918	924	5 - 6
.78	930	936	942	948	954	960	966	972	977	983	5 - 6
.79	989	995	001	007	013	019	025	032	038	044	6 - 7
1.80	6. 050	056	062	068	074	080	086	092	098	104	6
.81	110	117	123	129	135	141	147	153	160	166	6 - 7
.82	172	178	184	190	197	203	209	215	221	228	6 - 7
.83	234	240	246	253	259	265	271	278	284	290	6 - 7
.84	297	303	309	315	322	328	334	341	347	353	6 - 7
.85	360	366	373	379	385	392	398	404	411	417	6 - 7
.86	424	430	437	443	449	456	462	469	475	482	6 - 7
.87	488	495	501	508	514	521	527	534	540	547	6 - 7
.88	554	560	567	573	580	586	593	600	606	613	6 - 7
.89	619	626	633	639	646	653	659	666	673	679	6 - 7
1.90	686	693	699	706	713	719	726	733	740	746	6 - 7
.91	753	760	767	773	780	787	794	801	807	814	6 - 7
.92	821	828	835	841	848	855	862	869	876	883	6 - 7
.93	890	896	903	910	917	924	931	938	945	952	6 - 7
.94	959	966	973	980	987	994	001	008	015	022	7
.95	7. 029	036	043	050	057	064	071	078	085	092	7
.96	099	106	114	121	128	135	142	149	156	164	7 - 8
.97	171	178	185	192	199	207	214	221	228	236	7 - 8
.98	243	250	257	265	272	279	286	294	301	308	7 - 8
.99	316	323	330	338	345	352	360	367	374	382	7 - 8

$$e^x$$

x	0	1	2	3	4	5	6	7	8	9	Diff.
2.00	7. 389	396	404	411	419	426	434	441	448	456	7 - 8
.01	463	471	478	486	493	501	508	516	523	531	7 - 8
.02	538	546	553	561	569	576	584	591	599	606	7 - 8
.03	614	622	629	637	645	652	660	668	675	683	7 - 8
.04	691	698	706	714	721	729	737	745	752	760	7 - 8
.05	768	776	783	791	799	807	815	822	830	838	7 - 8
.06	846	854	862	870	877	885	893	901	909	917	7 - 8
.07	925	933	941	949	957	965	973	980	988	996	7 - 8
.08	8. 004	012	020	029	037	045	053	061	069	077	8 - 9
.09	085	093	101	109	117	125	134	142	150	158	8 - 9
2.10	166	174	183	191	199	207	215	224	232	240	8 - 9
.11	248	256	265	273	281	290	298	306	314	323	8 - 9
.12	331	339	348	356	365	373	381	390	398	406	8 - 9
.13	415	423	432	440	449	457	466	474	482	491	8 - 9
.14	499	508	516	525	534	542	551	559	568	576	8 - 9
.15	585	593	602	611	619	628	637	645	654	662	8 - 9
.16	671	680	688	697	706	715	723	732	741	750	8 - 9
.17	758	767	776	785	793	802	811	820	829	837	8 - 9
.18	846	855	864	873	882	891	900	908	917	926	8 - 9
.19	935	944	953	962	971	980	989	998	007	016	9
2.20	9. 025	034	043	052	061	070	079	088	098	107	9 - 10
.21	116	125	134	143	152	161	171	180	189	198	9 - 10
.22	207	217	226	235	244	253	263	272	281	291	9 - 10
.23	300	309	318	328	337	346	356	365	375	384	9 - 10
.24	393	403	412	422	431	440	450	459	469	478	9 - 10
.25	488	497	507	516	526	535	545	554	564	574	9 - 10
.26	583	593	602	612	621	631	641	650	660	670	9 - 10
.27	679	689	699	708	718	728	738	747	757	767	9 - 10
.28	777	786	796	806	816	826	836	845	855	865	9 - 10
.29	875	885	895	905	915	924	934	944	954	964	9 - 10
2.30	974	984	994	004	014	024	034	044	054	064	10
.31	10. 074	085	095	105	115	125	135	145	155	166	10 - 11
.32	176	186	196	206	216	227	237	247	257	268	10 - 11
.33	278	288	299	309	319	329	340	350	360	371	10 - 11
.34	381	392	402	412	423	433	444	454	465	475	10 - 11
.35	486	496	507	517	528	538	549	559	570	580	10 - 11
.36	591	602	612	623	633	644	655	665	676	687	10 - 11
.37	697	708	719	730	740	751	762	773	783	794	10 - 11
.38	805	816	827	837	848	859	870	881	892	903	10 - 11
.39	913	924	935	946	957	968	979	990	001	012	11
2.40	11. 023	034	045	056	067	078	090	101	112	123	11 - 12
.41	134	145	156	167	179	190	201	212	223	235	11 - 12
.42	246	257	268	280	291	302	314	325	336	348	11 - 12
.43	359	370	382	393	404	416	427	439	450	462	11 - 12
.44	473	485	496	508	519	531	542	554	565	577	11 - 12
.45	588	600	612	623	635	646	658	670	681	693	11 - 12
.46	705	717	728	740	752	763	775	787	799	811	11 - 12
.47	822	834	846	858	870	882	894	905	917	929	11 - 12
.48	941	953	965	977	989	001	013	025	037	049	12
.49	12. 061	073	085	098	110	122	134	146	158	170	12 - 13

$$e^x$$

x	0	1	2	3	4	5	6	7	8	9	Diff.
2.50	12. 182	195	207	219	231	244	256	268	280	293	12 - 13
.51	305	317	330	342	354	367	379	391	404	416	12 - 13
.52	429	441	453	466	478	491	503	516	528	541	12 - 13
.53	554	566	579	591	604	616	629	642	654	667	12 - 13
.54	680	692	705	718	730	743	756	769	782	794	12 - 13
.55	807	820	833	846	858	871	884	897	910	923	12 - 13
.56	936	949	962	975	988	001	014	027	040	053	13
.57	13. 066	079	092	105	118	131	144	158	171	184	13 - 14
.58	197	210	224	237	250	263	277	290	303	316	13 - 14
.59	330	343	356	370	383	397	410	423	437	450	13 - 14
2.60	464	477	491	504	518	531	545	558	572	585	13 - 14
.61	599	613	626	640	654	667	681	695	708	722	13 - 14
.62	736	749	763	777	791	805	818	832	846	860	13 - 14
.63	874	888	902	915	929	943	957	971	985	999	13 - 14
.64	14. 013	027	041	055	069	083	098	112	126	140	14 - 15
.65	154	168	182	197	211	225	239	253	268	282	14 - 15
.66	296	311	325	339	354	368	382	397	411	426	14 - 15
.67	440	454	469	483	498	512	527	541	556	571	14 - 15
.68	585	600	614	629	644	658	673	688	702	717	14 - 15
.69	732	746	761	776	791	806	820	835	850	865	14 - 15
2.70	880	895	910	924	939	954	969	984	999	014	14 - 15
.71	15. 029	044	059	074	090	105	120	135	150	165	15 - 16
.72	180	196	211	226	241	256	272	287	302	318	15 - 16
.73	333	348	364	379	394	410	425	441	456	472	15 - 16
.74	487	502	518	534	549	565	580	596	611	627	15 - 16
.75	643	658	674	690	705	721	737	753	768	784	15 - 16
.76	800	816	831	847	863	879	895	911	927	943	15 - 16
.77	959	975	991	007	023	039	055	071	087	103	16
.78	16. 119	135	151	167	184	200	216	232	248	265	16 - 17
.79	281	297	314	330	346	363	379	395	412	428	16 - 17
2.80	445	461	478	494	511	527	544	560	577	593	16 - 17
.81	610	627	643	660	676	693	710	727	743	760	16 - 17
.82	777	794	810	827	844	861	878	895	912	929	16 - 17
.83	945	962	979	996	013	030	047	064	082	099	17 - 18
.84	17. 116	133	150	167	184	202	219	236	253	271	17 - 18
.85	288	305	322	340	357	374	392	409	427	444	17 - 18
.86	462	479	496	514	532	549	567	584	602	619	17 - 18
.87	637	655	672	690	708	725	743	761	779	796	17 - 18
.88	814	832	850	868	886	904	921	939	957	975	17 - 18
.89	993	011	029	047	065	084	102	120	138	156	18 - 19
2.90	18. 174	192	211	229	247	265	284	302	320	338	18 - 19
.91	357	375	394	412	430	449	467	486	504	523	18 - 19
.92	541	560	578	597	616	634	653	672	690	709	18 - 19
.93	728	746	765	784	803	822	840	859	878	897	18 - 19
.94	916	935	954	973	992	011	030	049	068	087	19
.95	19. 106	125	144	163	183	202	221	240	259	279	19 - 20
.96	298	317	337	356	375	395	414	434	453	472	19 - 20
.97	492	511	531	550	570	590	609	629	648	668	19 - 20
.98	688	708	727	747	767	787	806	826	846	866	19 - 20
.99	886	906	925	945	965	985	005	025	045	065	19 - 21
	20.										

$$e^x$$

x	0	1	2	3	4	5	6	7	8	9	Diff.
3.00	20. 086	106	126	146	166	186	206	227	247	267	20
.01	287	308	328	348	369	389	409	430	450	471	
.02	491	512	532	553	573	594	615	635	656	677	
.03	697	718	739	759	780	801	822	843	863	884	
.04	905	926	947	968	989	010	031	052	073	094	21
.05	21. 115	136	158	179	200	221	242	264	285	306	
.06	328	349	370	392	413	434	456	477	499	520	
.07	542	563	585	607	628	650	672	693	715	737	
.08	758	780	802	824	846	867	889	911	933	955	
.09	977	999	021	043	065	087	109	131	154	176	22
3.10	22. 198	220	242	265	287	309	332	354	376	399	
.11	421	443	466	488	511	533	556	579	601	624	
.12	646	669	692	714	737	760	783	805	828	851	
.13	874	897	920	943	966	989	012	035	058	081	23
.14	23. 104	127	150	173	196	220	243	266	289	313	
.15	336	359	383	406	430	453	477	500	524	547	
.16	571	594	618	641	665	689	712	736	760	784	
.17	807	831	855	879	903	927	951	975	999	023	24
.18	24. 047	071	095	119	143	167	191	216	240	264	
.19	288	313	337	361	386	410	435	459	484	508	
3.20	533	557	582	606	631	656	680	705	730	754	
.21	779	804	829	854	878	903	928	953	978	003	25
.22	25. 028	053	078	103	128	154	179	204	229	254	
.23	280	305	330	356	381	406	432	457	483	508	
.24	534	559	585	610	636	662	687	713	739	765	
.25	790	816	842	868	894	920	946	972	997	024	26
.26	26. 050	076	102	128	154	180	206	233	259	285	
.27	311	338	364	390	417	443	470	496	523	549	
.28	576	602	629	656	682	709	736	762	789	816	
.29	843	870	897	924	950	977	004	031	058	086	27
3.30	27. 113	140	167	194	221	249	276	303	330	358	
.31	385	413	440	467	495	522	550	577	605	633	
.32	660	688	716	743	771	799	827	855	883	910	
.33	938	966	994	022	050	078	106	135	163	191	28
.34	28. 219	247	276	304	332	361	389	417	446	474	
.35	503	531	560	588	617	646	674	703	732	760	
.36	789	818	847	876	905	933	962	991	020	049	29
.37	29. 079	108	137	166	195	224	254	283	312	341	
.38	371	400	430	459	488	518	548	577	607	636	
.39	666	696	725	755	785	815	844	874	904	934	
3.40	964	994	024	054	084	114	144	175	205	235	30
.41	30. 265	296	326	356	387	417	447	478	508	539	
.42	569	600	631	661	692	723	753	784	815	846	
.43	877	908	938	969	000	031	062	094	125	156	31
.44	31. 187	218	249	281	312	343	375	406	437	469	
.45	500	532	563	595	627	658	690	722	753	785	
.46	817	849	881	913	944	976	008	040	073	105	32
.47	32. 137	169	201	233	266	298	330	362	395	427	
.48	460	492	525	557	590	622	655	688	720	753	
.49	786	819	852	884	917	950	983	016	049	082	33
	33.										

$$e^x$$

x	0	1	2	3	4	5	6	7	8	9	Diff.
3.50	33. 115	149	182	215	248	281	315	348	381	415	33
.51	448	482	515	549	582	616	650	683	717	751	
.52	784	818	852	886	920	954	988	022	056	090	34
.53	34. 124	158	192	226	261	295	329	364	398	432	
.54	467	501	536	570	605	640	674	709	744	779	
.55	813	848	883	918	953	988	023	058	093	128	35
.56	35. 163	198	234	269	304	339	375	410	446	481	
.57	517	552	588	623	659	695	730	766	802	838	
.58	874	909	945	981	017	053	089	126	162	198	36
.59	36. 234	270	307	343	379	416	452	489	525	562	
3.60	598	635	672	708	745	782	818	855	892	929	
.61	966	003	040	077	114	151	189	226	263	300	37
.62	37. 338	375	412	450	487	525	562	600	637	675	
.63	713	751	788	826	864	902	940	978	016	054	38
.64	38. 092	130	168	206	245	283	321	359	398	436	
.65	475	513	552	590	629	668	706	745	784	823	
.66	861	900	939	978	017	056	095	134	173	213	39
.67	39. 252	291	330	370	409	449	488	528	567	607	
.68	646	686	726	766	805	845	885	925	965	005	
.69	40. 045	085	125	165	205	246	286	326	366	407	40
3.70	447	488	528	569	609	650	691	731	772	813	
.71	854	895	936	977	018	059	100	141	182	223	41
.72	41. 264	306	347	388	430	471	513	554	596	637	
.73	679	721	763	804	846	888	930	972	014	056	42
.74	42. 098	140	182	224	267	309	351	394	436	479	
.75	521	564	606	649	692	734	777	820	863	905	
.76	948	991	034	077	121	164	207	250	293	337	43
.77	43. 380	423	467	510	554	598	641	685	728	772	
.78	816	860	904	948	992	036	080	124	168	212	44
.79	44. 256	301	345	389	434	478	523	567	612	657	
3.80	701	746	791	835	880	925	970	015	060	105	45
.81	45. 150	196	241	286	331	377	422	468	513	559	
.82	604	650	696	741	787	833	879	925	971	016	46
.83	46. 063	109	155	201	247	293	340	386	433	479	
.84	525	572	619	665	712	759	805	852	899	946	
.85	993	040	087	134	181	229	276	323	371	418	47
.86	47. 465	513	560	608	656	703	751	799	847	894	
.87	942	990	038	086	135	183	231	279	327	376	48
.88	48. 424	473	521	570	618	667	716	764	813	862	
.89	911	960	009	058	107	156	205	254	304	353	49
3.90	49. 402	452	501	551	600	650	700	749	799	849	
.91	899	949	999	049	099	149	199	249	300	350	50
.92	50. 400	451	501	552	602	653	704	754	805	856	
.93	907	958	009	060	111	162	213	265	316	367	51
.94	51. 419	470	522	573	625	676	728	780	832	883	
.95	935	987	039	091	144	196	248	300	353	405	52
.96	52. 457	510	562	615	668	720	773	826	879	932	
.97	985	038	091	144	197	250	303	357	410	464	53
.98	53. 517	571	624	678	732	785	839	893	947	001	54
.99	54. 055	109	163	217	272	326	380	435	489	544	

$$e^x$$

x	0	1	2	3	4	5	6	7	8	9	Diff.
4.00	54. 598	653	707	762	817	872	927	982	037	092	55
.01	55. 147	202	257	313	368	423	479	534	590	645	
.02	701	757	813	868	924	980	036	092	149	205	56
.03	56. 261	317	374	430	486	543	599	656	713	770	
.04	826	883	940	997	054	111	168	226	283	340	57
.05	57. 397	455	512	570	628	685	743	801	858	916	
.06	974	032	090	148	207	265	323	382	440	498	58
.07	58. 557	616	674	733	792	850	909	968	027	086	59
.08	59. 145	205	264	323	383	442	501	561	621	680	
.09	740	800	859	919	979	039	099	160	220	280	60
4.10	60. 340	401	461	522	582	643	703	764	825	886	
.11	947	008	069	130	191	252	313	375	436	498	61
.12	61. 559	621	682	744	806	868	930	992	054	116	62
.13	62. 178	240	302	365	427	490	552	615	677	740	
.14	803	866	929	992	055	118	181	244	307	371	63
.15	63. 434	497	561	625	688	752	816	880	944	007	64
.16	64. 072	136	200	264	328	393	457	522	586	651	
.17	715	780	845	910	975	040	105	170	235	301	65
.18	65. 366	431	497	562	628	694	759	825	891	957	
.19	66. 023	089	155	221	287	354	420	487	553	620	66
4.20	686	753	820	887	954	021	088	155	222	289	67
.21	67. 357	424	491	559	627	694	762	830	898	965	68
.22	68. 033	102	170	238	306	375	443	511	580	649	
.23	717	786	855	924	993	062	131	200	269	338	69
.24	69. 408	477	547	616	686	756	826	895	965	035	70
.25	70. 105	176	246	316	386	457	527	598	669	739	
.26	810	881	952	023	094	165	236	307	379	450	71
.27	71. 522	593	665	737	808	880	952	024	096	168	72
.28	72. 240	313	385	457	530	603	675	748	821	894	
.29	966	039	113	186	259	332	406	479	553	626	73
4.30	73. 700	774	847	921	995	069	143	218	292	366	74
.31	74. 440	515	590	664	739	814	888	963	038	113	75
.32	75. 189	264	339	415	490	566	641	717	793	868	
.33	944	020	096	172	249	325	401	478	554	631	76
.34	76. 708	784	861	938	015	092	169	246	324	401	77
.35	77. 478	556	634	711	789	867	945	023	101	179	78
.36	78. 257	335	414	492	571	649	728	807	886	965	
.37	79. 044	123	202	281	360	440	519	599	679	758	79
.38	838	918	998	078	158	238	319	399	479	560	80
.39	80. 640	721	802	883	964	045	126	207	288	369	81
4.40	81. 451	532	614	696	777	859	941	023	105	187	82
.41	82. 269	352	434	517	599	682	765	847	930	013	83
.42	83. 096	179	263	346	429	513	596	680	764	848	
.43	931	015	099	184	268	352	437	521	606	690	84
.44	84. 775	860	945	030	115	200	285	370	456	541	85
.45	85. 627	713	798	884	970	056	142	228	315	401	86
.46	86. 488	574	661	747	834	921	008	095	182	269	87
.47	87. 357	444	532	619	707	795	882	970	058	146	88
.48	88. 235	323	411	500	588	677	766	854	943	032	89
.49	89. 121	211	300	389	479	568	658	747	837	927	90

$$e^x$$

x	0	1	2	3	4	5	6	7	8	9	Diff.
4.50	90. 017	107	197	288	378	468	559	649	740	831	90
.51	922	013	104	195	286	378	469	561	652	744	91
.52	91. 836	927	019	112	204	296	388	481	573	666	92
.53	92. 759	851	944	037	130	224	317	410	504	597	93
.54	93. 691	785	878	972	066	160	255	349	443	538	94
.55	94. 632	727	822	917	012	107	202	297	393	488	95
.56	95. 583	679	775	871	967	063	159	255	351	448	96
.57	96. 544	641	737	834	931	028	125	222	320	417	97
.58	97. 514	612	710	807	905	003	101	199	298	396	98
.59	98. 494	593	692	790	889	988	087	186	286	385	99
4.60	99. 484	584	683	783	883	983	083	183	283	384	100
.61	100. 484	585	685	786	887	988	089	190	291	393	101
.62	101. 494	596	697	799	901	003	105	207	309	412	102
.63	102. 514	617	719	822	925	028	131	234	337	441	103
.64	103. 544	648	752	855	959	063	167	272	376	480	104
.65	104. 585	690	794	899	004	109	214	320	425	530	105
.66	105. 636	742	848	953	059	166	272	378	485	591	106
.67	106. 698	804	911	018	125	233	340	447	555	662	107
.68	107. 770	878	986	094	202	310	419	527	636	744	108
.69	108. 853	962	071	180	289	399	508	618	727	837	109
4.70	109. 947	057	167	278	388	498	609	720	830	941	110
	110.										111
.71	111. 052	163	274	386	497	609	720	832	944	056	112
.72	112. 168	280	393	505	618	730	843	956	069	182	113
.73	113. 296	409	522	636	750	863	977	091	206	320	114
.74	114. 434	549	663	778	893	008	123	238	353	469	115
.75	115. 584	700	816	932	048	164	280	396	513	629	116
.76	116. 746	863	980	097	214	331	449	566	684	801	117
.77	117. 919										118
	118.	037	155	274	392	510	629	748	866	985	119
.78	119. 104	224	343	462	582	701	821	941	061	181	120
.79	120. 301	422	542	663	784	904	025	146	268	389	121
4.80	121. 510	632	754	875	997	119	242	364	486	609	122
.81	122. 732	854	977	100	224	347	470	594	717	841	123
.82	123. 965										124
	124.	089	213	338	462	586	711	836	961	086	125
.83	125. 211	336	462	587	713	839	964	091	217	343	126
.84	126. 469	596	723	849	976	103	230	358	485	613	127
.85	127. 740	868	996	124	252	381	509	638	766	895	128
.85	128.										129
.86	129. 024	153	283	412	541	671	801	931	061	191	130
.87	130. 321	451	582	712	843	974	105	236	368	499	131
.88	131. 631	762	894	026	158	290	423	555	688	821	132
.89	132. 954										133
	133.	087	220	353	486	620	754	888	021	156	134
4.90	134. 290	424	559	693	828	963	098	233	368	504	135
.91	135. 639	775	911								136
	136.			047	183	319	456	592	729	866	137
.92	137. 003	140	277	414	552	689	827	965	103	241	138
.93	138. 380	518	657	795	934	073	212	352	491	631	139
.94	139. 770	910									140
	140.		050	190	330	471	611	752	893	034	141
.95	141. 175	316	458	599	741	883	025	167	309	451	142
.96	142. 594	736	879	022	165	309	452	595	739	883	143
	143.										144
.97	144. 027	171	315	460	604	749	894	039	184	329	145
.98	145. 474	620	766	911	057	204	350	496	643	790	146
.99	146. 936										147
	147.	083	231	378	525	673	821	969	117	265	148
5.00	148. 413										

$$e^{-x}$$

x	0	1	2	3	4	5	6	7	8	9	Diff. (Subtract)
.00	1.00 000	900	800	700	601	501	402	302	203	104	100-99
.01	0.99 005	906	807	708	610	511	413	314	216	118	99-98
.02	.98 020	922	824	726	629	531	434	336	239	142	98-97
.03	.97 045	948	851	754	657	561	464	368	271	175	97-96
.04	.96 079	983	887	791	695	600	504	409	313	218	96-95
.05	.95 123	028	933	838	743	649	554	459	365	271	95-94
.06	.94 176	082	988	894	800	707	613	520	426	333	94-93
.07	.93 239	146	053	960	867	774	682	589	496	404	93-92
.08	.92 312	219	127	035	943	851	759	668	576	485	93-91
.09	.91 393	302	211	119	028	937	846	756	665	574	92-90
.10	0.90 484	393	303	213	123	032	942	853	763	673	91-89
.11	.89 583	494	404	315	226	137	048	959	870	781	90-89
.12	.88 692	603	515	426	338	250	161	073	985	897	89-87
.13	.87 810	722	634	547	459	372	284	197	110	023	88-87
.14	.86 936	849	762	675	589	502	416	329	243	157	87-86
.15	071	985	899	813	727	642	556	470	385	300	86-85
.16	.85 214	129	044	959	874	789	705	620	535	451	85-84
.17	.84 366	282	198	114	030	946	862	778	694	611	84-83
.18	.83 527	444	360	277	194	110	027	944	861	779	84-82
.19	.82 696	613	531	448	366	283	201	119	037	955	83-82
.20	0.81 873	791	709	628	546	465	383	302	221	140	82-81
.21	058	977	896	816	735	654	574	493	413	332	81-80
.22	.80 252	172	092	011	932	852	772	692	612	533	81-79
.23	.79 453	374	295	215	136	057	978	899	820	741	80-78
.24	.78 663	584	506	427	349	270	192	114	036	958	79-78
.25	.77 880	802	724	647	569	492	414	337	260	182	78-77
.26	105	028	951	874	797	721	644	567	491	414	77-76
.27	.76 338	262	185	109	033	957	881	805	730	654	77-75
.28	.75 578	503	427	352	277	201	126	051	976	901	76-75
.29	.74 826	752	677	603	528	453	379	304	230	156	75-74
.30	0.74 082	008	934	860	786	712	639	565	492	418	74-73
.31	.73 345	271	198	125	052	979	906	833	760	688	74-72
.32	.72 615	542	470	397	325	253	181	108	036	964	73-72
.33	.71 892	821	749	677	605	534	462	391	320	248	72-71
.34	177	106	035	964	893	822	751	681	610	539	71-70
.35	.70 469	398	328	258	187	117	047	977	907	837	71-69
.36	.69 768	698	628	559	489	420	350	281	212	143	70-69
.37	073	004	935	867	798	729	660	592	523	455	69-68
.38	.68 386	318	250	181	113	045	977	909	841	773	69-67
.39	.67 706	638	570	503	435	368	301	233	166	099	68-67
.40	0.67 032	965	898	831	764	698	631	564	498	431	67-66
.41	.66 365	299	232	166	100	034	968	902	836	770	67-66
.42	.65 705	639	573	508	442	377	312	246	181	116	66-65
.43	051	986	921	856	791	726	662	597	533	468	65-64
.44	.64 404	339	275	211	147	082	018	954	890	827	65-63
.45	.63 763	699	635	572	508	445	381	318	255	192	64-63
.46	128	065	002	939	876	814	751	688	625	563	63-62
.47	.62 500	438	375	313	251	189	126	064	002	940	63-62
.48	.61 878	816	755	693	631	570	508	447	385	324	62-61
.49	263	201	140	079	018	957	896	835	774	714	62-60
.60											

$$e^{-x}$$

x	0	1	2	3	4	5	6	7	8	9	Diff. (Subtract)
.50	.60 653	592	532	471	411	351	290	230	170	110	61-60
.51	050	990	930	870	810	750	690	631	571	512	60-59
.52	.59 452	393	333	274	215	156	096	037	978	919	60-59
.53	.58 860	802	743	684	626	567	508	450	391	333	59-58
.54	275	217	158	100	042	984	926	868	810	753	59-57
.55	.57 695	637	580	522	465	407	350	293	235	178	58-57
.56	121	064	007	950	893	836	779	722	666	609	57-56
.57	.56 553	496	440	383	327	270	214	158	102	046	57-56
.58	.55 990	934	878	822	766	711	655	599	544	488	56-55
.59	433	377	322	267	211	156	101	046	991	936	56-5 5
.60	.54 881	826	772	717	662	607	553	498	444	389	55-54
.61	335	281	227	172	118	064	010	956	902	848	55-54
.62	.53 794	741	687	633	580	526	473	419	366	312	54-53
.63	259	206	153	100	047	994	941	888	835	782	53
.64	.52 729	677	624	571	519	466	414	361	309	257	53- 52
.65	205	152	100	048	996	944	892	840	789	737	53-51
.66	.51 685	633	582	530	479	427	376	325	273	222	52-51
.67	171	120	069	018	967	916	865	814	763	712	51-50
.68	.50 662	611	560	510	459	409	359	308	258	208	51-50
.69	158	107	057	007	957	907	858	808	758	708	51-49
.70	.49 659	609	559	510	460	411	361	312	263	214	50-49
.71	164	115	066	017	968	919	870	821	773	724	49-48
.72	.48 675	627	578	529	481	432	384	336	287	239	49-48
.73	191	143	095	047	999	951	903	855	807	759	48
.74	.47 711	664	616	568	521	473	426	379	331	284	48-47
.75	237	189	142	095	048	001	954	907	860	813	48-46
.76	.46 767	720	673	627	580	533	487	440	394	348	47-46
.77	301	255	209	163	116	070	024	978	932	886	47-45
.78	.45 841	795	749	703	658	612	566	521	475	430	46-45
.79	384	339	294	249	203	158	113	068	023	978	46-45
.80	.44 933	888	843	798	754	709	664	619	575	530	45-44
.81	486	441	397	353	308	264	220	175	131	087	45-44
.82	043	999	955	911	867	823	780	736	692	649	44-43
.83	.43 605	561	518	474	431	387	344	301	257	214	44-43
.84	171	128	085	042	999	956	913	870	827	784	43
.85	.42 741	699	656	613	571	528	486	443	401	359	43-42
.86	316	274	232	189	147	105	063	021	979	937	43-42
.87	.41 895	853	811	770	728	686	645	603	561	520	42-41
.88	478	437	395	354	313	271	230	189	148	107	42-41
.89	066	025	984	943	902	861	820	779	738	698	41-40
.90	.40 657	616	576	535	495	454	414	373	333	293	41-40
.91	252	212	172	132	092	052	012	972	932	892	40
.92	.39 852	812	772	733	693	653	614	574	534	495	40-39
.93	455	416	377	337	298	259	219	180	141	102	40-39
.94	063	024	985	946	907	868	829	790	752	713	39-38
.95	.38 674	635	597	558	520	481	443	404	366	328	39-38
.96	289	251	213	175	136	098	060	022	984	946	39-38
.97	.37 908	870	833	795	757	719	682	644	606	569	38-37
.98	531	494	456	419	381	344	307	269	232	195	38-37
.99	158	121	083	046	009	972	935	898	862	825	38-36
	.36										

$$e^{-x}$$

x	0	1	2	3	4	5	6	7	8	9	Diff. (Subtract)
1.00	.36 788	751	714	678	641	604	568	531	495	458	37-36
.01	422	385	349	313	277	240	204	168	132	096	37-36
.02	059	023	987	951	916	880	844	808	772	736	36-35
.03	.35 701	665	629	594	558	523	487	452	416	381	36-35
.04	345	310	275	240	204	169	134	099	064	029	36-35
.05	.34 994	959	924	889	854	819	784	750	715	680	35-34
.06	646	611	576	542	507	473	438	404	370	335	35-34
.07	301	267	232	198	164	130	096	062	028	994	35-34
.08	.33 960	926	892	858	824	790	756	723	689	655	34-33
.09	622	588	554	521	487	454	421	387	354	320	34-33
1.10	287	254	221	187	154	121	088	055	022	989	34-33
.11	.32 956	923	890	857	824	792	759	726	693	661	33-32
.12	628	595	563	530	498	465	433	400	368	336	33-32
.13	303	271	239	207	174	142	110	078	046	014	33-32
.14	.31 982	950	918	886	854	822	791	759	727	695	32-31
.15	664	632	600	569	537	506	474	443	411	380	32-31
.16	349	317	286	255	223	192	161	130	099	068	32-31
.17	037	006	975	944	913	882	851	820	789	759	31-30
.18	.30 728	697	666	636	605	575	544	514	483	453	31-30
.19	422	392	361	331	301	270	240	210	180	150	31-30
1.20	119	089	059	029	999	969	939	909	879	850	30-29
.21	.29 820	790	760	730	701	671	641	612	582	553	30-29
.22	523	494	464	435	405	376	346	317	288	259	30-29
.23	229	200	171	142	113	083	054	025	996	967	30-29
.24	.28 938	909	881	852	823	794	765	737	708	679	29-28
.25	650	622	593	565	536	508	479	451	422	394	29-28
.26	365	337	309	280	252	224	196	168	139	111	29-28
.27	083	055	027	999	971	943	915	887	859	832	28-27
.28	.27 804	776	748	720	693	665	637	610	582	555	28-27
.29	527	500	472	445	417	390	362	335	308	280	28-27
1.30	253	226	199	172	144	117	090	063	036	009	28-27
.31	.26 982	955	928	901	874	847	821	794	767	740	27-26
.32	714	687	660	634	607	580	554	527	501	474	27-26
.33	448	421	395	369	342	316	290	263	237	211	27-26
.34	185	158	132	106	080	054	028	002	976	950	27-26
.35	.25 924	898	872	846	821	795	769	743	717	692	26-25
.36	666	640	615	589	564	538	513	487	462	436	26-25
.37	411	385	360	335	309	284	259	233	208	183	26-25
.38	158	133	108	082	057	032	007	982	957	932	26-24
.39	.24 908	883	858	833	808	783	759	734	709	684	25-24
1.40	660	635	610	586	561	537	512	488	463	439	25-24
.41	414	390	366	341	317	293	268	244	220	196	25-24
.42	171	147	123	099	075	051	027	003	979	955	24
.43	.23 931	907	883	859	835	812	788	764	740	716	24-23
.44	693	669	645	622	598	575	551	528	504	480	24-23
.45	457	434	410	387	363	340	317	293	270	247	24-23
.46	224	200	177	154	131	108	085	062	039	016	24-23
.47	.22 993	970	947	924	901	878	855	832	809	787	23-22
.48	764	741	718	696	673	650	628	605	582	560	23-22
.49	537	515	492	470	447	425	402	380	358	335	23-22

$$e^{-x}$$

x	0	1	2	3	4	5	6	7	8	9	Diff. (Subtract)
1.50	.22 313	291	268	246	224	202	180	157	135	113	23-22
.51	091	069	047	025	003	981	959	937	915	893	22
.52	.21 871	849	827	806	784	762	740	719	697	675	22-21
.53	654	632	610	589	567	546	524	503	481	460	22-21
.54	438	417	395	374	353	331	310	289	267	246	22-21
.55	225	204	182	161	140	119	098	077	056	035	22-21
.56	014	993	972	951	930	909	888	867	846	825	21-20
.57	.20 805	784	763	742	721	701	680	659	639	618	21-20
.58	598	577	556	536	515	495	474	454	433	413	21-20
.59	393	372	352	331	311	291	271	250	230	210	21-20
1.60	190	169	149	129	109	089	069	049	029	009	21-20
.61	.19 989	969	949	929	909	889	869	849	829	810	20-19
.62	790	770	750	731	711	691	671	652	632	613	20-19
.63	593	573	554	534	515	495	476	456	437	417	20-19
.64	398	379	359	340	321	301	282	263	243	224	20-19
.65	205	186	167	147	128	109	090	071	052	033	20-19
.66	014	995	976	957	938	919	900	881	862	844	19-18
.67	.18 825	806	787	768	750	731	712	693	675	656	19-18
.68	637	619	600	582	563	544	526	507	489	470	19-18
.69	452	434	415	397	378	360	342	323	305	287	19-18
1.70	268	250	232	214	195	177	159	141	123	105	19-18
.71	087	069	050	032	014	996	978	960	942	925	19-17
.72	.17 907	889	871	853	835	817	799	782	764	746	18-17
.73	728	711	693	675	658	640	622	605	587	570	18-17
.74	552	534	517	499	482	464	447	430	412	395	18-17
.75	377	360	343	325	308	291	273	256	239	222	18-17
.76	204	187	170	153	136	119	102	084	067	050	18-17
.77	033	016	999	982	965	948	931	914	898	881	17-16
.78	.16 864	847	830	813	796	780	763	746	729	713	17-16
.79	696	679	663	646	629	613	596	580	563	546	17-16
1.80	530	513	497	480	464	447	431	415	398	382	17-16
.81	365	349	333	316	300	284	268	251	235	219	17-16
.82	203	186	170	154	138	122	106	090	073	057	17-16
.83	041	025	009	993	977	961	945	929	914	898	16-15
.84	.15 882	866	850	834	818	803	787	771	755	739	16-15
.85	724	708	692	677	661	645	630	614	598	583	16-15
.86	567	552	536	521	505	490	474	459	443	428	16-15
.87	412	397	382	366	351	335	320	305	290	274	16-15
.88	259	244	229	213	198	183	168	153	137	122	16-15
.89	107	092	077	062	047	032	017	002	987	972	15
1.90	.14 957	942	927	912	897	882	867	853	838	823	15-14
.91	808	793	778	764	749	734	719	705	690	675	15-14
.92	661	646	631	617	602	588	573	558	544	529	15-14
.93	515	500	486	471	457	442	428	414	399	385	15-14
.94	370	356	342	327	313	299	284	270	256	242	15-14
.95	227	213	199	185	171	156	142	128	114	100	15-14
.96	086	072	058	044	030	016	002	988	974	960	14
.97	.13 946	932	918	904	890	876	862	848	835	821	14-13
.98	807	793	779	766	752	738	724	711	697	683	14-13
.99	670	656	642	629	615	601	588	574	561	547	14-13

$$e^{-x}$$

x	0	1	2	3	4	5	6	7	8	9	Diff. (Subtract)
2.00	.13 534	520	506	493	480	466	453	439	426	412	14-13
.01	399	385	372	359	345	332	319	305	292	279	14-13
.02	266	252	239	226	213	199	186	173	160	147	14-13
.03	134	120	107	094	081	068	055	042	029	016	14-13
.04	003	990	977	964	951	938	925	912	899	886	13
.05	.12 873	861	848	835	822	809	796	784	771	758	13-12
.06	745	733	720	707	695	682	669	656	644	631	13-12
.07	619	606	593	581	568	556	543	531	518	506	13-12
.08	493	481	468	456	443	431	418	406	393	381	13-12
.09	369	356	344	332	319	307	295	282	270	258	13-12
2.10	246	233	221	209	197	185	172	160	148	136	13-12
.11	124	112	100	087	075	063	051	039	027	015	13-12
.12	003	991	979	967	955	943	931	919	908	896	12-11
.13	.11 884	872	860	848	836	824	813	801	789	777	12-11
.14	765	754	742	730	719	707	695	683	672	660	12-11
.15	648	637	625	614	602	590	579	567	556	544	12-11
.16	533	521	509	498	486	475	464	452	441	429	12-11
.17	418	406	395	384	372	361	349	338	327	315	12-11
.18	304	293	282	270	259	248	237	225	214	203	12-11
.19	192	180	169	158	147	136	125	114	102	091	12-11
2.20	080	069	058	047	036	025	014	003	992	981	11
.21	.10 970	959	948	937	926	915	904	894	883	872	11-10
.22	861	850	839	828	818	807	796	785	774	764	11-10
.23	753	742	731	721	710	699	689	678	667	657	11-10
.24	646	635	625	614	603	593	582	572	561	550	11-10
.25	540	529	519	508	498	487	477	466	456	445	11-10
.26	435	425	414	404	393	383	373	362	352	342	11-10
.27	331	321	311	300	290	280	269	259	249	239	11-10
.28	228	218	208	198	188	177	167	157	147	137	11-10
.29	127	117	106	096	086	076	066	056	046	036	11-10
2.30	026	016	006	996	986	976	966	956	946	936	10
.31	.09 926	916	906	896	886	877	867	857	847	837	10-9
.32	827	818	808	798	788	778	769	759	749	739	10-9
.33	730	720	710	700	691	681	671	662	652	642	10-9
.34	633	623	614	604	594	585	575	566	556	546	10-9
.35	537	527	518	508	499	489	480	470	461	451	10-9
.36	442	433	423	414	404	395	386	376	367	357	10-9
.37	348	339	329	320	311	301	292	283	274	264	10-9
.38	255	246	237	227	218	209	200	190	181	172	10-9
.39	163	154	145	136	126	117	108	099	090	081	10-9
2.40	072	063	054	045	036	027	018	009	000	991	9
.41	.08 982	973	964	955	946	937	928	919	910	901	9
.42	892	883	874	866	857	848	839	830	821	812	9-8
.43	804	795	786	777	769	760	751	742	734	725	9-8
.44	716	707	699	690	681	673	664	655	647	638	9-8
.45	629	621	612	604	595	586	578	569	561	552	9-8
.46	543	535	526	518	509	501	492	484	475	467	9-8
.47	458	450	442	433	425	416	408	399	391	383	9-8
.48	374	366	358	349	341	333	324	316	308	299	9-8
.49	291	283	274	266	258	250	241	233	225	217	9-8

$$e^{-x}$$

x	0	1	2	3	4	5	6	7	8	9	Diff. (Subtract)
2.50	.082 085	003	921	839	757	676	594	512	431	350	82-81
.51	.081 268	187	106	025	944	863	782	701	621	540	81-80
.52	.080 460	379	299	219	138	058	978	898	818	739	81-79
.53	.079 659	579	500	420	341	262	182	103	024	945	80-79
.54	.078 866	788	709	630	552	473	395	316	238	160	79-78
.55	082	004	926	848	770	692	615	537	460	382	78-77
.56	.077 305	227	150	073	996	919	842	765	689	612	78-76
.57	.076 536	459	383	306	230	154	078	002	926	850	77-76
.58	.075 774	698	623	547	472	396	321	245	170	095	76-75
.59	020	945	870	795	721	646	571	497	422	348	75-74
2.60	.074 274	199	125	051	977	903	829	755	682	608	75-73
.61	.073 535	461	388	314	241	168	095	022	949	876	74-73
.62	.072 803	730	657	585	512	440	367	295	223	151	73-72
.63	078	006	934	863	791	719	647	576	504	433	72-71
.64	.071 361	290	219	148	076	005	934	863	793	722	72-70
.65	.070 651	581	510	440	369	299	229	158	088	018	71-70
.66	.069 948	878	808	739	669	599	530	460	391	322	70-69
.67	252	183	114	045	976	907	838	769	700	632	69-68
.68	.068 563	495	426	358	289	221	153	085	017	949	69-68
.69	.067 881	813	745	678	610	542	475	407	340	273	68-67
2.70	206	138	071	004	937	870	803	737	670	603	68-66
.71	.066 537	470	404	337	271	205	139	073	007	941	67-66
.72	.065 875	809	743	677	612	546	481	415	350	285	66-65
.73	219	154	089	024	959	894	829	764	700	635	65-64
.74	.064 570	506	441	377	313	248	184	120	056	992	65-64
.75	.063 928	864	800	736	673	609	545	482	418	355	64-63
.76	292	229	165	102	039	976	913	850	787	725	64-62
.77	.062 662	599	537	474	412	349	287	225	163	101	63-62
.78	039	976	915	853	791	729	667	606	544	483	63-61
.79	.061 421	360	298	237	176	115	054	993	932	871	62-61
2.80	.060 810	749	689	628	567	507	446	386	326	265	61-60
.81	205	145	085	025	965	905	845	785	725	666	60-59
.82	.059 606	546	487	427	368	309	249	190	131	072	60-59
.83	013	954	895	836	777	719	660	601	543	484	59-58
.84	.058 426	367	309	251	192	134	076	018	960	902	59-58
.85	.057 844	787	729	671	613	556	498	441	383	326	58-57
.86	269	212	154	097	040	983	926	869	812	756	58-56
.87	.056 699	642	586	529	473	416	360	303	247	191	57-56
.88	135	079	023	967	911	855	799	743	687	632	56-55
.89	.055 576	521	465	410	354	299	244	189	133	078	56-55
2.90	023	968	913	858	804	749	694	639	585	530	55-54
.91	.054 476	421	367	313	258	204	150	096	042	988	55-54
.92	.053 934	880	826	772	718	665	611	557	504	450	54-53
.93	397	344	290	237	184	131	078	025	972	919	54-53
.94	.052 866	813	760	707	655	602	549	497	444	392	53-52
.95	340	287	235	183	131	079	027	975	923	871	53-52
.96	.051 819	767	715	664	612	560	509	457	406	355	52-51
.97	303	252	201	150	099	047	996	945	895	844	52-50
.98	.050 793	742	691	641	590	540	489	439	388	338	51-50
.99	287	237	187	137	087	037	987	937	887	837	50
	.049										

$$e^{-x}$$

x	0	1	2	3	4	5	6	7	8	9	Diff. (Subtract)
3.00	.049 787	737	688	638	588	539	489	440	390	341	50-49
.01	292	242	193	144	095	046	997	948	899	850	50-49
.02	.048 801	752	704	655	606	558	509	461	412	364	49-48
.03	316	267	219	171	123	075	027	979	931	883	49-48
.04	.047 835	787	739	692	644	596	549	501	454	406	48-47
.05	359	312	264	217	170	123	076	029	982	935	48-47
.06	.046 888	841	794	747	701	654	607	561	514	468	47-46
.07	421	375	328	282	236	190	143	097	051	005	47-46
.08	.045 959	913	867	822	776	730	684	639	593	547	46-45
.09	502	456	411	366	320	275	230	185	139	094	46-45
3.10	049	004	959	914	869	825	780	735	690	646	45-44
.11	.044 601	556	512	467	423	379	334	290	246	201	45-44
.12	157	113	069	025	981	937	893	849	805	762	44-43
.13	.043 718	674	630	587	543	500	456	413	369	326	44-43
.14	283	240	196	153	110	067	024	981	938	895	44-43
.15	.042 852	809	767	724	681	638	596	553	511	468	43-42
.16	426	383	341	299	256	214	172	130	088	046	43-42
.17	004	962	920	878	836	794	752	711	669	627	42-41
.18	.041 586	544	503	461	420	378	337	296	254	213	42-41
.19	172	131	090	049	008	967	926	885	844	803	41
3.20	.040 762	721	681	640	599	559	518	478	437	397	41-40
.21	357	316	276	236	196	155	115	075	035	995	41-40
.22	.039 955	915	875	835	796	756	716	676	637	597	40-39
.23	557	518	478	439	400	360	321	282	242	203	40-39
.24	164	125	086	047	008	969	930	891	852	813	39
.25	.038 774	735	697	658	619	581	542	504	465	427	39-38
.26	388	350	312	273	235	197	159	121	083	044	39-38
.27	006	968	930	893	855	817	779	741	704	666	38-37
.28	.037 628	591	553	516	478	441	403	366	328	291	38-37
.29	254	217	179	142	105	068	031	994	957	920	38-37
3.30	.036 883	846	809	773	736	699	663	626	589	553	37-36
.31	516	480	443	407	370	334	298	261	225	189	37-36
.32	153	117	081	045	009	973	937	901	865	829	36
.33	.035 793	757	722	686	650	615	579	543	508	472	36-35
.34	437	402	366	331	295	260	225	190	155	119	36-35
.35	084	049	014	979	944	909	874	840	805	770	35-34
.36	.034 735	701	666	631	597	562	527	493	458	424	35-34
.37	390	355	321	287	252	218	184	150	116	082	35-34
.38	047	013	979	945	912	878	844	810	776	742	34-33
.39	.033 709	675	641	608	574	541	507	474	440	407	34-33
3.40	373	340	307	273	240	207	174	140	107	074	34-33
.41	041	008	975	942	909	876	844	811	778	745	33-32
.42	.032 712	680	647	614	582	549	517	484	452	419	33-32
.43	387	355	322	290	258	225	193	161	129	097	33-32
.44	065	033	001	969	937	905	873	841	809	777	32-31
.45	.031 746	714	682	651	619	587	556	524	493	461	32-31
.46	430	398	367	336	304	273	242	211	179	148	32-31
.47	117	086	055	024	993	962	931	900	869	838	31
.48	.030 807	777	746	715	684	654	623	593	562	531	31-30
.49	501	470	440	410	379	349	318	288	258	228	31-30

$$e^{-x}$$

x	0	1	2	3	4	5	6	7	8	9	Diff. (Subtract)
3.50	.030 197	167	137	107	077	047	017	987	957	927	30
.51	.029 897	867	837	807	778	748	718	688	659	629	30-29
.52	599	570	540	511	481	452	422	393	364	334	30-29
.53	305	276	246	217	188	159	130	100	071	042	30-29
.54	013	984	955	926	898	869	840	811	782	753	29-28
.55	.028 725	696	667	639	610	581	553	524	496	467	29-28
.56	439	410	382	354	325	297	269	240	212	184	29-28
.57	156	128	100	072	043	015	987	959	932	904	29-27
.58	.027 876	848	820	792	764	737	709	681	654	626	28-27
.59	598	571	543	516	488	461	433	406	378	351	28-27
3.60	324	296	269	242	215	187	160	133	106	079	28-27
.61	052	025	998	971	944	917	890	863	836	809	27-26
.62	.026 783	756	729	702	676	649	622	596	569	543	27-26
.63	516	490	463	437	410	384	358	331	305	279	27-26
.64	252	226	200	174	148	121	095	069	043	017	27-26
.65	.025 991	965	939	913	887	861	836	810	784	758	26-25
.66	733	707	681	655	630	604	579	553	527	502	26-25
.67	476	451	426	400	375	349	324	299	273	248	26-25
.68	223	198	173	147	122	097	072	047	022	997	26-25
.69	.024 972	947	922	897	872	847	823	798	773	748	25-24
3.70	724	699	674	649	625	600	576	551	527	502	25-24
.71	478	453	429	404	380	355	331	307	282	258	25-24
.72	234	210	186	161	137	113	089	065	041	017	25-24
.73	.023 993	969	945	921	897	873	849	825	802	778	24-23
.74	754	730	707	683	659	636	612	588	565	541	24-23
.75	518	494	471	447	424	400	377	354	330	307	24-23
.76	284	260	237	214	191	168	144	121	098	075	24-23
.77	052	029	006	983	960	937	914	891	868	846	23-22
.78	.022 823	800	777	754	732	709	686	663	641	618	23-22
.79	596	573	550	528	505	483	460	438	416	393	23-22
3.80	371	348	326	304	281	259	237	215	193	170	23-22
.81	148	126	104	082	060	038	016	994	972	950	22
.82	.021 928	906	884	862	840	818	797	775	753	731	22-21
.83	710	688	666	645	623	601	580	558	537	515	22-21
.84	494	472	451	429	408	386	365	344	322	301	22-21
.85	280	258	237	216	195	174	152	131	110	089	22-21
.86	068	047	026	005	984	963	942	921	900	879	21
.87	.020 858	838	817	796	775	754	734	713	692	671	21-20
.88	651	630	610	589	568	548	527	507	486	466	21-20
.89	445	425	404	384	364	343	323	303	282	262	21-20
3.90	242	222	201	181	161	141	121	101	081	061	21-20
.91	041	020	000	980	960	941	921	901	881	861	21-19
.92	.019 841	821	801	782	762	742	722	703	683	663	20-19
.93	644	624	604	585	565	546	526	507	487	468	20-19
.94	448	429	409	390	371	351	332	313	293	274	20-19
.95	255	235	216	197	178	159	140	120	101	082	20-19
.96	063	044	025	006	987	968	949	930	911	892	19
.97	.018 873	855	836	817	798	779	761	742	723	704	19-18
.98	686	667	648	630	611	592	574	555	537	518	19-18
.99	500	481	463	444	426	407	389	371	352	334	19-18

$$e^{-x}$$

x	0	1	2	3	4	5	6	7	8	9	Diff. (Subtract)
4.00	.018 316	297	279	261	243	224	206	188	170	152	19-18
.01	133	115	097	079	061	043	025	007	9̄8̄9̄	9̄7̄1̄	18
.02	.017 953	935	917	899	881	863	846	828	810	792	18-17
.03	774	757	739	721	703	686	668	650	633	615	18-17
.04	597	580	562	545	527	510	492	475	457	440	18-17
.05	422	405	388	370	353	335	318	301	284	266	18-17
.06	249	232	215	197	180	163	146	129	112	094	18-17
.07	077	060	043	026	009	9̄9̄2̄	9̄7̄5̄	9̄5̄8̄	9̄4̄1̄	9̄2̄4̄	17
.08	.016 907	891	874	857	840	823	806	790	773	756	17-16
.09	739	723	706	689	672	656	639	622	606	589	17-16
4.10	573	556	540	523	507	490	474	457	441	424	17-16
.11	408	391	375	359	342	326	310	293	277	261	17-16
.12	245	228	212	196	180	163	1̲4̲7̲	1̲3̲1̲	1̲1̲5̲	0̲9̲9̲	17-16
.13	083	067	051	035	019	003	9̄8̄7̄	9̄7̄1̄	9̄5̄5̄	9̄3̄9̄	16
.14	.015 923	907	891	875	859	843	828	812	796	780	16-15
.15	764	749	733	717	701	686	670	654	639	623	16-15
.16	608	592	576	561	545	530	514	499	483	468	16-15
.17	452	437	421	406	391	375	360	344	329	314	16-15
.18	299	283	268	253	237	222	207	192	177	161	16-15
.19	146	131	116	101	086	071	056	041	026	011	15
4.20	.014 996	981	966	951	936	921	906	891	876	861	15
.21	846	832	817	802	787	772	758	743	728	713	15-14
.22	699	684	669	655	640	625	611	596	582	567	15-14
.23	552	538	523	509	494	480	465	451	436	422	15-14
.24	408	393	379	364	350	336	321	307	293	279	15-14
.25	264	250	236	222	207	193	179	165	151	1̲3̲6̲	15-14
.26	122	108	094	080	066	052	038	024	010	9̄9̄6̄	14
.27	.013 982	968	954	940	926	912	898	884	870	857	14-13
.28	843	829	815	801	787	774	760	746	732	719	14-13
.29	705	691	678	664	650	637	623	609	596	582	14-13
4.30	569	555	541	528	514	501	487	474	460	447	14-13
.31	434	420	407	393	380	367	353	340	327	313	14-13
.32	300	287	273	260	247	234	220	207	194	181	14-13
.33	168	154	141	128	115	102	089	076	063	050	14-13
.34	037	023	010	9̄9̄7̄	9̄8̄4̄	9̄7̄2̄	9̄5̄9̄	9̄4̄6̄	9̄3̄3̄	9̄2̄0̄	14-12
.35	.012 907	894	881	868	855	842	830	817	804	791	13-12
.36	778	766	753	740	727	715	702	689	677	664	13-12
.37	651	639	626	613	601	588	576	563	550	538	13-12
.38	525	513	500	488	475	463	450	438	426	413	13-12
.39	401	388	376	364	351	339	327	314	302	290	13-12
4.40	277	265	253	241	228	216	204	192	180	167	13-12
.41	155	143	131	1̲1̲9̲	1̲0̲7̲	0̲9̲5̲	0̲8̲2̲	0̲7̲0̲	0̲5̲8̲	0̲4̲6̲	13-12
.42	034	022	010	998	9̄8̄6̄	9̄7̄4̄	9̄6̄2̄	9̄5̄0̄	9̄3̄8̄	9̄2̄6̄	12
.43	.011 914	903	891	879	867	855	843	831	820	808	12-11
.44	796	784	772	761	749	737	725	714	702	690	12-11
.45	679	667	655	644	632	620	609	597	586	574	12-11
.46	562	551	539	528	516	505	493	482	470	459	12-11
.47	447	436	424	413	402	390	379	367	356	345	12-11
.48	333	322	311	299	288	277	266	254	243	232	12-11
.49	221	209	198	187	176	165	154	142	131	120	12-11

$$e^{-x}$$

x	0	1	2	3	4	5	6	7	8	9	Diff. (Subtract)
4.50	.011 109	098	087	076	065	054	043	032	020	009	12-11
.51	.010 998	987	976	966	955	944	933	922	911	900	11-10
.52	889	878	867	856	846	835	824	813	802	791	11-10
.53	781	770	759	748	738	727	716	705	695	684	11-10
.54	673	663	652	641	631	620	610	599	588	578	11-10
.55	567	557	546	536	525	515	504	493	483	473	11-10
.56	462	452	441	431	420	410	399	389	379	368	11-10
.57	358	348	337	327	317	306	296	286	275	265	11-10
.58	255	245	234	224	214	204	194	183	173	163	11-10
.59	153	143	133	122	112	102	092	082	072	062	11-10
4.60	052	042	032	022	012	002	992̄	982̄	972̄	962̄	10
.61	.009 952	942	932	922	912	902	892	882	873	863	10-9
.62	853	843	833	823	813	804	794	784	774	765	10-9
.63	755	745	735	726	716	706	696	687	677	667	10-9
.64	658	648	638	629	619	610	600	590	581	571	10-9
.65	562	552	542	533	523	514	504	495	485	476	10-9
.66	466	457	448	438	429	419	410	400	391	382	10-9
.67	372	363	354	344	335	326	316	307	298	288	10-9
.68	279	270	260	251	242	233	224	214	205	196	10-9
.69	187	178	168	159	150	141	132	123	113	104	10-9
4.70	095	086	077	068	059	050	041	032	023	014	9
.71	005	996̄	987̄	978̄	969̄	960̄	951̄	942̄	933̄	924̄	9
.72	.008 915	906	897	888	880	871	862	853	844	835	9-8
.73	826	818	809	800	791	782	774	765	756	747	9-8
.74	739	730	721	712	704	695	686	678	669	660	9-8
.75	652	643	634	626	617	609	600	591	583	574	9-8
.76	566	557	548	540	531	523	514	506	497	489	9-8
.77	480	472	463	455	447	438	430	421	413	404	9-8
.78	396	388	379	371	362	354	346	337	329	321	9-8
.79	312	304	296	288	279	271	263	254	246	238	9-8
4.80	230	222	213	205	197	189	181	172	164	156	9-8
.81	148	140	132	123	115	107	099	091	083	075	9-8
.82	067	059	051	043	035	027	019	011	003	995̄	8
.83	.007 987	979	971	963	955	947	939	931	923	915	8
.84	907	899	891	883	875	868	860	852	844	836	8-7
.85	828	821	813	805	797	789	782	774	766	758	8-7
.86	750	743	735	727	720	712	704	696	689	681	8-7
.87	673	666	658	650	643	635	627	620	612	605	8-7
.88	597	589	582	574	567	559	552	544	536	529	8-7
.89	521	514	506	499	491	484	476	469	461	454	8-7
4.90	447	439	432	424	417	409	402	395	387	380	8-7
.91	372	365	358	350	343	336	328	321	314	306	8-7
.92	299	292	285	277	270	263	255	248	241	234	8-7
.93	227	219	212	205	198	190	183	176	169	162	8-7
.94	155	147	140	133	126	119	112	105	098	090	8-7
.95	083	076	069	062	055	048	041	034	027	020	7
.96	013	006	999̄	992̄	985̄	978̄	971̄	964̄	957̄	950̄	7
.97	.006 943	936	929	922	915	909	902	895	888	881	7-6
.98	874	867	860	853	847	840	833	826	819	812	7-6
.99	806	799	792	785	778	772	765	758	751	745	7-6
5.00	738										

y	n	$10^{-n}e^{y}$	y	n	$10^{n}\,e^{-y}$
5	2	1.48413	5	3	6.73795
10	4	2.20265	10	5	4.53999
15	6	3.26902	15	7	3.05902
20	8	4.85165	20	9	2.06115
25	10	7.20049	25	11	1.38879
30	13	1.06865	30	14	9.35762
35	15	1.58601	35	16	6.30512
40	17	2.35385	40	18	4.24835
45	19	3.49343	45	20	2.86252
50	21	5.18471	50	22	1.92875
55	23	7.69479	55	24	1.29958
60	26	1.14201	60	27	8.75651
65	28	1.69489	65	29	5.90009
70	30	2.51544	70	31	3.97545
75	32	3.73324	75	33	2.67864
80	34	5.54062	80	35	1.80485
85	36	8.22301	85	37	1.21610
90	39	1.22040	90	40	8.19401
95	41	1.81124	95	42	5.52108
100	43	2.68812	100	44	3.72008

Examples:

$$10^{-2}e^{5} = 1.48413, \quad e^{5} = 1.48413 \times 10^{2}$$
$$10^{3}e^{-5} = 6.73795, \quad e^{-5} = 6.73795 \times 10^{-3}$$

When the exponent is numerically greater than 5, multiply the values in the tables by the appropriate value of e^{y} or e^{-y}. Note that

$$e^{y+x} = e^{y}.e^{x}$$

For large tables of e^{x} and e^{-x} see the tables of the Exponential Function published by the National Bureau of Standards, Washington, D.C.

Alpha	α	A
Beta	β	B
Gamma	γ	Γ
Delta	δ	Δ
Epsilon	ϵ	E
Zeta	ζ	Z
Eta	η	H
Theta	$\theta \ \vartheta$	Θ
Iota	ι	I
Kappa	κ	K
Lambda	λ	Λ
Mu	μ	M
Nu	ν	N
Xi	ξ	Ξ
Omicron	o	O
Pi	π	Π
Rho	ρ	P
Sigma	$\sigma \ \varsigma$	Σ
Tau	τ	T
Upsilon	υ	Υ
Phi	$\varphi \ \phi$	Φ
Chi	χ	X
Psi	ψ	Ψ
Omega	ω	Ω

$$\text{SINH } X = \frac{1}{2} (e^{X} - e^{-X})$$

x	0	1	2	3	4	5	6	7	8	9	Diff.
.00	.0 000	010	020	030	040	050	060	070	080	090	10
.01	100	110	120	130	140	150	160	170	180	190	10
.02	200	210	220	230	240	250	260	270	280	290	10
.03	300	310	320	330	340	350	360	370	380	390	10
.04	400	410	420	430	440	450	460	470	480	490	10
.05	500	510	520	530	540	550	560	570	580	590	10
.06	600	610	620	630	640	650	660	671	681	691	10 - 11
.07	701	711	721	731	741	751	761	771	781	791	10
.08	801	811	821	831	841	851	861	871	881	891	10
.09	901	911	921	931	941	951	961	972	982	992	10 - 11
.10	.1 002	012	022	032	042	052	062	072	082	092	10
.11	102	112	122	132	142	153	163	173	183	193	10 - 11
.12	203	213	223	233	243	253	263	273	283	294	10 - 11
.13	304	314	324	334	344	354	364	374	384	394	10 - 11
.14	405	415	425	435	445	455	465	475	485	496	10 - 11
.15	506	516	526	536	546	556	566	576	587	597	10 - 11
.16	607	617	627	637	647	657	668	678	688	698	10 - 11
.17	708	718	728	739	749	759	769	779	789	800	10 - 11
.18	810	820	830	840	850	861	871	881	891	901	10 - 11
.19	911	922	932	942	952	962	973	983	993	003	10 - 11
.20	.2 013	024	034	044	054	064	075	085	095	105	10 - 11
.21	115	126	136	146	156	167	177	187	197	208	10 - 11
.22	218	228	238	249	259	269	279	290	300	310	10 - 11
.23	320	331	341	351	361	372	382	392	403	413	10 - 11
.24	423	433	444	454	464	475	485	495	505	516	10 - 11
.25	526	536	547	557	567	578	588	598	609	619	10 - 11
.26	629	640	650	660	671	681	691	702	712	723	10 - 11
.27	733	743	754	764	774	785	795	806	816	826	10 - 11
.28	837	847	858	868	878	889	899	910	920	930	10 - 11
.29	941	951	962	972	983	993	003	014	024	035	10 - 11
.30	.3 045	056	066	077	087	098	108	118	129	139	10 - 11
.31	150	160	171	181	192	202	213	223	234	244	10 - 11
.32	255	265	276	286	297	308	318	329	339	350	10 - 11
.33	360	371	381	392	402	413	424	434	445	455	10 - 11
.34	466	476	487	498	508	519	529	540	551	561	10 - 11
.35	572	583	593	604	614	625	636	646	657	668	10 - 11
.36	678	689	700	710	721	732	742	753	764	774	10 - 11
.37	785	796	806	817	828	839	849	860	871	881	10 - 11
.38	892	903	914	924	935	946	957	967	978	989	10 - 11
.39	.4 000	010	021	032	043	054	064	075	086	097	10 - 11
.40	108	118	129	140	151	162	172	183	194	205	10 - 11
.41	216	227	238	248	259	270	281	292	303	314	10 - 11
.42	325	335	346	357	368	379	390	401	412	423	10 - 11
.43	434	445	456	467	478	488	499	510	521	532	10 - 11
.44	543	554	565	576	587	598	609	620	631	642	11
.45	653	664	675	687	698	709	720	731	742	753	11 - 12
.46	764	775	786	797	808	819	830	842	853	864	11 - 12
.47	875	886	897	908	919	931	942	953	964	975	11 - 12
.48	986	998	009	020	031	042	054	065	076	087	11 - 12
.49	.5 098	110	121	132	143	155	166	177	188	200	11 - 12

SINH X

x	0	1	2	3	4	5	6	7	8	9	Diff.
.50	.5 211	222	234	245	256	267	279	290	301	313	11 - 12
.51	324	335	347	358	369	381	392	403	415	426	11 - 12
.52	438	449	460	472	483	495	506	517	529	540	11 - 12
.53	552	563	575	586	597	609	620	632	643	655	11 - 12
.54	666	678	689	701	712	724	735	747	758	770	11 - 12
.55	782	793	805	816	828	839	851	863	874	886	11 - 12
.56	897	909	921	932	944	955	967	979	990	002	11 - 12
.57	.6 014	025	037	049	060	072	084	096	107	119	11 - 12
.58	131	142	154	166	178	189	201	213	225	237	11 - 12
.59	248	260	272	284	296	307	319	331	343	355	11 - 12
.60	367	378	390	402	414	426	438	450	462	473	11 - 12
.61	485	497	509	521	533	545	557	569	581	593	12
.62	605	617	629	641	653	665	677	689	701	713	12
.63	725	737	749	761	773	785	798	810	822	834	12 - 13
.64	846	858	870	882	894	907	919	931	943	955	12 - 13
.65	967	980	992	004	016	029	041	053	065	077	12 - 13
.66	.7 090	102	114	127	139	151	163	176	188	200	12 - 13
.67	213	225	237	250	262	274	287	299	312	324	12 - 13
.68	336	349	361	374	386	398	411	423	436	448	12 - 13
.69	461	473	486	498	511	523	536	548	561	573	12 - 13
.70	586	598	611	624	636	649	661	674	686	699	12 - 13
.71	712	724	737	750	762	775	788	800	813	826	12 - 13
.72	838	851	864	877	889	902	915	928	940	953	12 - 13
.73	966	979	991	004	017	030	043	056	068	081	12 - 13
.74	.8 094	107	120	133	146	159	171	184	197	210	12 - 13
.75	223	236	249	262	275	288	301	314	327	340	13
.76	353	366	379	392	405	418	431	444	458	471	13 - 14
.77	484	497	510	523	536	549	563	576	589	602	13 - 14
.78	615	629	642	655	668	681	695	708	721	734	13 - 14
.79	748	761	774	788	801	814	828	841	854	868	13 - 14
.80	881	894	908	921	935	948	961	975	988	002	13 - 14
.81	.9 015	029	042	056	069	083	096	110	123	137	13 - 14
.82	150	164	177	191	205	218	232	245	259	273	13 - 14
.83	286	300	314	327	341	355	368	382	396	410	13 - 14
.84	423	437	451	465	478	492	506	520	534	547	13 - 14
.85	561	575	589	603	617	630	644	658	672	686	13 - 14
.86	700	714	728	742	756	770	784	798	812	826	14
.87	840	854	868	882	896	910	924	938	952	966	14 - 15
.88	981	995	009	023	037	051	066	080	094	108	14 - 15
.89	1.0 122	137	151	165	179	194	208	222	237	251	14 - 15
.90	265	280	294	308	323	337	351	366	380	395	14 - 15
.91	409	423	438	452	467	481	496	510	525	539	14 - 15
.92	554	568	583	598	612	627	641	656	671	685	14 - 15
.93	700	714	729	744	758	773	788	803	817	832	14 - 15
.94	847	862	876	891	906	921	935	950	965	980	14 - 15
.95	995	010	025	039	054	069	084	099	114	129	14 - 15
.96	1.1 144	159	174	189	204	219	234	249	264	279	15
.97	294	309	324	340	355	370	385	400	415	431	15 - 16
.98	446	461	476	491	507	522	537	552	568	583	15 - 16
.99	598	614	629	644	660	675	690	706	721	737	15 - 16

SINH X

x	0	1	2	3	4	5	6	7	8	9	Diff.
1.00	1.1 752	767	783	798	814	829	845	860	876	891	15 - 16
1.01	907	922	938	954	969	985	000	016	032	047	15 - 16
1.02	1.2 063	079	094	110	126	141	157	173	189	205	15 - 16
1.03	220	236	252	268	284	299	315	331	347	363	15 - 16
1.04	379	395	411	427	443	459	475	491	507	523	16
1.05	539	555	571	587	603	619	635	651	667	683	16 - 17
1.06	700	716	732	748	764	781	797	813	829	846	16 - 17
1.07	862	878	894	911	927	943	960	976	993	009	16 - 17
1.08	1.3 025	042	058	075	091	108	124	141	157	174	16 - 17
1.09	190	207	223	240	257	273	290	306	323	340	16 - 17
1.10	356	373	390	407	423	440	457	474	490	507	16 - 17
1.11	524	541	558	575	591	608	625	642	659	676	16 - 17
1.12	693	710	727	744	761	778	795	812	829	846	17
1.13	863	880	897	914	932	949	966	983	000	018	17 - 18
1.14	1.4 035	052	069	087	104	121	138	156	173	190	17 - 18
1.15	208	225	243	260	277	295	312	330	347	365	17 - 18
1.16	382	400	417	435	452	470	488	505	523	540	17 - 18
1.17	558	576	593	611	629	647	664	682	700	718	17 - 18
1.18	735	753	771	789	807	825	843	860	878	896	17 - 18
1.19	914	932	950	968	986	004	022	040	058	077	18 - 19
1.20	1.5 095	113	131	149	167	185	204	222	240	258	18 - 19
1.21	276	295	313	331	350	368	386	405	423	441	18 - 19
1.22	460	478	497	515	534	552	571	589	608	626	18 - 19
1.23	645	663	682	700	719	738	756	775	794	812	18 - 19
1.24	831	850	869	887	906	925	944	963	981	000	18 - 19
1.25	1.6 019	038	057	076	095	114	133	152	171	190	19
1.26	209	228	247	266	285	304	323	343	362	381	19 - 20
1.27	400	419	439	458	477	496	516	535	554	574	19 - 20
1.28	593	612	632	651	671	690	710	729	749	768	19 - 20
1.29	788	807	827	846	866	885	905	925	944	964	19 - 20
1.30	984	004	023	043	063	083	102	122	142	162	19 - 20
1.31	1.7 182	202	222	241	261	281	301	321	341	361	19 - 20
1.32	381	401	422	442	462	482	502	522	542	563	20 - 21
1.33	583	603	623	644	664	684	705	725	745	766	20 - 21
1.34	786	806	827	847	868	888	909	929	950	970	20 - 21
1.35	991	012	032	053	073	094	115	135	156	177	20 - 21
1.36	1.8 198	218	239	260	281	302	323	343	364	385	20 - 21
1.37	406	427	448	469	490	511	532	553	574	595	21 - 22
1.38	617	638	659	680	701	723	744	765	786	808	21 - 22
1.39	829	850	872	893	914	936	957	979	000	022	21 - 22
1.40	1.9 043	065	086	108	129	151	172	194	216	237	21 - 22
1.41	259	281	303	324	346	368	390	411	433	455	21 - 22
1.42	477	499	521	543	565	587	609	631	653	675	22
1.43	697	719	741	763	785	808	830	852	874	897	22 - 23
1.44	919	941	963	986	008	031	053	075	098	120	22 - 23
1.45	2.0 143	165	188	210	233	255	278	301	323	346	22 - 23
1.46	369	391	414	437	460	482	505	528	551	574	22 - 23
1.47	597	619	642	665	688	711	734	757	780	803	22 - 23
1.48	827	850	873	896	919	942	966	989	012	035	23 - 24
1.49	2.1 059	082	105	129	152	175	199	222	246	269	23 - 24

SINH X

x	0	1	2	3	4	5	6	7	8	9	Diff.
1.50	2.1 293	316	340	363	387	411	434	458	482	505	23 - 24
1.51	529	553	577	600	624	648	672	696	720	744	23 - 24
1.52	768	792	816	840	864	888	912	936	960	984	24
1.53	2.2 008	032	057	081	105	129	154	178	202	227	24 - 25
1.54	251	275	300	324	349	373	398	422	447	472	24 - 25
1.55	496	521	545	570	595	619	644	669	694	719	24 - 25
1.56	743	768	793	818	843	868	893	918	943	968	25
1.57	993	018	043	068	093	119	144	169	194	220	25 - 26
1.58	2.3 245	270	296	321	346	372	397	423	448	474	25 - 26
1.59	499	525	550	576	601	627	653	678	704	730	25 - 26
1.60	756	781	807	833	859	885	911	937	963	989	25 - 26
1.61	2.4 015	041	067	093	119	145	171	197	223	250	26 - 27
1.62	276	302	329	355	381	408	434	460	487	513	26 - 27
1.63	540	566	593	619	646	673	699	726	753	779	26 - 27
1.64	806	833	859	886	913	940	967	994	021	048	26 - 27
1.65	2.5 075	102	129	156	183	210	237	264	291	319	27 - 28
1.66	346	373	400	428	455	482	510	537	565	592	27 - 28
1.67	620	647	675	702	730	757	785	813	840	868	27 - 28
1.68	896	924	951	979	007	035	063	091	119	147	27 - 28
1.69	2.6 175	203	231	259	287	315	343	372	400	428	28 - 29
1.70	456	485	513	541	570	598	626	655	683	712	28 - 29
1.71	740	769	798	826	855	884	912	941	970	999	28 - 29
1.72	2.7 027	056	085	114	143	172	201	230	259	288	29
1.73	317	346	375	404	433	463	492	521	550	580	29 - 30
1.74	609	638	668	697	727	756	786	815	845	875	29 - 30
1.75	904	934	963	993	023	053	082	112	142	172	29 - 30
1.76	2.8 202	232	262	292	322	352	382	412	442	472	30 - 31
1.77	503	533	563	593	624	654	684	715	745	776	30 - 31
1.78	806	837	867	898	928	959	990	020	051	082	30 - 31
1.79	2.9 112	143	174	205	236	267	298	329	360	391	31
1.80	422	453	484	515	546	577	609	640	671	703	31 - 32
1.81	734	765	797	828	860	891	923	954	986	018	31 - 32
1.82	3.0 049	081	113	144	176	208	240	272	303	335	31 - 32
1.83	367	399	431	463	495	528	560	592	624	656	32 - 33
1.84	689	721	753	786	818	850	883	915	948	980	32 - 33
1.85	3.1 013	046	078	111	144	176	209	242	275	307	32 - 33
1.86	340	373	406	439	472	505	538	571	605	638	33 - 34
1.87	671	704	737	771	804	837	871	904	938	971	33 - 34
1.88	3.2 005	038	072	105	139	173	206	240	274	308	33 - 34
1.89	341	375	409	443	477	511	545	579	613	647	34 - 35
1.90	682	716	750	784	819	853	887	922	956	991	34 - 35
1.91	3.3 025	060	094	129	163	198	233	267	302	337	34 - 35
1.92	372	407	441	476	511	546	581	616	652	687	34 - 36
1.93	722	757	792	827	863	898	933	969	004	040	35 - 36
1.94	3.4 075	111	146	182	218	253	289	325	360	396	35 - 36
1.95	432	468	504	540	576	612	648	684	720	756	36
1.96	792	829	865	901	937	974	010	047	083	120	36 - 37
1.97	3.5 156	193	229	266	303	339	376	413	450	486	36 - 37
1.98	523	560	597	634	671	708	745	783	820	857	37 - 38
1.99	894	931	969	006	044	081	118	156	193	231	37 - 38
	3.6										

SINH X

x	0	1	2	3	4	5	6	7	8	9	Diff.
2.00	3. 627	631	634	638	642	646	649	653	657	661	3 - 4
2.01	665	668	672	676	680	684	688	691	695	699	3 - 4
2.02	703	707	711	714	718	722	726	730	734	738	3 - 4
2.03	741	745	749	753	757	761	765	769	772	776	3 - 4
2.04	780	784	788	792	796	800	804	808	812	816	4
2.05	820	824	827	831	835	839	843	847	851	855	3 - 4
2.06	859	863	867	871	875	879	883	887	891	895	4
2.07	899	903	907	911	915	919	924	928	932	936	4 - 5
2.08	940	944	948	952	956	960	964	968	972	977	4 - 5
2.09	981	985	989	993	997	001	005	009	014	018	4 - 5
2.10	4. 022	026	030	034	038	043	047	051	055	059	4 - 5
2.11	064	068	072	076	080	084	089	093	097	101	4 - 5
2.12	106	110	114	118	122	127	131	135	139	144	4 - 5
2.13	148	152	157	161	165	169	174	178	182	187	4 - 5
2.14	191	195	200	204	208	212	217	221	225	230	4 - 5
2.15	234	239	243	247	252	256	260	265	269	274	4 - 5
2.16	278	282	287	291	296	300	304	309	313	318	4 - 5
2.17	322	326	331	335	340	344	349	353	358	362	4 - 5
2.18	367	371	376	380	385	389	394	398	403	407	4 - 5
2.19	412	416	421	425	430	434	439	443	448	453	4 - 5
2.20	457	462	466	471	475	480	485	489	494	498	4 - 5
2.21	503	508	512	517	521	526	531	535	540	545	4 - 5
2.22	549	554	559	563	568	573	577	582	587	591	4 - 5
2.23	596	601	606	610	615	620	624	629	634	639	4 - 5
2.24	643	648	653	658	662	667	672	677	682	686	4 - 5
2.25	691	696	701	706	710	715	720	725	730	735	4 - 5
2.26	739	744	749	754	759	764	769	773	778	783	4 - 5
2.27	788	793	798	803	808	813	817	822	827	832	4 - 5
2.28	837	842	847	852	857	862	867	872	877	882	5
2.29	887	892	897	902	907	912	917	922	927	932	5
2.30	937	942	947	952	957	962	967	972	977	982	5 - 6
2.31	988	993	998	003	008	013	018	023	028	034	5 - 6
2.32	5. 039	044	049	054	059	064	070	075	080	085	5 - 6
2.33	090	096	101	106	111	116	122	127	132	137	5 - 6
2.34	142	148	153	158	163	169	174	179	185	190	5 - 6
2.35	195	200	206	211	216	222	227	232	238	243	5 - 6
2.36	248	254	259	264	270	275	280	286	291	297	5 - 6
2.37	302	307	313	318	324	329	334	340	345	351	5 - 6
2.38	356	362	367	373	378	383	389	394	400	405	5 - 6
2.39	411	416	422	427	433	439	444	450	455	461	5 - 6
2.40	466	472	477	483	489	494	500	505	511	516	5 - 6
2.41	522	528	533	539	545	550	556	561	567	573	5 - 6
2.42	578	584	590	595	601	607	613	618	624	630	5 - 6
2.43	635	641	647	653	658	664	670	676	681	687	5 - 6
2.44	693	699	705	710	716	722	728	734	739	745	5 - 6
2.45	751	757	763	769	774	780	786	792	798	804	5 - 6
2.46	810	816	821	827	833	839	845	851	857	863	5 - 6
2.47	869	875	881	887	893	899	905	911	917	923	6
2.48	929	935	941	947	953	959	965	971	977	983	6
2.49	989	995	001	007	014	020	026	032	038	044	6 - 7
	6.										

SINH X

x	0	1	2	3	4	5	6	7	8	9	Diff.
2.50	6. 050	056	062	069	075	081	087	093	099	106	6 - 7
2.51	112	118	124	130	137	143	149	155	162	168	6 - 7
2.52	174	180	187	193	199	205	212	218	224	231	6 - 7
2.53	237	243	250	256	262	269	275	281	288	294	6 - 7
2.54	300	307	313	320	326	332	339	345	352	358	6 - 7
2.55	365	371	377	384	390	397	403	410	416	423	6 - 7
2.56	429	436	442	449	455	462	468	475	482	488	6 - 7
2.57	495	501	508	514	521	528	534	541	547	554	6 - 7
2.58	561	567	574	581	587	594	601	607	614	621	6 - 7
2.59	627	634	641	648	654	661	668	674	681	688	6 - 7
2.60	695	702	708	715	722	729	735	742	749	756	6 - 7
2.61	763	770	776	783	790	797	804	811	818	825	6 - 7
2.62	831	838	845	852	859	866	873	880	887	894	7
2.63	901	908	915	922	929	936	943	950	957	964	7
2.64	971	978	985	992	999	0̄0̄6̄	0̄1̄3̄	0̄2̄0̄	0̄2̄7̄	0̄3̄5̄	7 - 8
2.65	7. 042	049	056	063	070	077	084	092	099	106	7 - 8
2.66	113	120	128	135	142	149	156	164	171	178	7 - 8
2.67	185	193	200	207	214	222	229	236	244	251	7 - 8
2.68	258	266	273	280	288	295	302	310	317	325	7 - 8
2.69	332	339	347	354	362	369	376	384	391	399	7 - 8
2.70	406	414	421	429	436	444	451	459	466	474	7 - 8
2.71	481	489	496	504	512	519	527	534	542	550	7 - 8
2.72	557	565	572	580	588	595	603	611	618	626	7 - 8
2.73	634	642	649	657	665	672	680	688	696	703	7 - 8
2.74	711	719	727	735	742	750	758	766	774	782	7 - 8
2.75	789	797	805	813	821	829	837	845	852	860	7 - 8
2.76	868	876	884	892	900	908	916	924	932	940	8
2.77	948	956	964	972	980	988	996	0̄0̄4̄	0̄1̄2̄	0̄2̄0̄	8
2.78	8. 028	037	045	053	061	069	077	085	093	102	8 - 9
2.79	110	118	126	134	143	151	159	167	175	184	8 - 9
2.80	192	200	208	217	225	233	242	250	258	267	8 - 9
2.81	275	283	292	300	308	317	325	333	342	350	8 - 9
2.82	359	367	375	384	392	401	409	418	426	435	8 - 9
2.83	443	452	460	469	477	486	494	503	512	520	8 - 9
2.84	529	537	546	554	563	572	580	589	598	606	8 - 9
2.85	615	624	632	641	650	658	667	676	685	693	8 - 9
2.86	702	711	720	728	737	746	755	764	772	781	8 - 9
2.87	790	799	808	817	826	835	843	852	861	870	8 - 9
2.88	879	888	897	906	915	924	933	942	951	960	9
2.89	969	978	987	996	0̄0̄5̄	0̄1̄4̄	0̄2̄3̄	0̄3̄2̄	0̄4̄1̄	0̄5̄0̄	9 - 10
2.90	9. 060	069	078	087	096	105	114	124	133	142	9 - 10
2.91	151	160	170	179	188	197	207	216	225	234	9 - 10
2.92	244	253	262	272	281	290	300	309	318	328	9 - 10
2.93	337	347	356	365	375	384	394	403	413	422	9 - 10
2.94	431	441	450	460	470	479	489	498	508	517	9 - 10
2.95	527	536	546	556	565	575	584	594	604	613	9 - 10
2.96	623	633	642	652	662	672	681	691	701	711	9 - 10
2.97	720	730	740	750	759	769	779	789	799	809	9 - 10
2.98	819	828	838	848	858	868	878	888	898	908	9 - 10
2.99	918	928	938	948	958	968	978	988	998	0̄0̄8̄	10
3.00	10. 018										

$$\text{COSH } X \ = \ \frac{1}{2} \ (\ e^{X} + e^{-X}\ )$$

x	0	1	2	3	4	5	6	7	8	9	Diff.
.00	1.0 000	000	000	000	000	000	000	000	000	000	0
.01	001	001	001	001	001	001	001	001	002	002	0 - 1
.02	002	002	002	003	003	003	003	004	004	004	0 - 1
.03	005	005	005	005	006	006	006	007	007	008	0 - 1
.04	008	008	009	009	010	010	011	011	012	012	0 - 1
.05	013	013	014	014	015	015	016	016	017	017	0 - 1
.06	018	019	019	020	020	021	022	022	023	024	0 - 1
.07	025	025	026	027	027	028	029	030	030	031	0 - 1
.08	032	033	034	034	035	036	037	038	039	040	0 - 1
.09	041	041	042	043	044	045	046	047	048	049	0 - 1
.10	050	051	052	053	054	055	056	057	058	059	1
.11	061	062	063	064	065	066	067	069	070	071	1 - 2
.12	072	073	075	076	077	078	079	081	082	083	1 - 2
.13	085	086	087	089	090	091	093	094	095	097	1 - 2
.14	098	100	101	102	104	105	107	108	110	111	1 - 2
.15	113	114	116	117	119	120	122	123	125	127	1 - 2
.16	128	130	132	133	135	136	138	140	141	143	1 - 2
.17	145	147	148	150	152	154	155	157	159	161	1 - 2
.18	162	164	166	168	170	172	173	175	177	179	1 - 2
.19	181	183	185	187	189	191	193	195	197	199	2
.20	201	203	205	207	209	211	213	215	217	219	2
.21	221	223	226	228	230	232	234	236	239	241	2 - 3
.22	243	245	247	250	252	254	256	259	261	263	2 - 3
.23	266	268	270	273	275	277	280	282	285	287	2 - 3
.24	289	292	294	297	299	302	304	307	309	312	2 - 3
.25	314	317	319	322	324	327	329	332	335	337	2 - 3
.26	340	343	345	348	351	353	356	359	361	364	2 - 3
.27	367	369	372	375	378	381	383	386	389	392	2 - 3
.28	395	397	400	403	406	409	412	415	418	421	2 - 3
.29	423	426	429	432	435	438	441	444	447	450	3
.30	453	456	459	463	466	469	472	475	478	481	3 - 4
.31	484	488	491	494	497	500	503	507	510	513	3 - 4
.32	516	520	523	526	529	533	536	539	543	546	3 - 4
.33	549	553	556	560	563	566	570	573	577	580	3 - 4
.34	584	587	591	594	598	601	605	608	612	615	3 - 4
.35	619	622	626	630	633	637	640	644	648	651	3 - 4
.36	655	659	662	666	670	674	677	681	685	689	3 - 4
.37	692	696	700	704	708	711	715	719	723	727	3 - 4
.38	731	735	739	742	746	750	754	758	762	766	3 - 4
.39	770	774	778	782	786	790	794	798	803	807	4 - 5
.40	811	815	819	823	827	831	836	840	844	848	4 - 5
.41	852	857	861	865	869	874	878	882	886	891	4 - 5
.42	895	899	904	908	912	917	921	926	930	934	4 - 5
.43	939	943	948	952	957	961	966	970	975	979	4 - 5
.44	984	988	993	997	002	007	011	016	020	025	4 - 5
.45	1.1 030	034	039	044	048	053	058	063	067	072	4 - 5
.46	077	082	086	091	096	101	106	110	115	120	4 - 5
.47	125	130	135	140	145	149	154	159	164	169	4 - 5
.48	174	179	184	189	194	199	204	209	215	220	5 - 6
.49	225	230	235	240	245	250	256	261	266	271	5 - 6

COSH X

x	0	1	2	3	4	5	6	7	8	9	Diff.
.50	1.1 276	281	287	292	297	302	308	313	318	324	5 - 6
.51	329	334	340	345	350	356	361	366	372	377	5 - 6
.52	383	388	394	399	405	410	416	421	427	432	5 - 6
.53	438	443	449	454	460	466	471	477	482	488	5 - 6
.54	494	499	505	511	517	522	528	534	539	545	5 - 6
.55	551	557	563	568	574	580	586	592	598	604	5 - 6
.56	609	615	621	627	633	639	645	651	657	663	6
.57	669	675	681	687	693	699	705	711	717	724	6 - 7
.58	730	736	742	748	754	760	767	773	779	785	6 - 7
.59	792	798	804	810	817	823	829	836	842	848	6 - 7
.60	855	861	867	874	880	887	893	900	906	912	6 - 7
.61	919	925	932	938	945	951	958	965	971	978	6 - 7
.62	984	991	998	004	011	018	024	031	038	044	6 - 7
.63	1.2 051	058	064	071	078	085	092	098	105	112	6 - 7
.64	119	126	133	139	146	153	160	167	174	181	6 - 7
.65	188	195	202	209	216	223	230	237	244	251	7
.66	258	265	272	280	287	294	301	308	315	323	7 - 8
.67	330	337	344	351	359	366	373	381	388	395	7 - 8
.68	402	410	417	425	432	439	447	454	462	469	7 - 8
.69	476	484	491	499	506	514	521	529	537	544	7 - 8
.70	552	559	567	575	582	590	597	605	613	620	7 - 8
.71	628	636	644	651	659	667	675	682	690	698	7 - 8
.72	706	714	722	729	737	745	753	761	769	777	7 - 8
.73	785	793	801	809	817	825	833	841	849	857	8
.74	865	873	881	890	898	906	914	922	930	939	8 - 9
.75	947	955	963	972	980	988	996	005	013	021	8 - 9
.76	1.3 030	038	046	055	063	072	080	089	097	105	8 - 9
.77	114	122	131	139	148	156	165	174	182	191	8 - 9
.78	199	208	217	225	234	243	251	260	269	277	8 - 9
.79	286	295	304	313	321	330	339	348	357	365	8 - 9
.80	374	383	392	401	410	419	428	437	446	455	9
.81	464	473	482	491	500	509	518	527	536	546	9 - 10
.82	555	564	573	582	591	601	610	619	628	638	9 - 10
.83	647	656	665	675	684	693	703	712	722	731	9 - 10
.84	740	750	759	769	778	788	797	807	816	826	9 - 10
.85	835	845	854	864	874	883	893	903	912	922	9 - 10
.86	932	941	951	961	971	980	990	000	010	019	9 - 10
.87	1.4 029	039	049	059	069	079	089	099	108	118	9 - 10
.88	128	138	148	158	168	178	189	199	209	219	10 - 11
.89	229	239	249	259	270	280	290	300	310	321	10 - 11
.90	331	341	351	362	372	382	393	403	413	424	10 - 11
.91	434	445	455	466	476	486	497	507	518	529	10 - 11
.92	539	550	560	571	581	592	603	613	624	635	10 - 11
.93	645	656	667	677	688	699	710	721	731	742	10 - 11
.94	753	764	775	786	797	807	818	829	840	851	10 - 11
.95	862	873	884	895	906	917	928	940	951	962	11 - 12
.96	973	984	995	006	018	029	040	051	063	074	11 - 12
.97	1.5 085	096	108	119	130	142	153	165	176	187	11 - 12
.98	199	210	222	233	245	256	268	279	291	302	11 - 12
.99	314	326	337	349	361	372	384	396	407	419	11 - 12

COSH X

x		0	1	2	3	4	5	6	7	8	9	Diff.
1.00	1.5	431	443	454	466	478	490	502	513	525	537	11 - 12
1.01		549	561	573	585	597	609	621	633	645	657	12
1.02		669	681	693	705	717	729	742	754	766	778	12 - 13
1.03		790	803	815	827	839	852	864	876	889	901	12 - 13
1.04		913	926	938	951	963	975	988	000	013	025	12 - 13
1.05	1.6	038	050	063	076	088	101	113	126	139	151	12 - 13
1.06		164	177	190	202	215	228	241	253	266	279	12 - 13
1.07		292	305	318	331	344	356	369	382	395	408	12 - 13
1.08		421	434	447	461	474	487	500	513	526	539	13 - 14
1.09		552	566	579	592	605	619	632	645	659	672	13 - 14
1.10		685	699	712	725	739	752	766	779	793	806	13 - 14
1.11		820	833	847	860	874	887	901	915	928	942	13 - 14
1.12		956	969	983	997	011	024	038	052	066	080	13 - 14
1.13	1.7	093	107	121	135	149	163	177	191	205	219	14
1.14		233	247	261	275	289	303	317	332	346	360	14 - 15
1.15		374	388	403	417	431	445	460	474	488	503	14 - 15
1.16		517	531	546	560	575	589	604	618	633	647	14 - 15
1.17		662	676	691	706	720	735	749	764	779	794	14 - 15
1.18		808	823	838	853	867	882	897	912	927	942	14 - 15
1.19		957	971	986	001	016	031	046	061	076	091	14 - 16
1.20	1.8	107	122	137	152	167	182	197	213	228	243	15 - 16
1.21		258	274	289	304	320	335	350	366	381	397	15 - 16
1.22		412	428	443	459	474	490	505	521	536	552	15 - 16
1.23		568	583	599	615	630	646	662	678	693	709	15 - 16
1.24		725	741	757	773	788	804	820	836	852	868	15 - 16
1.25		884	900	916	932	948	965	981	997	013	029	16 - 17
1.26	1.9	045	062	078	094	110	127	143	159	176	192	16 - 17
1.27		208	225	241	258	274	291	307	324	340	357	16 - 17
1.28		373	390	407	423	440	457	473	490	507	524	16 - 17
1.29		540	557	574	591	608	624	641	658	675	692	16 - 17
1.30		709	726	743	760	777	794	811	829	846	863	17 - 18
1.31		880	897	914	932	949	966	983	001	018	035	17 - 18
1.32	2.0	053	070	088	105	122	140	157	175	192	210	17 - 18
1.33		228	245	263	280	298	316	333	351	369	387	17 - 18
1.34		404	422	440	458	476	494	512	529	547	565	17 - 18
1.35		583	601	619	637	655	674	692	710	728	746	18 - 19
1.36		764	782	801	819	837	856	874	892	911	929	18 - 19
1.37		947	966	984	003	021	040	058	077	095	114	18 - 19
1.38	2.1	132	151	170	188	207	226	244	263	282	301	18 - 19
1.39		320	338	357	376	395	414	433	452	471	490	18 - 19
1.40		509	528	547	566	585	604	624	643	662	681	19 - 20
1.41		700	720	739	758	778	797	816	836	855	875	19 - 20
1.42		894	914	933	953	972	992	011	031	051	070	19 - 20
1.43	2.2	090	110	129	149	169	189	209	228	248	268	19 - 20
1.44		288	308	328	348	368	388	408	428	448	468	20
1.45		488	509	529	549	569	589	610	630	650	671	20 - 21
1.46		691	711	732	752	773	793	814	834	855	875	20 - 21
1.47		896	916	937	958	978	999	020	041	061	082	20 - 21
1.48	2.3	103	124	145	166	186	207	228	249	270	291	20 - 21
1.49		312	333	355	376	397	418	439	460	482	503	21 - 22

COSH X

x	0	1	2	3	4	5	6	7	8	9	Diff.
1.50	2.3 524	545	567	588	609	631	652	674	695	717	21 - 22
1.51	738	760	781	803	825	846	868	889	911	933	21 - 22
1.52	955	976	998	020	042	064	086	108	130	152	21 - 22
1.53	2.4 174	196	218	240	262	284	306	328	350	373	22 - 23
1.54	395	417	439	462	484	506	529	551	574	596	22 - 23
1.55	619	641	664	686	709	731	754	777	799	822	22 - 23
1.56	845	868	890	913	936	959	982	005	028	050	22 - 23
1.57	2.5 073	096	120	143	166	189	212	235	258	281	23 - 24
1.58	305	328	351	375	398	421	445	468	491	515	23 - 24
1.59	538	562	585	609	633	656	680	703	727	751	23 - 24
1.60	775	798	822	846	870	894	918	942	966	989	23 - 24
1.61	2.6 013	038	062	086	110	134	158	182	206	231	24 - 25
1.62	255	279	304	328	352	377	401	426	450	474	24 - 25
1.63	499	524	548	573	597	622	647	671	696	721	24 - 25
1.64	746	771	795	820	845	870	895	920	945	970	24 - 25
1.65	995	020	045	070	096	121	146	171	197	222	25 - 26
1.66	2.7 247	273	298	323	349	374	400	425	451	476	25 - 26
1.67	502	528	553	579	605	631	656	682	708	734	25 - 26
1.68	760	786	811	837	863	889	916	942	968	994	25 - 27
1.69	2.8 020	046	072	099	125	151	178	204	230	257	26 - 27
1.70	283	310	336	363	389	416	442	469	496	522	26 - 27
1.71	549	576	603	629	656	683	710	737	764	791	26 - 27
1.72	818	845	872	899	926	953	981	008	035	062	27 - 28
1.73	2.9 090	117	144	172	199	227	254	282	309	337	27 - 28
1.74	364	392	420	447	475	503	531	558	586	614	27 - 28
1.75	642	670	698	726	754	782	810	838	866	894	28
1.76	922	951	979	007	035	064	092	121	149	177	28 - 29
1.77	3.0 206	234	263	292	320	349	377	406	435	464	28 - 29
1.78	492	521	550	579	608	637	666	695	724	753	29
1.79	782	811	840	870	899	928	957	987	016	045	29 - 30
1.80	3.1 075	104	134	163	193	222	252	281	311	341	29 - 30
1.81	371	400	430	460	490	520	549	579	609	639	29 - 30
1.82	669	699	730	760	790	820	850	881	911	941	30 - 31
1.83	972	002	032	063	093	124	154	185	215	246	30 - 31
1.84	3.2 277	307	338	369	400	431	461	492	523	554	30 - 31
1.85	585	616	647	678	710	741	772	803	854	866	31 - 32
1.86	897	928	960	991	023	054	086	117	149	180	31 - 32
1.87	3.3 212	244	276	307	339	371	403	435	467	498	31 - 32
1.88	530	562	595	627	659	691	723	755	788	820	32 - 33
1.89	852	885	917	949	982	014	047	079	112	145	32 - 33
1.90	3.4 177	210	243	276	308	341	374	407	440	473	32 - 33
1.91	506	539	572	605	638	671	705	738	771	804	33 - 34
1.92	838	871	905	938	972	005	039	072	106	140	33 - 34
1.93	3.5 173	207	241	275	308	342	376	410	444	478	33 - 34
1.94	512	546	580	615	649	683	717	752	786	820	34 - 35
1.95	855	889	924	958	993	027	062	097	131	166	34 - 35
1.96	3.6 201	236	271	305	340	375	410	445	480	516	34 - 36
1.97	551	586	621	656	692	727	762	798	833	869	35 - 36
1.98	904	940	975	011	046	082	118	154	189	225	35 - 36
1.99	3.7 261	297	333	369	405	441	477	513	549	586	36 - 37

COSH X

x	0	1	2	3	4	5	6	7	8	9	Diff.
2.00	3. 762	766	769	773	777	780	784	788	791	795	3 - 4
2.01	799	802	806	810	813	817	821	824	828	832	3 - 4
2.02	835	839	843	847	850	854	858	862	865	869	3 - 4
2.03	873	876	880	884	888	891	895	899	903	907	3 - 4
2.04	910	914	918	922	925	929	933	937	941	945	3 - 4
2.05	948	952	956	960	964	967	971	975	979	983	3 - 4
2.06	987	991	994	998	002	006	010	014	018	022	3 - 4
2.07	4. 026	029	033	037	041	045	049	053	057	061	3 - 4
2.08	065	069	073	077	080	084	088	092	096	100	3 - 4
2.09	104	108	112	116	120	124	128	132	136	140	4
2.10	144	148	152	156	160	164	169	173	177	181	4 - 5
2.11	185	189	193	197	201	205	209	213	217	221	4 - 5
2.12	226	230	234	238	242	246	250	254	259	263	4 - 5
2.13	267	271	275	279	283	288	292	296	300	304	4 - 5
2.14	309	313	317	321	325	330	334	338	342	346	4 - 5
2.15	351	355	359	363	368	372	376	380	385	389	4 - 5
2.16	393	398	402	406	410	415	419	423	428	432	4 - 5
2.17	436	441	445	449	454	458	462	467	471	475	4 - 5
2.18	480	484	488	493	497	502	506	510	515	519	4 - 5
2.19	524	528	532	537	541	546	550	555	559	563	4 - 5
2.20	568	572	577	581	586	590	595	599	604	608	4 - 5
2.21	613	617	622	626	631	635	640	644	649	653	4 - 5
2.22	658	663	667	672	676	681	685	690	695	699	4 - 5
2.23	704	708	713	718	722	727	731	736	741	745	4 - 5
2.24	750	755	759	764	769	773	778	783	787	792	4 - 5
2.25	797	801	806	811	815	820	825	830	834	839	4 - 5
2.26	844	848	853	858	863	867	872	877	882	887	4 - 5
2.27	891	896	901	906	911	915	920	925	930	·935	4 - 5
2.28	939	944	949	954	959	964	969	973	978	983	4 - 5
2.29	988	993	998	003	008	013	018	022	027	032	4 - 5
2.30	5. 037	042	047	052	057	062	067	072	077	082	5
2.31	087	092	097	102	107	112	117	122	127	132	5
2.32	137	142	147	152	157	162	167	172	177	183	5 - 6
2.33	188	193	198	203	208	213	218	223	229	234	5 - 6
2.34	239	244	249	254	259	265	270	275	280	285	5 - 6
2.35	290	296	301	306	311	317	322	327	332	337	5 - 6
2.36	343	348	353	358	364	369	374	380	385	390	5 - 6
2.37	395	401	406	411	417	422	427	433	438	443	5 - 6
2.38	449	454	459	465	470	476	481	486	492	497	5 - 6
2.39	503	508	513	519	524	530	535	541	546	551	5 - 6
2.40	557	562	568	573	579	584	590	595	601	606	5 - 6
2.41	612	617	623	628	634	640	645	651	656	662	5 - 6
2.42	667	673	679	684	690	695	701	707	712	718	5 - 6
2.43	723	729	735	740	746	752	757	763	769	774	5 - 6
2.44	780	786	791	797	803	809	814	820	826	832	5 - 6
2.45	837	843	849	855	860	866	872	878	884	889	5 - 6
2.46	895	901	907	913	918	924	930	936	942	948	5 - 6
2.47	954	959	965	971	977	983	989	995	001	007	5 - 6
2.48	6. 013	018	024	030	036	042	048	054	060	066	5 - 6
2.49	072	078	084	090	096	102	108	114	120	126	6

COSH X

x	0	1	2	3	4	5	6	7	8	9	Diff.
2.50	6. 132	138	144	150	157	163	169	175	181	187	6 - 7
2.51	193	199	205	211	218	224	230	236	242	248	6 - 7
2.52	255	261	267	273	279	285	292	298	304	310	6 - 7
2.53	317	323	329	335	342	348	354	360	367	373	6 - 7
2.54	379	386	392	398	405	411	417	424	430	436	6 - 7
2.55	443	449	455	462	468	474	481	487	494	500	6 - 7
2.56	507	513	519	526	532	539	545	552	558	565	6 - 7
2.57	571	578	584	591	597	604	610	617	623	630	6 - 7
2.58	636	643	650	656	663	669	676	683	689	696	6 - 7
2.59	702	709	716	722	729	736	742	749	756	762	6 - 7
2.60	769	776	782	789	796	803	809	816	823	830	6 - 7
2.61	836	843	850	857	863	870	877	884	891	897	6 - 7
2.62	904	911	918	925	932	939	945	952	959	966	6 - 7
2.63	973	980	987	994	001	008	014	021	028	035	6 - 7
2.64	7. 042	049	056	063	070	077	084	091	098	105	7
2.65	112	119	126	134	141	148	155	162	169	176	7 - 8
2.66	183	190	197	204	212	219	226	233	240	247	7 - 8
2.67	255	262	269	276	283	291	298	305	312	320	7 - 8
2.68	327	334	341	349	356	363	371	378	385	392	7 - 8
2.69	400	407	414	422	429	437	444	451	459	466	7 - 8
2.70	473	481	488	496	503	511	518	525	533	540	7 - 8
2.71	548	555	563	570	578	585	593	600	608	616	7 - 8
2.72	623	631	638	646	653	661	669	676	684	691	7 - 8
2.73	699	707	714	722	730	737	745	753	760	768	7 - 8
2.74	776	783	791	799	807	814	822	830	838	845	7 - 8
2.75	853	861	869	877	885	892	900	908	916	924	7 - 8
2.76	932	939	947	955	963	971	979	987	995	003	7 - 8
2.77	8. 011	019	027	035	043	050	058	066	074	083	7 - 9
2.78	091	099	107	115	123	131	139	147	155	163	8
2.79	171	179	187	196	204	212	220	228	236	245	8 - 9
2.80	253	261	269	277	286	294	302	310	319	327	8 - 9
2.81	335	343	352	360	368	377	385	393	402	410	8 - 9
2.82	418	427	435	443	452	460	469	477	485	494	8 - 9
2.83	502	511	519	528	536	545	553	562	570	579	8 - 9
2.84	587	596	604	613	621	630	638	647	656	664	8 - 9
2.85	673	681	690	699	707	716	725	733	742	751	8 - 9
2.86	759	768	777	786	794	803	812	821	829	838	8 - 9
2.87	847	856	864	873	882	891	900	909	917	926	8 - 9
2.88	935	944	953	962	971	980	989	998	007	015	8 - 9
2.89	9. 024	033	042	051	060	069	078	087	096	106	9 - 10
2.90	115	124	133	142	151	160	169	178	187	196	9 - 10
2.91	206	215	224	233	242	252	261	270	279	288	9 - 10
2.92	298	307	316	325	335	344	353	363	372	381	9 - 10
2.93	391	400	409	419	428	437	447	456	466	475	9 - 10
2.94	484	494	503	513	522	532	541	551	560	570	9 - 10
2.95	579	589	598	608	617	627	636	646	656	665	9 - 10
2.96	675	685	694	704	713	723	733	742	752	762	9 - 10
2.97	772	781	791	801	811	820	830	840	850	859	9 - 10
2.98	869	879	889	899	909	919	928	938	948	958	9 - 10
2.99	968	978	988	998	008	018	028	038	048	058	10
3.00	10. 068										

For large tables see: "Tables of the Circular and Hyperbolic Sines and Cosines," Natl. Bur. of Stds., ed. of 1953, with x, 0(.0001)2(.1)10, and "Table of Hyperbolic Sines and Cosines," Natl. Bur. of Stds., ed. of 1955, with x, 2(.001)10.

HYPERBOLIC FUNCTIONS

$$\text{Tanh } x = \frac{e^x - e^{-x}}{e^x + e^{-x}} = \frac{e^{2x} - 1}{e^{2x} + 1}$$

x	0	1	2	3	4	5	6	7	8	9	Diff.
.00	.0 000	010	020	030	040	050	060	070	080	090	10
.01	100	110	120	130	140	150	160	170	180	190	10
.02	200	210	220	230	240	250	260	270	280	290	10
.03	300	310	320	330	340	350	360	370	380	390	10
.04	400	410	420	430	440	450	460	470	480	490	10
.05	500	510	520	530	539	549	559	569	579	589	9 - 10
.06	599	609	619	629	639	649	659	669	679	689	10
.07	699	709	719	729	739	749	759	768	778	788	9 - 10
.08	798	808	818	828	838	848	858	868	878	888	10
.09	898	907	917	927	937	947	957	967	977	987	9 - 10
.10	997	007	016	026	036	046	056	066	076	086	9 - 10
.11	.1 096	105	115	125	135	145	155	165	175	184	9 - 10
.12	194	204	214	224	234	244	253	263	273	283	9 - 10
.13	293	303	312	322	332	342	352	361	371	381	9 - 10
.14	391	401	411	420	430	440	450	460	469	479	9 - 10
.15	489	499	508	518	528	538	547	557	567	577	9 - 10
.16	586	596	606	616	625	635	645	655	664	674	9 - 10
.17	684	694	703	713	723	732	742	752	761	771	9 - 10
.18	781	790	800	810	820	829	839	849	858	868	9 - 10
.19	877	887	897	906	916	926	935	945	955	964	9 - 10
.20	974	983	993	003	012	022	031	041	051	060	9 - 10
.21	.2 070	079	089	098	108	117	127	137	146	156	9 - 10
.22	165	175	184	194	203	213	222	232	241	251	9 - 10
.23	260	270	279	289	298	308	317	327	336	346	9 - 10
.24	355	364	374	383	393	402	412	421	430	440	9 - 10
.25	449	459	468	477	487	496	506	515	524	534	9 - 10
.26	543	552	562	571	580	590	599	608	618	627	9 - 10
.27	636	646	655	664	673	683	692	701	711	720	9 - 10
.28	729	738	748	757	766	775	784	794	803	812	9 - 10
.29	821	831	840	849	858	867	876	886	895	904	9 - 10
.30	913	922	931	941	950	959	968	977	986	995	9 - 10
.31	.3 004	013	023	032	041	050	059	068	077	086	9 - 10
.32	095	104	113	122	131	140	149	158	167	176	9
.33	185	194	203	212	221	230	239	248	257	266	9
.34	275	284	293	302	310	319	328	337	346	355	8 - 9
.35	364	373	381	390	399	408	417	426	435	443	8 - 9
.36	452	461	470	479	487	496	505	514	522	531	8 - 9
.37	540	549	557	566	575	584	592	601	610	618	8 - 9
.38	627	636	644	653	662	670	679	688	696	705	8 - 9
.39	714	722	731	739	748	757	765	774	782	791	8 - 9
.40	799	808	817	825	834	842	851	859	868	876	8 - 9
.41	885	893	902	910	919	927	936	944	952	961	8 - 9
.42	969	978	986	995	003	011	020	028	036	045	8 - 9
.43	.4 053	062	070	078	087	095	103	112	120	128	8 - 9
.44	136	145	153	161	170	178	186	194	203	211	8 - 9
.45	219	227	235	244	252	260	268	276	285	293	8 - 9
.46	301	309	317	325	333	342	350	358	366	374	8 - 9
.47	382	390	398	406	414	422	430	438	446	454	8
.48	462	470	478	486	494	502	510	518	526	534	8
.49	542	550	558	566	574	582	590	598	605	613	7 - 8

TANH X

x	0	1	2	3	4	5	6	7	8	9	Diff.
.50	.4 621	629	637	645	653	660	668	676	684	692	7 - 8
.51	699	707	715	723	731	738	746	754	762	769	7 - 8
.52	777	785	792	800	808	815	823	831	839	846	7 - 8
.53	854	861	869	877	884	892	900	907	915	922	7 - 8
.54	930	937	945	953	960	968	975	983	990	998	7 - 8
.55	.5 005	013	020	028	035	043	050	057	065	072	7 - 8
.56	080	087	095	102	109	117	124	132	139	146	7 - 8
.57	154	161	168	176	183	190	198	205	212	219	7 - 8
.58	227	234	241	248	256	263	270	277	285	292	7 - 8
.59	299	306	313	320	328	335	342	349	356	363	7 - 8
.60	370	378	385	392	399	406	413	420	427	434	7 - 8
.61	441	448	455	462	469	476	483	490	497	504	7
.62	511	518	525	532	539	546	553	560	567	574	7
.63	581	587	594	601	608	615	622	629	635	642	6 - 7
.64	649	656	663	669	676	683	690	696	703	710	6 - 7
.65	717	723	730	737	744	750	757	764	770	777	6 - 7
.66	784	790	797	804	810	817	823	830	837	843	6 - 7
.67	850	856	863	869	876	883	889	896	902	909	6 - 7
.68	915	922	928	935	941	948	954	961	967	973	6 - 7
.69	980	986	993	999	005	012	018	025	031	037	6 - 7
.70	.6 044	050	056	063	069	075	082	088	094	100	6 - 7
.71	107	113	119	126	132	138	144	150	157	163	6 - 7
.72	169	175	181	188	194	200	206	212	218	225	6 - 7
.73	231	237	243	249	255	261	267	273	279	285	6
.74	291	297	304	310	316	322	328	334	340	346	6 - 7
.75	351	357	363	369	375	381	387	393	399	405	6
.76	411	417	423	428	434	440	446	452	458	463	5 - 6
.77	469	475	481	487	492	498	504	510	516	521	5 - 6
.78	527	533	539	544	550	556	561	567	573	578	5 - 6
.79	584	590	595	601	607	612	618	624	629	635	5 - 6
.80	640	646	652	657	663	668	674	679	685	690	5 - 6
.81	696	701	707	712	718	723	729	734	740	745	5 - 6
.82	751	756	762	767	772	778	783	789	794	799	5 - 6
.83	805	810	815	821	826	832	837	842	847	853	5 - 6
.84	858	863	869	874	879	884	890	895	900	905	5 - 6
.85	911	916	921	926	932	937	942	947	952	957	5 - 6
.86	963	968	973	978	983	988	993	998	004	009	5 - 6
.87	.7 014	019	024	029	034	039	044	049	054	059	5
.88	064	069	074	079	084	089	094	099	104	109	5
.89	114	119	124	129	134	139	143	148	153	158	4 - 5
.90	163	168	173	178	182	187	192	197	202	207	4 - 5
.91	211	216	221	226	230	235	240	245	249	254	4 - 5
.92	259	264	268	273	278	283	287	292	297	301	4 - 5
.93	306	311	315	320	325	329	334	338	343	348	4 - 5
.94	352	357	361	366	371	375	380	384	389	393	4 - 5
.95	398	402	407	411	416	420	425	429	434	438	4 - 5
.96	443	447	452	456	461	465	469	474	478	483	4 - 5
.97	487	491	496	500	505	509	513	518	522	526	4 - 5
.98	531	535	539	544	548	552	557	561	565	569	4 - 5
.99	574	578	582	586	591	595	599	603	608	612	4 - 5

TANH X

x	0	1	2	3	4	5	6	7	8	9	Diff.
1.00	.76 159	201	243	285	327	369	410	452	493	535	41 - 42
1.01	576	618	659	700	741	782	823	864	905	946	41 - 42
1.02	987	027	068	109	149	190	230	270	310	351	40 - 41
1.03	.77 391	431	471	511	551	591	630	670	710	749	39 - 40
1.04	789	828	868	907	946	985	025	064	103	142	39 - 40
1.05	.78 181	219	258	297	336	374	413	451	490	528	38 - 39
1.06	566	605	643	681	719	757	795	833	871	908	37 - 39
1.07	946	984	021	059	096	134	171	208	246	283	37 - 38
1.08	.79 320	357	394	431	468	505	541	578	615	651	36 - 37
1.09	688	724	761	797	833	870	906	942	978	014	36 - 37
1.10	.80 050	086	122	157	193	229	264	300	335	371	35 - 36
1.11	406	442	477	512	547	582	617	652	687	722	35 - 36
1.12	757	792	826	861	896	930	965	999	033	068	34 - 35
1.13	.81 102	136	170	204	238	272	306	340	374	408	33 - 34
1.14	441	475	509	542	576	609	642	676	709	742	33 - 34
1.15	775	809	842	875	907	940	973	006	039	071	32 - 34
1.16	.82 104	137	169	202	234	266	299	331	363	395	32 - 33
1.17	427	459	491	523	555	587	619	650	682	714	31 - 32
1.18	745	777	808	840	871	902	933	965	996	027	31 - 32
1.19	.83 058	089	120	151	182	212	243	274	304	335	30 - 31
1.20	365	396	426	457	487	517	548	578	608	638	30 - 31
1.21	668	698	728	758	788	817	847	877	906	936	29 - 30
1.22	965	995	024	054	083	112	142	171	200	229	29 - 30
1.23	.84 258	287	316	345	374	402	431	460	488	517	28 - 29
1.24	546	574	603	631	659	688	716	744	772	800	28 - 29
1.25	828	856	884	912	940	968	996	023	051	079	27 - 28
1.26	.85 106	134	161	189	216	244	271	298	325	353	27 - 28
1.27	380	407	434	461	488	515	542	568	595	622	26 - 27
1.28	648	675	702	728	755	781	808	834	860	886	26 - 27
1.29	913	939	965	991	017	043	069	095	121	147	25 - 26
1.30	.86 172	198	224	249	275	300	326	351	377	402	25 - 26
1.31	428	453	478	503	528	554	579	604	629	654	24 - 26
1.32	678	703	728	753	778	802	827	851	876	900	24 - 25
1.33	925	949	974	998	022	047	071	095	119	143	24 - 25
1.34	.87 167	191	215	239	263	287	311	334	358	382	23 - 24
1.35	405	429	452	476	499	523	546	570	593	616	23 - 24
1.36	639	662	686	709	732	755	778	801	824	846	22 - 24
1.37	869	892	915	937	960	983	005	028	050	073	22 - 23
1.38	.88 095	117	140	162	184	207	229	251	273	295	22 - 23
1.39	317	339	361	383	405	427	448	470	492	514	21 - 22
1.40	535	557	578	600	621	643	664	686	707	728	21 - 22
1.41	749	771	792	813	834	855	876	897	918	939	21 - 22
1.42	960	981	002	022	043	064	084	105	126	146	20 - 21
1.43	.89 167	187	208	228	248	269	289	309	329	350	20 - 21
1.44	370	390	410	430	450	470	490	510	530	549	19 - 20
1.45	569	589	609	628	648	668	687	707	726	746	19 - 20
1.46	765	785	804	823	843	862	881	900	920	939	19 - 20
1.47	958	977	996	015	034	053	072	090	109	128	18 - 19
1.48	.90 147	166	184	203	221	240	259	277	296	314	18 - 19
1.49	332	351	369	388	406	424	442	460	479	497	18 - 19

TANH X

x	0	1	2	3	4	5	6	7	8	9	Diff.
1.50	.90 515	533	551	569	587	605	623	641	658	676	17 - 18
1.51	694	712	729	747	765	782	800	817	835	852	17 - 18
1.52	870	887	905	922	939	957	974	991	008	025	17 - 18
1.53	.91 042	060	077	094	111	128	145	161	178	195	16 - 18
1.54	212	229	246	262	279	296	312	329	345	362	16 - 17
1.55	379	395	411	428	444	461	477	493	510	526	16 - 17
1.56	542	558	574	591	607	623	639	655	671	687	16 - 17
1.57	703	718	734	750	766	782	797	813	829	845	15 - 16
1.58	860	876	891	907	922	938	953	969	984	000	15 - 16
1.59	.92 015	030	046	061	076	091	106	122	137	152	15 - 16
1.60	167	182	197	212	227	242	257	272	286	301	14 - 15
1.61	316	331	346	360	375	390	404	419	433	448	14 - 15
1.62	462	477	491	506	520	535	549	563	578	592	14 - 15
1.63	606	620	635	649	663	677	691	705	719	733	14 - 15
1.64	747	761	775	789	803	817	831	844	858	872	13 - 14
1.65	886	899	913	927	940	954	968	981	995	008	13 - 14
1.66	.93 022	035	049	062	075	089	102	115	129	142	13 - 14
1.67	155	168	182	195	208	221	234	247	260	273	13 - 14
1.68	286	299	312	325	338	351	364	376	389	402	12 - 13
1.69	415	427	440	453	465	478	491	503	516	528	12 - 13
1.70	541	553	566	578	591	603	615	628	640	652	12 - 13
1.71	665	677	689	701	714	726	738	750	762	774	12 - 13
1.72	786	798	810	822	834	846	858	870	882	894	12
1.73	906	917	929	941	953	964	976	988	999	011	11 - 12
1.74	.94 023	034	046	057	069	080	092	103	115	126	11 - 12
1.75	138	149	160	172	183	194	205	217	228	239	11 - 12
1.76	250	261	273	284	295	306	317	328	339	350	11 - 12
1.77	361	372	383	394	405	415	426	437	448	459	10 - 11
1.78	470	480	491	502	512	523	534	544	555	565	10 - 11
1.79	576	587	597	608	618	629	639	649	660	670	10 - 11
1.80	681	691	701	712	722	732	742	753	763	773	10 - 11
1.81	783	793	803	814	824	834	844	854	864	874	10 - 11
1.82	884	894	904	914	924	933	943	953	963	973	9 - 10
1.83	983	992	002	012	022	031	041	051	060	070	9 - 10
1.84	.95 080	089	099	108	118	127	137	146	156	165	9 - 10
1.85	175	184	193	203	212	221	231	240	249	259	9 - 10
1.86	268	277	286	296	305	314	323	332	341	350	9 - 10
1.87	359	368	378	387	396	405	413	422	431	440	8 - 10
1.88	449	458	467	476	485	493	502	511	520	529	8 - 9
1.89	537	546	555	563	572	581	589	598	607	615	8 - 9
1.90	624	632	641	649	658	666	675	683	692	700	8 - 9
1.91	709	717	725	734	742	750	759	767	775	783	8 - 9
1.92	792	800	808	816	825	833	841	849	857	865	8 - 9
1.93	873	881	889	898	906	914	922	930	938	945	7 - 9
1.94	953	961	969	977	985	993	001	009	016	024	7 - 8
1.95	.96 032	040	047	055	063	071	078	086	094	101	7 - 8
1.96	109	117	124	132	139	147	155	162	170	177	7 - 8
1.97	185	192	200	207	214	222	229	237	244	251	7 - 8
1.98	259	266	273	281	288	295	303	310	317	324	7 - 8
1.99	331	339	346	353	360	367	374	382	389	396	7 - 8

TANH X

x	0	1	2	3	4	5	6	7	8	9	Diff.
2.00	.96 403	410	417	424	431	438	445	452	459	466	7
2.01	473	480	487	493	500	507	514	521	528	535	6 - 7
2.02	541	548	555	562	568	575	582	589	595	602	6 - 7
2.03	609	615	622	629	635	642	648	655	662	668	6 - 7
2.04	675	681	688	694	701	707	714	720	727	733	6 - 7
2.05	740	746	752	759	765	771	778	784	790	797	6 - 7
2.06	803	809	816	822	828	834	841	847	853	859	6 - 7
2.07	865	872	878	884	890	896	902	908	914	920	6 - 7
2.08	926	933	939	945	951	957	963	969	975	980	5 - 7
2.09	986	992	998	004	010	016	022	028	034	039	5 - 6
2.10	.97 045	051	057	063	068	074	080	086	091	097	5 - 6
2.11	103	109	114	120	126	131	137	143	148	154	5 - 6
2.12	159	165	171	176	182	187	193	198	204	209	5 - 6
2.13	215	220	226	231	237	242	248	253	258	264	5 - 6
2.14	269	275	280	285	291	296	301	307	312	317	5 - 6
2.15	323	328	333	338	344	349	354	359	365	370	5 - 6
2.16	375	380	385	390	396	401	406	411	416	421	5 - 6
2.17	426	431	436	441	446	452	457	462	467	472	5 - 6
2.18	477	482	487	491	496	501	506	511	516	521	4 - 5
2.19	526	531	536	541	545	550	555	560	565	570	4 - 5
2.20	574	579	584	589	593	598	603	608	612	617	4 - 5
2.21	622	626	631	636	640	645	650	654	659	664	4 - 5
2.22	668	673	678	682	687	691	696	700	705	709	4 - 5
2.23	714	718	723	727	732	736	741	745	750	754	4 - 5
2.24	759	763	768	772	776	781	785	790	794	798	4 - 5
2.25	803	807	811	816	820	824	829	833	837	841	4 - 5
2.26	846	850	854	858	863	867	871	875	879	884	4 - 5
2.27	888	892	896	900	905	909	913	917	921	925	4 - 5
2.28	929	933	937	942	946	950	954	958	962	966	4 - 5
2.29	970	974	978	982	986	990	994	998	002	006	4
2.30	.98 010	014	018	021	025	029	033	037	041	045	3 - 4
2.31	049	053	056	060	064	068	072	076	079	083	3 - 4
2.32	087	091	095	098	102	106	110	113	117	121	3 - 4
2.33	124	128	132	136	139	143	147	150	154	158	3 - 4
2.34	161	165	169	172	176	179	183	187	190	194	3 - 4
2.35	197	201	204	208	212	215	219	222	226	229	3 - 4
2.36	233	236	240	243	247	250	254	257	261	264	3 - 4
2.37	267	271	274	278	281	285	288	291	295	298	3 - 4
2.38	301	305	308	312	315	318	322	325	328	331	3 - 4
2.39	335	338	341	345	348	351	354	358	361	364	3 - 4
2.40	367	371	374	377	380	384	387	390	393	396	3 - 4
2.41	400	403	406	409	412	415	418	422	425	428	3 - 4
2.42	431	434	437	440	443	446	450	453	456	459	3 - 4
2.43	462	465	468	471	474	477	480	483	486	489	3
2.44	492	495	498	501	504	507	510	513	516	519	3
2.45	522	525	528	530	533	536	539	542	545	548	2 - 3
2.46	551	554	556	559	562	565	568	571	574	576	2 - 3
2.47	579	582	585	588	590	593	596	599	602	604	2 - 3
2.48	607	610	613	615	618	621	624	626	629	632	2 - 3
2.49	635	637	640	643	645	648	651	653	656	659	2 - 3

TANH X

x	0	1	2	3	4	5	6	7	8	9	Diff.
2.50	.986 614	641	667	694	720	747	773	799	825	852	26 - 27
2.51	878	904	930	956	981	007	033	059	085	110	25 - 26
2.52	.987 136	161	187	212	238	263	288	313	339	364	25 - 26
2.53	389	414	439	464	489	514	538	563	588	612	24 - 25
2.54	637	662	686	711	735	759	784	808	832	856	24 - 25
2.55	880	904	928	952	976	000	024	048	072	095	23 - 24
2.56	.988 119	143	166	190	213	236	260	283	306	330	23 - 24
2.57	353	376	399	422	445	468	491	514	537	559	22 - 23
2.58	582	605	627	650	673	695	718	740	762	785	22 - 23
2.59	807	829	851	874	896	918	940	962	984	006	22 - 23
2.60	.989 027	049	071	093	114	136	158	179	201	222	21 - 22
2.61	244	265	286	308	329	350	371	392	413	434	21 - 22
2.62	455	476	497	518	539	560	580	601	622	643	20 - 21
2.63	663	684	704	725	745	765	786	806	826	847	20 - 21
2.64	867	887	907	927	947	967	987	007	027	047	19 - 20
2.65	.990 066	086	106	126	145	165	184	204	223	243	19 - 20
2.66	262	281	301	320	339	359	378	397	416	435	19 - 20
2.67	454	473	492	511	530	549	567	586	605	624	18 - 19
2.68	642	661	679	698	716	735	753	772	790	808	18 - 19
2.69	827	845	863	881	899	917	936	954	972	990	18 - 19
2.70	.991 007	025	043	061	079	097	114	132	150	167	17 - 18
2.71	185	202	220	237	255	272	289	307	324	341	17 - 18
2.72	359	376	393	410	427	444	461	478	495	512	17
2.73	529	546	563	579	596	613	630	646	663	679	16 - 17
2.74	696	712	729	745	762	778	795	811	827	843	16 - 17
2.75	860	876	892	908	924	940	956	972	988	004	16
2.76	.992 020	036	052	068	084	099	115	131	146	162	15 - 16
2.77	178	193	209	224	240	255	271	286	301	317	15 - 16
2.78	332	347	362	378	393	408	423	438	453	468	15 - 16
2.79	483	498	513	528	543	558	573	587	602	617	14 - 15
2.80	632	646	661	675	690	705	719	734	748	762	14 -.15
2.81	777	791	806	820	834	849	863	877	891	905	14 - 15
2.82	919	934	948	962	976	990	004	018	031	045	13 - 15
2.83	.993 059	073	087	101	114	128	142	155	169	183	13 - 14
2.84	196	210	223	237	250	264	277	290	304	317	13 - 14
2.85	330	344	357	370	383	397	410	423	436	449	13 - 14
2.86	462	475	488	501	514	527	540	553	565	578	12 - 13
2.87	591	604	617	629	642	655	667	680	692	705	12 - 13
2.88	718	730	743	755	767	780	792	805	817	829	12 - 13
2.89	842	854	866	878	891	903	915	927	939	951	12 - 13
2.90	963	975	987	999	011	023	035	047	059	071	11 - 12
2.91	.994 082	094	106	118	129	141	153	164	176	188	11 - 12
2.92	199	211	222	234	245	257	268	280	291	302	11 - 12
2.93	314	325	336	348	359	370	381	393	404	415	11 - 12
2.94	426	437	448	459	470	481	492	503	514	525	11
2.95	536	547	558	569	580	590	601	612	623	633	10 - 11
2.96	644	655	665	676	687	697	708	718	729	739	10 - 11
2.97	750	760	771	781	791	802	812	823	833	843	10 - 11
2.98	853	864	874	884	894	905	915	925	935	945	10 - 11
2.99	955	965	975	985	995	005	015	025	035	045	10
3.00	.995 055										

For a large table see "Table of Circular and Hyperbolic Tangents and Cotangents for Radian Arguments," Columbia University Press, New York, N.Y.

HYPERBOLIC FUNCTIONS

SINH^{-1} X

x	0	1	2	3	4	5	6	7	8	9	Diff.
.00	.0 000	010	020	030	040	050	060	070	080	090	10
.01	100	110	120	130	140	150	160	170	180	190	10
.02	200	210	220	230	240	250	260	270	280	290	10
.03	300	310	320	330	340	350	360	370	380	390	10
.04	400	410	420	430	440	450	460	470	480	490	10
.05	500	510	520	530	540	550	560	570	580	590	10
.06	600	610	620	630	640	650	660	669	679	689	9 - 10
.07	699	709	719	729	739	749	759	769	779	789	10
.08	799	809	819	829	839	849	859	869	879	889	10
.09	899	909	919	929	939	949	959	968	978	988	9 - 10
.10	998	008̄	018̄	028̄	038̄	048̄	058̄	068̄	078̄	088̄	10
.11	.1 098	108	118	128	138	147	157	167	177	187	9 - 10
.12	197	207	217	227	237	247	257	267	277	286	9 - 10
.13	296	306	316	326	336	346	356	366	376	386	9 - 10
.14	395	405	415	425	435	445	455	465	475	485	9 - 10
.15	494	504	514	524	534	544	554	564	573	583	9 - 10
.16	593	603	613	623	633	643	652	662	672	682	9 - 10
.17	692	702	712	721	731	741	751	761	771	781	9 - 10
.18	790	800	810	820	830	840	849	859	869	879	9 - 10
.19	889	899	908	918	928	938	948	957	967	977	9 - 10
.20	987	997	007̄	016̄	026̄	036̄	046̄	055̄	065̄	075̄	9 - 10
.21	.2 085	095	104	114	124	134	144	153	163	173	9 - 10
.22	183	192	202	212	222	231	241	251	261	270	9 - 10
.23	280	290	300	309	319	329	339	348	358	368	9 - 10
.24	378	387	397	407	416	426	436	446	455	465	9 - 10
.25	475	484	494	504	513	523	533	543	552	562	9 - 10
.26	572	581	591	601	610	620	630	639	649	659	9 - 10
.27	668	678	688	697	707	716	726	736	745	755	9 - 10
.28	765	774	784	794	803	813	822	832	842	851	9 - 10
.29	861	870	880	890	899	909	918	928	938	947	9 - 10
.30	957	966	976	985	995	005̄	014̄	024̄	033̄	043̄	9 - 10
.31	.3 052	062	071	081	091	100	110	119	129	138	9 - 10
.32	148	157	167	176	186	195	205	214	224	233	9 - 10
.33	243	252	262	271	281	290	300	309	319	328	9 - 10
.34	338	347	357	366	376	385	394	404	413	423	9 - 10
.35	432	442	451	461	470	479	489	498	508	517	9 - 10
.36	526	536	545	555	564	573	583	592	602	611	9 - 10
.37	620	630	639	649	658	667	677	686	695	705	9 - 10
.38	714	723	733	742	751	761	770	779	789	798	9 - 10
.39	807	817	826	835	845	854	863	872	882	891	9 - 10
.40	900	910	919	928	937	947	956	965	975	984	9 - 10
.41	993	002̄	012̄	021̄	030̄	039̄	048̄	058̄	067̄	076̄	9 - 10
.42	.4 085	095	104	113	122	131	141	150	159	168	9 - 10
.43	177	187	196	205	214	223	232	242	251	260	9 - 10
.44	269	278	287	297	306	315	324	333	342	351	9 - 10
.45	360	370	379	388	397	406	415	424	433	442	9 - 10
.46	452	461	470	479	488	497	506	515	524	533	9
.47	542	551	560	569	578	587	596	605	614	624	9 - 10
.48	633	642	651	660	669	678	687	696	705	714	8 - 9
.49	722	731	740	749	758	767	776	785	794	803	9

SINH $^{-1}$ X

x	0	1	2	3	4	5	6	7	8	9	Diff.
.50	.4 812	821	830	839	848	857	866	875	884	892	8 - 9
.51	901	910	919	928	937	946	955	964	973	981	8 - 9
.52	990	999	008	017	026	035	043	052	061	070	8 - 9
.53	.5 079	088	096	105	114	123	132	141	149	158	8 - 9
.54	167	176	185	193	202	211	220	229	237	246	8 - 9
.55	255	264	272	281	290	299	307	316	325	334	8 - 9
.56	342	351	360	368	377	386	395	403	412	421	8 - 9
.57	429	438	447	455	464	473	481	490	499	507	8 - 9
.58	516	525	533	542	551	559	568	576	585	594	8 - 9
.59	602	611	620	628	637	645	654	663	671	680	8 - 9
.60	688	697	705	714	723	731	740	748	757	765	8 - 9
.61	774	782	791	799	808	816	825	833	842	850	8 - 9
.62	859	867	876	884	893	901	910	918	927	935	8 - 9
.63	944	952	961	969	978	986	994	003	011	020	8 - 9
.64	.6 028	037	045	053	062	070	079	087	095	104	8 - 9
.65	112	121	129	137	146	154	162	171	179	188	8 - 9
.66	196	204	213	221	229	238	246	254	263	271	8 - 9
.67	279	287	296	304	312	321	329	337	346	354	8 - 9
.68	362	370	379	387	395	403	412	420	428	436	8 - 9
.69	445	453	461	469	477	486	494	502	510	518	8 - 9
.70	527	535	543	551	559	568	576	584	592	600	8 - 9
.71	608	617	625	633	641	649	657	665	674	682	8 - 9
.72	690	698	706	714	722	730	738	746	755	763	8 - 9
.73	771	779	787	795	803	811	819	827	835	843	8
.74	851	859	867	875	883	891	899	907	915	923	8
.75	931	939	947	955	963	971	979	987	995	003	8
.76	.7 011	019	027	035	043	051	059	067	075	083	8
.77	091	099	107	114	122	130	138	146	154	162	7 - 8
.78	170	178	186	193	201	209	217	225	233	241	7 - 8
.79	248	256	264	272	280	288	295	303	311	319	7 - 8
.80	327	334	342	350	358	366	373	381	389	397	7 - 8
.81	405	412	420	428	436	443	451	459	467	474	7 - 8
.82	482	490	498	505	513	521	528	536	544	552	7 - 8
.83	559	567	575	582	590	598	605	613	621	628	7 - 8
.84	636	644	651	659	667	674	682	689	697	705	7 - 8
.85	712	720	728	735	743	750	758	766	773	781	7 - 8
.86	788	796	804	811	819	826	834	841	849	856	7 - 8
.87	864	872	879	887	894	902	909	917	924	932	7 - 8
.88	939	947	954	962	969	977	984	992	999	007	7 - 8
.89	.8 014	022	029	037	044	051	059	066	074	081	7 - 8
.90	089	096	104	111	118	126	133	141	148	155	7 - 8
.91	163	170	178	185	192	200	207	214	222	229	7 - 8
.92	237	244	251	259	266	273	281	288	295	303	7 - 8
.93	310	317	325	332	339	347	354	361	368	376	7 - 8
.94	383	390	398	405	412	419	427	434	441	448	7 - 8
.95	456	463	470	477	485	492	499	506	514	521	7 - 8
.96	528	535	542	550	557	564	571	578	586	593	7 - 8
.97	600	607	614	622	629	636	643	650	657	664	7 - 8
.98	672	679	686	693	700	707	714	722	729	736	7 - 8
.99	743	750	757	764	771	778	785	793	800	807	7 - 8

$$\text{SINH}^{-1} X$$

x	0	1	2	3	4	5	6	7	8	9	Diff.
1.00	.8 814	821	828	835	842	849	856	863	870	877	7
.01	884	891	898	905	912	919	926	933	940	947	7
.02	954	961	968	975	982	989	996	003	010	017	7
.03	.9 024	031	038	045	052	059	066	073	080	087	7
.04	094	101	108	115	121	128	135	142	149	156	6 − 7
.05	163	170	177	184	190	197	204	211	218	225	6 − 7
.06	232	239	245	252	259	266	273	280	286	293	6 − 7
.07	300	307	314	321	327	334	341	348	355	361	6 − 7
.08	368	375	382	389	395	402	409	416	423	429	6 − 7
.09	436	443	450	456	463	470	477	483	490	497	6 − 7
1.10	503	510	517	524	530	537	544	550	557	564	6 − 7
.11	571	577	584	591	597	604	611	617	624	631	6 − 7
.12	637	644	651	657	664	671	677	684	691	697	6 − 7
.13	704	710	717	724	730	737	743	750	757	763	6 − 7
.14	770	776	783	790	796	803	809	816	823	829	6 − 7
.15	836	842	849	855	862	868	875	882	888	895	6 − 7
.16	901	908	914	921	927	934	940	947	953	960	6 − 7
.17	966	973	979	986	992	999	005	012	018	025	6 − 7
.18	1.0 031	038	044	050	057	063	070	076	083	089	6 − 7
.19	096	102	108	115	121	128	134	141	147	153	6 − 7
1.20	160	166	173	179	185	192	198	204	211	217	6 − 7
.21	224	230	236	243	249	255	262	268	274	281	6 − 7
.22	287	293	300	306	312	319	325	331	338	344	6 − 7
.23	350	357	363	369	376	382	388	394	401	407	6 − 7
.24	413	420	426	432	438	445	451	457	463	470	6 − 7
.25	476	482	488	495	501	507	513	520	526	532	6 − 7
.26	538	544	551	557	563	569	575	582	588	594	6 − 7
.27	600	606	613	619	625	631	637	643	650	656	6 − 7
.28	662	668	674	680	687	693	699	705	711	717	6 − 7
.29	723	730	736	742	748	754	760	766	772	778	6 − 7
1.30	785	791	797	803	809	815	821	827	833	839	6
.31	845	851	857	864	870	876	882	888	894	900	6 − 7
.32	906	912	918	924	930	936	942	948	954	960	6
.33	966	972	978	984	990	996	002	008	014	020	6
.34	1.1 026	032	038	044	050	056	062	068	074	080	6
.35	086	092	098	104	110	115	121	127	133	139	5 − 6
.36	145	151	157	163	169	175	181	187	192	198	5 − 6
.37	204	210	216	222	228	234	240	245	251	257	5 − 6
.38	263	269	275	281	286	292	298	304	310	316	5 − 6
.39	322	327	333	339	345	351	357	362	368	374	5 − 6
1.40	380	386	391	397	403	409	415	420	426	432	5 − 6
.41	438	444	449	455	461	467	472	478	484	490	5 − 6
.42	496	501	507	513	519	524	530	536	541	547	5 − 6
.43	553	559	564	570	576	582	587	593	599	604	5 − 6
.44	610	616	622	627	633	639	644	650	656	661	5 − 6
.45	667	673	678	684	690	695	701	707	712	718	5 − 6
.46	724	729	735	741	746	752	758	763	769	774	5 − 6
.47	780	786	791	797	803	808	814	819	825	831	5 − 6
.48	836	842	847	853	859	864	870	875	881	886	5 − 6
.49	892	898	903	909	914	920	925	931	937	942	5 − 6

$$\text{SINH}^{-1}\ X$$

x	0	1	2	3	4	5	6	7	8	9	Diff.
1.50	1.1 948	953	959	964	970	975	981	986	992	997	5 - 6
.51	1.2 003	008	014	020	025	031	036	042	047	053	5 - 6
.52	058	064	069	075	080	086	091	096	102	107	5 - 6
.53	113	118	124	129	135	140	146	151	157	162	5 - 6
.54	167	173	178	184	189	195	200	206	211	216	5 - 6
.55	222	227	233	238	243	249	254	260	265	271	5 - 6
.56	276	281	287	292	297	303	308	314	319	324	5 - 6
.57	330	335	340	346	351	357	362	367	373	378	5 - 6
.58	383	389	394	399	405	410	415	421	426	431	5 - 6
.59	437	442	447	453	458	463	469	474	479	485	5 - 6
1.60	490	495	500	506	511	516	522	527	532	537	5 - 6
.61	543	548	553	559	564	569	574	580	585	590	5 - 6
.62	595	601	606	611	616	622	627	632	637	643	5 - 6
.63	648	653	658	663	669	674	679	684	690	695	5 - 6
.64	700	705	710	716	721	726	731	736	742	747	5 - 6
.65	752	757	762	767	773	778	783	788	793	798	5 - 6
.66	804	809	814	819	824	829	835	840	845	850	5 - 6
.67	855	860	865	870	876	881	886	891	896	901	5 - 6
.68	906	911	917	922	927	932	937	942	947	952	5 - 6
.69	957	962	968	973	978	983	988	993	998	$\overline{003}$	5 - 6
1.70	1.3 008	013	018	023	028	034	039	044	049	054	5 - 6
.71	059	064	069	074	079	084	089	094	099	104	5
.72	109	114	119	124	129	134	139	144	149	154	5
.73	159	164	169	174	179	184	189	194	199	204	5
.74	209	214	219	224	229	234	239	244	249	254	5
.75	259	264	269	274	279	284	289	294	299	304	4 - 5
.76	308	313	318	323	328	333	338	343	348	353	5
.77	358	363	368	373	377	382	387	392	397	402	4 - 5
.78	407	412	417	422	426	431	436	441	446	451	4 - 5
.79	456	461	465	470	475	480	485	490	495	500	4 - 5
1.80	504	509	514	519	524	529	534	538	543	548	4 - 5
.81	553	558	563	567	572	577	582	587	591	596	4 - 5
.82	601	606	611	616	620	625	630	635	640	644	4 - 5
.83	649	654	659	664	668	673	678	683	687	692	4 - 5
.84	697	702	707	711	716	721	726	730	735	740	4 - 5
.85	745	749	754	759	764	768	773	778	783	787	4 - 5
.86	792	797	802	806	811	816	821	825	830	835	4 - 5
.87	839	844	849	854	858	863	868	872	877	882	4 - 5
.88	886	891	896	901	905	910	915	919	924	929	4 - 5
.89	933	938	943	947	952	957	961	966	971	975	4 - 5
1.90	980	985	989	994	999	$\overline{003}$	$\overline{008}$	$\overline{013}$	$\overline{017}$	$\overline{022}$	4 - 5
.91	1.4 026	031	036	040	045	050	054	059	064	068	4 - 5
.92	073	077	082	087	091	096	100	105	110	114	4 - 5
.93	119	123	128	133	137	142	146	151	156	160	4 - 5
.94	165	169	174	178	183	188	192	197	201	206	4 - 5
.95	210	215	220	224	229	233	238	242	247	251	4 - 5
.96	256	261	265	270	274	279	283	288	292	297	4 - 5
.97	301	306	310	315	319	324	329	333	338	342	4 - 5
.98	347	351	356	360	365	369	374	378	383	387	4 - 5
.99	392	396	401	405	409	414	418	423	427	432	4 - 5

$$\text{SINH}^{-1}\ \text{X}$$

x	0	1	2	3	4	5	6	7	8	9	Diff.
2.0	1.4 436	481	525	570	614	658	702	745	789	832	43 – 45
2.1	875	918	960	$\overline{003}$	$\overline{045}$	$\overline{088}$	$\overline{130}$	$\overline{172}$	$\overline{214}$	$\overline{255}$	41 – 43
2.2	1.5 297	338	379	420	461	502	542	583	623	$\overline{663}$	40 – 41
2.3	703	743	782	822	861	900	939	978	$\overline{017}$	$\overline{056}$	38 – 40
2.4	1.6 094	133	171	209	247	285	323	360	398	435	37 – 39
2.5	472	509	546	583	620	$\overline{656}$	$\overline{693}$	729	765	$\overline{801}$	36 – 37
2.6	837	873	909	945	980	$\overline{015}$	$\overline{051}$	$\overline{086}$	$\overline{121}$	$\overline{156}$	35 – 36
2.7	1.7 191	225	260	294	329	363	397	431	465	499	33 – 35
2.8	532	566	599	633	666	$\overline{699}$	$\overline{732}$	765	798	$\overline{831}$	32 – 34
2.9	863	896	928	961	993	$\overline{025}$	$\overline{057}$	$\overline{089}$	$\overline{121}$	$\overline{153}$	31 – 33
3.0	1.8 184	216	248	279	310	341	373	404	434	465	30 – 32
3.1	496	527	557	588	618	648	679	$\overline{709}$	$\overline{739}$	$\overline{769}$	30 – 31
3.2	799	828	858	888	917	947	976	$\overline{005}$	$\overline{035}$	$\overline{064}$	29 – 30
3.3	1.9 093	122	151	179	208	237	265	294	322	351	28 – 29
3.4	379	407	435	463	491	519	547	574	602	630	27 – 28
3.5	657	685	712	$\overline{739}$	767	$\overline{794}$	$\overline{821}$	848	875	$\overline{902}$	26 – 28
3.6	928	955	982	$\overline{008}$	$\overline{035}$	$\overline{061}$	$\overline{088}$	$\overline{114}$	$\overline{140}$	$\overline{166}$	26 – 27
3.7	2.0 193	219	245	271	296	322	348	374	399	425	25 – 26
3.8	450	476	501	526	552	577	602	627	652	677	25 – 26
3.9	702	727	751	776	801	825	850	874	899	923	24 – 25
4.0	947	971	996	$\overline{020}$	$\overline{044}$	$\overline{068}$	$\overline{092}$	$\overline{116}$	$\overline{139}$	$\overline{163}$	23 – 25
4.1	2.1 187	211	234	258	281	305	328	351	375	398	23 – 24
4.2	421	444	467	490	513	536	559	582	605	627	22 – 23
4.3	650	673	695	718	740	763	785	808	830	852	22 – 23
4.4	874	896	918	940	962	984	$\overline{006}$	$\overline{028}$	$\overline{050}$	$\overline{072}$	21 – 23
4.5	2.2 093	115	137	158	180	201	223	244	266	287	21 – 22
4.6	308	329	351	372	393	414	435	456	477	498	20 – 22
4.7	518	539	560	581	601	622	643	663	684	704	20 – 21
4.8	724	745	765	785	$\overline{806}$	$\overline{826}$	$\overline{846}$	$\overline{866}$	$\overline{886}$	$\overline{906}$	20 – 21
4.9	926	946	966	986	$\overline{006}$	$\overline{026}$	$\overline{046}$	$\overline{065}$	$\overline{085}$	$\overline{105}$	19 – 20
5.0	2.3 124	144	164	183	203	222	241	261	280	299	19 – 20
5.1	319	338	357	376	395	414	433	452	471	490	19
5.2	509	528	547	566	585	603	622	641	659	678	18 – 19
5.3	696	715	733	752	770	789	807	825	844	862	18 – 19
5.4	880	898	916	935	953	971	989	$\overline{007}$	$\overline{025}$	$\overline{043}$	18 – 19
5.5	2.4 061	078	096	114	132	150	167	185	203	220	17 – 18
5.6	238	255	273	291	308	325	343	360	378	395	17 – 18
5.7	412	429	447	464	481	498	515	532	550	567	17 – 18
5.8	584	601	617	634	651	668	685	702	719	735	16 – 17
5.9	752	769	785	802	819	835	852	868	885	901	16 – 17
6.0	918	934	951	967	983	$\overline{000}$	$\overline{016}$	$\overline{032}$	$\overline{048}$	$\overline{065}$	16 – 17
6.1	2.5 081	097	113	129	145	161	177	193	209	225	16
6.2	241	257	273	289	305	321	336	352	368	384	15 – 16
6.3	399	415	431	446	462	477	493	509	524	539	15 – 16
6.4	555	570	586	601	616	632	647	662	678	693	15 – 16
6.5	708	723	739	754	769	784	799	814	829	844	15 – 16
6.6	859	874	889	904	919	934	949	963	978	993	14 – 15
6.7	2.6 008	023	037	052	067	081	096	111	125	140	14 – 15
6.8	154	169	183	198	212	227	241	256	270	284	14 – 15
6.9	299	313	327	342	356	370	384	399	413	427	14 – 15

$$\text{SINH}^{-1} X$$

x	0	1	2	3	4	5	6	7	8	9	Diff.
7.0	2.6 441	455	469	484	498	512	526	540	554	568	14 - 15
7.1	582	596	610	623	637	651	665	679	693	706	13 - 14
7.2	720	734	748	761	775	789	802	816	830	843	13 - 14
7.3	857	870	884	897	911	924	938	951	965	978	13 - 14
7.4	992	005	018	032	045	058	072	085	098	111	13 - 14
7.5	2.7 125	138	151	164	177	191	204	217	230	243	13 - 14
7.6	256	269	282	295	308	321	334	347	360	373	13
7.7	386	398	411	424	437	450	463	475	488	501	12 - 13
7.8	514	526	539	552	564	577	590	602	615	627	12 - 13
7.9	640	652	665	678	690	703	715	727	740	752	12 - 13
8.0	765	777	789	802	814	827	839	851	863	876	12 - 13
8.1	888	900	912	925	937	949	961	973	986	998	12 - 13
8.2	2.8 010	022	034	046	058	070	082	094	106	118	12
8.3	130	142	154	166	178	190	202	214	225	237	11 - 12
8.4	249	261	273	284	296	308	320	331	343	355	11 - 12
8.5	367	378	390	402	413	425	436	448	460	471	11 - 12
8.6	483	494	506	517	529	540	552	563	575	586	11 - 12
8.7	598	609	620	632	643	655	666	677	689	700	11 - 12
8.8	711	722	734	745	756	767	779	790	801	812	11 - 12
8.9	823	835	846	857	868	879	890	901	912	923	11 - 12
9.0	934	945	957	968	979	990	000	011	022	033	10 - 12
9.1	2.9 044	055	066	077	088	099	110	120	131	142	10 - 11
9.2	153	164	175	185	196	207	218	228	239	250	10 - 11
9.3	260	271	282	292	303	314	324	335	346	356	10 - 11
9.4	367	377	388	398	409	419	430	441	451	462	10 - 11
9.5	472	482	493	503	514	524	535	545	555	566	10 - 11
9.6	576	586	597	607	617	628	638	648	659	669	10 - 11
9.7	679	689	700	710	720	730	741	751	761	771	10 - 11
9.8	781	791	802	812	822	832	842	852	862	872	10 - 11
9.9	882	892	902	912	922	932	942	952	962	972	10
10.0	982										

If $\sinh y = x$, then $y = \sinh^{-1} x$.

$$\sinh^{-1} x = \log_n \left(x + \sqrt{x^2 + 1} \right)$$

$$\text{COSH}^{-1} X$$

x	0	1	2	3	4	5	6	7	8	9	Diff.
1.00	0.0 000	447	632	774	894	000	095	183	264	341	72 - 447
.01	.1 413	482	548	611	671	730	786	841	895	946	51 - 69
.02	997	046	094	141	187	231	275	319	361	403	40 - 49
.03	.2 443	484	523	562	600	638	675	712	748	784	35 - 41
.04	819	854	888	922	956	989	022	054	086	118	31 - 35
.05	.3 149	180	211	242	272	302	331	361	390	418	28 - 31
.06	447	475	503	531	559	586	613	640	667	694	26 - 28
.07	720	746	772	798	824	849	874	900	924	949	24 - 26
.08	974	998	023	047	071	094	118	142	165	188	23 - 25
.09	.4 211	234	257	280	303	325	347	370	392	414	22 - 23
1.10	436	457	479	501	522	543	565	586	607	628	20 - 22
.11	648	669	690	710	731	751	771	791	811	831	20 - 21
.12	851	871	891	910	930	949	969	988	007	026	19 - 20
.13	.5 045	064	083	102	121	139	158	177	195	213	18 - 19
.14	232	250	268	286	304	322	340	358	376	393	17 - 18
.15	411	429	446	464	481	498	516	533	550	567	17 - 18
.16	584	601	618	635	652	668	685	702	718	735	16 - 17
.17	751	768	784	801	817	833	849	865	881	897	16 - 17
.18	913	929	945	961	977	993	008	024	040	055	15 - 16
.19	.6 071	086	102	117	132	148	163	178	193	209	15 - 16
1.20	224	239	254	269	284	298	313	328	343	358	14 - 15
.21	372	387	402	416	431	445	460	474	489	503	14 - 15
.22	517	532	546	560	574	588	603	617	631	645	14 - 15
.23	659	673	686	700	714	728	742	756	769	783	13 - 14
.24	797	810	824	837	851	864	878	891	905	918	13 - 14
.25	931	945	958	971	985	998	011	024	037	050	13 - 14
.26	.7 063	076	089	102	115	128	141	154	167	180	12 - 13
.27	192	205	218	231	243	256	269	281	294	306	12 - 13
.28	319	331	344	356	369	381	394	406	418	431	12 - 13
.29	443	455	467	479	492	504	516	528	540	552	12 - 13
1.30	564	576	588	600	612	624	636	648	660	672	12
.31	684	695	707	719	731	742	754	766	777	789	11 - 12
.32	801	812	824	835	847	858	870	881	893	904	11 - 12
.33	916	927	939	950	961	973	984	995	006	018	11 - 12
.34	.8 029	040	051	062	074	085	096	107	118	129	11 - 12
.35	140	151	162	173	184	195	206	217	228	239	10 - 11
.36	249	260	271	282	293	303	314	325	336	346	10 - 11
.37	357	368	378	389	400	410	421	431	442	452	10 - 11
.38	463	473	484	494	505	515	526	536	547	557	10 - 11
.39	567	578	588	598	609	619	629	639	650	660	10 - 11
1.40	670	680	691	701	711	721	731	741	751	761	10 - 11
.41	771	782	792	802	812	822	832	842	851	861	9 - 11
.42	871	881	891	901	911	921	931	940	950	960	9 - 10
.43	970	980	989	999	009	019	028	038	048	057	9 - 10
.44	.9 067	077	086	096	106	115	125	134	144	153	9 - 10
.45	163	172	182	191	201	210	220	229	239	248	9 - 10
.46	258	267	276	286	295	304	314	323	332	342	9 - 10
.47	351	360	369	379	388	397	406	416	425	434	9 - 10
.48	443	452	461	471	480	489	498	507	516	525	9 - 10
.49	534	543	552	561	570	579	588	597	606	615	9

$$\text{COSH}^{-1} X$$

x	0	1	2	3	4	5	6	7	8	9	Diff.
1.50	.9 624	633	642	651	660	669	678	687	695	704	8 - 9
.51	713	722	731	740	748	757	766	775	784	792	8 - 9
.52	801	810	818	827	836	845	853	862	871	879	8 - 9
.53	888	897	905	914	922	931	940	948	957	965	8 - 9
.54	974	982	991	999	008	016	025	033	042	050	8 - 9
.55	1.0 059	067	076	084	092	101	109	118	126	134	8 - 9
.56	143	151	159	168	176	184	193	201	209	217	8 - 9
.57	226	234	242	250	259	267	275	283	292	300	8 - 9
.58	308	316	324	332	341	349	357	365	373	381	8 - 9
.59	389	397	405	413	421	430	438	446	454	462	8 - 9
1.60	470	478	486	494	502	510	518	526	533	541	7 - 8
.61	549	557	565	573	581	589	597	605	612	620	7 - 8
.62	628	636	644	652	660	667	675	683	691	698	7 - 8
.63	706	714	722	730	737	745	753	760	768	776	7 - 8
.64	784	791	799	807	814	822	830	837	845	853	7 - 8
.65	860	868	875	883	891	898	906	913	921	928	7 - 8
.66	936	944	951	959	966	974	981	989	996	004	7 - 8
.67	1.1 011	019	026	033	041	048	056	063	071	078	7 - 8
.68	086	093	100	108	115	122	130	137	145	152	7 - 8
.69	159	167	174	181	189	196	203	210	218	225	7 - 8
1.70	232	240	247	254	261	269	276	283	290	298	7 - 8
.71	305	312	319	326	334	341	348	355	362	369	7 - 8
.72	376	384	391	398	405	412	419	426	433	441	7 - 8
.73	448	455	462	469	476	483	490	497	504	511	7
.74	518	525	532	539	546	553	560	567	574	581	7
.75	588	595	602	609	616	623	630	637	644	651	6 - 7
.76	657	664	671	678	685	692	699	706	712	719	6 - 7
.77	726	733	740	747	754	760	767	774	781	788	6 - 7
.78	794	801	808	815	822	828	835	842	849	855	6 - 7
.79	862	869	875	882	889	896	902	909	916	922	6 - 7
1.80	929	936	942	949	956	962	969	976	982	989	6 - 7
.81	996	002	009	016	022	029	035	042	049	055	6 - 7
.82	1.2 062	068	075	081	088	094	101	108	114	121	6 - 7
.83	127	134	140	147	153	160	166	173	179	186	6 - 7
.84	192	199	205	212	218	224	231	237	244	250	6 - 7
.85	257	263	270	276	282	289	295	302	308	314	6 - 7
.86	321	327	333	340	346	352	359	365	372	378	6 - 7
.87	384	391	397	403	409	416	422	428	435	441	6 - 7
.88	447	454	460	466	472	479	485	491	497	504	6 - 7
.89	510	516	522	529	535	541	547	553	560	566	6 - 7
1.90	572	578	584	591	597	603	609	615	621	627	6 - 7
.91	634	640	646	652	658	664	670	677	683	689	6 - 7
.92	695	701	707	713	719	725	731	737	744	750	6 - 7
.93	756	762	768	774	780	786	792	798	804	810	6
.94	816	822	828	834	840	846	852	858	864	870	6
.95	876	882	888	894	900	906	912	918	924	930	5 - 6
.96	935	941	947	953	959	965	971	977	983	989	6
.97	995	001	006	012	018	024	030	036	042	047	5 - 6
.98	1.3 053	059	065	071	077	083	088	094	100	106	5 - 6
.99	112	117	123	129	135	141	146	152	158	164	5 - 6

$$\text{COSH}^{-1}\ X$$

x	0	1	2	3	4	5	6	7	8	9	Diff.
2.0	1.3 170	227	284	341	397	454	509	565	620	674	54 - 57
2.1	729	783	836	890	943	995	$\overline{048}$	$\overline{100}$	$\overline{152}$	$\overline{203}$	51 - 54
2.2	1.4 254	305	356	406	456	506	$\overline{555}$	$\overline{604}$	$\overline{653}$	$\overline{702}$	48 - 51
2.3	750	799	846	894	942	989	$\overline{036}$	$\overline{082}$	$\overline{129}$	$\overline{175}$	46 - 49
2.4	1.5 221	267	312	357	402	447	492	536	580	624	44 - 46
2.5	668	712	755	798	841	884	926	969	$\overline{011}$	$\overline{053}$	41 - 44
2.6	1.6 094	136	177	219	260	300	341	382	422	462	40 - 42
2.7	502	542	581	$\overline{621}$	$\overline{660}$	699	738	777	816	854	38 - 40
2.8	892	931	969	$\overline{006}$	$\overline{044}$	$\overline{082}$	$\overline{119}$	$\overline{156}$	$\overline{193}$	$\overline{230}$	37 - 39
2.9	1.7 267	304	340	377	413	449	485	521	556	592	35 - 37
3.0	627	663	698	733	768	803	837	872	906	940	34 - 36
3.1	975	$\overline{009}$	$\overline{042}$	$\overline{076}$	$\overline{110}$	$\overline{143}$	$\overline{177}$	$\overline{210}$	$\overline{243}$	$\overline{276}$	33 - 34
3.2	1.8 309	342	375	408	440	472	505	537	569	601	32 - 33
3.3	633	665	696	728	759	790	822	853	884	915	31 - 32
3.4	946	976	$\overline{007}$	$\overline{037}$	$\overline{068}$	$\overline{098}$	$\overline{128}$	$\overline{159}$	$\overline{189}$	$\overline{219}$	29 - 31
3.5	1.9 248	278	308	338	367	396	426	455	484	513	29 - 30
3.6	542	571	600	628	657	686	714	742	771	799	28 - 29
3.7	827	855	883	911	939	966	994	$\overline{021}$	$\overline{049}$	$\overline{076}$	27 - 28
3.8	2.0 104	131	158	185	212	239	266	293	319	346	26 - 27
3.9	373	399	426	452	478	504	531	557	583	609	25 - 27
4.0	634	660	686	712	737	763	788	813	839	864	25 - 26
4.1	889	914	939	964	989	$\overline{014}$	$\overline{039}$	$\overline{064}$	$\overline{088}$	$\overline{113}$	24 - 25
4.2	2.1 137	162	186	211	235	259	283	308	332	356	24 - 25
4.3	380	403	427	451	475	498	522	546	569	592	23 - 24
4.4	616	639	662	686	709	732	755	778	801	824	22 - 24
4.5	846	869	892	915	937	960	982	$\overline{005}$	$\overline{027}$	$\overline{049}$	22 - 23
4.6	2.2 072	094	116	138	160	182	204	226	248	270	22
4.7	292	314	335	357	379	400	422	443	465	486	21 - 22
4.8	507	529	550	571	592	613	634	655	676	697	21 - 22
4.9	718	739	760	780	801	822	842	863	883	904	20 - 21
5.0	924	945	965	985	$\overline{006}$	$\overline{026}$	$\overline{046}$	$\overline{066}$	$\overline{086}$	$\overline{106}$	20 - 21
5.1	2.3 126	146	166	186	206	226	246	265	285	305	19 - 20
5.2	324	344	363	383	402	422	441	461	480	499	19 - 20
5.3	518	538	557	576	595	614	633	652	671	690	19 - 20
5.4	709	727	746	765	784	802	821	840	858	877	18 - 19
5.5	895	914	932	951	969	987	$\overline{006}$	$\overline{024}$	$\overline{042}$	$\overline{060}$	18 - 19
5.6	2.4 078	097	115	133	151	169	187	205	223	240	17 - 19
5.7	258	276	294	312	329	347	365	382	400	417	17 - 18
5.8	435	452	470	487	505	522	539	557	574	591	17 - 18
5.9	608	626	643	660	677	694	711	728	745	762	17 - 18
6.0	779	796	813	829	846	863	880	897	913	930	16 - 17
6.1	946	963	980	996	$\overline{013}$	$\overline{029}$	$\overline{046}$	$\overline{062}$	$\overline{079}$	$\overline{095}$	16 - 17
6.2	2.5 111	128	144	160	176	193	209	225	241	257	16 - 17
6.3	273	289	305	321	337	353	369	385	401	417	16
6.4	433	449	464	480	496	512	527	543	559	574	15 - 16
6.5	590	605	621	636	652	667	683	698	714	729	15 - 16
6.6	744	760	775	790	805	821	836	851	866	881	15 - 16
6.7	896	911	927	942	957	972	987	$\overline{001}$	$\overline{016}$	$\overline{031}$	14 - 16
6.8	2.6 046	061	076	091	105	120	135	150	164	179	14 - 15
6.9	194	208	223	238	252	267	281	296	310	325	14 - 15

$$\cosh^{-1} X$$

x	0	1	2	3	4	5	6	7	8	9	Diff.
7.0	2.6 339	354	368	382	397	411	425	440	454	468	14 - 15
7.1	482	497	511	525	539	553	567	582	596	610	14 - 15
7.2	624	638	652	666	680	694	707	721	735	749	13 - 14
7.3	763	777	791	804	818	832	846	859	873	887	13 - 14
7.4	900	914	928	941	955	968	982	995	009	022	13 - 14
7.5	2.7 036	049	063	076	089	103	116	129	143	156	13 - 14
7.6	169	183	196	209	222	236	249	262	276	288	13 - 14
7.7	301	314	327	340	353	367	380	393	405	418	12 - 14
7.8	431	444	457	470	483	496	509	521	534	547	12 - 13
7.9	560	573	585	598	611	623	636	649	661	674	12 - 13
8.0	687	699	712	724	737	749	762	774	787	799	12 - 13
8.1	812	824	837	849	861	874	886	898	911	923	12 - 13
8.2	935	948	960	972	984	997	009	021	033	045	12 - 13
8.3	2.8 058	070	082	094	106	118	130	142	154	166	12
8.4	178	190	202	214	226	238	250	262	274	285	11 - 12
8.5	297	309	321	333	345	356	368	380	392	403	11 - 12
8.6	415	427	439	450	462	473	485	497	508	520	11 - 12
8.7	532	543	555	566	578	589	601	612	624	635	11 - 12
8.8	647	658	669	681	692	704	715	726	738	749	11 - 12
8.9	760	772	783	794	805	817	828	839	850	862	11 - 12
9.0	873	884	895	906	917	928	940	951	962	973	11 - 12
9.1	984	995	006	017	028	039	050	061	072	083	11
9.2	2.9 094	105	116	127	137	148	159	170	181	192	10 - 11
9.3	203	213	224	235	246	257	267	278	289	299	10 - 11
9.4	310	321	332	342	353	364	374	385	395	406	10 - 11
9.5	417	427	438	448	459	469	480	490	501	511	10 - 11
9.6	522	532	543	553	564	574	585	595	605	616	10 - 11
9.7	626	636	647	657	667	678	688	698	709	719	10 - 11
9.8	729	739	750	760	770	780	791	801	811	821	10 - 11
9.9	831	841	851	862	872	882	892	902	912	922	10 - 11
10.0	932										

If $\cosh y = x$, then $y = \cosh^{-1} x$.

$$\cosh^{-1} x = \pm \operatorname{logn} (x + \sqrt{x^2 - 1}), \qquad (x > 1.)$$

Only the positive values are here tabulated.

$$\text{TANH}^{-1} X$$

x	0	1	2	3	4	5	6	7	8	9	Diff.
.00	.0 000	010	020	030	040	050	060	070	080	090	10
.01	100	110	120	130	140	150	160	170	180	190	10
.02	200	210	220	230	240	250	260	270	280	290	10
.03	300	310	320	330	340	350	360	370	380	390	10
.04	400	410	420	430	440	450	460	470	480	490	10
.05	500	510	520	530	541	551	561	571	581	591	10 - 11
.06	601	611	621	631	641	651	661	671	681	691	10
.07	701	711	721	731	741	751	761	772	782	792	10 - 11
.08	802	812	822	832	842	852	862	872	882	892	10
.09	902	913	923	933	943	953	963	973	983	993	10 - 11
.10	.1 003	013	024	034	044	054	064	074	084	094	10 - 11
.11	104	115	125	135	145	155	165	175	186	196	10 - 11
.12	206	216	226	236	246	257	267	277	287	297	10 - 11
.13	307	318	328	338	348	358	368	379	389	399	10 - 11
.14	409	419	430	440	450	460	471	481	491	501	10 - 11
.15	511	522	532	542	552	563	573	583	593	604	10 - 11
.16	614	624	634	645	655	665	676	686	696	706	10 - 11
.17	717	727	737	748	758	768	779	789	799	809	10 - 11
.18	820	830	841	851	861	872	882	892	903	913	10 - 11
.19	923	934	944	955	965	975	986	996	007	017	10 - 11
.20	.2 027	038	048	059	069	079	090	100	111	121	10 - 11
.21	132	142	153	163	174	184	195	205	216	226	10 - 11
.22	237	247	258	268	279	289	300	310	321	331	10 - 11
.23	342	352	363	374	384	395	405	416	427	437	10 - 11
.24	448	458	469	480	490	501	512	522	533	543	10 - 11
.25	554	565	575	586	597	608	618	629	640	650	10 - 11
.26	661	672	683	693	704	715	726	736	747	758	10 - 11
.27	769	779	790	801	812	823	833	844	855	866	10 - 11
.28	877	888	899	909	920	931	942	953	964	975	10 - 11
.29	986	997	008	018	029	040	051	062	073	084	10 - 11
.30	.3 095	106	117	128	139	150	161	172	183	194	11
.31	205	217	228	239	250	261	272	283	294	305	11 - 12
.32	316	328	339	350	361	372	383	395	406	417	11 - 12
.33	428	440	451	462	473	484	496	507	518	530	11 - 12
.34	541	552	564	575	586	598	609	620	632	643	11 - 12
.35	654	666	677	689	700	712	723	734	746	757	11 - 12
.36	769	780	792	803	815	826	838	850	861	873	11 - 12
.37	884	896	907	919	931	942	954	966	977	989	11 - 12
.38	.4 001	012	024	036	047	059	071	083	094	106	11 - 12
.39	118	130	142	153	165	177	189	201	213	225	11 - 12
.40	236	248	260	272	284	296	308	320	332	344	12
.41	356	368	380	392	404	416	428	441	453	465	12 - 13
.42	477	489	501	513	526	538	550	562	574	587	12 - 13
.43	599	611	624	636	648	660	673	685	698	710	12 - 13
.44	722	735	747	760	772	784	797	809	822	834	12 - 13
.45	847	860	872	885	897	910	922	935	948	960	12 - 13
.46	973	986	999	011	024	037	049	062	075	088	12 - 13
.47	.5 101	114	126	139	152	165	178	191	204	217	12 - 13
.48	230	243	256	269	282	295	308	321	334	347	13 - 14
.49	361	374	387	400	413	427	440	453	466	480	13 - 14

$$\text{TANH}^{-1} X$$

x	0	1	2	3	4	5	6	7	8	9	Diff.
.50	.5 493	506	520	533	547	560	573	587	600	614	13 - 14
.51	627	641	654	668	682	695	709	722	736	750	13 - 14
.52	763	777	791	805	818	832	846	860	874	888	13 - 14
.53	901	915	929	943	957	971	985	999	013	027	14 - 15
.54	.6 042	056	070	084	098	112	127	141	155	169	14 - 15
.55	184	198	213	227	241	256	270	285	299	314	14 - 15
.56	328	343	358	372	387	401	416	431	446	460	14 - 15
.57	475	490	505	520	535	550	565	580	595	610	15
.58	625	640	655	670	685	700	716	731	746	761	15 - 16
.59	777	792	807	823	838	854	869	885	900	916	15 - 16
.60	931	947	963	978	994	010	026	042	057	073	15 - 16
.61	.7 089	105	121	137	153	169	185	201	218	234	16 - 17
.62	250	266	283	299	315	332	348	365	381	398	16 - 17
.63	414	431	447	464	481	498	514	531	548	565	16 - 17
.64	582	599	616	633	650	667	684	701	718	736	17 - 18
.65	753	770	788	805	823	840	858	875	893	910	17 - 18
.66	928	946	964	981	999	017	035	053	071	089	17 - 18
.67	.8 107	126	144	162	180	199	217	236	254	273	18 - 19
.68	291	310	328	347	366	385	404	423	441	460	18 - 19
.69	480	499	518	537	556	576	595	614	634	653	19 - 20
.70	673	693	712	732	752	772	792	812	832	852	19 - 20
.71	872	892	912	933	953	973	994	014	035	056	20 - 21
.72	.9 076	097	118	139	160	181	202	223	245	266	21 - 22
.73	287	309	330	352	373	395	417	439	461	483	21 - 22
.74	505	527	549	571	594	616	639	661	684	707	22 - 23
.75	730	752	775	798	822	845	868	892	915	939	22 - 24
.76	962	986	010	034	058	082	106	130	154	179	24 - 25
.77	1.0 203	228	253	277	302	327	352	378	403	428	24 - 26
.78	454	479	505	531	557	583	609	635	661	688	25 - 27
.79	714	741	768	795	822	849	876	903	931	958	27 - 28
.80	986	014	042	070	098	127	155	184	212	241	28 - 29
.81	1.1 270	299	329	358	388	417	447	477	507	538	29 - 31
.82	568	599	630	660	692	723	754	786	817	849	30 - 32
.83	881	914	946	979	011	044	077	111	144	178	32 - 34
.84	1.2 212	246	280	315	349	384	419	454	490	526	34 - 36
.85	562	598	634	671	707	745	782	819	857	895	36 - 38
.86	933	972	011	050	089	129	169	209	249	290	39 - 41
.87	1.3 331	372	414	456	498	540	583	626	670	714	41 - 44
.88	758	802	847	892	938	984	030	077	124	171	44 - 48
.89	1.4 219	268	316	365	415	465	516	566	618	670	48 - 52
.90	722	775	828	882	937	992	047	103	160	217	53 - 58
.91	1.5 275	334	393	453	513	574	636	698	762	826	59 - 64
.92	890	956	022	089	157	226	296	366	436	510	66 - 74
.93	1.6 584	658	734	811	888	967	047	129	211	295	74 - 85
	1.7										

X	TANH^{-1} X	X	TANH^{-1} X
.940	1.7380	.970	2.0923
.941	1.7467	.971	2.1095
.942	1.7555	.972	2.1273
.943	1.7645	.973	2.1457
.944	1.7736	.974	2.1649
.945	1.7828	.975	2.1847
.946	1.7923	.976	2.2054
.947	1.8019	.977	2.2269
.948	1.8117	.978	2.2494
.949	1.8216	.979	2.2729
.950	1.8318	.980	2.2976
.951	1.8421	.981	2.3235
.952	1.8527	.982	2.3507
.953	1.8635	.983	2.3796
.954	1.8745	.984	2.4101
.955	1.8857	.985	2.4427
.956	1.8972	.986	2.4774
.957	1.9090	.987	2.5147
.958	1.9210	.988	2.5550
.959	1.9333	.989	2.5987
.960	1.9459	.990	2.6467
.961	1.9588	.991	2.6996
.962	1.9721	.992	2.7587
.963	1.9857	.993	2.8257
.964	1.9996	.994	2.9031
.965	2.0139	.995	2.9945
.966	2.0287	.996	3.1063
.967	2.0439	.997	3.2504
.968	2.0595	.998	3.4534
.969	2.0756	.999	3.8002
		1.000	Infin.

If tanh y = x, then y = tanh^{-1} x.

$$\tanh^{-1} x = \frac{1}{2} \text{ logn } \frac{1+x}{1-x}, \qquad (x^2 < 1).$$

For large tables see "Tables of Inverse Hyperbolic Functions," published by the Staff of the Computation Laboratory, Harvard University, H. H. Aiken, Director, Harvard University Press, 1949.

$$K = \int_0^{\pi/2} \frac{d\phi}{(1 - k^2\sin^2\phi)^{1/2}}$$

k^2	0	1	2	3	4	5	6	7	8	9	Diff.
.00	1.5 708	712	716	720	724	728	732	736	740	743	3 - 4
.01	747	751	755	759	763	767	771	775	779	783	4
.02	787	791	795	799	804	808	812	816	820	824	4 - 5
.03	828	832	836	840	844	848	852	856	860	865	4 - 5
.04	869	873	877	881	885	889	893	898	902	906	4 - 5
.05	910	914	918	923	927	931	935	939	943	948	4 - 5
.06	952	956	960	965	969	973	977	981	986	990	4 - 5
.07	994	998	0̄03	0̄07	0̄11	0̄16	0̄20	0̄24	0̄28	0̄33	4 - 5
.08	1.6 037	041	046	050	054	059	063	067	072	076	4 - 5
.09	080	085	089	094	098	102	107	111	116	120	4 - 5
.10	124	129	133	138	142	147	151	155	160	164	4 - 5
.11	169	173	178	182	187	191	196	200	205	209	4 - 5
.12	214	218	223	228	232	237	241	246	250	255	4 - 5
.13	260	264	269	273	278	283	287	292	296	301	4 - 5
.14	306	310	315	320	324	329	334	338	343	348	4 - 5
.15	353	357	362	367	371	376	381	386	390	395	4 - 5
.16	400	405	410	414	419	424	429	434	438	443	4 - 5
.17	448	453	458	463	467	472	477	482	487	492	4 - 5
.18	497	502	507	512	516	521	526	531	536	541	4 - 5
.19	546	551	556	561	566	571	576	581	586	591	5
.20	596	601	606	611	616	622	627	632	637	642	5 - 6
.21	647	652	657	662	668	673	678	683	688	693	5 - 6
.22	699	704	709	714	719	725	730	735	740	745	5 - 6
.23	751	756	761	767	772	777	782	788	793	798	5 - 6
.24	804	809	814	820	825	831	836	841	847	852	5 - 6
.25	858	863	868	874	879	885	890	896	901	907	5 - 6
.26	912	918	923	929	934	940	945	951	956	962	5 - 6
.27	967	973	979	984	990	996	0̄01	0̄07	0̄12	0̄18	5 - 6
.28	1.7 024	029	035	041	046	052	058	064	069	075	5 - 6
.29	081	087	092	098	104	110	116	121	127	133	5 - 6
.30	139	145	151	156	162	168	174	180	186	192	5 - 6
.31	198	204	210	216	222	228	234	240	246	252	6
.32	258	264	270	276	282	288	294	300	306	313	6 - 7
.33	319	325	331	337	343	349	356	362	368	374	6 - 7
.34	381	387	393	399	406	412	418	425	431	437	6 - 7
.35	444	450	456	463	469	475	482	488	495	501	6 - 7
.36	508	514	520	527	533	540	546	553	560	566	6 - 7
.37	573	579	586	592	599	606	612	619	626	632	6 - 7
.38	639	646	652	659	666	673	679	686	693	700	6 - 7
.39	706	713	720	727	734	741	748	754	761	768	6 - 7
.40	775	782	789	796	803	810	817	824	831	838	7
.41	845	852	859	866	874	881	888	895	902	909	7 - 8
.42	917	924	931	938	945	953	960	967	975	982	7 - 8
.43	989	997	0̄04	0̄11	0̄19	0̄26	0̄33	0̄41	0̄48	0̄56	7 - 8
.44	1.8 063	071	078	086	093	101	108	116	124	131	7 - 8
.45	139	146	154	162	169	177	185	193	200	208	7 - 8
.46	216	224	232	239	247	255	263	271	279	287	7 - 8
.47	295	303	311	319	327	335	343	351	359	367	8
.48	375	383	391	399	408	416	424	432	440	449	8 - 9
.49	457	465	474	482	490	499	507	515	524	532	8 - 9

K

k^2	0	1	2	3	4	5	6	7	8	9	Diff.
.50	1.8 541	549	558	566	575	583	592	601	609	618	8 - 9
.51	626	635	644	652	661	670	679	688	696	705	8 - 9
.52	714	723	732	741	750	759	768	777	786	795	9
.53	804	813	822	831	840	849	858	868	877	886	9 - 10
.54	895	905	$\overline{914}$	$\overline{923}$	$\overline{933}$	$\overline{942}$	$\overline{951}$	$\overline{961}$	$\overline{970}$	$\overline{980}$	9 - 10
.55	989	999	$\overline{008}$	$\overline{018}$	$\overline{027}$	$\overline{037}$	$\overline{047}$	$\overline{056}$	$\overline{066}$	$\overline{076}$	9 - 10
.56	1.9 085	095	105	115	125	134	144	154	164	174	9 - 10
.57	184	194	204	214	224	234	244	255	265	275	10 - 11
.58	285	296	306	316	326	337	347	358	368	379	10 - 11
.59	389	400	410	421	431	442	453	463	474	485	10 - 11
.60	496	506	517	528	539	550	561	572	583	594	10 - 11
.61	605	616	627	639	650	661	672	684	695	706	11 - 12
.62	718	729	741	752	764	775	787	799	810	822	11 - 12
.63	834	845	857	869	881	893	905	917	929	941	11 - 12
.64	953	965	977	990	$\overline{002}$	$\overline{014}$	$\overline{026}$	$\overline{039}$	$\overline{051}$	$\overline{064}$	12 - 13
.65	2.0 076	088	101	114	126	139	152	164	177	190	12 - 13
.66	203	216	229	242	255	268	281	294	307	320	13 - 14
.67	334	347	360	374	387	401	414	428	442	455	13 - 14
.68	469	483	497	510	524	538	552	566	580	595	13 - 15
.69	609	623	637	652	666	681	695	710	724	739	14 - 15
.70	754	768	783	798	813	828	843	858	873	888	14 - 16
.71	904	919	934	950	965	981	996	$\overline{012}$	$\overline{028}$	$\overline{044}$	15 - 16
.72	2.1 059	075	091	107	123	140	156	172	188	205	16 - 17
.73	221	238	254	271	288	305	322	338	355	373	16 - 17
.74	390	407	424	442	459	477	494	512	529	547	17 - 18
.75	565	583	601	619	637	656	674	692	711	730	18 - 19
.76	748	767	786	805	824	843	862	881	901	920	19 - 20
.77	940	959	979	999	$\overline{019}$	$\overline{039}$	$\overline{059}$	$\overline{079}$	$\overline{099}$	$\overline{120}$	19 - 21
.78	2.2 140	161	181	202	223	244	265	286	308	329	20 - 22
.79	351	372	394	416	438	460	482	504	527	549	21 - 23
.80	572	595	618	641	664	687	711	734	758	782	23 - 24
.81	805	830	854	878	903	927	952	977	$\overline{002}$	$\overline{027}$	24 - 25
.82	2.3 052	078	103	129	155	181	207	234	260	287	25 - 27
.83	314	341	368	396	423	451	479	507	535	564	27 - 29
.84	593	621	651	680	$\overline{709}$	$\overline{739}$	$\overline{769}$	$\overline{799}$	$\overline{829}$	$\overline{859}$	28 - 31
.85	890	921	952	984	$\overline{015}$	$\overline{047}$	$\overline{079}$	$\overline{111}$	$\overline{144}$	$\overline{176}$	31 - 33
.86	2.4 209	243	276	310	344	378	413	447	482	518	33 - 36
.87	553	589	$\overline{626}$	$\overline{662}$	$\overline{699}$	$\overline{736}$	$\overline{773}$	$\overline{811}$	$\overline{849}$	$\overline{888}$	36 - 39
.88	926	965	$\overline{005}$	$\overline{045}$	$\overline{085}$	$\overline{125}$	$\overline{166}$	$\overline{207}$	$\overline{249}$	$\overline{291}$	39 - 42
.89	2.5 333	376	419	463	507	552	597	642	688	734	43 - 47
.90	781	828	876	924	973	$\overline{023}$	$\overline{072}$	$\overline{123}$	$\overline{174}$	$\overline{226}$	47 - 52
.91	2.6 278	331	384	$\overline{438}$	$\overline{493}$	$\overline{548}$	$\overline{604}$	$\overline{661}$	$\overline{718}$	$\overline{777}$	53 - 59
.92	836	895	956	$\overline{017}$	$\overline{079}$	$\overline{142}$	$\overline{206}$	$\overline{271}$	$\overline{336}$	$\overline{403}$	59 - 68
.93	2.7 471	539	609	680	752	824	899	974	$\overline{051}$	$\overline{128}$	68 - 80
.94	2.8 208	288	370	453	538	625	713	803	895	$\overline{988}$	80 - 95
.95	2.9 083	181	280	382	485	591	700	811	925	$\overline{042}$	98 -119
.96	3.0 161										

k^2	K	k^2	K
.960	3.0161	.980	3.3541
.961	3.0284	.981	3.3793
.962	3.0410	.982	3.4059
.963	3.0539	.983	3.4340
.964	3.0672	.984	3.4638
.965	3.0809	.985	3.4955
.966	3.0950	.986	3.5295
.967	3.1095	.987	3.5661
.968	3.1244	.988	3.6056
.969	3.1399	.989	3.6485
.970	3.1559	.990	3.6956
.971	3.1724	.991	3.7478
.972	3.1895	.992	3.8061
.973	3.2073	.993	3.8723
.974	3.2257	.994	3.9487
.975	3.2449	.995	4.0393
.976	3.2648	.996	4.1502
.977	3.2857	.997	4.2933
.978	3.3074		
.979	3.3302		

k^2	0	1	2	3	4	5	6	7	8	9	Diff.
.9970	4.2 933	950	967	983	000	017	034	051	068	085	16 - 17
.9971	4.3 102	119	137	154	171	189	206	224	241	259	17 - 18
.9972	277	295	313	331	349	367	385	403	421	440	18 - 19
.9973	458	477	495	514	532	551	570	589	608	627	18 - 19
.9974	646	665	685	704	723	743	762	782	802	822	19 - 20
.9975	841	861	881	902	922	942	962	983	003	024	20 - 21
.9976	4.4 045	066	087	107	129	150	171	192	214	235	20 - 22
.9977	257	279	300	322	344	366	389	411	433	456	21 - 23
.9978	478	501	524	547	570	593	616	640	663	687	23 - 24
.9979	710	734	758	782	806	830	855	879	904	929	24 - 26
.9980	953	978	004	029	054	080	105	131	157	183	25 - 26
.9981	4.5 209	235	262	289	315	342	369	396	424	451	26 - 28
.9982	479	507	534	563	591	619	648	677	705	735	27 - 30
.9983	764	793	823	853	883	913	943	973	004	035	29 - 31
.9984	4.6 066	097	129	161	192	224	257	289	322	355	31 - 33
.9985	388	421	455	489	523	557	592	626	661	697	33 - 36
.9986	732	768	804	840	877	914	951	988	026	064	36 - 38
.9987	4.7 102	140	179	218	258	298	338	378	419	460	38 - 41
.9988	501	543	585	628	671	714	757	801	846	890	42 - 46
.9989	936	981	027	074	120	168	216	264	312	362	45 - 50
.9990	4.8 411	461	512	563	615	667	720	774	828	882	50 - 55
.9991	937	993	049	107	164	223	282	342	402	463	56 - 62
.9992	4.9 525	588	652	716	781	848	942	983	051	121	63 - 71
.9993	5.0 192	264	337	411	486	562	640	718	798	879	72 - 83
.9994	962	046	131	218	307	397	488	582	677	774	. 84 - 99
.9995	5.1 873										

k^2	K	k^2	K	k^2	K
.99950	5.1873	.9999900	7.1428	.9999950	7.4893
51	5.1974	01	7.1478	51	7.4994
52	5.2077	02	7.1529	52	7.5097
53	5.2182	03	7.1580	53	7.5203
54	5.2289	04	7.1632	54	7.5310
55	5.2399	05	7.1684	55	7.5420
56	5.2511	06	7.1737	56	7.5533
57	5.2626	07	7.1791	57	7.5647
58	5.2744	08	7.1845	58	7.5765
59	5.2864	09	7.1899	59	7.5886
.99960	5.2987	.9999910	7.1955	.9999960	7.6009
61	5.3114	11	7.2010	61	7.6136
62	5.3244	12	7.2067	62	7.6266
63	5.3377	13	7.2124	63	7.6399
64	5.3514	14	7.2182	64	7.6536
65	5.3655	15	7.2240	65	7.6677
66	5.3799	16	7.2299	66	7.6822
67	5.3949	17	7.2359	67	7.6971
68	5.4102	18	7.2420	68	7.7125
69	5.4261	19	7.2481	69	7.7284
.99970	5.4425	.9999920	7.2543	.9999970	7.7447
71	5.4594	21	7.2606	71	7.7617
72	5.4770	22	7.2670	72	7.7792
73	5.4951	23	7.2735	73	7.7974
74	5.5140	24	7.2800	74	7.8163
75	5.5336	·25	7.2866	75	7.8359
76	5.5540	26	7.2933	76	7.8563
77	5.5753	27	7.3001	77	7.8776
78	5.5975	28	7.3070	78	7.8998
79	5.6207	29	7.3140	79	7.9231
.99980	5.6451	.9999930	7.3211	.9999980	7.9475
81	5.6708	31	7.3283	81	7.9731
82	5.6978	32	7.3356	82	8.0002
83	5.7264	33	7.3430	83	8.0287
84	5.7567	34	7.3505	84	8.0591
85	5.7889	35	7.3582	85	8.0913
86	5.8234	36	7.3659	86	8.1258
87	5.8604	37	7.3738	87	8.1629
88	5.9005	38	7.3818	88	8.2029
89	5.9439	39	7.3899	89	8.2464
.99990	5.9916	.9999940	7.3982	.9999990	8.2941
91	6.0443	41	7.4066	91	8.3467
92	6.1031	42	7.4151	92	8.4056
93	6.1699	43	7.4238	93	8.4724
94	6.2470	44	7.4327	94	8.5495
95	6.3381	45	7.4417	95	8.6406
96	6.4497	46	7.4509	96	8.7522
97	6.5935	47	7.4602	97	8.8960
98	6.7962	48	7.4697	98	9.0988
.99999	7.1428	.9999949	7.4794	.9999999	9.4453
				1.0	Infin.

Rather than interpolating from the table, for large values of k, it is sometimes better to use the following series:

$$K = \text{logn } \frac{4}{k'} + \frac{1^2}{2^2} \left(\text{logn } \frac{4}{k'} - \frac{2}{1 \text{x} 2} \right) k'^2$$

$$+ \frac{1^2 \text{x } 3^2}{2^2 \text{x } 4^2} \left(\text{logn } \frac{4}{k'} - \frac{2}{1 \text{x} 2} - \frac{2}{3 \text{x} 4} \right) k'^4 \ldots$$

where $\qquad\qquad k'^2 = 1 - k^2$

and where logn denotes natural logarithm.

For large tables of the complete elliptic integrals of the first and second kinds, see :-

"Ten-figure Table of the Complete Elliptic Integrals," by L. M. Milne-Thomson, Proc. Lond. Math. Soc., ser. 2, v. 33.

"Tafeln der Besselschen, Theta-, Kugel- und anderer Funktionen," by K. Hayashi.

"Tafeln für die Differenzenrechnung," by K. Hayashi.

See also the additional tables in "Toroidal Functions and the Complete Elliptic Integrals," by J. R. Airey, Phil. Mag., ser. 7, v. 19, p. 177, Jan., 1935.

$$E = \int_0^{\pi/2} (1 - k^2\sin^2\phi)^{1/2}d\phi$$

k^2	0	1	2	3	4	5	6	7	8	9	Diff. (Subtract)
.00	1.57 080	040	001	962	922	883	844	804	765	726	39 - 40
.01	1.56 686	647	607	568	528	489	449	410	370	331	39 - 40
.02	291	252	212	172	133	093	054	014	974	935	39 - 40
.03	1.55 895	855	815	776	736	696	656	616	577	537	39 - 40
.04	497	457	417	377	337	297	257	217	177	137	40
.05	097	057	017	977	937	897	857	817	777	736	40 - 41
.06	1.54 696	656	616	576	535	495	455	415	374	334	40 - 41
.07	294	253	213	172	132	092	051	011	970	930	40 - 41
.08	1.53 889	849	808	768	727	687	646	605	565	524	40 - 41
.09	483	443	402	361	321	280	239	198	157	117	40 - 41
.10	076	035	994	953	912	871	830	789	748	708	40 - 41
.11	1.52 667	625	584	543	502	461	420	379	338	297	41 - 42
.12	256	214	173	132	091	049	008	967	926	884	41 - 42
.13	1.51 843	801	760	719	677	636	594	553	511	470	41 - 42
.14	428	387	345	304	262	221	179	137	096	054	41 - 42
.15	012	970	929	887	845	803	762	720	678	636	41 - 42
.16	1.50 594	552	510	468	426	384	342	300	258	216	42
.17	174	132	090	048	006	964	922	879	837	795	42 - 43
.18	1.49 753	710	668	626	583	541	499	456	414	371	42 - 43
.19	329	287	244	202	159	116	074	031	989	946	42 - 43
.20	1.48 904	861	818	775	733	690	647	604	562	519	42 - 43
.21	476	433	390	347	305	262	219	176	133	090	42 - 43
.22	047	004	961	917	874	831	788	745	702	658	43 - 44
.23	1.47 615	572	529	485	442	399	355	312	269	225	43 - 44
.24	182	138	095	051	008	964	921	877	833	790	43 - 44
.25	1.46 746	703	659	615	571	528	484	440	396	352	43 - 44
.26	309	265	221	177	133	089	045	001	957	913	44
.27	1.45 869	825	781	736	692	648	604	560	515	471	44 - 45
.28	427	383	338	294	249	205	161	116	072	027	44 - 45
.29	1.44 983	938	894	849	804	760	715	670	626	581	44 - 45
.30	536	492	447	402	357	312	267	222	178	133	44 - 45
.31	088	043	998	953	907	862	817	772	727	682	45 - 46
.32	1.43 637	591	546	501	456	410	365	319	274	229	45 - 46
.33	183	138	092	047	001	956	910	864	819	773	45 - 46
.34	1.42 727	682	636	590	544	499	453	407	361	315	45 - 46
.35	269	223	177	131	085	039	993	947	901	855	46 - 47
.36	1.41 808	762	716	670	623	577	531	484	438	391	46 - 47
.37	345	299	252	206	159	112	066	019	972	926	46 - 47
.38	1.40 879	832	786	739	692	645	598	551	504	457	46 - 47
.39	411	363	316	269	222	175	128	081	034	986	47 - 48
.40	1.39 939	892	845	797	750	703	655	608	560	513	47 - 48
.41	465	418	370	322	275	227	179	132	084	036	47 - 48
.42	1.38 988	940	893	845	797	749	701	653	605	557	47 - 48
.43	509	460	412	364	316	268	219	171	123	074	48 - 49
.44	026	977	929	880	832	783	735	686	638	589	48 - 49
.45	1.37 540	491	443	394	345	296	247	198	149	100	48 - 49
.46	051	002	953	904	855	806	757	707	658	609	49 - 50
.47	1.36 560	510	461	411	362	312	263	213	164	114	49 - 50
.48	064	015	965	915	866	816	766	716	666	616	49 - 50
.49	1.35 566	516	466	416	366	316	265	215	165	115	50 - 51

E

k²	0	1	2	3	4	5	6	7	8	9	Diff. (Subtract)
.50	1.35 064	014	964	913	863	812	762	711	661	610	50 - 51
.51	1.34 559	509	458	407	356	305	254	204	153	102	50 - 51
.52	051	999	948	897	846	795	744	692	641	590	51 - 52
.53	1.33 538	487	435	384	332	281	229	177	126	074	51 - 52
.54	022	970	919	867	815	763	711	659	607	555	51 - 53
.55	1.32 502	450	398	346	293	241	189	136	084	031	52 - 53
.56	1.31 979	926	874	821	768	715	663	610	557	504	52 - 53
.57	451	398	345	292	239	186	132	079	026	973	53 - 54
.58	1.30 919	866	812	759	705	652	598	544	491	437	53 - 54
.59	383	329	275	222	168	114	059	005	951	897	53 - 55
.60	1.29 843	789	734	680	625	571	516	462	407	353	54 - 55
.61	298	243	188	134	079	024	969	914	859	804	54 - 56
.62	1.28 748	693	638	583	527	472	416	361	305	250	55 - 56
.63	194	138	083	027	971	915	859	803	747	691	55 - 56
.64	1.27 635	579	523	466	410	354	297	241	184	127	56 - 57
.65	071	014	957	900	844	787	730	673	616	558	56 - 58
.66	1.26 501	444	387	329	272	214	157	099	042	984	57 - 58
.67	1.25 926	869	811	753	695	637	579	521	462	404	57 - 59
.68	346	287	229	171	112	053	995	936	877	818	58 - 59
.69	1.24 759	700	641	582	523	464	405	345	286	227	59 - 60
.70	167	107	048	988	928	869	809	749	689	629	59 - 61
.71	1.23 568	508	448	388	327	267	206	145	085	024	60 - 61
.72	1.22 963	902	841	780	719	658	597	536	474	413	61 - 62
.73	351	290	228	166	104	043	981	919	856	794	61 - 63
.74	1.21 732	670	607	545	482	420	357	294	232	169	62 - 63
.75	106	043	979	916	853	789	726	662	599	535	63 - 64
.76	1.20 471	408	344	280	215	151	087	023	958	894	63 - 65
.77	1.19 829	764	700	635	570	505	440	374	309	244	64 - 66
.78	178	113	047	981	915	849	783	717	651	585	65 - 67
.79	1.18 518	452	385	319	252	185	118	051	984	916	66 - 68
.80	1.17 849	782	714	646	579	511	443	375	306	238	67 - 69
.81	170	101	033	964	895	826	757	688	619	549	68 - 70
.82	1.16 480	410	341	271	201	131	061	990	920	849	69 - 71
.83	1.15 779	708	637	566	495	424	352	281	209	137	71 - 72
.84	066	994	921	849	777	704	632	559	486	413	72 - 73
.85	1.14 340	266	193	119	045	971	897	823	749	674	73 - 75
.86	1.13 600	525	450	375	300	224	149	073	997	921	75 - 76
.87	1.12 845	769	692	616	539	462	385	307	230	152	76 - 78
.88	074	996	918	840	761	682	603	524	445	365	78 - 80
.89	1.11 286	206	126	045	965	884	803	722	641	559	80 - 82
.90	1.10 477	396	313	231	148	065	982	899	816	732	81 - 84
.91	1.09 648	563	479	394	309	224	138	053	967	880	84 - 87
.92	1.08 794	707	620	532	445	357	268	180	091	002	87 - 90
.93	1.07 912	822	732	642	551	460	368	276	184	092	90 - 93
.94	1.06 999	905	812	718	623	528	433	337	241	144	93 - 97
.95	047	950	852	754	655	555	455	355	254	152	97 -102
.96	1.05 050	1.04 948	844	740	636	531	425	318	211	103	102 -108
.97	1.03 995	885	775	664	552	439	325	210	094	978	110 -119
.98	1.02 859	740	620	498	375	250	123	995	865	734	119 -135
.99	1.01 599	463	323	181	035	885	730	569	400	217	136 -217
1.00	1.00 000										

SINE INTEGRAL

$$Si(x) = \int_0^x \frac{\sin u}{u}\, du$$

x	0	1	2	3	4	5	6	7	8	9	Diff.
.0	.0 000	100	200	300	400	500	600	700	800	900	100 - 99
.1	999	099	199	299	398	498	598	697	797	896	100 - 99
.2	.1 996	095	194	293	392	491	590	689	788	886	99 - 98
.3	.2 985	083	182	280	378	476	574	672	770	867	99 - 97
.4	.3 965	062	159	256	353	450	546	643	739	835	97 - 96
.5	.4 931	027	123	218	313	408	503	598	693	787	96 - 94
.6	.5 881	975	069	163	256	349	442	535	628	720	94 - 92
.7	.6 812	904	996	087	179	270	360	451	541	631	92 - 90
.8	.7 721	811	900	989	078	166	254	342	430	518	90 - 87
.9	.8 605	692	778	865	951	036	122	207	292	377	87 - 84
1.0	.9 461	545	629	712	795	878	960	042	124	206	84 - 81
.1	1.0 287	368	448	528	608	688	767	846	924	003	81 - 78
.2	1.1 080	158	235	312	388	464	540	616	691	765	78 - 74
.3	840	914	987	060	133	206	278	349	421	492	74 - 70
.4	1.2 562	632	702	772	841	909	978	046	113	180	70 - 67
.5	1.3 247	313	379	445	510	574	639	703	766	829	66 - 63
.6	892	954	016	077	138	199	259	319	378	437	62 - 59
.7	1.4 496	554	612	669	726	782	838	894	949	004	58 - 54
.8	1.5 058	112	166	219	271	323	375	426	477	528	54 - 50
.9	578	627	676	725	774	821	869	916	962	008	49 - 46
2.0	1.6 054	099	144	189	233	276	319	362	404	446	45 - 41
.1	487	528	568	608	648	687	726	764	802	839	41 - 37
.2	876	913	949	985	020	055	089	123	156	189	37 - 33
.3	1.7 222	254	286	317	348	379	409	439	468	496	32 - 28
.4	525	553	580	607	634	660	686	712	736	761	28 - 24
.5	785	809	832	855	878	900	921	943	963	984	24 - 20
.6	1.8 004	024	043	062	080	098	116	133	150	166	20 - 16
.7	182	198	213	228	242	256	270	283	296	309	16 - 12
.8	321	333	344	355	366	376	386	396	405	413	12 - 8
.9	422	430	438	445	452	459	465	471	476	482	8 - 5
3.0	487	491	495	499	503	506	509	511	513	515	4 - 2
.1	517	518	519	519	519	519	519	518	517	516	0 - 2
.2	514	512	510	507	504	501	498	494	490	485	2 - 5
.3	481	476	471	465	459	453	447	440	434	427	5 - 8
.4	419	411	404	395	387	378	369	360	351	341	7 - 10
.5	331	321	311	300	289	278	267	255	244	232	10 - 13
.6	219	207	194	182	169	155	142	128	114	100	12 - 14
.7	086	072	057	042	027	012	997	981	966	950	14 - 16
.8	1.7 934	918	901	885	868	851	834	817	800	783	16 - 18
.9	765	747	729	711	693	675	657	638	620	601	18 - 19
4.0	582	563	544	525	505	486	467	447	427	407	19 - 20
.1	387	367	347	327	307	287	266	246	225	204	20 - 21
.2	184	163	142	121	100	079	058	037	016	994	21 - 22
.3	1.6 973	952	931	909	888	866	845	823	802	780	21 - 22
.4	758	737	715	693	672	650	628	607	585	563	21 - 22
.5	541	520	498	476	455	433	411	390	368	346	21 - 22
.6	325	303	281	260	238	217	195	174	153	131	21 - 22
.7	110	089	068	046	025	004	983	962	941	921	22 - 20
.8	1.5 900	879	858	838	817	797	776	756	736	716	21 - 20
.9	696	676	656	636	616	596	577	557	538	519	20 - 19

Si(x)

x	0	1	2	3	4	5	6	7	8	9	Diff.
5.0	1.5 499	480	461	442	423	405	386	367	349	331	19 - 18
.1	313	294	276	259	241	223	206	188	171	154	19 - 17
.2	137	120	103	086	070	053	037	021	005	989	17 - 16
.3	1.4 973	958	942	927	911	896	881	867	852	837	16 - 14
.4	823	809	795	781	767	753	740	726	713	700	14 - 13
.5	687	674	662	649	637	625	613	601	590	578	13 - 11
.6	567	555	544	534	523	512	502	492	482	472	12 - 10
.7	462	452	443	434	425	416	407	398	390	382	10 - 8
.8	374	366	358	350	343	336	329	322	315	308	8 - 6
.9	302	296	290	284	278	272	267	262	257	252	6 - 5
6.0	247	242	238	234	230	226	222	218	215	212	5 - 3
.1	209	206	203	200	198	196	194	192	190	188	3 - 1
.2	187	186	185	184	183	182	182	182	182	182	1 - 0
.3	182	182	183	183	184	185	186	187	189	190	0 - 2
.4	192	194	196	198	201	203	206	209	212	215	2 - 3
.5	218	221	225	229	232	236	240	245	249	254	3 - 5
.6	258	263	268	273	278	283	289	295	300	306	5 - 6
.7	312	318	324	331	337	344	351	357	364	371	6 - 8
.8	379	386	393	401	409	416	424	432	440	449	7 - 9
.9	457	465	474	483	491	500	509	518	527	537	8 - 10
7.0	546	555	565	575	584	594	604	614	624	634	9 - 10
.1	644	655	665	675	686	697	707	718	729	740	10 - 11
.2	751	762	773	784	796	807	818	830	841	853	11 - 12
.3	864	876	888	900	911	923	935	947	959	971	11 - 12
.4	983	996	008	020	032	045	057	069	082	094	12 - 13
.5	1.5 107	119	132	144	157	170	182	195	208	220	12 - 13
.6	233	246	259	271	284	297	310	323	335	348	12 - 13
.7	361	374	387	400	412	425	438	451	464	477	12 - 13
.8	489	502	515	528	540	553	566	579	591	604	12 - 13
.9	617	629	642	655	667	680	692	705	717	729	12 - 13
8.0	742	754	767	779	791	803	815	828	840	852	12 - 13
.1	864	876	888	899	911	923	935	946	958	969	12 - 11
.2	981	992	004	015	026	038	049	060	071	082	12 - 11
.3	1.6 093	104	114	125	136	146	157	167	178	188	11 - 10
.4	198	208	218	228	238	248	258	267	277	287	10 - 9
.5	296	305	315	324	333	342	351	360	368	377	10 - 8
.6	386	394	403	411	419	427	435	443	451	459	9 - 8
.7	467	474	482	489	496	503	511	518	524	531	8 - 6
.8	538	545	551	557	564	570	576	582	588	594	7 - 5
.9	599	605	610	616	621	626	631	636	641	646	6 - 4
9.0	650	655	659	664	668	672	676	680	684	687	5 - 3
.1	691	694	698	701	704	707	710	713	715	718	4 - 2
.2	720	723	725	727	729	731	733	735	736	738	3 - 1
.3	739	741	742	743	744	745	745	746	747	747	2 - 0
.4	747	748	748	748	747	747	747	747	746	745	0 - 1
.5	745	744	743	742	741	739	738	737	735	733	1 - 2
.6	732	730	728	726	724	721	719	716	714	711	2 - 3
.7	708	706	703	700	696	693	690	687	683	679	2 - 4
.8	676	672	668	664	660	656	652	647	643	638	4 - 5
.9	634	629	624	620	615	610	605	599	594	589	4 - 6
10.0	583										

$$\text{Ci}(x) = \int_{\infty}^{x} \frac{\cos u}{u}\, du$$

x	Ci(x)	x	Ci(x)
.00	- Infin.	.50	-.1778
.01	-4.0280	.51	-.1605
.02	-3.3349	.52	-.1436
.03	-2.9296	.53	-.1271
.04	-2.6421	.54	-.1110
.05	-2.4191	.55	-.0953
.06	-2.2371	.56	-.0800
.07	-2.0833	.57	-.0650
.08	-1.9501	.58	-.0504
.09	-1.8328	.59	-.0362
.10	-1.7279	.60	-.0223
.11	-1.6331	.61	-.0087
.12	-1.5466	.62	.0046
.13	-1.4672	.63	.0176
.14	-1.3938	.64	.0303
.15	-1.3255	.65	.0426
.16	-1.2618	.66	.0548
.17	-1.2020	.67	.0666
.18	-1.1457	.68	.0782
.19	-1.0925	.69	.0895
.20	-1.0422	.70	.1005
.21	-.9944	.71	.1113
.22	-.9490	.72	.1219
.23	-.9057	.73	.1322
.24	-.8643	.74	.1423
.25	-.8247	.75	.1522
.26	-.7867	.76	.1618
.27	-.7503	.77	.1712
.28	-.7153	.78	.1805
.29	-.6816	.79	.1895
.30	-.6492	.80	.1983
.31	-.6179	.81	.2069
.32	-.5877	.82	.2153
.33	-.5585	.83	.2235
.34	-.5304	.84	.2316
.35	-.5031	.85	.2394
.36	-.4767	.86	.2471
.37	-.4511	.87	.2546
.38	-.4263	.88	.2619
.39	-.4022	.89	.2691
.40	-.3788	.90	.2761
.41	-.3561	.91	.2829
.42	-.3341	.92	.2896
.43	-.3126	.93	.2961
.44	-.2918	.94	.3024
.45	-.2715	.95	.3086
.46	-.2517	.96	.3147
.47	-.2325	.97	.3206
.48	-.2138	.98	.3263
.49	-.1956	.99	.3319

Ci(x)

x	0	1	2	3	4	5	6	7	8	9	Diff.
1.0	.3 374	427	479	530	579	627	674	720	764	807	53 - 42
.1	849	889	929	967	$\overline{004}$	$\overline{040}$	$\overline{075}$	$\overline{109}$	$\overline{142}$	$\overline{174}$	40 - 31
.2	.4 205	234	263	291	317	343	368	392	414	436	29 - 21
.3	457	478	497	515	533	549	565	580	594	608	21 - 12
.4	620	632	643	653	662	671	679	686	693	698	12 - 5
.5	704	708	712	715	717	719	720	720	720	719	4 - 0
.6	717	715	712	709	705	701	696	690	684	677	2 - 7
.7	670	662	653	645	635	625	615	604	592	580	8 - 12
.8	568	555	542	528	514	499	484	469	453	436	13 - 17
.9	419	402	385	367	348	329	310	291	271	250	17 - 21
2.0	230	209	187	166	144	122	099	076	053	029	21 - 24
.1	005	$\overline{981}$	$\overline{956}$	$\overline{932}$	$\overline{907}$	$\overline{881}$	$\overline{856}$	$\overline{830}$	$\overline{804}$	$\overline{777}$	24 - 27
.2	.3 751	724	697	669	642	614	586	558	529	501	27 - 29
.3	472	443	413	384	354	325	295	264	234	204	29 - 31
.4	173	142	111	080	049	017	$\overline{986}$	$\overline{954}$	$\overline{923}$	$\overline{891}$	31 - 32
.5	.2 859	827	794	762	730	697	665	632	599	566	32 - 33
.6	533	500	467	434	401	368	334	301	268	234	33 - 34
.7	201	167	134	100	067	033	999	$\overline{966}$	$\overline{932}$	$\overline{899}$	33 - 34
.8	.1 865	831	798	764	730	697	663	630	596	562	33 - 34
.9	529	495	462	429	395	362	329	296	262	229	33 - 34
3.0	196	163	130	098	065	032	000	$\overline{967}$	$\overline{935}$	$\overline{902}$	33 - 32
.1	.0 870	838	806	774	742	710	678	647	615	584	32 - 31
.2	553	521	490	460	429	398	368	337	307	277	32 - 30
.3	247	217	187	158	128	099	070	041	012	$\overline{017}$	30 - 28
.4	-.0 045	074	102	130	158	185	213	240	267	294	29 - 27
.5	321	348	374	401	427	453	479	504	530	555	27 - 25
.6	580	605	629	654	678	702	726	749	773	796	25 - 23
.7	819	842	864	887	909	931	953	974	996	$\overline{017}$	23 - 21
.8	-.1 038	058	079	099	119	139	159	178	197	216	21 - 19
.9	235	253	272	290	308	325	343	360	377	393	19 - 16
4.0	410	426	442	458	473	489	504	519	533	548	16 - 14
.1	562	576	589	603	616	629	642	654	666	678	14 - 12
.2	690	702	713	724	735	746	756	766	776	786	12 - 9
.3	795	804	813	822	831	839	847	855	862	870	9 - 7
.4	877	883	890	897	903	909	914	920	925	930	7 - 5
.5	935	939	944	948	952	955	959	962	965	968	5 - 2
.6	970	973	975	977	978	980	981	982	983	984	3 - 0
.7	984	984	984	984	983	983	982	981	979	978	0 - 2
.8	976	974	972	970	967	964	961	958	955	952	2 - 4
.9	948	944	940	936	931	926	922	916	911	906	4 - 6

COSINE INTEGRAL

Ci(x)

x	0	1	2	3	4	5	6	7	8	9	Diff.
5.0	-.1 900	895	889	882	876	870	863	856	849	842	5 - 7
.1	835	827	820	812	804	796	787	779	770	761	7 - 9
.2	753	743	734	725	715	706	696	686	676	665	9 - 11
.3	655	645	634	623	612	601	590	579	567	556	10 - 12
.4	544	532	520	508	496	484	471	459	446	433	12 - 13
.5	421	408	395	381	368	355	341	328	314	301	13 - 14
.6	287	273	259	245	231	216	202	188	173	159	14 - 15
.7	144	129	115	100	085	070	055	040	025	010	14 - 16
.8	-.0 994	979	964	948	933	917	902	886	871	855	15 - 16
.9	839	824	808	792	776	760	744	728	713	697	15 - 16
6.0	681	665	649	632	616	600	584	568	552	536	16 - 17
.1	520	504	488	471	455	439	423	407	391	375	16 - 17
.2	359	343	327	311	295	279	263	247	231	215	16
.3	199	183	167	151	136	120	104	089	073	057	16 - 15
.4	042	026	011	0̄0̄5̄	0̄2̄0̄	0̄3̄5̄	0̄5̄0̄	0̄6̄6̄	0̄8̄1̄	0̄9̄6̄	16 - 15
.5	.0 111	126	141	156	171	185	200	215	229	244	15 - 14
.6	258	273	287	301	315	329	343	357	371	385	15 - 14
.7	399	412	426	439	452	466	479	492	505	518	14 - 13
.8	531	544	556	569	581	594	606	618	630	642	13 - 12
.9	654	666	677	689	700	712	723	734	745	756	12 - 11
7.0	767	778	788	799	809	819	830	840	850	859	11 - 9
.1	869	879	888	897	907	916	925	934	942	951	10 - 8
.2	960	968	976	984	992	0̄0̄0̄	0̄0̄8̄	0̄1̄6̄	0̄2̄3̄	0̄3̄1̄	8 - 7
.3	.1 038	045	052	059	066	072	079	085	091	098	7 - 6
.4	104	109	115	121	126	132	137	142	147	152	6 - 4
.5	156	161	165	170	174	178	182	185	189	193	5 - 3
.6	196	199	202	205	208	211	213	216	218	220	3 - 2
.7	222	224	226	228	229	231	232	233	234	235	2 - 1
.8	236	236	237	237	238	238	238	238	237	237	1 - 0
.9	236	236	235	234	233	232	231	229	228	226	0 - 2
8.0	224	222	220	218	216	214	211	209	206	203	2 - 3
.1	200	197	194	191	187	184	180	176	172	168	3 - 4
.2	164	160	156	152	147	142	138	133	128	123	4 - 5
.3	118	112	107	102	096	090	085	079	073	067	5 - 6
.4	061	054	048	042	035	029	022	015	008	001	6 - 7
.5	.0 994	987	980	973	965	958	950	943	935	927	7 - 8
.6	919	911	903	895	887	879	871	862	854	845	8 - 9
.7	837	828	819	811	802	793	784	775	766	757	8 - 9
.8	748	738	729	720	710	701	691	682	672	663	9 - 10
.9	653	643	633	623	614	604	594	584	574	564	9 - 11
9.0	553	543	533	523	513	502	492	482	471	461	10 - 11
.1	451	440	430	419	409	398	388	377	367	356	10 - 11
.2	346	335	324	314	303	292	282	271	260	250	10 - 11
.3	239	228	218	207	196	186	175	164	154	143	10 - 11
.4	133	122	111	101	090	079	069	058	048	037	10 - 11
.5	027	016	006	0̄0̄5̄	0̄1̄5̄	0̄2̄5̄	0̄3̄6̄	0̄4̄6̄	0̄5̄6̄	0̄6̄7̄	10 - 11
.6	-.0 077	087	098	108	118	128	138	148	158	168	10 - 11
.7	178	188	198	208	217	227	237	247	256	266	10 - 9
.8	275	285	294	303	313	322	331	340	350	359	10 - 9
.9	368	377	385	394	403	412	421	429	438	446	9 - 8
10.0	455										

$$\text{Ei} (x) = \int_{-\infty}^{x} \frac{e^u}{u} du$$

x	Ei(x)	x	Ei(x)
.00	-Infin.	.50	.4542
.01	-4.0179	.51	.4870
.02	-3.3147	.52	.5195
.03	-2.8991	.53	.5517
.04	-2.6013	.54	.5836
.05	-2.3679	.55	.6153
.06	-2.1753	.56	.6467
.07	-2.0108	.57	.6778
.08	-1.8669	.58	.7087
.09	-1.7387	.59	.7394
.10	-1.6228	.60	.7699
.11	-1.5170	.61	.8002
.12	-1.4193	.62	.8302
.13	-1.3287	.63	.8601
.14	-1.2438	.64	.8898
.15	-1.1641	.65	.9194
.16	-1.0887	.66	.9488
.17	-1.0172	.67	.9780
.18	-.9491	.68	1.0071
.19	-.8841	.69	1.0361
.20	-.8218	.70	1.0649
.21	-.7619	.71	1.0936
.22	-.7042	.72	1.1222
.23	-.6485	.73	1.1507
.24	-.5947	.74	1.1791
.25	-.5425	.75	1.2073
.26	-.4919	.76	1.2355
.27	-.4427	.77	1.2636
.28	-.3949	.78	1.2916
.29	-.3482	.79	1.3195
.30	-.3027	.80	1.3474
.31	-.2582	.81	1.3752
.32	-.2147	.82	1.4029
.33	-.1721	.83	1.4306
.34	-.1304	.84	1.4582
.35	-.0894	.85	1.4857
.36	-.0493	.86	1.5132
.37	-.0098	.87	1.5407
.38	.0290	.88	1.5681
.39	.0672	.89	1.5955
.40	.1048	.90	1.6228
.41	.1418	.91	1.6501
.42	.1783	.92	1.6774
.43	.2143	.93	1.7047
.44	.2498	.94	1.7319
.45	.2849	.95	1.7591
.46	.3195	.96	1.7864
.47	.3537	.97	1.8136
.48	.3876	.98	1.8407
.49	.4211	.99	1.8679

EXPONENTIAL INTEGRAL

$$10^{-1}Ei(x)$$

x	0	1	2	3	4	5	6	7	8	9	Diff.
1.0	.1 895	922	949	977	004	031	058	086	113	140	27 - 28
.1	.2 167	195	222	249	277	304	332	359	387	414	27 - 28
.2	442	470	498	525	553	581	609	637	665	693	27 - 28
.3	721	750	778	806	835	863	892	921	949	978	28 - 29
.4	.3 007	036	065	094	124	153	183	212	242	271	29 - 30
.5	301	331	361	391	422	452	482	513	544	574	30 - 31
.6	605	636	667	699	730	762	793	825	857	889	31 - 32
.7	921	953	986	018	051	084	117	150	183	216	32 - 34
.8	.4 250	284	317	351	386	420	454	489	524	559	33 - 35
.9	594	629	664	700	736	772	808	844	881	917	35 - 37
2.0	954	991	028	066	104	141	179	217	256	294	37 - 39
.1	.5 333	372	411	451	490	530	570	611	651	692	39 - 41
.2	733	774	815	857	899	941	983	025	068	111	41 - 43
.3	.6 154	198	242	286	330	374	419	464	509	555	44 - 46
.4	601	647	693	740	787	834	881	929	977	025	46 - 49
.5	.7 074	123	172	221	271	321	372	422	473	524	49 - 52
.6	576	628	680	733	786	839	893	947	001	055	52 - 55
.7	.8 110	166	221	277	334	390	447	505	563	621	55 - 58
.8	679	738	798	857	917	978	039	100	162	224	59 - 62
.9	.9 286	349	412	476	540	605	670	735	801	867	63 - 67
3.0	934										
	1.	000	007	014	021	027	034	041	048	055	6 - 8
.1	063	070	077	084	092	099	106	114	122	129	7 - 8
.2	137	144	152	160	168	176	184	192	200	208	7 - 8
.3	216	224	233	241	249	258	266	275	284	292	8 - 9
.4	301	310	319	328	337	346	355	364	374	383	9 - 10
.5	393	402	412	421	431	441	451	460	470	480	9 - 11
.6	491	501	511	521	532	542	553	564	574	585	10 - 11
.7	596	607	618	629	640	652	663	675	686	698	11 - 12
.8	709	721	733	745	757	769	782	794	806	819	12 - 13
.9	832	844	857	870	883	896	909	923	936	949	12 - 14
4.0	963	977	991	005	019	033	047	061	076	090	14 - 15
.1	2. 105	120	135	150	165	180	195	211	226	242	15 - 16
.2	258	274	290	306	322	339	355	372	389	406	16 - 17
.3	423	440	457	475	492	510	528	546	564	582	17 - 19
.4	601	619	638	657	676	695	715	734	754	773	18 - 20
.5	793	813	834	854	875	895	916	937	958	980	20 - 22
.6	3. 001	023	045	067	089	112	134	157	180	203	22 - 23
.7	226	250	274	297	321	346	370	395	420	445	23 - 25
.8	470	495	521	547	573	599	625	652	679	706	25 - 27
.9	733	761	788	816	845	873	902	931	960	989	27 - 30
5.0	4. 019	048	078	109	139	170	201	232	264	296	29 - 32
.1	328	360	392	425	458	492	525	559	593	628	32 - 35
.2	662	697	733	768	804	840	877	914	951	988	35 - 38
.3	5. 026	064	102	140	179	218	258	298	338	379	38 - 41
.4	419	461	502	544	586	629	671	715	758	802	41 - 45
.5	847	891	936	982	027	074	120	167	214	262	44 - 48
.6	6. 310	359	408	457	507	557	607	658	709	761	49 - 52
.7	813	866	919	973	027	081	136	191	247	303	53 - 57
.8	7. 360	417	475	533	592	651	710	770	831	892	57 - 62
.9	954										
	8.	016	079	142	205	270	334	400	466	532	62 - 67

$$10^{-3}Ei(x)$$

x	0	1	2	3	4	5	6	7	8	9	Diff.
6.0	.08 599	666	735	803	872	942	013	084	155	227	67 - 73
.1	.09 300	374	448	522	598	673	750	827	905	983	74 - 80
.2	.1 006	014	022	030	039	047	055	064	072	081	8 - 9
.3	089	098	107	115	124	133	142	151	161	170	8 - 10
.4	179	189	198	208	218	227	237	247	257	267	9 - 10
.5	277	288	298	309	319	330	340	351	362	373	10 - 11
.6	384	395	407	418	430	441	453	465	476	488	11 - 13
.7	501	513	525	537	550	562	575	588	601	614	12 - 13
.8	627	640	654	667	681	695	708	722	736	751	13 - 15
.9	765	779	794	809	823	838	853	869	884	899	14 - 16
7.0	915	931	947	963	979	995	012	028	045	062	16 - 17
.1	.2 079	096	113	131	148	166	184	202	220	238	17 - 19
.2	257	276	294	313	333	352	371	391	411	431	18 - 20
.3	451	472	492	513	534	555	576	597	619	641	20 - 22
.4	663	685	708	730	753	776	799	822	846	870	22 - 24
.5	894	918	943	967	992	017	042	068	094	120	24 - 26
.6	.3 146	172	199	226	253	280	308	335	364	392	26 - 29
.7	420	449	478	508	537	567	597	627	658	689	29 - 31
.8	720	751	783	815	847	880	913	946	979	013	31 - 34
.9	.4 047	081	116	151	186	222	257	293	330	367	34 - 37
8.0	404	441	479	517	555	594	633	673	713	753	37 - 40
.1	793	834	875	917	959	001	044	087	130	174	41 - 44
.2	.5 218	263	308	353	399	445	492	539	586	634	45 - 48
.3	682	731	780	830	880	930	981	032	084	136	49 - 53
.4	.6 189	242	296	350	405	460	515	571	628	685	53 - 58
.5	743	801	859	918	978	038	099	160	222	284	58 - 63
.6	.7 347	411	475	539	604	670	736	803	871	939	64 - 68
.7	.8 007	077	147	217	288	360	433	506	579	654	70 - 75
.8	729	805	881	958	036	114	194	273	354	435	76 - 82
.9	.9 517	600	684	768	853	938					83 - 87
	1.						002	011	020	029	9
9.0	038	047	056	065	075	084	093	103	113	122	9 - 10
.1	132	142	152	162	172	182	193	203	214	224	10 - 11
.2	235	246	257	268	279	290	301	313	324	336	11 - 12
.3	347	359	371	383	395	408	420	432	445	458	12 - 13
.4	471	483	496	510	523	536	550	563	577	591	12 - 14
.5	605	619	633	648	662	677	692	707	722	737	14 - 15
.6	752	768	783	799	815	831	847	863	880	896	15 - 17
.7	913	930	947	964	982	999	017	035	053	071	17 - 19
.8	2. 089	108	126	145	164	183	202	222	242	262	18 - 20
.9	282	302	322	343	364	385	406	427	449	470	20 - 22
10.0	492										

EXPONENTIAL INTEGRAL

$$-\text{Ei}\ (-x)\ =\ \int_{x}^{\infty} \frac{e^{-u}}{u}\ du$$

x	-Ei(-x)	x	-Ei(-x)
.00	Infin.	.50	.5598
.01	4.0379	.51	.5478
.02	3.3547	.52	.5362
.03	2.9591	.53	.5250
.04	2.6812	.54	.5140
.05	2.4679	.55	.5034
.06	2.2953	.56	.4930
.07	2.1508	.57	.4830
.08	2.0269	.58	.4732
.09	1.9187	.59	.4636
.10	1.8229	.60	.4544
.11	1.7371	.61	.4454
.12	1.6595	.62	.4366
.13	1.5889	.63	.4280
.14	1.5241	.64	.4197
.15	1.4645	.65	.4115
.16	1.4092	.66	.4036
.17	1.3578	.67	.3959
.18	1.3098	.68	.3883
.19	1.2649	.69	.3810
.20	1.2227	.70	.3738
.21	1.1829	.71	.3668
.22	1.1454	.72	.3599
.23	1.1099	.73	.3532
.24	1.0762	.74	.3467
.25	1.0443	.75	.3403
.26	1.0139	.76	.3341
.27	.9849	.77	.3280
.28	.9573	.78	.3221
.29	.9309	.79	.3163
.30	.9057	.80	.3106
.31	.8815	.81	.3050
.32	.8583	.82	.2996
.33	.8361	.83	.2943
.34	.8147	.84	.2891
.35	.7942	.85	.2840
.36	.7745	.86	.2790
.37	.7554	.87	.2742
.38	.7371	.88	.2694
.39	.7194	.89	.2647
.40	.7024	.90	.2602
.41	.6859	.91	.2557
.42	.6700	.92	.2513
.43	.6546	.93	.2470
.44	.6397	.94	.2429
.45	.6253	.95	.2387
.46	.6114	.96	.2347
.47	.5979	.97	.2308
.48	.5848	.98	.2269
.49	.5721	.99	.2231

-10 Ei(-x)

x	0	1	2	3	4	5	6	7	8	9	Diff. (Subtract)
1.0	2. 194	157	122	087	052	019	986	953	922	890	37 - 30
.1	1. 860	830	801	772	743	716	688	662	635	609	30 - 25
.2	584	559	535	511	487	464	441	419	397	376	25 - 21
.3	355	334	313	293	274	254	235	216	198	180	21 - 18
.4	162	145	128	111	094	078	062	046	030	015	17 - 15
.5	000										
	.9	854	709	567	426	288	152	019	587	758	145 - 127
.6	.8 631	506	383	261	142	025	909	796	684	574	125 - 109
.7	.7 465	359	254	151	049	949	850	753	658	564	106 - 93
.8	.6 471	380	290	202	115	029	945	862	780	700	91 - 80
.9	.5 620	542	465	390	315	241	169	098	027	958	78 - 68
2.0	.4 890	823	757	692	627	564	502	440	380	320	67 - 59
.1	261	204	147	090	035	980	927	874	821	770	57 - 51
.2	.3 719	669	620	571	523	476	430	384	339	294	50 - 44
.3	250	207	164	122	081	040	000	960	921	882	43 - 38
.4	.2 844	806	769	733	697	662	627	592	558	525	38 - 33
.5	491	459	427	395	364	333	303	273	243	214	32 - 29
.6	185	157	129	101	074	047	021	994	969	943	28 - 25
.7	.1 918	893	869	845	821	798	775	752	730	707	25 - 21
.8	686	664	643	622	601	581	560	540	521	502	22 - 19
.9	482	464	445	427	409	391	373	356	338	322	19 - 16
3.0	305	288	272	256	240	225	209	194	179	164	17 - 15
.1	149	135	121	107	093	079	066	052	039	026	14 - 13
.2	013	001									
	.09		882	758	637	517	398	281	166	052	124 - 113
.3	.08 939	828	718	610	503	398	294	191	090	990	111 - 99
.4	.07 891	793	697	602	508	416	324	234	145	057	98 - 87
.5	.06 970	884	800	716	634	552	472	393	314	237	86 - 77
.6	160	085	011	937	864	793	722	652	583	515	75 - 67
.7	.05 448	381	316	251	187	124	062	000	939	879	67 - 59
.8	.04 820	762	704	647	591	535	480	426	372	319	58 - 52
.9	267	216	165	114	065	016	967	919	872	825	51 - 46
4.0	.03 779	734	689	645	601	557	515	472	431	390	45 - 41
.1	349	309	269	230	191	153	115	078	041	005	40 - 36
.2	.02 969	933	898	864	829	796	762	729	697	665	36 - 32
.3	633	602	571	540	510	480	450	421	393	364	31 - 28
.4	336	308	281	254	227	201	175	149	123	098	28 - 25
.5	073	049	025	001	977	954	931	908	885	863	24 - 22
.6	.01 841	819	798	777	756	735	715	694	674	655	22 - 19
.7	635	616	597	578	560	541	523	505	488	470	19 - 17
.8	453	436	419	402	386	370	354	338	322	307	17 - 15
.9	291	276	261	247	232	218	204	189	176	162	15 - 13
5.0	148	135	122	109	096	083	070	058	045	033	13 - 12
.1	021	009									
	.009		977	861	746	633	521	410	301	193	116 - 107
.2	086	981	877	774	672	571	472	374	277	181	105 - 95
.3	.008 086	992	900	809	718	629	541	453	367	282	94 - 84
.4	.007 198	115	033	952	871	792	714	636	560	484	83 - 75
.5	.006 409	335	262	190	119	048	979	910	842	775	74 - 67
.6	.005 708	643	578	514	450	388	326	265	204	145	65 - 59
.7	085	027	969	912	856	800	745	691	637	584	58 - 52
.8	.004 532	480	428	378	328	278	229	181	133	086	52 - 47
.9	039										
	.003	993	947	902	858	814	770	727	684	642	46 - 41

EXPONENTIAL INTEGRAL

$$-10^4 \mathrm{Ei}(-x)$$

x	0	1	2	3	4	5	6	7	8	9	Diff. (Subtract)
6.0	3. 601	560	519	479	439	400	361	323	285	248	41 - 37
.1	211	174	138	102	067	032	998	964	930	897	37 - 33
.2	2. 864	831	799	767	736	705	674	644	614	584	33 - 29
.3	555	526	497	469	441	413	386	359	332	306	29 - 26
.4	279	254	228	203	178	153	129	105	081	058	26 - 23
.5	034	011	989	966	944	922	900	879	858	837	23 - 21
.6	1. 816	795	775	755	735	716	696	677	658	640	21 - 18
.7	621	603	585	567	549	532	515	498	481	464	18 - 16
.8	448	431	415	399	384	368	353	337	322	308	17 - 14
.9	293	278	264	250	236	222	208	195	181	168	15 - 13
7.0	155	142	129	116	104	092	079	067	055	043	13 - 11
.1	032	020	009								
.9				974	863	752	643	535	429	323	111 - 104
.2	219	116	014	913	813	715	617	521	426	332	103 - 93
.3	.8 239	147	056	966	877	789	702	616	531	447	92 - 83
.4	.7 364	282	201	120	041	962	885	808	732	657	82 - 74
.5	.6 583	510	437	366	295	225	155	087	019	952	73 - 66
.6	.5 886	820	756	692	628	566	504	443	382	322	66 - 59
.7	263	205	147	090	033	977	922	867	813	760	58 - 53
.8	.4 707	655	603	552	502	452	402	354	305	258	52 - 47
.9	210	164	118	072	027	982	938	895	851	809	46 - 42
8.0	.3 767	725	684	643	603	563	523	484	446	408	42 - 38
.1	370	333	296	259	223	188	153	118	083	049	37 - 34
.2	015	982	949	917	884	853	821	790	759	729	33 - 30
.3	.2 699	669	639	610	582	553	525	497	470	442	30 - 27
.4	415	389	362	336	311	285	260	235	211	186	27 - 24
.5	162	138	115	091	068	046	023	001	979	957	24 - 21
.6	.1 936	914	893	872	852	832	811	791	772	752	22 - 19
.7	733	714	695	677	658	640	622	604	587	569	19 - 17
.8	552	535	518	501	485	469	452	437	421	405	17 - 15
.9	390	375	359	345	330	315	301	287	272	259	16 - 13
9.0	245	231	218	204	191	178	165	152	140	127	14 - 12
.1	115	103	091	079	067	055	044	032	021	010	12 - 11
.2	.09 988	879	771	664	558	454	351	248	147	047	109 - 99
.3	.08 948	851	754	658	564	470	378	286	196	106	97 - 88
.4	018										
.07		930	844	758	674	590	507	425	344	264	86 - 79
.5	185	106	029	952	876	802	727	654	582	510	79 - 71
.6	.06 439	369	299	231	163	096	029	964	899	834	70 - 63
.7	.05 771	708	646	584	524	464	404	345	287	230	63 - 57
.8	173	116	061	006	951	897	844	791	739	688	57 - 51
.9	.04 637	586	537	487	439	390	343	295	249	203	51 - 46
10.0	157										

See "Tables of Sine, Cosine and Exponential Integrals," vols. I and II, 1940, and "Table of Sine and Cosine Integrals," 1942, A. N. Lowan, Technical Director, Work Projects Administration for the City of New York, sponsored by the National Bureau of Standards, Washington, D.C.

r	$_1C_r$	r	$_2C_r$	r	$_3C_r$	r	$_4C_r$	r	$_5C_r$	r	$_6C_r$
0,1	1	0,2	1	0,3	1	0,4	1	0,5	1	0,6	1
		1	2	1,2	3	1,3	4	1,4	5	1,5	6
						2	6	2,3	10	2,4	15
										3	20

r	$_7C_r$	r	$_8C_r$	r	$_9C_r$	r	$_{10}C_r$	r	$_{11}C_r$
0,7	1	0,8	1	0,9	1	0,10	1	0,11	1
1,6	7	1,7	8	1,8	9	1, 9	10	1,10	11
2,5	21	2,6	28	2,7	36	2, 8	45	2, 9	55
3,4	35	3,5	56	3,6	84	3, 7	120	3, 8	165
		4	70	4,5	126	4, 6	210	4, 7	330
						5	252	5, 6	462

r	$_{12}C_r$	r	$_{13}C_r$	r	$_{14}C_r$	r	$_{15}C_r$	r	$_{16}C_r$
0,12	1	0,13	1	0,14	1	0,15	1	0,16	1
1,11	12	1,12	13	1,13	14	1,14	15	1,15	16
2,10	66	2,11	78	2,12	91	2,13	105	2,14	120
3, 9	220	3,10	286	3,11	364	3,12	455	3,13	560
4, 8	495	4, 9	715	4,10	1001	4,11	1365	4,12	1820
5, 7	792	5, 8	1287	5, 9	2002	5,10	3003	5,11	4368
6	924	6, 7	1716	6, 8	3003	6, 9	5005	6,10	8008
				7	3432	7, 8	6435	7, 9	11440
								8	12870

r	$_{17}C_r$	r	$_{18}C_r$	r	$_{19}C_r$	r	$_{20}C_r$
0,17	1	0,18	1	0,19	1	0,20	1
1,16	17	1,17	18	1,18	19	1,19	20
2,15	136	2,16	153	2,17	171	2,18	190
3,14	680	3,15	816	3,16	969	3,17	1 140
4,13	2 380	4,14	3 060	4,15	3 876	4,16	4 845
5,12	6 188	5,13	8 568	5,14	11 628	5,15	15 504
6,11	12 376	6,12	18 564	6,13	27 132	6,14	38 760
7,10	19 448	7,11	31 824	7,12	50 388	7,13	77 520
8, 9	24 310	8,10	43 758	8,11	75 582	8,12	125 970
		9	48 620	9,10	92 378	9,11	167 960
						10	184 756

r	$_{21}C_r$	r	$_{22}C_r$	r	$_{23}C_r$
0,21	1	0,22	1	0,23	1
1,20	21	1,21	22	1,22	23
2,19	210	2,20	231	2,21	253
3,18	1 330	3,19	1 540	3,20	1 771
4,17	5 985	4,18	7 315	4,19	8 855
5,16	20 349	5,17	26 334	5,18	33 649
6,15	54 264	6,16	74 613	6,17	100 947
7,14	116 280	7,15	170 544	7,16	245 157
8,13	203 490	8,14	319 770	8,15	490 314
9,12	293 930	9,13	497 420	9,14	817 190
10,11	352 716	10,12	646 646	10,13	1 144 066
		11	705 432	11,12	1 352 078

r	$_{24}C_r$	r	$_{25}C_r$
0,24	1	0,25	1
1,23	24	1,24	25
2,22	276	2,23	300
3,21	2 024	3,22	2 300
4,20	10 626	4,21	12 650
5,19	42 504	5,20	53 130
6,18	134 596	6,19	177 100
7,17	346 104	7,18	480 700
8,16	735 471	8,17	1 081 575
9,15	1 307 504	9,16	2 042 975
10,14	1 961 256	10,15	3 268 760.
11,13	2 496 144	11,14	4 457 400
12	2 704 156	12,13	5 200 300

Note that

$$_nC_r = \frac{n!}{(n-r)!\ r!}$$

where

$$n! = n(n-1)(n-2)\ldots.1$$

$$0! = 1$$

For a large table, see "Zehnstellige Logarithmen der Zahlen von 1 bis 100 000", by J. Peters and J. Stein, 1922, vol. 1, second section, p. 69.

$$\frac{(a^2 + b^2)^{1/2}}{a}$$

$\frac{b}{a}$	0	1	2	3	4	5	6	7	8	9	Diff.
.00	1.0 000	000	000	000	000	000	000	000	000	000	
.01	000	001	001	001	001	001	001	001	002	002	
.02	002	002	002	003	003	003	003	004	004	004	
.03	004	005	005	005	006	006	006	007	007	008	
.04	008	008	009	009	010	010	011	011	012	012	
.05	012	013	014	014	015	015	016	016	017	017	
.06	018	019	019	020	020	021	022	022	023	024	
.07	024	025	026	027	027	028	029	030	030	031	
.08	032	033	034	034	035	036	037	038	039	040	
.09	040	041	042	043	044	045	046	047	048	049	1
.10	1.0 050	051	052	053	054	055	056	057	058	059	
.11	060	061	063	064	065	066	067	068	069	071	
.12	072	073	074	075	077	078	079	080	082	083	
.13	084	085	087	088	089	091	092	093	095	096	
.14	098	099	100	102	103	105	106	107	109	110	
.15	112	113	115	116	118	119	121	122	124	126	
.16	127	129	130	132	134	135	137	138	140	142	
.17	143	145	147	149	150	152	154	155	157	159	
.18	161	162	164	166	168	170	172	173	175	177	
.19	179	181	183	185	186	188	190	192	194	196	
.20	1.0 198	200	202	204	206	208	210	212	214	216	2
.21	218	220	222	224	226	229	231	233	235	237	
.22	239	241	243	246	248	250	252	254	257	259	
.23	261	263	266	268	270	272	275	277	279	282	
.24	284	286	289	291	293	296	298	301	303	305	
.25	308	310	313	315	318	320	322	325	327	330	
.26	332	335	338	340	343	345	348	350	353	355	
.27	358	361	363	366	369	371	374	377	379	382	
.28	385	387	390	393	395	398	401	404	406	409	
.29	412	415	418	420	423	426	429	432	435	437	
.30	1.0 440	443	446	449	452	455	458	461	464	467	3
.31	469	472	475	478	481	484	487	490	493	496	
.32	500	503	506	509	512	515	518	521	524	527	
.33	530	534	537	540	543	546	549	553	556	559	
.34	562	565	569	572	575	578	582	585	588	592	
.35	595	598	601	605	608	611	615	618	622	625	
.36	628	632	635	638	642	645	649	652	656	659	
.37	663	666	670	673	676	680	684	687	691	694	
.38	698	701	705	708	712	716	719	723	726	730	
.39	734	737	741	745	748	752	756	759	763	767	
.40	1.0 770	774	778	782	785	789	793	797	800	804	
.41	808	812	815	819	823	827	831	835	838	842	
.42	846	850	854	858	862	866	870	873	877	881	
.43	885	889	893	897	901	905	909	913	917	921	4
.44	925	929	933	937	941	945	950	954	958	962	
.45	966	970	974	978	982	986	991	995	999	003	
.46	1.1 007	011	016	020	024	028	032	037	041	045	
.47	049	054	058	062	067	071	075	079	084	088	
.48	092	097	101	105	110	114	118	123	127	132	
.49	136	140	145	149	154	158	163	167	171	176	

$$\frac{(a^2 + b^2)^{1/2}}{a}$$

b/a	0	1	2	3	4	5	6	7	8	9	Diff.
.50	1.1 180	185	189	194	198	203	207	212	216	221	
.51	225	230	235	239	244	248	253	257	262	267	
.52	271	276	280	285	290	294	299	304	308	313	
.53	318	322	327	332	336	341	346	351	355	360	
.54	365	370	374	379	384	389	393	398	403	408	
.55	413	418	422	427	432	437	442	447	451	456	
.56	461	466	471	476	481	486	491	496	501	505	
.57	510	515	520	525	530	535	540	545	550	555	5
.58	560	565	570	575	580	585	590	596	601	606	
.59	611	616	621	626	631	636	641	646	652	657	
.60	662	667	672	677	683	688	693	698	703	708	
.61	714	719	724	729	735	740	745	750	756	761	
.62	766	771	777	782	787	792	798	803	808	814	
.63	819	824	830	835	840	846	851	857	862	867	
.64	873	878	883	889	894	900	905	911	916	921	
.65	927	932	938	943	949	954	960	965	971	976	
.66	982	987	993	998	004	009	015	020	026	031	
.67	1.2 037	043	048	054	059	065	071	076	082	087	
.68	093	099	104	110	116	121	127	132	138	144	
.69	149	155	161	167	172	178	184	189	195	201	
.70	207	212	218	224	230	235	241	247	253	258	
.71	264	270	276	282	287	293	299	305	311	316	
.72	322	328	334	340	346	352	357	363	369	375	
.73	381	387	393	399	405	411	417	422	428	434	
.74	440	446	452	458	464	470	476	482	488	494	
.75	500	506	512	518	524	530	536	542	548	554	6
.76	560	566	572	578	584	591	597	603	609	615	
.77	621	627	633	639	645	652	658	664	670	676	
.78	682	688	695	701	707	713	719	725	732	738	
.79	744	750	756	763	769	775	781	788	794	800	
.80	806	812	819	825	831	838	844	850	856	863	
.81	869	875	882	888	894	900	907	913	919	926	
.82	932	938	945	951	958	964	970	977	983	989	
.83	996	002	009	015	021	028	034	041	047	053	
.84	1.3 060	066	073	079	086	092	099	105	111	118	
.85	124	131	137	144	150	157	163	170	176	183	
.86	189	196	202	209	216	222	229	235	242	248	
.87	255	261	268	275	281	288	294	301	307	314	
.88	321	327	334	340	347	354	360	367	374	380	
.89	387	394	400	407	414	420	427	434	440	447	
.90	454	460	467	474	480	487	494	501	507	514	
.91	521	527	534	541	548	554	561	568	575	581	
.92	588	595	602	609	615	622	629	636	643	649	
.93	656	663	670	677	683	690	697	704	711	718	
.94	724	731	738	745	752	759	766	772	779	786	
.95	793	800	807	814	821	828	835	841	848	855	7
.96	862	869	876	883	890	897	904	911	918	925	
.97	932	939	946	953	959	966	973	980	987	994	
.98	1.4 001	008	015	022	029	036	043	051	058	065	
.99	072	079	086	093	100	107	114	121	128	135	
1.00	142										

See "Tables for Converting Rectangular to Polar Co-ordinates"
by J. C. P. Miller, published by Scientific Computing Service Ltd.,
23 Bedford Square, London, W. C. 1.

n! = n(n-1)(n-2)....1

n		log$_{10}$(n!)
50		64.483 0749

n	n!	log$_{10}$(n!)
1	1	0
2	2	.301 0300
3	6	.778 1513
4	24	1.380 2112
5	120	2.079 1812
6	720	2.857 3325
7	5 040	3.702 4305
8	40 320	4.605 5205
9	362 880	5.559 7630
10	3 628 800	6.559 7630
11	3.991 680 x 10^7	7.601 1557
12	4.790 016 x 10^8	8.680 3370
13	6.227 021 x 10^9	9.794 2803
14	8.717 829 x 10^{10}	10.940 4084
15	1.307 674 x 10^{12}	12.116 4996
16	2.092 279 x 10^{13}	13.320 6196
17	3.556 874 x 10^{14}	14.551 0685
18	6.402 374 x 10^{15}	15.806 3410
19	1.216 451 x 10^{17}	17.085 0946
20	2.432 902 x 10^{18}	18.386 1246
21	5.109 094 x 10^{19}	19.708 3439
22	1.124 001 x 10^{21}	21.050 7666
23	2.585 202 x 10^{22}	22.412 4944
24	6.204 484 x 10^{23}	23.792 7057
25	1.551 121 x 10^{25}	25.190 6457
26	4.032 915 x 10^{26}	26.605 6190
27	1.088 887 x 10^{28}	28.036 9828
28	3.048 883 x 10^{29}	29.484 1408
29	8.841 762 x 10^{30}	30.946 5388
30	2.652 529 x 10^{32}	32.423 6601
31	8.222 839 x 10^{33}	33.915 0218
32	2.631 308 x 10^{35}	35.420 1717
33	8.683 318 x 10^{36}	36.938 6857
34	2.952 328 x 10^{38}	38.470 1646
35	1.033 315 x 10^{40}	40.014 2326
36	3.719 933 x 10^{41}	41.570 5351
37	1.376 375 x 10^{43}	43.138 7369
38	5.230 226 x 10^{44}	44.718 5205
39	2.039 788 x 10^{46}	46.309 5851
40	8.159 153 x 10^{47}	47.911 6451
41	3.345 253 x 10^{49}	49.524 4289
42	1.405 006 x 10^{51}	51.147 6782
43	6.041 526 x 10^{52}	52.781 1467
44	2.658 272 x 10^{54}	54.424 5993
45	1.196 222 x 10^{56}	56.077 8119
46	5.502 622 x 10^{57}	57.740 5697
47	2.586 232 x 10^{59}	59.412 6676
48	1.241 392 x 10^{61}	61.093 9088
49	6.082 819 x 10^{62}	62.784 1049
50	3.041 409 x 10^{64}	64.483 0749

n	log$_{10}$(n!)
50	64.483 0749
51	66.190 6450
52	67.906 6484
53	69.630 9243
54	71.363 3180
55	73.103 6807
56	74.851 8687
57	76.607 7436
58	78.371 1716
59	80.142 0236
60	81.920 1748
61	83.705 5047
62	85.497 8964
63	87.297 2369
64	89.103 4169
65	90.916 3303
66	92.735 8742
67	94.561 9490
68	96.394 4579
69	98.233 3070
70	100.078 4050
71	101.929 6634
72	103.786 9959
73	105.650 3187
74	107.519 5505
75	109.394 6117
76	111.275 4253
77	113.161 9160
78	115.054 0106
79	116.951 6377
80	118.854 7277
81	120.763 2127
82	122.677 0266
83	124.596 1047
84	126.520 3840
85	128.449 8029
86	130.384 3013
87	132.323 8206
88	134.268 3033
89	136.217 6933
90	138.171 9358
91	140.130 9772
92	142.094 7650
93	144.063 2480
94	146.036 3758
95	148.014 0994
96	149.996 3707
97	151.983 1424
98	153.974 3685
99	155.970 0037

n	$\log_{10}(n!)$	n	$\log_{10}(n!)$	n	$\log_{10}(n!)$
100	157.970 0037	150	262.756 8934	200	374.896 8886
101	159.974 3250	151	264.935 8704	201	377.200 0847
102	161.982 9252	152	267.117 7139	202	379.505 4361
103	163.995 7624	153	269.302 4054	203	381.812 9321
104	166.012 7958	154	271.489 9261	204	384.122 5623
105	168.033 9851	155	273.680 2578	205	386.434 3161
106	170.059 2909	156	275.873 3824	206	388.748 1834
107	172.088 6747	157	278.069 2820	207	391.064 1537
108	174.122 0985	158	280.267 9391	208	393.382 2170
109	176.159 5250	159	282.469 3363	209	395.702 3633
110	178.200 9176	160	284.673 4562	210	398.024 5826
111	180.246 2406	161	286.880 2821	211	400.348 8651
112	182.295 4586	162	289.089 7971	212	402.675 2009
113	184.348 5371	163	291.301 9847	213	405.003 5805
114	186.405 4419	164	293.516 8286	214	407.333 9943
115	188.466 1398	165	295.734 3125	215	409.666 4328
116	190.530 5978	166	297.954 4206	216	412.000 8865
117	192.598 7836	167	300.177 1371	217	414.337 3463
118	194.670 6656	168	302.402 4464	218	416.675 8027
119	196.746 2126	169	304.630 3331	219	419.016 2469
120	198.825 3938	170	306.860 7820	220	421.358 6695
121	200.908 1792	171	309.093 7781	221	423.703 0618
122	202.994 5390	172	311.329 3066	222	426.049 4148
123	205.084 4442	173	313.567 3527	223	428.397 7197
124	207.177 8658	174	315.807 9019	224	430.747 9677
125	209.274 7759	175	318.050 9400	225	433.100 1502
126	211.375 1464	176	320.296 4526	226	435.454 2586
127	213.478 9501	177	322.544 4259	227	437.810 2845
128	215.586 1601	178	324.794 8459	228	440.168 2193
129	217.696 7498	179	327.047 6989	229	442.528 0548
130	219.810 6932	180	329.302 9714	230	444.889 7827
131	221.927 9645	181	331.560 6500	231	447.253 3946
132	224.048 5384	182	333.820 7214	232	449.618 8826
133	226.172 3900	183	336.083 1725	233	451.986 2385
134	228.299 4948	184	338.347 9903	234	454.355 4544
135	230.429 8286	185	340.615 1620	235	456.726 5223
136	232.563 3675	186	342.884 6750	236	459.099 4343
137	234.700 0881	187	345.156 5166	237	461.474 1826
138	236.839 9672	188	347.430 6744	238	463.850 7596
139	238.982 9820	189	349.707 1362	239	466.229 1575
140	241.129 1100	190	351.985 8898	240	468.609 3687
141	243.278 3291	191	354.266 9232	241	470.991 3857
142	245.430 6174	192	356.550 2244	242	473.375 2011
143	247.585 9535	193	358.835 7817	243	475.760 8074
144	249.744 3160	194	361.123 5835	244	478.148 1972
145	251.905 6840	195	363.413 6181	245	480.537 3633
146	254.070 0368	196	365.705 8742	246	482.928 2984
147	256.237 3542	197	368.000 3404	247	485.320 9954
148	258.407 6159	198	370.297 0056	248	487.715 4470
149	260.580 8022	199	372.595 8586	249	490.111 6464
				250	492.509 5864

For a large table, see "Zehnstellige Logarithmen der Zahlen von 1 bis 100 000", by J. Peters and J. Stein, 1922, vol. 1, second section, p. 58 - 68.

p	$p^C{}_2$ (exact)	$p^C{}_3$ (exact)	$p^C{}_4$	$p^C{}_5$	$p^C{}_6$
0	0	0	0	0	0
.01	-.004 95	.003 2835	-.002 4544	.001 9586	-.001 6289
.02	-.009 8	.006 468	-.004 8187	.003 8357	-.003 1836
.03	-.014 55	.009 5545	-.007 0942	.005 6328	-.004 6658
.04	-.019 2	.012 544	-.009 2826	.007 3518	-.006 0775
.05	-.023 75	.015 4375	-.011 3852	.008 9943	-.007 4203
.06	-.028 2	.018 236	-.013 4035	.010 5619	-.008 6960
.07	-.032 55	.020 9405	-.015 3389	.012 0564	-.009 9063
.08	-.036 8	.023 552	-.017 1930	.013 4793	-.011 0530
.09	-.040 95	.026 0715	-.018 9670	.014 8322	-.012 1377
.10	-.045	.028 5	-.020 6625	.016 1167	-.013 1620
.11	-.048 95	.030 8385	-.022 2808	.017 3345	-.014 1276
.12	-.052 8	.033 088	-.023 8234	.018 4869	-.015 0360
.13	-.056 55	.035 2495	-.025 2915	.019 5756	-.015 8889
.14	-.060 2	.037 324	-.026 6867	.020 6021	-.016 6877
.15	-.063 75	.039 3125	-.028 0102	.021 5678	-.017 4340
.16	-.067 2	.041 216	-.029 2634	.022 4743	-.018 1292
.17	-.070 55	.043 0355	-.030 4476	.023 3229	-.018 7749
.18	-.073 8	.044 772	-.031 5643	.024 1151	-.019 3725
.19	-.076 95	.046 4265	-.032 6146	.024 8523	-.019 9233
.20	-.08	.048	-.033 6	.025 536	-.020 4288
.21	-.082 95	.049 4935	-.034 5217	.026 1675	-.020 8904
.22	-.085 8	.050 908	-.035 3811	.026 7481	-.021 3093
.23	-.088 55	.052 2445	-.036 1793	.027 2792	-.021 6870
.24	-.091 2	.053 504	-.036 9178	.027 7622	-.022 0246
.25	-.093 75	.054 6875	-.037 5977	.028 1982	-.022 3236
.26	-.096 2	.055 796	-.038 2203	.028 5888	-.022 5851
.27	-.098 55	.056 8305	-.038 7868	.028 9350	-.022 8104
.28	-.100 8	.057 792	-.039 2986	.029 2381	-.023 0007
.29	-.102 95	.058 6815	-.039 7567	.029 4995	-.023 1571
.30	-.105	.059 5	-.040 1625	.029 7202	-.023 2809
.31	-.106 95	.060 2485	-.040 5171	.029 9016	-.023 3731
.32	-.108 8	.060 928	-.040 8218	.030 0448	-.023 4350
.33	-.110 55	.061 5395	-.041 0776	.030 1510	-.023 4675
.34	-.112 2	.062 084	-.041 2859	.030 2212	-.023 4718
.35	-.113 75	.062 5625	-.041 4477	.030 2568	-.023 4490
.36	-.115 2	.062 976	-.041 5642	.030 2587	-.023 4001
.37	-.116 55	.063 3255	-.041 6365	.030 2281	-.023 3260
.38	-.117 8	.063 612	-.041 6659	.030 1661	-.023 2279
.39	-.118 95	.063 8365	-.041 6533	.030 0737	-.023 1066
.40	-.12	.064	-.041 6	.029 952	-.022 9632
.41	-.120 95	.064 1035	-.041 5070	.029 8020	-.022 7986
.42	-.121 8	.064 148	-.041 3755	.029 6248	-.022 6136
.43	-.122 55	.064 1345	-.041 2064	.029 4214	-.022 4093
.44	-.123 2	.064 064	-.041 0010	.029 1927	-.022 1864
.45	-.123 75	.063 9375	-.040 7602	.028 9397	-.021 9459
.46	-.124 2	.063 756	-.040 4851	.028 6634	-.021 6887
.47	-.124 55	.063 5205	-.040 1767	.028 3648	-.021 4154
.48	-.124 8	.063 232	-.039 8362	.028 0447	-.021 1270
.49	-.124 95	.062 8915	-.039 4644	.027 7040	-.020 8242

$$p^C{}_r = \frac{p(p-1)(p-2)\ldots(p-r+1)}{r(r-1)(r-2)\ldots 1}$$

where p is a decimal number < 1 and r is an integer.

p	pC_2	pC_3	pC_4	pC_5	pC_6
	(exact)	(exact)			
.50	-.125	.062 5	-.039 0625	.027 3437	-.020 5078
.51	-.124 95	.062 0585	-.038 6314	.026 9647	-.020 1786
.52	-.124 8	.061 568	-.038 1722	.026 5678	-.019 8373
.53	-.124 55	.061 0295	-.037 6857	.026 1539	-.019 4846
.54	-.124 2	.060 444	-.037 1731	.025 7238	-.019 1213
.55	-.123 75	.059 8125	-.036 6352	.025 2783	-.018 7480
.56	-.123 2	.059 136	-.036 0730	.024 8182	-.018 3655
.57	-.122 55	.058 4155	-.035 4874	.024 3444	-.017 9743
.58	-.121 8	.057 652	-.034 8795	.023 8576	-.017 5751
.59	-.120 95	.056 8465	-.034 2500	.023 3585	-.017 1685
.60	-.12	.056	-.033 6	.022 848	-.016 7552
.61	-.118 95	.055 1135	-.032 9303	.022 3268	-.016 3357
.62	-.117 8	.054 188	-.032 2419	.021 7955	-.015 9107
.63	-.116 55	.053 2245	-.031 5355	.021 2549	-.015 4807
.64	-.115 2	.052 224	-.030 8122	.020 7058	-.015 0462
.65	-.113 75	.051 1875	-.030 0727	.020 1487	-.014 6078
.66	-.112 2	.050 116	-.029 3179	.019 5843	-.014 1660
.67	-.110 55	.049 0105	-.028 5486	.019 0134	-.013 7213
.68	-.108 8	.047 872	-.027 7658	.018 4365	-.013 2743
.69	-.106 95	.046 7015	-.026 9701	.017 8542	-.012 8253
.70	-.105	.045 5	-.026 1625	.017 2672	-.012 3749
.71	-.102 95	.044 2685	-.025 3437	.016 6762	-.011 9235
.72	-.100 8	.043 008	-.024 5146	.016 0816	-.011 4715
.73	-.098 55	.041 7195	-.023 6758	.015 4840	-.011 0194
.74	-.096 2	.040 404	-.022 8283	.014 8840	-.010 5677
.75	-.093 75	.039 0625	-.021 9727	.014 2822	-.010 1166
.76	-.091 2	.037 696	-.021 1098	.013 6791	-.009 6666
.77	-.088 55	.036 3055	-.020 2403	.013 0752	-.009 2180
.78	-.085 8	.034 892	-.019 3651	.012 4711	-.008 7713
.79	-.082 95	.033 4565	-.018 4847	.011 8672	-.008 3268
.80	-.08	.032	-.017 6	.011 264	-.007 8848
.81	-.076 95	.030 5235	-.016 7116	.010 6620	-.007 4456
.82	-.073 8	.029 028	-.015 8203	.010 0617	-.007 0096
.83	-.070 55	.027 5145	-.014 9266	.009 4635	-.006 5771
.84	-.067 2	.025 984	-.014 0314	.008 8678	-.006 1484
.85	-.063 75	.024 4375	-.013 1352	.008 2751	-.005 7236
.86	-.060 2	.022 876	-.012 2387	.007 6859	-.005 3033
.87	-.056 55	.021 3005	-.011 3425	.007 1004	-.004 8875
.88	-.052 8	.019 712	-.010 4474	.006 5192	-.004 4765
.89	-.048 95	.018 1115	-.009 5538	.005 9425	-.004 0706
.90	-.045	.016 5	-.008 6625	.005 3707	-.003 6700
.91	-.040 95	.014 8785	-.007 7740	.004 8043	-.003 2750
.92	-.036 8	.013 248	-.006 8890	.004 2436	-.002 8856
.93	-.032 55	.011 6095	-.006 0079	.003 6889	-.002 5023
.94	-.028 2	.009 964	-.005 1315	.003 1405	-.002 1250
.95	-.023 75	.008 3125	-.004 2602	.002 5987	-.001 7541
.96	-.019 2	.006 656	-.003 3946	.002 0639	-.001 3897
.97	-.014 55	.004 9955	-.002 5352	.001 5363	-.001 0319
.98	-.009 8	.003 332	-.001 6827	.001 0163	-.000 6809
.99	-.004 95	.001 6665	-.000 8374	.000 5041	-.000 3369
1.00	0	0	0	0	0

For a large table, with columns of differences, see "Tables of the Higher Mathematical Functions", by H. T. Davis, The Principia Press, Bloomington, Indiana, vol. 1, pages 102 - 109.

LAGRANGIAN INTERPOLATION COEFFICIENTS

for interpolating without columns of differences.

Interpolation using Three Tabulated Values.

Let three successive tabulated values at equal intervals h of the argument be

$$f(-h) \ , \quad f(0) \quad \text{and} \quad f(h)$$

then

$$f(ph) = K_{-1} \, f(-h) + K_0 \, f(0) + K_1 \, f(h)$$

where K_n is taken from the following table:

p	K_{-1}	K_0	K_1	
.1	-.045	.990	.055	-.1
.2	-.080	.960	.120	-.2
.3	-.105	.910	.195	-.3
.4	-.120	.840	.280	-.4
.5	-.125	.750	.375	-.5
.6	-.120	.640	.480	-.6
.7	-.105	.510	.595	-.7
.8	-.080	.360	.720	-.8
.9	-.045	.190	.855	-.9
	K_1	K_0	K_{-1}	p

By using the letters at the bottom of the table, p may have negative values less than 1, and by choosing appropriate values of $f(0)$, the same interpolated value of the function may be obtained by two different calculations, which may be used to check each other, one from a positive value of p and the other from a negative value of p. The number of figures in these two solutions which agree gives an approximate estimate of the number of figures which are correct. The computation of an interpolated value of $f(x)$ is one continuous operation with a modern computing machine.

Interpolation using Five Tabulated Values.

Let five successive tabulated values at equal intervals h of the argument be

$$f(-2h) \ , \quad f(-h) \ , \quad f(0) \ , \quad f(h) \quad \text{and} \quad f(2h)$$

then

$$f(ph) = K_{-2} \, f(-2h) + K_{-1} \, f(-h) + K_0 \, f(0) + K_1 \, f(h) + K_2 \, f(2h)$$

where K_n is taken from the following table:

p	K_{-2}	K_{-1}	K_0	K_1	K_2	
.1	.0078375	-.0598500	.9875250	.0731500	-.0086625	-.1
.2	.0144000	-.1056000	.9504000	.1584000	-.0176000	-.2
.3	.0193375	-.1368500	.8895250	.2541500	-.0261625	-.3
.4	.0224000	-.1536000	.8064000	.3584000	-.0336000	-.4
.5	.0234375	-.1562500	.7031250	.4687500	-.0390625	-.5
.6	.0224000	-.1456000	.5824000	.5824000	-.0416000	-.6
.7	.0193375	-.1228500	.4475250	.6961500	-.0401625	-.7
.8	.0144000	-.0896000	.3024000	.8064000	-.0336000	-.8
.9	.0078375	-.0478500	.1515250	.9091500	-.0206625	-.9
	K_2	K_1	K_0	K_{-1}	K_{-2}	p

The coefficients in this table are complete in 7 decimal places or less, as given.

LAGRANGIAN INTERPOLATION COEFFICIENTS

for interpolating without columns of differences.

Interpolation using Seven Tabulated Values.

Let seven successive tabulated values at equal intervals h of the argument be

$$f(-3h) , \quad f(-2h) , \quad f(-h) , \quad f(0) , \quad f(h) , \quad f(2h) \quad \text{and} \quad f(3h)$$

then
$$f(ph) = K_{-3} f(-3h) + K_{-2} f(-2h) + K_{-1} f(-h) + K_0 f(0)$$
$$+ K_1 f(h) + K_2 f(2h) + K_3 f(3h)$$

where K_n is taken from the following table:

p	K_{-3}	K_{-2}	K_{-1}	K_0	K_1	K_2	K_3	
.1	−.0015910	.0140918	−.0672564	.9864277	.0822023	−.0155752	.0017007	−.1
.2	−.0029568	.0258048	−.1182720	.9461760	.1774080	−.0315392	.0033792	−.2
.3	−.0040029	.0344594	−.1524167	.8806297	.2830596	−.0466216	.0048924	−.3
.4	−.0046592	.0396032	−.1697280	.7920640	.3960320	−.0594048	.0060928	−.4
.5	−.0048828	.0410156	−.1708984	.6835937	.5126953	−.0683594	.0068359	−.5
.6	−.0046592	.0387072	−.1572480	.5591040	.6289920	−.0718848	.0069888	−.6
.7	−.0040029	.0329124	−.1306817	.4231597	.7405296	−.0683566	.0064394	−.7
.8	−.0029568	.0240768	−.0936320	.2808960	.8426880	−.0561792	.0051072	−.8
.9	−.0015910	.0128378	−.0489864	.1378877	.9307423	−.0338452	.0029547	−.9
	K_3	K_2	K_1	K_0	K_{-1}	K_{-2}	K_{-3}	p

Most of the coefficients in the third table require 10 decimal places to be complete. See "Tables and Methods of Extending Tables for Interpolation without Differences", by Geo. Rutledge and Prescott Crout, Jour. of Math. and Phys., v. 9, 1930, p. 166.

If any seven tabulated values of the function $y = f(x)$, just described, are known, at equal intervals h of the argument, the first derivative dy/dx where $x = 0$, that is, at the middle one of the seven values, may be obtained by the following expression given by Professor R. D. Douglass and A. S. Avakian:

$$\frac{dy}{dx} = \frac{397}{1512} \frac{\sum ky}{h} - \frac{7}{216} \frac{\sum k^3 y}{h}$$

where k is the coefficient of h in the parentheses giving the values of x, that is, k has the values $-3, -2, -1, 0, 1, 2$ and 3, and where h is the constant interval between the values of x.

See "Applied Mathematics in Chemical Engineering" by T. K. Sherwood and C. E. Reed, 1939, page 287, eq. (38).

SURFACE ZONAL HARMONICS

$$P_n(x) = \frac{1}{2^n \, n!} \frac{d^n}{dx^n} (x^2 - 1)^n$$

x	$P_1(x)$	$P_2(x)$	$P_3(x)$	$P_4(x)$	$P_5(x)$
0	0	-.5	0	.375	0
.01	.01	-.49985	-.0149975	.37463	.018741
.02	.02	-.4994	-.02998	.37350	.037430
.03	.03	-.49865	-.0449325	.37163	.056014
.04	.04	-.4976	-.05984	.36901	.074441
.05	.05	-.49625	-.0746875	.36565	.092659
.06	.06	-.4946	-.08946	.36156	.11062
.07	.07	-.49265	-.10414	.35673	.12826
.08	.08	-.4904	-.11872	.35118	.14555
.09	.09	-.48785	-.13318	.34491	.16242
.10	.10	-.485	-.1475	.33794	.17883
.11	.11	-.48185	-.16167	.33027	.19473
.12	.12	-.4784	-.17568	.32191	.21008
.13	.13	-.47465	-.18951	.31287	.22482
.14	.14	-.4706	-.20314	.30318	.23891
.15	.15	-.46625	-.21656	.29284	.25232
.16	.16	-.4616	-.22976	.28187	.26499
.17	.17	-.45665	-.24272	.27028	.27688
.18	.18	-.4514	-.25542	.25809	.28796
.19	.19	-.44585	-.26785	.24533	.29818
.20	.20	-.44	-.28	.232	.30752
.21	.21	-.43385	-.29185	.21813	.31593
.22	.22	-.4274	-.30338	.20375	.32339
.23	.23	-.42065	-.31458	.18887	.32986
.24	.24	-.4136	-.32544	.17352	.33531
.25	.25	-.40625	-.33594	.15771	.33972
.26	.26	-.3986	-.34606	.14149	.34307
.27	.27	-.39065	-.35579	.12488	.34532
.28	.28	-.3824	-.36512	.10789	.34647
.29	.29	-.37385	-.37403	.09057	.34650
.30	.30	-.365	-.3825	.07294	.34539
.31	.31	-.35585	-.39052	.05503	.34312
.32	.32	-.3464	-.39808	.03688	.33970
.33	.33	-.33665	-.40516	.01851	.33512
.34	.34	-.3266	-.41174	-.00004	.32937
.35	.35	-.31625	-.41781	-.01872	.32245
.36	.36	-.3056	-.42336	-.03752	.31438
.37	.37	-.29465	-.42837	-.05638	.30514
.38	.38	-.2834	-.43282	-.07528	.29477
.39	.39	-.27185	-.43670	-.09416	.28326
.40	.40	-.26	-.44	-.113	.27064
.41	.41	-.24785	-.44270	-.13175	.25693
.42	.42	-.2354	-.44478	-.15036	.24215
.43	.43	-.22265	-.44623	-.16880	.22633
.44	.44	-.2096	-.44704	-.18702	.20951
.45	.45	-.19625	-.44719	-.20497	.19172
.46	.46	-.1826	-.44666	-.22261	.17301
.47	.47	-.16865	-.44544	-.23989	.15341
.48	.48	-.1544	-.44352	-.25676	.13298
.49	.49	-.13985	-.44088	-.27316	.11177

SURFACE ZONAL HARMONICS

x	$P_6(x)$	$P_7(x)$	$P_8(x)$	$P_9(x)$	$P_{10}(x)$	$P_{11}(x)$
0	-.3125	0	.27344	0	-.2461	0
.01	-.31184	-.02186	.27245	.0246	-.2447	-.0270
.02	-.30988	-.04359	.26951	.0489	-.2407	-.0537
.03	-.30661	-.06509	.26462	.0729	-.2340	-.0796
.04	-.30205	-.08624	.25783	.0961	-.2247	-.1046
.05	-.29622	-.10693	.24917	.1186	-.2130	-.1281
.06	-.28913	-.12703	.23870	.1400	-.1989	-.1500
.07	-.28081	-.14644	.22649	.1601	-.1825	-.1700
.08	-.27130	-.16506	.21263	.1789	-.1642	-.1877
.09	-.26063	-.18278	.19721	.1960	-.1440	-.2029
.10	-.24883	-.19949	.18032	.2114	-.1221	-.2155
.11	-.23595	-.21511	.16209	.2249	-.0989	-.2252
.12	-.22204	-.22955	.14264	.2364	-.0745	-.2319
.13	-.20715	-.24271	.12209	.2457	-.0492	-.2356
.14	-.19133	-.25453	.10060	.2529	-.0233	-.2361
.15	-.17465	-.26492	.07831	.2577	.0030	-.2334
.16	-.15716	-.27383	.05537	.2601	.0293	-.2276
.17	-.13894	-.28119	.03194	.2602	.0553	-.2186
.18	-.12005	-.28695	.00820	.2579	.0808	-.2066
.19	-.10057	-.29107	-.01569	.2531	.1055	-.1918
.20	-.08058	-.29352	-.03956	.2460	.1291	-.1743
.21	-.06014	-.29426	-.06324	.2365	.1513	-.1543
.22	-.03936	-.29327	-.08654	.2247	.1718	-.1321
.23	-.01830	-.29055	-.10929	.2108	.1905	-.1080
.24	.00294	-.28610	-.13132	.1948	.2070	-.0822
.25	.02428	-.27992	-.15245	.1768	.2212	-.0552
.26	.04562	-.27203	-.17253	.1571	.2339	-.0272
.27	.06687	-.26246	-.19138	.1357	.2419	.0013
.28	.08795	-.25124	-.20886	.1129	.2480	.0300
.29	.10875	-.23843	-.22480	.0888	.2512	.0584
.30	.12918	-.22407	-.23907	.0637	.2515	.0861
.31	.14915	-.20824	-.25155	.0378	.2487	.1128
.32	.16856	-.19100	-.26209	.0114	.2428	.1380
.33	.18732	-.17244	-.27061	-.0154	.2339	.1613
.34	.20534	-.15266	-.27699	-.0422	.2220	.1825
.35	.22251	-.13176	-.28116	-.0688	.2073	.2010
.36	.23875	-.10984	-.28305	-.0948	.1899	.2167
.37	.25397	-.08704	-.28261	-.1201	.1699	.2292
.38	.26808	-.06347	-.27979	-.1444	.1475	.2383
.39	.28100	-.03927	-.27459	-.1674	.1231	.2438
.40	.29264	-.01459	-.26700	-.1888	.0968	.2456
.41	.30291	.01042	-.25704	-.2083	.0690	.2434
.42	.31176	.03561	-.24474	-.2258	.0401	.2374
.43	.31909	.06082	-.23017	-.2410	.0102	.2275
.44	.32486	.08587	-.21340	-.2537	-.0200	.2138
.45	.32898	.11060	-.19454	-.2637	-.0504	.1964
.46	.33141	.13483	-.17369	-.2708	-.0803	.1756
.47	.33209	.15838	-.15101	-.2748	-.1095	.1516
.48	.33098	.18107	-.12665	-.2758	-.1375	.1247
.49	.32804	.20272	-.10079	-.2735	-.1639	.0953

SURFACE ZONAL HARMONICS

x	$P_1(x)$	$P_2(x)$	$P_3(x)$	$P_4(x)$	$P_5(x)$
.50	.50	-.125	-.4375	-.28906	.08984
.51	.51	-.10985	-.43337	-.30440	.06726
.52	.52	-.0944	-.42848	-.31912	.04409
.53	.53	-.07865	-.42281	-.33317	.02041
.54	.54	-.0626	-.41634	-.34649	-.00372
.55	.55	-.04625	-.40906	-.35904	-.02819
.56	.56	-.0296	-.40096	-.37074	-.05294
.57	.57	-.01265	-.39202	-.38155	-.07786
.58	.58	.0046	-.38222	-.39140	-.10285
.59	.59	.02215	-.37155	-.40024	-.12781
.60	.60	.04	-.36	-.408	-.15264
.61	.61	.05815	-.34755	-.41462	-.17721
.62	.62	.0766	-.33418	-.42004	-.20142
.63	.63	.09535	-.31988	-.42418	-.22512
.64	.64	.1144	-.30464	-.42700	-.24819
.65	.65	.13375	-.28844	-.42841	-.27049
.66	.66	.1534	-.27126	-.42836	-.29188
.67	.67	.17335	-.25309	-.42676	-.31220
.68	.68	.1936	-.23392	-.42356	-.33131
.69	.69	.21415	-.21373	-.41869	-.34903
.70	.70	.235	-.1925	-.41206	-.36520
.71	.71	.25615	-.17022	-.40361	-.37964
.72	.72	.2776	-.14688	-.39327	-.39217
.73	.73	.29935	-.12246	-.38095	-.40260
.74	.74	.3214	-.09694	-.36659	-.41074
.75	.75	.34375	-.07031	-.35010	-.41638
.76	.76	.3664	-.04256	-.33140	-.41931
.77	.77	.38935	-.01367	-.31043	-.41932
.78	.78	.4126	.01638	-.28709	-.41618
.79	.79	.43615	.04760	-.26131	-.40966
.80	.80	.46	.08	-.233	-.39952
.81	.81	.48415	.11360	-.20208	-.38552
.82	.82	.5086	.14842	-.16847	-.36739
.83	.83	.53335	.18447	-.13207	-.34489
.84	.84	.5584	.22176	-.09281	-.31774
.85	.85	.58375	.26031	-.05060	-.28566
.86	.86	.6094	.30014	-.00534	-.24838
.87	.87	.63535	.34126	.04305	-.20559
.88	.88	.6616	.38368	.09467	-.15699
.89	.89	.68815	.42742	.14960	-.10228
.90	.90	.715	.4725	.20794	-.04114
.91	.91	.74215	.51893	.26978	.02676
.92	.92	.7696	.56672	.33522	.10175
.93	.93	.79735	.61589	.40435	.18417
.94	.94	.8254	.66646	.47728	.27438
.95	.95	.85375	.71844	.55409	.37274
.96	.96	.8824	.77184	.63489	.47962
.97	.97	.91135	.82668	.71978	.59539
.98	.98	.9406	.88298	.80886	.72045
.99	.99	.97015	.94075	.90223	.85518
1.00	1	1	1	1	1

SURFACE ZONAL HARMONICS

x	$P_6(x)$	$P_7(x)$	$P_8(x)$	$P_9(x)$	$P_{10}(x)$	$P_{11}(x)$
.50	.32324	.22314	-.07364	-.2679	-.1882	.0639
.51	.31655	.24217	-.04541	-.2590	-.2101	.0309
.52	.30796	.25961	-.01635	-.2468	-.2291	-.0031
.53	.29747	.27530	.01330	-.2314	-.2450	-.0375
.54	.28506	.28906	.04325	-.2128	-.2573	-.0718
.55	.27077	.30074	.07321	-.1913	-.2658	-.1052
.56	.25460	.31016	.10289	-.1669	-.2701	-.1371
.57	.23660	.31719	.13197	-.1399	-.2702	-.1669
.58	.21681	.32169	.16013	-.1105	-.2659	-.1940
.59	.19528	.32353	.18703	-.0791	-.2570	-.2176
.60	.17210	.32260	.21234	-.0461	-.2437	-.2372
.61	.14733	.31880	.23572	-.0118	-.2258	-.2522
.62	.12109	.31207	.25682	.0234	-.2036	-.2622
.63	.09348	.30232	.27533	.0589	-.1773	-.2668
.64	.06462	.28954	.29091	.0943	-.1471	-.2655
.65	.03467	.27371	.30324	.1290	-.1136	-.2582
.66	.00379	.25483	.31203	.1625	-.0771	-.2448
.67	-.02785	.23295	.31701	.1941	-.0382	-.2253
.68	-.06006	.20813	.31792	.2233	.0024	-.1999
.69	-.09261	.18049	.31455	.2495	.0440	-.1688
.70	-.12529	.15016	.30670	.2721	.0858	-.1327
.71	-.15782	.11731	.29426	.2904	.1269	-.0920
.72	-.18994	.08217	.27712	.3039	.1663	-.0477
.73	-.22136	.04499	.25527	.3120	.2030	-.0007
.74	-.25175	.00609	.22873	.3143	.2361	.0477
.75	-.28078	-.03418	.19761	.3103	.2644	.0964
.76	-.30807	-.07541	.16210	.2997	.2869	.1438
.77	-.33325	-.11713	.12249	.2823	.3027	.1884
.78	-.35589	-.15881	.07914	.2578	.3108	.2285
.79	-.37557	-.19987	.03256	.2263	.3103	.2623
.80	-.39180	-.23965	-.01666	.1879	.3005	.2882
.81	-.40409	-.27743	-.06776	.1429	.2809	.3045
.82	-.41193	-.31240	-.11987	.0920	.2512	.3097
.83	-.41475	-.34368	-.17195	.0359	.2114	.3023
.84	-.41198	-.37033	-.22280	-.0243	.1617	.2814
.85	-.40300	-.39130	-.27102	-.0873	.1029	.2464
.86	-.38716	-.40545	-.31503	-.1513	.0362	.1971
.87	-.36379	-.41156	-.35304	-.2143	-.0366	.1341
.88	-.33217	-.40829	-.38304	-.2738	-.1130	.0590
.89	-.29156	-.39423	-.40276	-.3267	-.1899	-.0257
.90	-.24116	-.36782	-.40969	-.3695	-.2631	-.1162
.91	-.18018	-.32743	-.40103	-.3983	-.3277	-.2072
.92	-.10774	-.27129	-.37370	-.4083	-.3773	-.2916
.93	-.02295	-.19749	-.32430	-.3941	-.4046	-.3600
.94	.07512	-.10404	-.24910	-.3498	-.4006	-.4008
.95	.18745	.01123	-.14402	-.2684	-.3549	-.3996
.96	.31506	.15060	-.00460	-.1422	-.2552	-.3385
.97	.45899	.31650	.17402	.0375	-.0875	-.1961
.98	.62035	.51151	.39710	.2804	.1647	.0532
.99	.80029	.73838	.67037	.5972	.5201	.4400
1.00	1	1	1	1	1	1

SURFACE ZONAL HARMONICS

θ deg.	$P_1(\cos\theta)$	$P_2(\cos\theta)$	$P_3(\cos\theta)$	$P_4(\cos\theta)$	$P_5(\cos\theta)$
0	1	1	1	1	1
1	.99985	.99954	.99909	.99848	.99772
2	.99939	.99817	.99635	.99392	.99088
3	.99863	.99589	.99179	.98634	.97954
4	.99756	.99270	.98543	.97577	.96377
5	.99619	.98861	.97728	.96227	.94368
6	.99452	.98361	.96736	.94589	.91939
7	.99255	.97772	.95569	.92670	.89108
8	.99027	.97095	.94232	.90480	.85893
9	.98769	.96329	.92726	.88026	.82315
10	.98481	.95477	.91057	.85321	.78399
11	.98163	.94539	.89228	.82376	.74170
12	.97815	.93516	.87244	.79204	.69656
13	.97437	.92410	.85111	.75819	.64888
14	.97030	.91221	.82833	.72235	.59895
15	.96593	.89952	.80416	.68470	.54713
16	.96126	.88604	.77868	.64537	.49373
17	.95630	.87178	.75194	.60456	.43911
18	.95106	.85676	.72401	.56244	.38363
19	.94552	.84101	.69497	.51918	.32763
20	.93969	.82453	.66488	.47498	.27149
21	.93358	.80736	.63384	.43002	.21556
22	.92718	.78950	.60190	.38450	.16019
23	.92050	.77099	.56917	.33862	.10573
24	.91355	.75185	.53572	.29256	.05252
25	.90631	.73209	.50163	.24653	.00088
26	.89879	.71175	.46699	.20072	-.04887
27	.89101	.69084	.43190	.15531	-.09642
28	.88295	.66939	.39644	.11051	-.14151
29	.87462	.64744	.36069	.06649	-.18388
30	.86603	.62500	.32476	.02344	-.22327
31	.85717	.60210	.28873	-.01847	-.25949
32	.84805	.57878	.25269	-.05907	-.29233
33	.83867	.55505	.21673	-.09820	-.32163
34	.82904	.53095	.18094	-.13570	-.34726
35	.81915	.50652	.14542	-.17142	-.36910
36	.80902	.48176	.11025	-.20524	-.38707
37	.79864	.45673	.07551	-.23701	-.40113
38	.78801	.43144	.04129	-.26664	-.41124
39	.77715	.40593	.00769	-.29400	-.41741
40	.76604	.38024	-.02523	-.31900	-.41968
41	.75471	.35438	-.05738	-.34157	-.41811
42	.74314	.32840	-.08869	-.36163	-.41279
43	.73135	.30232	-.11907	-.37913	-.40385
44	.71934	.27617	-.14845	-.39401	-.39141
45	.70711	.25000	-.17678	-.40625	-.37565
46	.69466	.22383	-.20397	-.41582	-.35677
47	.68200	.19768	-.22997	-.42273	-.33496
48	.66913	.17160	-.25471	-.42696	-.31048
49	.65606	.14562	-.27815	-.42856	-.28357

For $P_n(\cos\theta)$, use the definition of $P_n(x)$ given on the first page of this table, and put $x = \cos\theta$.

SURFACE ZONAL HARMONICS

θ deg.	$P_6(\cos \theta)$	$P_7(\cos \theta)$	$P_8(\cos \theta)$	$P_9(\cos \theta)$	$P_{10}(\cos \theta)$	$P_{11}(\cos \theta)$
0	1	1	1	1	1	1
1	.99680	.99574	.99452	.9932	.9916	.9900
2	.98725	.98301	.97819	.9728	.9668	.9602
3	.97142	.96198	.95125	.9393	.9260	.9115
4	.94947	.93291	.91416	.8933	.8704	.8455
5	.92160	.89616	.86751	.8358	.8012	.7640
6	.88808	.85220	.81205	.7680	.7203	.6694
7	.84922	.80158	.74869	.6911	.6296	.5646
8	.80538	.74493	.67844	.6069	.5312	.4526
9	.75698	.68296	.60242	.5168	.4277	.3366
10	.70447	.61644	.52185	.4228	.3214	.2200
11	.64833	.54619	.43799	.3266	.2150	.1059
12	.58909	.47307	.35216	.2302	.1108	-.0023
13	.52729	.39798	.26571	.1353	.0113	-.1020
14	.46350	.32183	.17995	.0437	-.0813	-.1904
15	.39831	.24554	.09618	-.0428	-.1651	-.2655
16	.33229	.17001	.01567	-.1227	-.2381	-.3255
17	.26606	.09614	-.06042	-.1946	-.2992	-.3693
18	.20020	.02477	-.13100	-.2573	-.3471	-.3963
19	.13529	-.04327	-.19509	-.3100	-.3813	-.4064
20	.07190	-.10723	-.25184	-.3517	-.4013	-.4001
21	.01059	-.16640	-.30055	-.3821	-.4072	-.3785
22	-.04813	-.22017	-.34066	-.4009	-.3996	-.3430
23	-.10376	-.26800	-.37177	-.4082	-.3793	-.2955
24	-.15585	-.30942	-.39364	-.4042	-.3473	-.2383
25	-.20398	-.34408	-.40623	-.3896	-.3052	-.1740
26	-.24779	-.37172	-.40962	-.3650	-.2547	-.1052
27	-.28694	-.39216	-.40408	-.3315	-.1975	-.0346
28	-.32117	-.40534	-.39003	-.2902	-.1358	.0349
29	-.35025	-.41130	-.36803	-.2424	-.0716	.1008
30	-.37402	-.41018	-.33878	-.1896	-.0070	.1607
31	-.39238	-.40221	-.30309	-.1332	.0558	.2125
32	-.40527	-.38771	-.26188	-.0749	.1151	.2543
33	-.41269	-.36710	-.21616	-.0161	.1689	.2850
34	-.41471	-.34086	-.16697	.0415	.2157	.3036
35	-.41145	-.30956	-.11544	.0965	.2542	.3097
36	-.40307	-.27382	-.06268	.1476	.2833	.3034
37	-.38980	-.23432	-.00981	.1935	.3024	.2852
38	-.37191	-.19178	.04206	.2331	.3111	.2561
39	-.34972	-.14695	.09187	.2655	.3093	.2176
40	-.32357	-.10060	.13863	.2900	.2973	.1712
41	-.29387	-.05351	.18142	.3062	.2758	.1190
42	-.26104	-.00645	.21943	.3137	.2455	.0631
43	-.22554	.03982	.25195	.3127	.2077	.0058
44	-.18784	.08455	.27840	.3031	.1637	-.0507
45	-.14844	.12706	.29834	.2855	.1151	-.1042
46	-.10783	.16668	.31146	.2605	.0635	-.1526
47	-.06654	.20283	.31759	.2288	.0107	-.1941
48	-.02508	.23497	.31673	.1915	-.0416	-.2273
49	.01606	.26263	.30901	.1495	-.0918	-.2508

SURFACE ZONAL HARMONICS

θ deg.	$P_1(\cos\theta)$	$P_2(\cos\theta)$	$P_3(\cos\theta)$	$P_4(\cos\theta)$	$P_5(\cos\theta)$
50	.64279	.11976	-.30022	-.42753	-.25449
51	.62932	.09407	-.32088	-.42394	-.22353
52	.61566	.06856	-.34009	-.41784	-.19097
53	.60182	.04327	-.35781	-.40929	-.15712
54	.58779	.01824	-.37399	-.39837	-.12229
55	.57358	-.00652	-.38861	-.38519	-.08679
56	.55919	-.03095	-.40164	-.36983	-.05093
57	.54464	-.05505	-.41307	-.35241	-.01503
58	.52992	-.07878	-.42286	-.33306	.02060
59	.51504	-.10210	-.43100	-.31189	.05566
60	.50000	-.12500	-.43750	-.28906	.08984
61	.48481	-.14744	-.44234	-.26471	.12287
62	.46947	-.16939	-.44552	-.23899	.15446
63	.45399	-.19084	-.44706	-.21205	.18436
64	.43837	-.21175	-.44695	-.18407	.21232
65	.42262	-.23209	-.44522	-.15521	.23811
66	.40674	-.25185	-.44188	-.12564	.26152
67	.39073	-.27099	-.43696	-.09554	.28238
68	.37461	-.28950	-.43049	-.06508	.30051
69	.35837	-.30736	-.42249	-.03444	.31577
70	.34202	-.32453	-.41301	-.00380	.32807
71	.32557	-.34101	-.40208	.02667	.33730
72	.30902	-.35676	-.38975	.05680	.34340
73	.29237	-.37178	-.37608	.08641	.34634
74	.27564	-.38604	-.36110	.11534	.34611
75	.25882	-.39952	-.34488	.14343	.34273
76	.24192	-.41221	-.32749	.17051	.33624
77	.22495	-.42410	-.30897	.19644	.32672
78	.20791	-.43516	-.28940	.22107	.31425
79	.19081	-.44539	-.26885	.24427	.39897
80	.17365	-.45477	-.24738	.26590	.28102
81	.15643	-.46329	-.22508	.28585	.26056
82	.13917	-.47095	-.20202	.30401	.23777
83	.12187	-.47772	-.17828	.32027	.21288
84	.10453	-.48361	-.15394	.33455	.18610
85	.08716	-.48861	-.12908	.34677	.15766
86	.06976	-.49270	-.10379	.35686	.12784
87	.05234	-.49589	-.07815	.36476	.09668
88	.03490	-.49817	-.05224	.37044	.06507
89	.01745	-.49954	-.02617	.37386	.03268
90	0	-.50000	0	.37500	0

SURFACE ZONAL HARMONICS

θ deg.	$P_6(\cos\theta)$	$P_7(\cos\theta)$	$P_8(\cos\theta)$	$P_9(\cos\theta)$	$P_{10}(\cos\theta)$	$P_{11}(\cos\theta)$
50	.05638	.28543	.29468	.1041	-.1381	-.2641
51	.09539	.30308	.27416	.0565	-.1792	-.2666
52	.13265	.31535	.24797	.0080	-.2138	-.2586
53	.16772	.32213	.21674	-.0400	-.2408	-.2403
54	.20020	.32336	.18120	-.0862	-.2594	-.2127
55	.22972	.31910	.14217	-.1296	-.2692	-.1769
56	.25597	.30949	.10052	-.1689	-.2699	-.1346
57	.27866	.29475	.05716	-.2032	-.2617	-.0874
58	.29756	.27518	.01306	-.2315	-.2449	-.0372
59	.31246	.25117	-.03086	-.2533	-.2201	.0139
60	.32324	.22314	-.07364	-.2679	-.1882	.0639
61	.32980	.19162	-.11439	-.2751	-.1504	.1108
62	.33210	.15715	-.15225	-.2747	-.1080	.1529
63	.33016	.12034	-.18645	-.2669	-.0624	.1885
64	.32403	.08181	-.21628	-.2518	-.0151	.2163
65	.31383	.04222	-.24114	-.2300	.0323	.2352
66	.29971	.00223	-.26055	-.2022	.0783	.2446
67	.28189	-.03748	-.27412	-.1690	.1212	.2441
68	.26062	-.07627	-.28161	-.1315	.1599	.2339
69	.23617	-.11348	-.28290	-.0906	.1929	.2144
70	.20888	-.14853	-.27802	-.0476	.2193	.1864
71	.17910	-.18082	-.26709	-.0035	.2382	.1513
72	.14721	-.20986	-.25040	.0404	.2491	.1102
73	.11363	-.23516	-.22834	.0829	.2516	.0650
74	.07878	-.25634	-.20141	.1230	.2457	.0175
75	.04310	-.27305	-.17022	.1595	.2316	-.0305
76	.00704	-.28504	-.13545	.1915	.2099	-.0771
77	-.02896	-.29214	-.09788	.2181	.1813	-.1204
78	-.06444	-.29424	-.05832	.2386	.1468	-.1587
79	-.09897	-.29133	-.01763	.2526	.1074	-.1905
80	-.13212	-.28348	.02331	.2596	.0647	-.2146
81	-.16348	-.27083	.06361	.2595	.0199	-.2300
82	-.19267	-.25360	.10241	.2523	-.0254	-.2362
83	-.21933	-.23211	.13887	.2383	-.0698	-.2329
84	-.24313	-.20671	.17222	.2177	-.1118	-.2203
85	-.26378	-.17784	.20175	.1913	-.1499	-.1988
86	-.28103	-.14598	.22681	.1596	-.1830	-.1695
87	-.29467	-.11168	.24688	.1237	-.2099	-.1334
88	-.30454	-.07551	.26153	.0844	-.2298	-.0920
89	-.31050	-.03807	.27044	.0428	-.2420	-.0469
90	-.31250	0	.27344	0	-.2461	

For larger tables, see:-

"Report of the British Association for the Advancement of Science,"
1879, pages 54 - 57.

"Six-Place Tables of the First 16 Surface Zonal Harmonics $P_n(x)$,"
by H. Tallquist, Acta Societatis Scientiarum Fennicae, Helsingfors,
Finland, 1937, Ser. A, v. 2, No. 4.

"Six-Place Tables of the First 32 Surface Zonal Harmonics $P_n(\cos\theta)$,"
by H. Tallquist, Acta Societatis Scientiarum Fennicae, Helsingfors,
Finland, 1938, Ser. A, v. 2, No. 11.

"Tafeln der Besselschen, Theta-, Kugel- und anderer Funktionen,"
by K. Hayashi.

SURFACE ZONAL HARMONICS — FIRST DERIVATIVES

$$P_n'(x) = \frac{d}{dx} P_n(x) \qquad\qquad P_0'(x) = 0 \ , \ P_1'(x) = 1$$

x	$P_2'(x)$	$P_3'(x)$ (Exact)	$P_4'(x)$	$P_5'(x)$	$P_6'(x)$	$P_7'(x)$	$P_8'(x)$
0	0	-1.5	0	1.875	0	-2.1875	0
.01	.03	-1.49925	-.0750	1.8724	.1312	-2.1816	-.1967
.02	.06	-1.497	-.1499	1.8645	.2619	-2.1639	-.3920
.03	.09	-1.49325	-.2245	1.8514	.3916	-2.1345	-.5848
.04	.12	-1.488	-.2989	1.8331	.5200	-2.0936	-.7737
.05	.15	-1.48125	-.3728	1.8096	.6464	-2.0412	-.9575
.06	.18	-1.473	-.4462	1.7810	.7706	-1.9777	-1.1349
.07	.21	-1.46325	-.5190	1.7473	.8919	-1.9033	-1.3048
.08	.24	-1.452	-.5910	1.7086	1.0100	-1.8183	-1.4660
.09	.27	-1.43925	-.6622	1.6650	1.1244	-1.7232	-1.6173
.10	.30	-1.425	-.7325	1.6164	1.2346	-1.6183	-1.7578
.11	.33	-1.40925	-.8017	1.5631	1.3403	-1.5042	-1.8864
.12	.36	-1.392	-.8698	1.5052	1.4411	-1.3813	-2.0021
.13	.39	-1.37325	-.9366	1.4426	1.5365	-1.2503	-2.1042
.14	.42	-1.353	-1.0020	1.3756	1.6261	-1.1117	-2.1919
.15	.45	-1.33125	-1.0659	1.3043	1.7095	-.9661	-2.2643
.16	.48	-1.308	-1.1283	1.2288	1.7865	-.8143	-2.3209
.17	.51	-1.28325	-1.1890	1.1493	1.8567	-.6569	-2.3612
.18	.54	-1.257	-1.2479	1.0658	1.9196	-.4948	-2.3847
.19	.57	-1.22925	-1.3050	.9787	1.9751	-.3287	-2.3910
.20	.60	-1.2	-1.36	.888	2.0227	-.1595	-2.3800
.21	.63	-1.16925	-1.4129	.7940	2.0623	.0121	-2.3515
.22	.66	-1.137	-1.4637	.6967	2.0936	.1851	-2.3054
.23	.69	-1.10325	-1.5121	.5966	2.1164	.3587	-2.2419
.24	.72	-1.068	-1.5581	.4936	2.1303	.5319	-2.1611
.25	.75	-1.03125	-1.6016	.3882	2.1354	.7038	-2.0634
.26	.78	-.993	-1.6424	.2804	2.1313	.8735	-1.9491
.27	.81	-.95325	-1.6805	.1706	2.1180	1.0400	-1.8189
.28	.84	-.912	-1.7158	.0590	2.0954	1.2023	-1.6733
.29	.87	-.86925	-1.7482	-.0541	2.0633	1.3596	-1.5132
.30	.90	-.825	-1.7775	-.1686	2.0217	1.5108	-1.3393
.31	.93	-.77925	-1.8037	-.2840	1.9707	1.6550	-1.1529
.32	.96	-.732	-1.8266	-.4001	1.9102	1.7912	-.9548
.33	.99	-.68325	-1.8461	-.5167	1.8402	1.9185	-.7464
.34	1.02	-.633	-1.8622	-.6333	1.7609	2.0361	-.5290
.35	1.05	-.58125	-1.8747	-.7498	1.6723	2.1429	-.3041
.36	1.08	-.528	-1.8835	-.8657	1.5746	2.2381	-.0730
.37	1.11	-.47325	-1.8886	-.9807	1.4680	2.3210	.1625
.38	1.14	-.417	-1.8897	-1.0945	1.3527	2.3906	.4007
.39	1.17	-.35925	-1.8869	-1.2067	1.2289	2.4463	.6399
.40	1.20	-.3	-1.88	-1.317	1.0970	2.4873	.8782
.41	1.23	-.23925	-1.8689	-1.4250	.9573	2.5129	1.1137
.42	1.26	-.177	-1.8535	-1.5303	.8102	2.5226	1.3444
.43	1.29	-.11325	-1.8336	-1.6325	.6560	2.5158	1.5683
.44	1.32	-.048	-1.8093	-1.7312	.4953	2.4919	1.7834
.45	1.35	.01875	-1.7803	-1.8260	.3286	2.4508	1.9876
.46	1.38	.087	-1.7466	-1.9165	.1564	2.3918	2.1789
.47	1.41	.15675	-1.7081	-2.0023	-.0206	2.3150	2.3551
.48	1.44	.228	-1.6646	-2.0828	-.2019	2.2200	2.5141
.49	1.47	.30075	-1.6161	-2.1577	-.3867	2.1068	2.6541

SURFACE ZONAL HARMONICS — FIRST DERIVATIVES

x	$P_2'(x)$	$P_3'(x)$ (Exact)	$P_4'(x)$	$P_5'(x)$	$P_6'(x)$	$P_7'(x)$	$P_8'(x)$
.50	1.50	.375	-1.5625	-2.2266	-.5742	1.9756	2.7729
.51	1.53	.45075	-1.5036	-2.2888	-.7637	1.8264	2.8688
.52	1.56	.528	-1.4394	-2.3441	-.9544	1.6595	2.9398
.53	1.59	.60675	-1.3697	-2.3917	-1.1452	1.4753	2.9843
.54	1.62	.687	-1.2944	-2.4314	-1.3353	1.2744	3.0007
.55	1.65	.76875	-1.2134	-2.4626	-1.5236	1.0574	2.9874
.56	1.68	.852	-1.1267	-2.4847	-1.7090	.8251	2.9434
.57	1.71	.93675	-1.0341	-2.4972	-1.8905	.5786	2.8673
.58	1.74	1.023	-.9355	-2.4996	-2.0669	.3189	2.7584
.59	1.77	1.11075	-.8309	-2.4914	-2.2368	.0473	2.6161
.60	1.80	1.2	-.72	-2.472	-2.3990	-.2348	2.4399
.61	1.83	1.29075	-.6028	-2.4408	-2.5522	-.5255	2.2299
.62	1.86	1.383	-.4793	-2.3973	-2.6948	-.8232	1.9861
.63	1.89	1.47675	-.3492	-2.3409	-2.8255	-1.1257	1.7094
.64	1.92	1.572	-.2125	-2.2710	-2.9426	-1.4309	1.4006
.65	1.95	1.66875	-.0691	-2.1869	-3.0445	-1.7362	1.0611
.66	1.98	1.767	.0812	-2.0882	-3.1295	-2.0389	.6929
.67	2.01	1.86675	.2384	-1.9741	-3.1959	-2.3362	.2983
.68	2.04	1.968	.4026	-1.8441	-3.2418	-2.6249	-.1198
.69	2.07	2.07075	.5739	-1.6974	-3.2654	-2.9014	-.5581
.70	2.10	2.175	.7525	-1.5336	-3.2647	-3.1623	-1.0124
.71	2.13	2.28075	.9384	-1.3518	-3.2376	-3.4034	-1.4780
.72	2.16	2.388	1.1318	-1.1514	-3.1821	-3.6207	-1.9496
.73	2.19	2.49675	1.3328	-.9318	-3.0959	-3.8095	-2.4210
.74	2.22	2.607	1.5414	-.6923	-2.9767	-3.9650	-2.8854
.75	2.25	2.71875	1.7578	-.4321	-2.8224	-4.0822	-3.3351
.76	2.28	2.832	1.9821	-.1506	-2.6304	-4.1556	-3.7615
.77	2.31	2.94675	2.2143	.1529	-2.3982	-4.1794	-4.1552
.78	2.34	3.063	2.4547	.4792	-2.1233	-4.1475	-4.5055
.79	2.37	3.18075	2.7032	.8290	-1.8031	-4.0534	-4.8012
.80	2.40	3.3	2.96	1.203	-1.4347	-3.8903	-5.0295
.81	2.43	3.42075	3.2252	1.6020	-1.0155	-3.6512	-5.1768
.82	2.46	3.543	3.4989	2.0268	-.5424	-3.3282	-5.2283
.83	2.49	3.66675	3.7813	2.4781	-.0125	-2.9136	-5.1678
.84	2.52	3.792	4.0733	2.9567	.5772	-2.3990	-4.9779
.85	2.55	3.91875	4.3732	3.4634	1.2299	-1.7756	-4.6597
.86	2.58	4.047	4.6810	3.9989	1.9488	-1.0741	-4.1330
.87	2.61	4.17675	4.9988	4.5642	2.7374	-.1650	-3.4360
.88	2.64	4.308	5.3258	5.1600	3.5989	.8418	-2.5256
.89	2.67	4.44075	5.6620	5.7871	4.5369	1.9969	-1.3766
.90	2.70	4.575	6.0075	6.4464	5.5549	3.3113	.0376
.91	2.73	4.71075	6.3625	7.1398	6.6568	4.7965	1.7453
.92	2.76	4.848	6.7270	7.8650	7.8463	6.4644	3.7770
.93	2.79	4.98675	7.1012	8.6259	9.1271	8.3276	6.1647
.94	2.82	5.127	7.4852	9.4225	10.5034	10.3991	8.9428
.95	2.85	5.26875	7.8791	10.2556	11.9792	12.6925	12.1477
.96	2.88	5.412	8.2829	11.1260	13.5587	15.2217	15.8176
.97	2.91	5.55675	8.6968	12.0348	15.2461	18.0016	19.9935
.98	2.94	5.703	9.1209	12.9827	17.0458	21.0473	24.7185
.99	2.97	5.85075	9.5552	13.9708	18.9622	24.3746	30.0379
1.00	3	6	10	15	21	28	36

For a more complete table, see "Tables of the Spherical
Function $P_n(x)$ and its Derived Functions", by H. Tallquist,
Acta Societatis Scientiarum Fennicae, Helsingfors, Finland,
vol. 32, 1906, pages 5 - 27.

$$\frac{d}{d\theta} \, P_n(\cos \theta)$$

θ deg.	$\frac{d}{d\theta} P_1$	$\frac{d}{d\theta} P_2$	$\frac{d}{d\theta} P_3$	$\frac{d}{d\theta} P_4$	$\frac{d}{d\theta} P_5$	$\frac{d}{d\theta} P_6$	$\frac{d}{d\theta} P_7$	$\frac{d}{d\theta} P_8$
0	0	0	0	0	0	0	0	0
1	-.01745	-.0523	-.1047	-.1744	-.2615	-.3659	-.4877	-.6266
2	-.03490	-.1046	-.2091	-.3480	-.5213	-.7284	-.9692	-1.2430
3	-.05234	-.1568	-.3129	-.5201	-.7775	-1.0841	-1.4334	-1.8392
4	-.06976	-.2088	-.4160	-.6899	-1.0286	-1.4295	-1.8896	-2.4056
5	-.08716	-.2605	-.5180	-.8567	-1.2728	-1.7614	-2.3170	-2.9330
6	-.10453	-.3119	-.6196	-1.0197	-1.5085	-2.0768	-2.7152	-3.4130
7	-.12187	-.3629	-.7176	-1.1782	-1.7341	-2.3727	-3.0795	-3.8380
8	-.13917	-.4135	-.8148	-1.3315	-1.9481	-2.6464	-3.4053	-4.2015
9	-.15643	-.4635	-.9099	-1.4789	-2.1492	-2.8954	-3.6887	-4.4980
10	-.17365	-.5130	-1.0026	-1.6199	-2.3360	-3.1174	-3.9263	-4.7230
11	-.19081	-.5619	-1.0928	-1.7537	-2.5074	-3.3104	-4.1156	-4.8737
12	-.20791	-.6101	-1.1801	-1.8798	-2.6621	-3.4729	-4.2544	-4.9482
13	-.22495	-.6576	-1.2643	-1.9978	-2.7993	-3.6034	-4.3413	-4.9433
14	-.24192	-.7042	-1.3453	-2.1069	-2.9181	-3.7008	-4.3758	-4.8687
15	-.25882	-.7500	-1.4229	-2.2069	-3.0178	-3.7646	-4.3580	-4.7179
16	-.27564	-.7949	-1.4968	-2.2973	-3.0978	-3.7943	-4.2885	-4.4972
17	-.29237	-.8388	-1.5668	-2.3777	-3.1576	-3.7899	-4.1688	-4.2115
18	-.30902	-.8817	-1.6328	-2.4478	-3.1970	-3.7518	-4.0012	-3.8666
19	-.32557	-.9235	-1.6946	-2.5073	-3.2158	-3.6806	-3.7884	-3.4693
20	-.34202	-.9642	-1.7521	-2.5560	-3.2141	-3.5774	-3.5338	-3.0273
21	-.35837	-1.0037	-1.8050	-2.5937	-3.1920	-3.4435	-3.2413	-2.5490
22	-.37461	-1.0420	-1.8534	-2.6203	-3.1497	-3.2804	-2.9153	-2.0432
23	-.39073	-1.0790	-1.8970	-2.6358	-3.0878	-3.0902	-2.5607	-1.5194
24	-.40674	-1.1147	-1.9358	-2.6400	-3.0067	-2.8749	-2.1827	-.9871
25	-.42262	-1.1491	-1.9696	-2.6330	-2.9073	-2.6371	-1.7867	-.4559
26	-.43837	-1.1820	-1.9984	-2.6150	-2.7903	-2.3794	-1.3782	.0649
27	-.45399	-1.2135	-2.0222	-2.5861	-2.6568	-2.1045	-.9633	.5660
28	-.46947	-1.2436	-2.0408	-2.5464	-2.5077	-1.8156	-.5476	1.0389
29	-.48481	-1.2721	-2.0542	-2.4961	-2.3444	-1.5155	-.1369	1.4755
30	-.50000	-1.2990	-2.0625	-2.4357	-2.1680	-1.2077	.2632	1.8686
31	-.51504	-1.3244	-2.0656	-2.3654	-1.9799	-.8953	.6472	2.2120
32	-.52992	-1.3482	-2.0634	-2.2855	-1.7817	-.5815	1.0102	2.5003
33	-.54464	-1.3703	-2.0562	-2.1966	-1.5748	-.2697	1.3472	2.7293
34	-.55919	-1.3908	-2.0437	-2.0991	-1.3608	.0370	1.6540	2.8960
35	-.57358	-1.4095	-2.0262	-1.9934	-1.1413	.3354	1.9267	2.9987
36	-.58779	-1.4266	-2.0037	-1.8802	-.9179	.6225	2.1620	3.0367
37	-.60182	-1.4419	-1.9761	-1.7600	-.6924	.8955	2.3573	3.0108
38	-.61566	-1.4554	-1.9438	-1.6334	-.4664	1.1516	2.5103	2.9227
39	-.62932	-1.4672	-1.9066	-1.5011	-.2415	1.3885	2.6196	2.7757
40	-.64279	-1.4772	-1.8648	-1.3637	-.0194	1.6038	2.6845	2.5737
41	-.65606	-1.4854	-1.8185	-1.2219	.1983	1.7955	2.7047	2.3221
42	-.66913	-1.4918	-1.7678	-1.0764	.4100	1.9620	2.6807	2.0267
43	-.68200	-1.4963	-1.7129	-.9279	.6142	2.1017	2.6138	1.6944
44	-.69466	-1.4991	-1.6539	-.7772	.8094	2.2136	2.5057	1.3326
45	-.70711	-1.5000	-1.5910	-.6250	.9944	2.2969	2.3589	.9492
46	-.71934	-1.4991	-1.5244	-.4720	1.1677	2.3510	2.1761	.5524
47	-.73135	-1.4963	-1.4542	-.3190	1.3282	2.3757	1.9609	.1506
48	-.74314	-1.4918	-1.3808	-.1668	1.4749	2.3713	1.7172	-.2479
49	-.75471	-1.4854	-1.3042	-.0160	1.6067	2.3382	1.4491	-.6350

$$\frac{d}{d\theta} P_n(\cos\theta)$$

θ	$\frac{d}{d\theta} P_1$	$\frac{d}{d\theta} P_2$	$\frac{d}{d\theta} P_3$	$\frac{d}{d\theta} P_4$	$\frac{d}{d\theta} P_5$	$\frac{d}{d\theta} P_6$	$\frac{d}{d\theta} P_7$	$\frac{d}{d\theta} P_8$
deg.								
50	-.76604	-1.4772	-1.2248	.1327	1.7228	2.2771	1.1614	-1.0027
51	-.77715	-1.4672	-1.1427	.2784	1.8225	2.1892	.8588	-1.3439
52	-.78801	-1.4554	-1.0581	.4205	1.9052	2.0759	.5463	-1.6517
53	-.79864	-1.4419	-.9714	.5584	1.9704	1.9387	.2292	-1.9202
54	-.80902	-1.4266	-.8828	.6914	2.0178	1.7797	-.0877	-2.1443
55	-.81915	-1.4095	-.7925	.8188	2.0473	1.6008	-.3990	-2.3200
56	-.82904	-1.3908	-.7007	.9401	2.0587	1.4046	-.7001	-2.4441
57	-.83867	-1.3703	-.6078	1.0547	2.0522	1.1934	-.9860	-2.5146
58	-.84805	-1.3482	-.5140	1.1620	2.0280	.9699	-1.2524	-2.5306
59	-.85717	-1.3244	-.4196	1.2617	1.9865	.7369	-1.4953	-2.4925
60	-.86603	-1.2990	-.3248	1.3532	1.9283	.4973	-1.7109	-2.4014
61	-.87462	-1.2721	-.2299	1.4361	1.8538	.2540	-1.8960	-2.2600
62	-.88295	-1.2436	-.1351	1.5101	1.7640	.0098	-2.0480	-2.0715
63	-.89101	-1.2135	-.0408	1.5748	1.6596	-.2321	-2.1646	-1.8405
64	-.89879	-1.1820	.0528	1.6300	1.5418	-.4691	-2.2443	-1.5721
65	-.90631	-1.1491	.1454	1.6755	1.4114	-.6983	-2.2861	-1.2722
66	-.91355	-1.1147	.2368	1.7111	1.2698	-.9170	-2.2896	-.9476
67	-.92050	-1.0790	.3268	1.7366	1.1183	-1.1226	-2.2550	-.6051
68	-.92718	-1.0420	.4149	1.7520	.9580	-1.3129	-2.1833	-.2522
69	-.93358	-1.0037	.5011	1.7573	.7905	-1.4855	-2.0757	.1037
70	-.93969	-.9642	.5851	1.7525	.6173	-1.6386	-1.9344	.4549
71	-.94552	-.9235	.6666	1.7377	.4397	-1.7704	-1.7617	.7942
72	-.95106	-.8817	.7455	1.7131	.2593	-1.8794	-1.5608	1.1144
73	-.95630	-.8388	.8214	1.6787	.0776	-1.9645	-1.3350	1.4088
74	-.96126	-.7949	.8941	1.6349	-.1037	-2.0248	-1.0882	1.6713
75	-.96593	-.7500	.9636	1.5819	-.2833	-2.0596	-.8245	1.8966
76	-.97030	-.7042	1.0295	1.5201	-.4595	-2.0687	-.5483	2.0800
77	-.97437	-.6576	1.0918	1.4498	-.6309	-2.0520	-.2641	2.2178
78	-.97815	-.6101	1.1501	1.3714	-.7961	-2.0098	.0234	2.3074
79	-.98163	-.5619	1.2044	1.2854	-.9536	-1.9428	.3094	2.3469
80	-.98481	-.5130	1.2545	1.1923	-1.1023	-1.8519	.5892	2.3357
81	-.98769	-.4635	1.3003	1.0926	-1.2407	-1.7382	.8584	2.2742
82	-.99027	-.4135	1.3415	.9869	-1.3679	-1.6031	1.1125	2.1639
83	-.99255	-.3629	1.3783	.8758	-1.4827	-1.4484	1.3473	2.0072
84	-.99452	-.3119	1.4103	.7598	-1.5842	-1.2760	1.5592	1.8076
85	-.99619	-.2605	1.4375	.6396	-1.6715	-1.0881	1.7446	1.5693
86	-.99756	-.2088	1.4599	.5160	-1.7439	-.8868	1.9006	1.2976
87	-.99863	-.1568	1.4774	.3895	-1.8009	-.6747	2.0246	.9982
88	-.99939	-.1046	1.4900	.2608	-1.8420	-.4544	2.1146	.6775
89	-.99985	-.0523	1.4975	.1308	-1.8667	-.2286	2.1692	.3424
90	-1.00000	0	1.5000	0	-1.8750	0	2.1875	0

Note that $\qquad \frac{d}{dx} P_n(x) = \frac{-1}{\sin\theta} \frac{d}{d\theta} P_n(\cos\theta)$

where $\qquad\qquad\qquad x = \cos\theta$

See the table of a slightly different arrangement of this function by H. Tallquist, Acta Societatis Scientiarum Fennicae, Helsingfors, Finland, v. 33, No. 9, 1908.

n	B_n	$\log_{10} B_n$
1	$\dfrac{1}{6}$	$\overline{1}.221\ 8487$
2	$\dfrac{1}{30}$	$\overline{2}.522\ 8787$
3	$\dfrac{1}{42}$	$\overline{2}.376\ 7507$
4	$\dfrac{1}{30}$	$\overline{2}.522\ 8787$
5	$\dfrac{5}{66}$	$\overline{2}.879\ 4261$
6	$\dfrac{691}{2730}$	$\overline{1}.403\ 3154$
7	$\dfrac{7}{6}$	$.066\ 9468$
8	$\dfrac{3617}{510}$	$.850\ 7783$
9	$\dfrac{43\ 867}{798}$	$1.740\ 1350$
10	$\dfrac{174\ 611}{330}$	$2.723\ 5577$
11	$\dfrac{854\ 513}{138}$	$3.791\ 8396$
12	$\dfrac{2.363\ 641 \times 10^{8}}{2730}$	$4.937\ 4189$
13	$\dfrac{8.553\ 103 \times 10^{6}}{6}$	$6.153\ 9725$
14	$\dfrac{2.374\ 946 \times 10^{10}}{870}$	$7.436\ 1345$
15	$\dfrac{8.615\ 841 \times 10^{12}}{14322}$	$8.779\ 2940$
16	$\dfrac{7.709\ 321 \times 10^{12}}{510}$	$10.179\ 4460$
17	$\dfrac{2.577\ 688 \times 10^{12}}{6}$	$11.633\ 0791$
18	$\dfrac{2.631\ 527 \times 10^{19}}{1919190}$	$13.137\ 0899$
19	$\dfrac{2.929\ 994 \times 10^{15}}{6}$	$14.688\ 7155$
20	$\dfrac{2.610\ 827 \times 10^{20}}{13530}$	$16.285\ 4803$
21	$\dfrac{1.520\ 098 \times 10^{21}}{1806}$	$17.925\ 1537$
22	$\dfrac{2.783\ 327 \times 10^{22}}{690}$	$19.605\ 7151$
23	$\dfrac{5.964\ 511 \times 10^{23}}{282}$	$21.325\ 3257$
24	$\dfrac{5.609\ 403 \times 10^{27}}{46410}$	$23.082\ 3051$
25	$\dfrac{4.950\ 572 \times 10^{26}}{66}$	$24.875\ 1115$
26	$\dfrac{8.011\ 657 \times 10^{29}}{1590}$	$26.702\ 3252$
27	$\dfrac{2.914\ 996 \times 10^{31}}{798}$	$28.562\ 6351$
28	$\dfrac{2.479\ 393 \times 10^{33}}{870}$	$30.454\ 8261$
29	$\dfrac{8.448\ 361 \times 10^{34}}{354}$	$32.377\ 7692$
30	$\dfrac{1.215\ 233 \times 10^{42}}{56\ 786\ 730}$	$34.330\ 4127$
31	$\dfrac{1.230\ 059 \times 10^{37}}{6}$	$36.311\ 7745$
32	$\dfrac{1.067\ 838 \times 10^{41}}{510}$	$38.320\ 9353$
33	$\dfrac{1.472\ 600 \times 10^{45}}{64722}$	$40.357\ 0329$
34	$\dfrac{7.877\ 313 \times 10^{43}}{30}$	$42.419\ 2569$
35	$\dfrac{1.505\ 381 \times 10^{48}}{4686}$	$44.506\ 8442$

B_n may be defined by the series

$$1 - x \cot x = \frac{2^2 B_1}{2!} x^2 + \frac{2^4 B_2}{4!} x^4 + \cdots + \frac{2^{2n} B_n}{(2n)!} x^{2n} + \cdots$$

n	E_n	$\log_{10}E_n$
1	1	0
2	5	.698 9700
3	61	1.785 3298
4	1 385	3.141 4498
5	50 521	4.703 4719
6	2 702 765	6.431 8083
7	$1.993\ 610 \times 10^{8}$	8.299 6402
8	$1.939\ 151 \times 10^{10}$	10.287 6117
9	$2.404\ 880 \times 10^{12}$	12.381 0934
10	$3.703\ 712 \times 10^{14}$	14.568 6372
11	$6.934\ 887 \times 10^{16}$	16.841 0394
12	$1.551\ 453 \times 10^{19}$	19.190 7387
13	$4.087\ 073 \times 10^{21}$	21.611 4123
14	$1.252\ 260 \times 10^{24}$	24.097 6944
15	$4.415\ 439 \times 10^{26}$	26.644 9739
16	$1.775\ 194 \times 10^{29}$	29.249 2458
17	$8.072\ 330 \times 10^{31}$	31.906 9989
18	$4.122\ 206 \times 10^{34}$	34.615 1297
19	$2.348\ 958 \times 10^{37}$	37.370 8753
20	$1.485\ 115 \times 10^{40}$	40.171 7601
21	$1.036\ 462 \times 10^{43}$	43.015 5535
22	$7.947\ 579 \times 10^{45}$	45.900 2349
23	$6.667\ 538 \times 10^{48}$	48.823 9655
24	$6.096\ 279 \times 10^{51}$	51.785 0648
25	$6.053\ 285 \times 10^{54}$	54.781 9911
26	$6.506\ 162 \times 10^{57}$	57.813 3249
27	$7.546\ 660 \times 10^{60}$	60.877 7548
28	$9.420\ 322 \times 10^{63}$	63.974 0657
29	$1.262\ 202 \times 10^{67}$	67.101 1288
30	$1.810\ 891 \times 10^{70}$	70.257 8923
31	$2.775\ 710 \times 10^{73}$	73.443 3741
32	$4.535\ 810 \times 10^{76}$	76.656 6549
33	$7.886\ 284 \times 10^{79}$	79.896 8724
34	$1.456\ 184 \times 10^{83}$	83.163 2164
35	$2.850\ 518 \times 10^{86}$	86.454 9238

E_n may be defined by the series

$$\sec x = 1 + E_1 \frac{x^2}{2!} + E_2 \frac{x^4}{4!} + \cdots + E_n \frac{x^{2n}}{(2n)!} + \cdots$$

Bernoulli's and Euler's numbers appear in the coefficients of many series. See "Traité Élémentaire des Nombres de Bernoulli", by N. Nielsen.

There are several different notations in use for these numbers and it is desirable when using the letters B_n and E_n for them, to state explicitly the values of the first few numbers, as $B_1 = 1/6$, $B_2 = 1/30$, $B_3 = 1/42$, etc.

For large tables of these numbers, see "Tables of the Higher Mathematical Functions", by H. T. Davis, v. 2, p. 230 - 242 and 294 - 302, and "Zehnstellige Logarithmen der Zahlen von 1 bis 100 000", by J. Peters and J. Stein, 1922, vol. 1, second section.

GAMMA FUNCTION

$$\Gamma(n) = \int_0^\infty x^{n-1} e^{-x}\, dx \qquad\qquad (n > 0)$$

n	0	1	2	3	4	5	6	7	8	9	Diff. (Subtract)
1.00	1.00 000	942	885	828	771	714	657	601	545	488	55 - 58
.01	0.99 433	377	321	266	211	156	101	047	993	938	54 - 56
.02	.98 884	831	777	724	670	617	565	512	459	407	52 - 54
.03	355	303	251	200	148	097	046	995	945	894	50 - 52
.04	.97 844	794	744	694	644	595	546	497	448	399	49 - 50
.05	350	302	254	206	158	110	063	015	968	921	47 - 48
.06	.96 874	828	781	735	689	643	597	551	506	460	45 - 47
.07	415	370	325	281	236	192	148	104	060	016	43 - 45
.08	.95 973	929	886	843	800	757	715	672	630	588	42 - 44
.09	546	504	463	421	380	339	298	257	216	175	40 - 42
1.10	135	095	055	015	975	935	896	857	817	778	38 - 40
.11	.94 740	701	662	624	586	547	509	472	434	396	37 - 39
.12	359	322	285	248	211	174	138	101	065	029	36 - 37
.13	.93 993	957	922	886	851	816	781	746	711	676	34 - 36
.14	642	607	573	539	505	471	437	404	370	337	33 - 35
.15	304	271	238	206	173	141	108	076	044	012	32 - 33
.16	.92 980	949	917	886	855	823	793	762	731	700	30 - 32
.17	670	640	609	579	550	520	490	461	431	402	29 - 31
.18	373	344	315	286	258	229	201	172	144	116	27 - 29
.19	089	061	033	006	978	951	924	897	870	843	26 - 28
1.20	.91 817	790	764	738	712	686	660	634	609	583	25 - 27
.21	558	532	507	482	457	433	408	383	359	335	24 - 26
.22	311	287	263	239	215	192	168	145	122	098	23 - 24
.23	075	053	030	007	985	962	940	918	896	874	22 - 23
.24	.90 852	830	809	787	766	745	724	703	682	661	21 - 22
.25	640	620	599	579	559	539	519	499	479	459	19 - 21
.26	440	420	401	382	363	344	325	306	287	269	18 - 20
.27	250	232	214	196	178	160	142	124	107	089	17 - 18
.28	072	055	037	020	003	987	970	953	937	920	16 - 18
.29	.89 904	888	872	856	840	824	809	793	778	762	15 - 16
1.30	747	732	717	702	687	672	658	643	629	615	14 - 15
.31	600	586	572	558	545	531	517	504	491	477	13 - 14
.32	464	451	438	425	412	400	387	375	362	350	12 - 13
.33	338	326	314	302	290	278	267	255	244	233	11 - 12-
.34	222	210	199	189	178	167	157	146	136	125	10 - 12
.35	115	105	095	085	075	066	056	046	037	028	9 - 10
.36	018	009	000	991	982	974	965	956	948	940	8 - 9
.37	.88 931	923	915	907	899	891	884	876	868	861	7 - 8
.38	854	846	839	832	825	818	812	805	798	792	6 - 8
.39	785	779	773	767	761	755	749	743	737	732	5 - 6
1.40	726	721	716	710	705	700	695	690	686	681	4 - 6
.41	676	672	668	663	659	655	651	647	643	639	3 - 5
.42	636	632	628	625	622	618	615	612	609	606	2 - 4
.43	604	601	598	596	593	591	589	587	584	582	1 - 3
.44	581	579	577	575	574	572	571	570	568	567	1 - 2
.45	566	565	564	564	563	562	562	561	561	561	0 - 1
.46	560	560	560	560	561	561	561	562	562	563	(Add) 0 - 1
.47	563	564	565	566	567	568	569	570	572	573	1 - 2
.48	575	576	578	580	582	584	586	588	590	592	1 - 3
.49	595	597	599	602	605	608	610	613	616	620	2 - 4

GAMMA FUNCTION

n	0	1	2	3	4	5	6	7	8	9	Diff. (Add)
1.50	.88 623	626	629	633	636	640	644	647	651	655	3 - 4
.51	659	663	667	672	676	680	685	690	694	699	4 - 5
.52	704	709	714	719	724	729	735	740	746	751	5 - 6
.53	757	762	768	774	780	786	792	799	805	811	5 - 7
.54	818	824	831	838	844	851	858	865	872	880	6 - 8
.55	887	894	902	909	917	924	932	940	948	956	7 - 8
.56	964	972	980	989	997	005	014	023	031	040	8 - 9
.57	.89 049	058	067	076	085	094	104	113	123	132	9 - 10
.58	142	152	161	171	181	191	202	212	222	232	9 - 11
.59	243	253	264	275	285	296	307	318	329	340	10 - 12
1.60	352	363	374	386	397	409	421	432	444	456	10 - 12
.61	468	480	492	505	517	529	542	554	567	580	12 - 13
.62	592	605	618	631	644	657	671	684	697	711	13 - 14
.63	724	738	752	766	779	793	807	821	836	850	13 - 15
.64	864	879	893	908	922	937	952	967	982	997	14 - 15
.65	.90 012	027	042	057	073	088	104	119	135	151	15 - 16
.66	167	183	199	215	231	247	264	280	296	313	16 - 17
.67	330	346	363	380	397	414	431	448	465	483	16 - 18
.68	500	518	535	553	570	588	606	624	642	660	17 - 18
.69	678	696	715	733	752	770	789	807	826	845	18 - 19
1.70	864	883	902	921	940	960	979	998	018	037	19 - 20
.71	.91 057	077	097	117	137	157	177	197	217	238	20 - 21
.72	258	279	299	320	341	361	382	403	424	445	20 - 22
.73	467	488	509	531	552	574	595	617	639	661	21 - 22
.74	683	705	727	749	771	793	816	838	861	884	22 - 23
.75	906	929	952	975	998	021	044	067	091	114	23 - 24
.76	.92 137	161	185	208	232	256	280	304	328	352	23 - 24
.77	376	401	425	449	474	499	523	548	573	598	24 - 25
.78	623	648	673	698	723	749	774	800	825	851	25 - 26
.79	877	903	928	954	980	007	033	059	085	112	25 - 27
1.80	.93 138	165	192	218	245	272	299	326	353	380	26 - 28
.81	408	435	462	490	517	545	573	601	629	656	27 - 29
.82	685	713	741	769	797	826	854	883	912	940	28 - 29
.83	969	998	027	056	085	114	143	173	202	232	29 - 30
.84	.94 261	291	321	350	380	410	440	470	501	531	29 - 31
.85	561	592	622	653	683	714	745	776	807	838	30 - 31
.86	869	900	931	962	994	025	057	089	120	152	31 - 32
.87	.95 184	216	248	280	312	345	377	409	442	474	32 - 33
.88	507	540	573	606	638	672	705	738	771	804	32 - 34
.89	838	871	905	939	972	006	040	074	108	142	33 - 35
1.90	.96 177	211	245	280	314	349	384	418	453	488	34 - 35
.91	523	558	593	629	664	699	735	770	806	842	35 - 36
.92	877	913	949	985	021	058	094	130	167	203	36 - 37
.93	.97 240	276	313	350	387	424	461	498	535	573	36 - 38
.94	610	647	685	723	760	798	836	874	912	950	37 - 38
.95	988	026	065	103	142	180	219	258	296	335	38 - 39
.96	.98 374	413	452	492	531	570	610	649	689	729	39 - 40
.97	768	808	848	888	928	969	009	049	090	130	40 - 41
.98	.99 171	212	252	293	334	375	416	457	499	540	40 - 42
.99	581	623	664	706	748	790	832	874	916	958	41 - 42
2.00	1.00 000										

For larger tables, see "Tables of the Higher Mathematical Functions," by H. T. Davis, v. 1, p. 196 - 273.
"Sieben- und mehrstellige Tafeln der Kreis- und Hyperbelfunktionen," by K. Hayashi, p. 248 - 264.

NORMAL PROBABILITY INTEGRAL $\qquad \dfrac{1}{\sqrt{2\pi}} \displaystyle\int_{-x}^{x} e^{-\frac{1}{2}t^2}\,dt$

x	0	1	2	3	4	5	6	7	8	9	Diff.
.00	.00 000	080	160	239	319	399	479	559	638	718	79-80
.01	798	878	957	$\overline{037}$	$\overline{117}$	$\overline{197}$	$\overline{277}$	$\overline{356}$	$\overline{436}$	$\overline{516}$	79-80
.02	.01 596	675	755	835	915	995	$\overline{074}$	$\overline{154}$	$\overline{234}$	$\overline{314}$	79-80
.03	.02 393	473	553	633	712	792	872	951	$\overline{031}$	$\overline{111}$	79-80
.04	.03 191	$\overline{270}$	$\overline{350}$	$\overline{430}$	510	589	669	749	828	908	79-80
.05	988	$\overline{067}$	$\overline{147}$	$\overline{227}$	$\overline{306}$	$\overline{386}$	$\overline{466}$	$\overline{545}$	$\overline{625}$	$\overline{705}$	79-80
.06	.04 784	864	944	$\overline{023}$	103	183	262	$\overline{342}$	$\overline{421}$	$\overline{501}$	79-80
.07	.05 581	660	740	819	899	979	$\overline{058}$	$\overline{138}$	$\overline{217}$	$\overline{297}$	79-80
.08	.06 376	456	535	615	694	774	853	933	$\overline{012}$	$\overline{092}$	79-80
.09	.07 171	251	330	410	489	569	648	727	807	886	79-80
.10	966	$\overline{045}$	$\overline{124}$	$\overline{204}$	$\overline{283}$	$\overline{362}$	$\overline{442}$	$\overline{521}$	$\overline{600}$	$\overline{680}$	79-80
.11	.08 759	838	918	997	$\overline{076}$	$\overline{155}$	$\overline{235}$	$\overline{314}$	$\overline{393}$	$\overline{472}$	79-80
.12	.09 552	631	710	789	868	948	$\overline{027}$	$\overline{106}$	$\overline{185}$	$\overline{264}$	79-80
.13	.10 343	422	502	581	660	739	818	897	976	$\overline{055}$	79-80
.14	.11 134	$\overline{213}$	$\overline{292}$	$\overline{371}$	450	529	608	687	766	845	79
.15	924	$\overline{002}$	$\overline{081}$	$\overline{160}$	$\overline{239}$	$\overline{318}$	$\overline{397}$	$\overline{476}$	$\overline{554}$	$\overline{633}$	78-79
.16	.12 712	791	869	948	$\overline{027}$	$\overline{106}$	$\overline{184}$	$\overline{263}$	$\overline{342}$	$\overline{420}$	78-79
.17	.13 499	578	656	735	813	892	971	$\overline{049}$	$\overline{128}$	$\overline{206}$	78-79
.18	.14 285	363	442	520	599	677	756	834	912	991	78-79
.19	.15 069	147	226	304	382	461	539	617	695	774	78-79
.20	852	930	$\overline{008}$	$\overline{086}$	$\overline{165}$	$\overline{243}$	$\overline{321}$	$\overline{399}$	$\overline{477}$	$\overline{555}$	78-79
.21	.16 633	711	789	867	945	$\overline{023}$	$\overline{101}$	$\overline{179}$	$\overline{257}$	$\overline{335}$	78
.22	.17 413	491	569	646	724	802	880	958	$\overline{035}$	$\overline{113}$	77-78
.23	.18 191	269	346	424	502	579	657	734	812	889	77-78
.24	967	$\overline{044}$	$\overline{122}$	$\overline{199}$	$\overline{277}$	$\overline{354}$	$\overline{432}$	$\overline{509}$	$\overline{587}$	$\overline{664}$	77-78
.25	.19 741	819	896	973	$\overline{050}$	$\overline{128}$	$\overline{205}$	$\overline{282}$	$\overline{359}$	$\overline{436}$	77-78
.26	.20 514	591	668	745	822	899	976	$\overline{053}$	$\overline{130}$	$\overline{207}$	77
.27	.21 284	361	438	515	592	668	745	822	899	976	76-77
.28	.22 052	129	206	$\overline{282}$	$\overline{359}$	$\overline{436}$	$\overline{512}$	$\overline{589}$	$\overline{665}$	$\overline{742}$	76-77
.29	818	895	971	$\overline{048}$	$\overline{124}$	$\overline{201}$	$\overline{277}$	$\overline{353}$	$\overline{430}$	$\overline{506}$	76-77
.30	.23 582	659	735	811	887	963	$\overline{040}$	$\overline{116}$	$\overline{192}$	$\overline{268}$	76-77
.31	.24 344	420	496	572	648	724	800	876	952	$\overline{027}$	75-76
.32	.25 103	179	$\overline{255}$	$\overline{330}$	$\overline{406}$	$\overline{482}$	$\overline{558}$	$\overline{633}$	$\overline{709}$	$\overline{784}$	75-76
.33	860	936	$\overline{011}$	$\overline{087}$	$\overline{162}$	$\overline{237}$	$\overline{313}$	$\overline{388}$	$\overline{464}$	$\overline{539}$	75-76
.34	.26 614	690	765	840	915	991	$\overline{066}$	$\overline{141}$	$\overline{216}$	$\overline{291}$	75-76
.35	.27 366	441	516	591	666	741	816	891	966	$\overline{040}$	74-75
.36	.28 115	190	265	340	414	489	563	638	713	787	74-75
.37	862	936	$\overline{011}$	$\overline{085}$	$\overline{160}$	$\overline{234}$	$\overline{308}$	$\overline{383}$	$\overline{457}$	$\overline{531}$	74-75
.38	.29 605	680	754	828	902	976	$\overline{050}$	$\overline{124}$	$\overline{198}$	$\overline{272}$	74-75
.39	.30 346	420	494	568	642	716	789	863	937	$\overline{011}$	73-74
.40	.31 084	158	232	305	379	452	526	599	673	746	73-74
.41	819	893	966	$\overline{039}$	$\overline{113}$	$\overline{186}$	$\overline{259}$	$\overline{332}$	$\overline{405}$	$\overline{478}$	73-74
.42	.32 551	624	697	770	843	916	989	$\overline{062}$	$\overline{135}$	$\overline{208}$	72-73
.43	.33 280	353	426	499	571	644	716	789	861	934	72-73
.44	.34 006	079	151	223	$\overline{296}$	$\overline{368}$	$\overline{440}$	$\overline{512}$	$\overline{585}$	$\overline{657}$	72-73
.45	729	801	873	945	$\overline{017}$	$\overline{089}$	$\overline{161}$	$\overline{233}$	$\overline{305}$	$\overline{377}$	71-72
.46	.35 448	520	592	664	735	807	878	950	$\overline{022}$	$\overline{093}$	71-72
.47	.36 164	236	$\overline{307}$	$\overline{379}$	$\overline{450}$	$\overline{521}$	$\overline{593}$	$\overline{664}$	$\overline{735}$	$\overline{806}$	71-72
.48	877	948	$\overline{019}$	$\overline{090}$	$\overline{161}$	$\overline{232}$	$\overline{303}$	$\overline{374}$	$\overline{445}$	$\overline{516}$	71
.49	.37 587	657	728	799	869	940	$\overline{011}$	$\overline{081}$	$\overline{152}$	$\overline{222}$	70-71
	.38										

NORMAL PROBABILITY INTEGRAL $\quad \dfrac{1}{\sqrt{2\pi}} \displaystyle\int_{-x}^{x} e^{-\frac{1}{2}t^2}\, dt$

x	0	1	2	3	4	5	6	7	8	9	Diff.
.50	.38 292	363	433	504	574	644	714	785	855	925	70-71
.51	995	065	135	205	275	345	415	484	554	624	69-70
.52	.39 694	763	833	903	972	042	111	181	250	319	69-70
.53	.40 389	458	527	597	666	735	804	873	942	011	69-70
.54	.41 080	149	218	287	356	425	493	562	631	699	68-69
.55	768	837	905	974	042	111	179	247	316	384	68-69
.56	.42 452	520	588	657	725	793	861	929	997	064	67-69
.57	.43 132	200	268	336	403	471	538	606	674	741	67-68
.58	809	876	943	011	078	145	212	280	347	414	67-68
.59	.44 481	548	615	682	749	816	882	949	016	083	66-67
.60	.45 149	216	283	349	416	482	549	615	681	748	66-67
.61	814	880	946	012	078	145	211	277	342	408	65-67
.62	.46 474	540	606	672	737	803	869	934	000	065	65-66
.63	.47 131	196	261	327	392	457	522	588	653	718	65-66
.64	783	848	913	978	042	107	172	237	302	366	64-65
.65	.48 431	495	560	624	689	753	818	882	946	010	64-65
.66	.49 075	139	203	267	331	395	459	523	587	650	63-64
.67	714	778	842	905	969	032	096	159	223	286	63-64
.68	.50 350	413	476	539	602	666	729	792	855	918	63-64
.69	981	043	106	169	232	294	357	420	482	545	62-63
.70	.51 607	670	732	794	857	919	981	043	105	166	62-63
.71	.52 230	292	354	415	477	539	601	663	724	786	61-62
.72	848	909	971	032	093	155	216	277	339	400	61-62
.73	.53 461	522	583	644	705	766	827	888	949	009	60-61
.74	.54 070	131	191	252	312	373	433	494	554	614	60-61
.75	675	735	795	855	915	975	035	095	155	215	60
.76	.55 275	334	394	454	513	573	632	692	751	811	59-60
.77	870	929	989	048	107	166	225	284	343	402	59-60
.78	.56 461	520	579	637	696	755	813	872	930	989	58-59
.79	.57 047	106	164	222	280	339	397	455	513	571	58-59
.80	629	687	745	803	860	918	976	033	091	148	57-58
.81	.58 206	263	321	378	436	493	550	607	664	721	57-58
.82	778	835	892	949	006	063	120	176	233	290	56-57
.83	.59 346	403	459	516	572	628	685	741	797	853	56-57
.84	909	965	021	077	133	189	245	300	356	412	55-56
.85	.60 467	523	579	634	690	745	800	856	911	966	55-56
.86	.61 021	076	131	186	241	296	351	406	461	515	54-55
.87	570	625	679	734	788	843	897	951	006	060	54-55
.88	.62 114	168	222	276	330	384	438	492	546	600	53-54
.89	653	707	761	814	868	921	975	028	081	135	53-54
.90	.63 188	241	294	347	400	453	506	559	612	665	53
.91	718	770	823	876	928	981	033	086	138	190	52-53
.92	.64 243	295	347	399	451	503	555	607	659	711	52
.93	763	815	866	918	970	021	073	124	176	227	51-52
.94	.65 278	330	381	432	483	534	585	636	687	738	51-52
.95	789	840	890	941	992	042	093	143	194	244	50-51
.96	.66 294	345	395	445	495	546	596	646	696	745	49-51
.97	795	845	895	945	994	044	094	143	193	242	49-50
.98	.67 291	341	390	439	488	538	587	636	685	734	49-50
.99	783	831	880	929	978	026	075	124	172	221	48-49
	.68										

NORMAL PROBABILITY INTEGRAL $\dfrac{1}{\sqrt{2\pi}} \displaystyle\int_{-x}^{x} e^{-\frac{1}{2}t^2}\, dt$

x	0	1	2	3	4	5	6	7	8	9	Diff.
1.00	.68 269	317	366	414	462	510	558	607	655	703	48-49
1.01	750	798	846	894	942	989	037	085	132	180	47-48
1.02	.69 227	275	322	369	416	464	511	558	605	652	47-48
1.03	699	746	793	840	886	933	980	026	073	120	46-47
1.04	.70 166	212	259	305	351	398	444	490	536	582	46-47
1.05	628	674	720	766	812	857	903	949	994	040	45-46
1.06	.71 086	131	176	222	267	312	358	403	448	493	45-46
1.07	538	583	628	673	718	763	807	852	897	941	44-45
1.08	986	030	075	119	164	208	252	296	340	385	44-45
1.09	.72 429	473	517	561	605	648	692	736	780	823	43-44
1.10	867	910	954	997	041	084	127	171	214	257	43-44
1.11	.73 300	343	386	429	472	515	558	601	643	686	42-43
1.12	729	771	814	856	899	941	983	026	068	110	42-43
1.13	.74 152	194	237	279	321	362	404	446	488	530	41-43
1.14	571	613	655	696	738	779	820	862	903	944	41-42
1.15	986	027	068	109	150	191	232	273	314	354	40-41
1.16	.75 395	436	476	517	558	598	639	679	719	760	40-41
1.17	800	840	880	920	960	001	041	080	120	160	39-41
1.18	.76 200	240	279	319	359	398	438	477	517	556	39-40
1.19	595	635	674	713	752	791	830	869	908	947	39-40
1.20	986	025	064	102	141	180	218	257	295	334	38-39
1.21	.77 372	410	449	487	525	563	602	640	678	716	38-39
1.22	754	791	829	867	905	942	980	018	055	093	37-38
1.23	.78 130	168	205	242	280	317	354	391	428	465	37-38
1.24	502	539	576	613	650	687	724	760	797	833	36-37
1.25	870	907	943	979	016	052	088	125	161	197	36-37
1.26	.79 233	269	305	341	377	413	449	484	520	556	35-36
1.27	592	627	663	698	734	769	804	840	875	910	35-36
1.28	945	981	016	051	086	121	156	191	225	260	34-36
1.29	.80 295	330	364	399	433	468	502	537	571	606	34-35
1.30	640	674	708	743	777	811	845	879	913	947	33-35
1.31	980	014	048	082	115	149	183	216	250	283	33-34
1.32	.81 316	350	383	416	450	483	516	549	582	615	33-34
1.33	648	681	714	747	780	812	845	878	910	943	32-33
1.34	975	008	040	073	105	137	170	202	234	266	32-33
1.35	.82 298	330	362	394	426	458	490	522	554	585	31-32
1.36	617	649	680	712	743	775	806	837	869	900	31-32
1.37	931	963	994	025	056	087	118	149	180	211	30-32
1.38	.83 241	272	303	334	364	395	425	456	486	517	30-31
1.39	547	577	608	638	668	698	729	759	789	819	30-31
1.40	849	879	908	938	968	998	028	057	087	116	29-30
1.41	.84 146	176	205	234	264	293	322	352	381	410	29-30
1.42	439	468	497	526	555	584	613	642	671	700	28-29
1.43	728	757	786	814	843	871	900	928	957	985	28-29
1.44	.85 013	042	070	098	126	154	182	210	238	266	28-29
1.45	294	322	350	378	405	433	461	488	516	543	27-28
1.46	571	598	626	653	681	708	735	762	790	817	27-28
1.47	844	871	898	925	952	979	006	032	059	086	26-27
1.48	.86 113	139	166	193	219	246	272	299	325	351	26-27
1.49	378	404	430	456	482	509	535	561	587	613	26-27

NORMAL PROBABILITY INTEGRAL $\dfrac{1}{\sqrt{2\pi}}\displaystyle\int_{-x}^{x} e^{-\frac{1}{2}t^2}\,dt$

x	0	1	2	3	4	5	6	7	8	9	Diff.
1.50	.86 639	664	690	716	742	768	793	819	845	870	25-26
1.51	896	921	947	972	997	023	048	073	099	124	25-26
1.52	.87 149	174	199	224	249	274	299	324	349	374	24-25
1.53	398	423	448	472	497	522	546	571	595	620	24-25
1.54	644	668	693	717	741	765	790	814	838	862	24-25
1.55	886	910	934	958	982	005	029	053	077	100	23-24
1.56	.88 124	148	171	195	218	242	265	289	312	335	23-24
1.57	358	382	405	428	451	474	497	520	543	566	23-24
1.58	589	612	635	658	681	703	726	749	771	794	22-23
1.59	817	839	862	884	906	929	951	973	996	018	22-23
1.60	.89 040	062	084	107	129	151	173	195	216	238	21-23
1.61	260	282	304	326	347	369	391	412	434	455	21-22
1.62	477	498	520	541	562	584	605	626	648	669	21-22
1.63	690	711	732	753	774	795	816	837	858	879	20-21
1.64	899	920	941	962	982	003	024	044	065	085	20-21
1.65	.90 106	126	147	167	187	208	228	248	268	288	20-21
1.66	309	329	349	369	389	409	429	449	468	488	19-20
1.67	508	528	548	567	587	607	626	646	665	685	19-20
1.68	704	724	743	762	782	801	820	840	859	878	19-20
1.69	897	916	935	954	973	992	011	030	049	068	19
1.70	.91 087	106	124	143	162	181	199	218	236	255	18-19
1.71	273	292	310	329	347	365	384	402	420	439	18-19
1.72	457	475	493	511	529	547	565	583	601	619	18
1.73	637	655	673	690	708	726	744	761	779	797	17-18
1.74	814	832	849	867	884	902	919	936	954	971	17-18
1.75	988	005	023	040	057	074	091	108	125	142	17-18
1.76	.92 159	176	193	210	227	244	260	277	294	311	16-17
1.77	327	344	361	377	394	410	427	443	460	476	16-17
1.78	492	509	525	541	558	574	590	606	622	639	16-17
1.79	655	671	687	703	719	735	751	766	782	798	15-16
1.80	814	830	845	861	877	893	908	924	939	955	15-16
1.81	970	986	001	017	032	048	063	078	094	109	15-16
1.82	.93 124	139	155	170	185	200	215	230	245	260	15-16
1.83	275	290	305	320	335	349	364	379	394	408	14-15
1.84	423	438	452	467	482	496	511	525	540	554	14-15
1.85	569	583	597	612	626	640	655	669	683	697	14-15
1.86	711	726	740	754	768	782	796	810	824	838	14-15
1.87	852	865	879	893	907	921	934	948	962	976	13-14
1.88	989	003	016	030	044	057	071	084	097	111	13-14
1.89	.94 124	138	151	164	177	191	204	217	230	244	13-14
1.90	257	270	283	296	309	322	335	348	361	374	13
1.91	387	400	412	425	438	451	463	476	489	502	12-13
1.92	514	527	539	552	565	577	590	602	614	627	12-13
1.93	639	652	664	676	689	701	713	725	738	750	12-13
1.94	762	774	786	798	810	823	835	847	859	870	11-13
1.95	882	894	906	918	930	942	953	965	977	989	11-12
1.96	.95 000	012	024	035	047	059	070	082	093	105	11-12
1.97	116	128	139	150	162	173	185	196	207	218	11-12
1.98	230	241	252	263	274	286	297	308	319	330	11-12
1.99	341	352	363	374	385	396	407	417	428	439	10-11

NORMAL PROBABILITY INTEGRAL $\dfrac{.1}{\sqrt{2\pi}}\displaystyle\int_{-x}^{x} e^{-\frac{1}{2}t^2}\,dt$

x	0	1	2	3	4	5	6	7	8	9	Diff.
2.00	.95 450	461	472	482	493	504	514	525	536	546	10-11
2.01	557	567	578	589	599	610	620	630	641	651	10-11
2.02	662	672	682	693	703	713	724	734	744	754	10-11
2.03	764	775	785	795	805	815	825	835	845	855	10-11
2.04	865	875	885	895	905	915	924	934	944	954	9-10
2.05	964	973	983	993	002	012	022	031	041	051	9-10
2.06	.96 060	070	079	089	098	108	117	127	136	145	9-10
2.07	155	164	173	183	192	201	211	220	229	238	9-10
2.08	247	257	266	275	284	293	302	311	320	329	9-10
2.09	338	347	356	365	374	383	392	401	409	418	8-9
2.10	427	436	445	453	462	471	480	488	497	506	8-9
2.11	514	523	531	540	548	557	566	574	582	591	8-9
2.12	599	608	616	625	633	641	650	658	666	675	8-9
2.13	683	691	699	708	716	724	732	740	748	756	8-9
2.14	765	773	781	789	797	805	813	821	829	837	7-8
2.15	844	852	860	868	876	884	892	899	907	915	7-8
2.16	923	930	938	946	954	961	969	977	984	992	7-8
2.17	999	007	014	022	029	037	044	052	059	067	7-8
2.18	.97 074	082	089	096	104	111	118	126	133	140	7-8
2.19	148	155	162	169	176	184	191	198	205	212	7-8
2.20	219	226	233	241	248	255	262	269	276	283	6-8
2.21	289	296	303	310	317	324	331	338	345	351	6-7
2.22	358	365	372	378	385	392	399	405	412	419	6-7
2.23	425	432	439	445	452	458	465	471	478	484	6-7
2.24	491	497	504	510	517	523	530	536	542	549	6-7
2.25	555	561	568	574	580	587	593	599	605	612	6-7
2.26	618	624	630	636	643	649	655	661	667	673	6-7
2.27	679	685	691	697	703	709	715	721	727	733	6
2.28	739	745	751	757	763	769	775	780	786	792	5-6
2.29	798	804	809	815	821	827	832	838	844	850	5-6
2.30	855	861	866	872	878	883	889	895	900	906	5-6
2.31	911	917	922	928	933	939	944	950	955	960	5-6
2.32	966	971	977	982	987	993	998	003	009	014	5-6
2.33	.98 019	025	030	035	040	046	051	056	061	066	5-6
2.34	072	077	082	087	092	097	102	107	113	118	5-6
2.35	123	128	133	138	143	148	153	158	163	168	5
2.36	173	177	182	187	192	197	202	207	212	216	4-5
2.37	221	226	231	236	240	245	250	255	259	264	4-5
2.38	269	273	278	283	287	292	297	301	306	311	4-5
2.39	315	320	324	329	333	338	342	347	352	356	4-5
2.40	360	365	369	374	378	383	387	392	396	400	4-5
2.41	405	409	413	418	422	426	431	435	439	444	4-5
2.42	448	452	456	461	465	469	473	478	482	486	4-5
2.43	490	494	498	503	507	511	515	519	523	527	4-5
2.44	531	535	539	543	547	551	555	559	563	567	4
2.45	571	575	579	583	587	591	595	599	603	607	4
2.46	611	614	618	622	626	630	634	637	641	645	3-4
2.47	649	653	656	660	664	668	671	675	679	682	3-4
2.48	686	690	694	697	701	704	708	712	715	719	3-4
2.49	723	726	730	733	737	740	744	748	751	755	3-4

NORMAL PROBABILITY INTEGRAL $\dfrac{1}{\sqrt{2\pi}}\displaystyle\int_{-x}^{x} e^{-\frac{1}{2}t^2}\,dt$

x	0	1	2	3	4	5	6	7	8	9	Diff.
2.5	.98 758	793	826	859	891	923	953	983	012	040	28-35
2.6	.99 068	095	121	146	171	195	219	241	264	285	21-27
2.7	307	327	347	367	386	404	422	439	456	473	16-20
2.8	489	505	520	535	549	563	576	590	602	615	12-16
2.9	627	639	650	661	672	682	692	702	712	721	9-12
3.0	730	739	747	755	763	771	779	786	793	800	6-9
3.1	806	813	819	825	831	837	842	848	853	858	5-7
3.2	863	867	872	876	880	885	889	892	896	900	3-5
3.3	903	907	910	913	916	919	922	925	928	930	2-4
3.4	933	935	937	940	942	944	946	948	950	952	1-3
3.5	953	955	957	958	960	961	963	964	966	967	1-2
3.6	968	969	971	972	973	974	975	976	977	978	0-2
3.7	978	979	980	981	982	982	983	984	984	985	0-1
3.8	986	986	987	987	988	988	989	989	990	990	0-1
3.9	990	991	991	992	992	992	993	993	993	993	0-1
4.0	994	994	994	994	995	995	995	995	995	996	0-1
4.1	996	996	996	996	997	997	997	997	997	997	0-1
4.2	997	997	998	998	998	998	998	998	998	998	0-1
4.3	998	998	998	999	999	999	999	999	999	999	0-1
4.4	999	999	999	999	999	999	999	999	999	999	0
4.5	999	999	999	999	999	999	999	000	000	000	0-1
1.00											

For a large table of this integral and its first derivative, of 15 decimal places, see Vol. II, "Tables of Probability Functions," A. N. Lowan, Technical Director, Work Projects Administration for the City of New York, sponsored and sold by the National Bureau of Standards, Washington, D. C.

ERROR FUNCTION, OR PROBABILITY INTEGRAL

$$\text{erf } x = \frac{2}{\sqrt{\pi}} \int_0^x e^{-x^2} dx$$

x	0	1	2	3	4	5	6	7	8	9	Diff.
.00	.00 000	113	226	339	451	564	677	790	903	016	112-113
.01	.01 128	241	354	467	580	692	805	918	031	144	112-113
.02	.02 256	369	482	595	708	820	933	046	159	271	112-113
.03	.03 384	497	610	722	835	948	060	173	286	398	112-113
.04	.04 511	624	736	849	962	074	187	299	412	525	112-113
.05	.05 637	750	862	975	087	200	312	425	537	650	112-113
.06	.06 762	875	987	099	212	324	437	549	661	773	112-113
.07	.07 886	998									
	.08		110	223	335	447	559	671	784	896	112-113
.08	.09 008	120	232	344	456	568	680	792	904	016	112
.09	.10 128	240	352	464	576	687	799	911	023	135	111-112
.10	.11 246	358	470	581	693	805	916	028	139	251	111-112
.11	.12 362	474	585	697	808	919	031	142	253	365	111-112
.12	.13 476	587	698	809	921	032	143	254	365	476	111-112
.13	.14 587	698	809	919	030	141	252	363	473	584	110-111
.14	.15 695	805	916	027	137	248	358	468	579	689	110-111
.15	.16 800	910	020	130	241	351	461	571	681	791	110-111
.16	.17 901	011	121	231	341	451	560	670	780	890	109-110
.17	.18 999										
	.19		109	218	328	437	547	656	766	875	984	109-110
.18	.20 094	203	312	421	530	639	748	857	966	075	109
.19	.21 184	293	402	510	619	728	836	945	053	162	108-109
.20	.22 270	379	487	595	704	812	920	028	136	244	108-109
.21	.23 352	460	568	676	784	891	999	107	214	322	107-108
.22	.24 430	537	645	752	859	967	074	181	288	395	107-108
.23	.25 502	609	716	823	930	037	144	250	357	463	106-107
.24	.26 570	677	783	889	996	102	208	314	421	527	106-107
.25	.27 633	739	845	950	056	162	268	373	479	584	105-106
.26	.28 690	795	901	006	111	217	322	427	532	637	105-106
.27	.29 742	847	952	056	161	266	370	475	579	684	104-105
.28	.30 788	892	997	101	205	309	413	517	621	725	103-105
.29	.31 828	922	036	139	243	346	450	553	656	760	103-104
.30	.32 863	966	069	172	275	378	480	583	686	788	102-103
.31	.33 891	993	096	198	300	403	505	607	709	811	102-103
.32	.34 913	014	116	218	319	421	523	624	725	827	101-102
.33	.35 928	029	130	231	332	433	534	635	735	836	100-101
.34	.36 936	037	137	238	338	438	538	636	738	838	100-101
.35	.37 938	038	138	237	337	436	536	635	735	834	99-100
.36	.38 933	032	131	230	329	428	526	625	724	822	98-99
.37	.39 921	019	117	215	314	412	510	608	705	803	97-99
.38	.40 901	999	096	194	291	388	486	583	680	777	97-98
.39	.41 874	971	068	164	261	358	454	550	647	743	96-97
.40	.42 839	935	031	127	223	319	415	510	606	701	95-96
.41	.43 797	892	988	083	178	273	368	463	557	652	94-96
.42	.44 747	841	936	030	124	219	313	407	501	595	94-95
.43	.45 689	782	876	970	063	157	250	343	436	529	93-94
.44	.46 623	715	808	901	994	086	179	271	364	456	92-93
.45	.47 548	640	732	824	916	008	100	191	283	374	91-92
.46	.48 466	557	648	739	830	921	012	103	193	284	90-91
.47	.49 375	465	555	646	736	826	916	006	096	185	89-91
.48	.50 275	365	454	543	633	722	811	900	989	078	89-90
.49	.51 167	256	344	433	521	609	698	786	874	962	88-89

x	0	1	2	3	4	5	6	7	8	9	Diff.
.50	.52 050	138	226	313	401	488	576	663	750	837	87 - 88
.51	924	011	098	185	272	358	445	531	617	704	86 - 87
.52	.53 790	876	962	048	134	219	305	390	476	561	85 - 86
.53	.54 646	732	817	902	987	071	156	241	325	410	84 - 86
.54	.55 494	578	662	746	830	914	998	082	165	249	83 - 84
.55	.56 332	416	499	582	665	748	831	914	996	079	82 - 84
.56	.57 162	244	326	409	491	573	655	737	818	900	81 - 83
.57	982	063	144	226	307	388	469	550	631	712	80 - 82
.58	.58 792	873	953	034	114	194	274	354	434	514	80 - 81
.59	.59 594	673	753	832	912	991	070	149	228	307	79 - 80
.60	.60 386	464	543	621	700	778	856	934	012	090	78 - 79
.61	.61 168	246	323	401	478	556	633	710	787	864	77 - 78
.62	941	018	095	171	248	324	400	477	553	629	76 - 77
.63	.62 705	780	856	932	007	083	158	233	309	384	75 - 76
.64	.63 459	533	608	683	757	832	906	981	055	129	74 - 75
.65	.64 203	277	351	424	498	572	645	718	791	865	73 - 74
.66	938	011	083	156	229	301	374	446	519	591	72 - 73
.67	.65 663	735	807	878	950	022	093	165	236	307	71 - 72
.68	.66 378	449	520	591	662	732	803	873	944	014	70 - 71
.69	.67 084	154	224	294	364	433	503	572	642	711	69 - 70
.70	780	849	918	987	056	125	193	262	330	398	68 - 69
.71	.68 467	535	603	671	738	806	874	941	009	076	67 - 68
.72	.69 143	210	278	344	411	478	545	611	678	744	66 - 68
.73	810	877	943	009	075	140	206	272	337	403	65 - 67
.74	.70 468	533	598	663	728	793	858	922	987	051	64 - 65
.75	.71 116	180	244	308	372	436	500	563	627	690	63 - 64
.76	754	817	880	943	006	069	132	195	257	320	62 - 63
.77	.72 382	444	507	569	631	693	755	816	878	940	61 - 63
.78	.73 001	062	124	185	246	307	368	429	489	550	60 - 62
.79	610	671	731	791	851	911	971	031	091	151	59 - 61
.80	.74 210	270	329	388	447	506	565	624	683	742	59 - 60
.81	800	859	917	976	034	092	150	208	266	323	57 - 59
.82	.75 381	439	496	553	611	668	725	782	839	896	56 - 58
.83	952	009	066	122	178	234	291	347	403	459	55 - 57
.84	.76 514	570	626	681	736	792	847	902	957	012	55 - 56
.85	.77 067	122	176	231	285	340	394	448	502	556	54 - 55
.86	610	664	718	771	825	878	932	985	038	091	53 - 54
.87	.78 144	197	250	302	355	408	460	512	565	617	52 - 53
.88	669	721	773	824	876	928	979	031	082	133	51 - 52
.89	.79 184	235	286	337	388	439	489	540	590	641	50 - 51
.90	691	741	791	841	891	941	990	040	090	139	49 - 50
.91	.80 188	238	287	336	385	434	482	531	580	628	48 - 50
.92	677	725	773	822	870	918	966	013	061	109	47 - 49
.93	.81 156	204	251	299	346	393	440	487	534	580	46 - 48
.94	627	674	720	767	813	859	905	951	997	043	46 - 47
.95	.82 089	135	180	226	271	317	362	407	452	497	45 - 46
.96	542	587	632	677	721	766	810	855	899	943	44 - 45
.97	987	031	075	119	162	206	250	293	337	380	43 - 44
.98	.83 423	466	509	552	595	638	681	723	766	808	42 - 43
.99	851	893	935	977	020	061	103	145	187	229	41 - 42
.84											

x	0	1	2	3	4	5	6	7	8	9	Diff.
1.00	.84 270	312	353	394	435	477	518	559	600	640	40 - 42
1.01	681	722	762	803	843	883	924	964	004	044	40 - 41
1.02	.85 084	124	163	203	243	282	322	361	400	439	39 - 40
1.03	478	517	556	595	634	673	711	750	788	827	38 - 39
1.04	865	903	941	979	017	055	093	131	169	206	37 - 38
1.05	.86 244	281	318	356	393	430	467	504	541	578	36 - 38
1.06	614	651	688	724	760	797	833	869	905	941	36 - 37
1.07	977	013	049	085	120	156	191	227	262	297	35 - 36
1.08	.87 333	368	403	438	473	507	542	577	611	646	34 - 35
1.09	680	715	749	783	817	851	885	919	953	987	34 - 35
1.10	.88 021	054	088	121	155	188	221	254	287	320	33 - 34
1.11	353	386	419	452	484	517	549	582	614	647	32 - 33
1.12	679	711	743	775	807	839	871	902	934	966	31 - 32
1.13	997	029	060	091	122	154	185	216	247	277	30 - 32
1.14	.89 308	339	370	400	431	461	492	522	552	582	30 - 31
1.15	612	642	672	702	732	762	792	821	851	880	29 - 30
1.16	910	939	968	997	027	056	085	114	142	171	28 - 30
1.17	.90 200	229	257	286	314	343	371	399	428	456	28 - 29
1.18	484	512	540	568	595	623	651	678	706	733	27 - 28
1.19	761	788	815	843	870	897	924	951	978	005	26 - 28
1.20	.91 031	058	085	111	138	164	191	217	243	269	26 - 27
1.21	296	322	348	374	399	425	451	477	502	528	25 - 26
1.22	553	579	604	630	655	680	705	730	755	780	25 - 26
1.23	805	830	855	879	904	929	953	978	002	026	24 - 25
1.24	.92 051	075	099	123	147	171	195	219	243	266	23 - 24
1.25	290	314	337	361	384	408	431	454	477	500	23 - 24
1.26	524	547	570	593	615	638	661	684	706	729	22 - 23
1.27	751	774	796	819	841	863	885	907	929	951	22 - 23
1.28	973	995	017	039	061	082	104	126	147	168	21 - 22
1.29	.93 190	211	232	254	275	296	317	338	359	380	21 - 22
1.30	401	422	442	463	484	504	525	545	566	586	20 - 21
1.31	606	627	647	667	687	707	727	747	767	787	20 - 21
1.32	807	826	846	866	885	905	924	944	963	982	19 - 20
1.33	.94 002	021	040	059	078	097	116	135	154	173	18 - 19
1.34	191	210	229	247	266	284	303	321	340	358	18 - 19
1.35	376	394	413	431	449	467	485	503	521	538	17 - 19
1.36	556	574	592	609	627	644	662	679	697	714	17 - 18
1.37	731	748	766	783	800	817	834	851	868	885	17 - 18
1.38	902	918	935	952	968	985	002	018	035	051	16 - 17
1.39	.95 067	084	100	116	132	148	165	181	197	213	16 - 17
1.40	229	244	260	276	292	307	323	339	354	370	15 - 16
1.41	385	401	416	431	447	462	477	492	507	523	15 - 16
1.42	538	553	568	582	597	612	627	642	656	671	14 - 15
1.43	686	700	715	729	744	758	773	787	801	815	14 - 15
1.44	830	844	858	872	886	900	914	928	942	956	14
1.45	970	983	997	011	024	038	051	065	078	092	13 - 14
1.46	.96 105	119	132	145	159	172	185	198	211	224	13 - 14
1.47	237	250	263	276	289	302	315	327	340	353	12 - 13
1.48	365	378	391	403	416	428	440	453	465	478	12 - 13
1.49	490	502	514	526	539	551	563	575	587	599	12 - 13

x	0	1	2	3	4	5	6	7	8	9	Diff.
1.5	.96 611	728	841	952	059	$\overline{162}$	$\overline{263}$	$\overline{360}$	$\overline{455}$	$\overline{546}$	89 - 117
1.6	.97 635	721	804	884	962	$\overline{038}$	$\overline{110}$	$\overline{181}$	$\overline{249}$	$\overline{315}$	64 - 86
1.7	.98 379	441	500	$\underline{558}$	613	667	719	769	817	864	45 - 62
1.8	909	952	994	035	074	111	147	182	216	248	31 - 43
1.9	.99 279	309	338	366	392	418	443	466	489	511	21 - 30
2.0	532	552	572	591	609	626	642	658	673	688	14 - 20
2.1	702	715	728	741	753	764	775	785	795	805	9 - 13
2.2	814	822	831	839	846	854	861	867	874	880	6 - 9
2.3	886	891	897	902	906	911	915	920	924	928	3 - 6
2.4	931	935	938	941	944	947	950	952	955	957	2 - 4
2.5	959	961	963	965	967	969	971	972	974	975	1 - 2
2.6	976	978	979	980	981	982	983	984	985	986	1 - 2
2.7	987	987	988	989	989	990	991	991	992	992	0 - 1
2.8	992	993	993	994	994	994	995	995	995	996	0 - 1
2.9	996	996	996	997	997	997	997	997	997	998	0 - 1
3.0	998	998	998	998	998	998	998	999	999	999	0 - 1
3.1	999	999	999	$\underline{999}$	999	999	999	999	999	999	0
3.2	999	999	999	$\overline{000}$	$\overline{000}$	$\overline{000}$	$\overline{000}$	$\overline{000}$	$\overline{000}$	$\overline{000}$	0 - 1
1.00											

Adapted from "A Short Table of Integrals," by
B. O. Peirce, pages 116 - 120, Ginn and Company, Boston.

For a large table of the error function and its first derivative, see Vol. I, "Tables of Probability Functions," published by the National Bureau of Standards, Washington, D.C.

$$J_0(x)$$

x	0	1	2	3	4	5	6	7	8	9	Diff.
.0	1.0 000	000	999	998	996	994	991	988	984	980	0 - 5
.1	.9 975	970	964	958	951	944	936	928	919	910	5 - 10
.2	900	890	879	868	857	844	832	819	805	791	10 - 15
.3	776	761	746	730	713	696	679	661	642	623	15 - 19
.4	604	584	564	543	522	500	478	455	432	409	20 - 24
.5	385	360	335	310	284	258	231	204	177	149	25 - 29
.6	120	091	062	032	002	971	940	909	877	845	29 - 33
.7	.8 812	779	745	711	677	642	607	572	536	500	33 - 37
.8	463	426	388	350	312	274	235	195	156	116	37 - 41
.9	075	034	993	952	910	868	825	783	739	696	41 - 44
1.0	.7 652	608	563	519	473	428	382	336	290	243	44 - 47
.1	196	149	101	054	006	957	909	860	810	761	47 - 50
.2	.6 711	661	611	561	510	459	408	356	305	253	50 - 52
.3	201	149	096	043	990	937	884	830	777	723	52 - 54
.4	.5 669	614	560	505	450	395	340	285	230	174	55 - 56
.5	118	062	006	950	894	838	781	725	668	611	56 - 57
.6	.4 554	497	440	383	325	268	210	153	095	038	57 - 58
.7	.3 980	922	864	806	748	690	632	574	516	458	58
.8	400	342	284	225	167	109	051	993	934	876	58 - 59
.9	.2 818	760	702	644	586	528	470	412	354	297	57 - 58
2.0	239	181	124	066	009	951	894	837	780	723	57 - 58
.1	.1 666	609	553	496	440	383	327	271	215	159	55 - 57
.2	104	048	993	937	882	827	773	718	664	609	54 - 56
.3	.0 555	502	448	394	341	288	235	182	130	077	52 - 54
.4	025	027	079	130	181	232	283	334	384	434	50 - 52
.5	-.0 484	533	583	632	681	729	778	826	873	921	47 - 50
.6	968	015	062	108	154	200	245	291	336	380	44 - 47
.7	-.1 424	469	512	556	599	641	684	726	768	809	41 - 45
.8	850	891	932	972	012	051	090	129	167	205	38 - 41
.9	-.2 243	280	317	354	390	426	462	497	532	566	34 - 37
3.0	601	634	668	701	733	765	797	829	860	890	30 - 34
.1	921	951	980	009	038	066	094	122	149	176	26 - 30
.2	-.3 202	228	253	278	303	328	351	375	398	421	22 - 26
.3	443	465	486	507	528	548	568	587	606	625	18 - 22
.4	643	661	678	695	711	727	743	758	773	787	14 - 18
.5	801	815	828	841	853	865	876	887	898	908	10 - 14
.6	918	927	936	944	953	960	967	974	981	987	5 - 9
.7	992	997	002	007	011	014	017	020	022	024	2 - 5
.8	-.4 026	027	027	028	027	027	026	025	023	021	0 - 3
.9	018	015	012	008	004	000	995	990	984	978	3 - 7
4.0	-.3 971	965	958	950	942	934	925	916	907	897	6 - 10
.1	887	876	865	854	842	831	818	806	793	779	11 - 14
.2	766	752	737	722	707	692	676	660	644	627	14 - 17
.3	610	593	575	557	539	520	501	482	463	443	17 - 20
.4	423	402	381	360	339	318	296	274	251	228	21 - 23
.5	205	182	159	135	111	087	062	037	012	987	23 - 26
.6	-.2 961	936	910	883	857	830	803	776	749	721	25 - 28
.7	693	665	637	609	580	551	522	493	464	434	28 - 30
.8	404	374	344	314	283	253	222	191	160	129	30 - 32
.9	097	066	034	002	970	938	906	874	841	809	31 - 33
	-.1										

$$J_0(x)$$

x	0	1	2	3	4	5	6	7	8	9	Diff.
5.0	-.1 776	743	710	677	644	611	578	544	511	477	33 - 34
.1	443	410	376	342	308	274	240	206	171	137	33 - 35
.2	103	069	034	000	965	931	896	862	827	793	34 - 35
.3	-.0 758	723	689	654	620	585	550	516	481	447	34 - 35
.4	412	378	343	309	274	240	205	171	137	103	34 - 35
.5	068	034	000	034	068	102	135	169	203	236	33 - 34
.6	.0 270	303	336	370	403	436	469	501	534	567	32 - 33
.7	599	632	664	696	728	760	791	823	855	886	31 - 33
.8	917	948	979	010	040	071	101	131	161	191	29 - 31
.9	.1 220	250	279	308	337	366	394	423	451	479	27 - 30
6.0	506	534	561	589	616	642	669	695	721	747	26 - 28
.1	773	798	824	849	873	898	922	947	970	994	23 - 26
.2	.2 017	041	064	086	109	131	153	175	196	217	21 - 23
.3	238	259	279	299	319	339	358	377	396	415	18 - 21
.4	433	451	469	486	504	521	537	554	570	585	15 - 18
.5	601	616	631	646	660	674	688	702	715	728	12 - 15
.6	740	753	765	777	788	799	810	821	831	841	10 - 13
.7	851	860	869	878	886	895	902	910	917	924	7 - 9
.8	931	937	943	949	955	960	965	969	973	977	4 - 6
.9	981	984	987	990	993	995	997	998	999	000	1 - 3
7.0	.3 001	001	001	001	000	999	998	997	995	993	0 - 2
.1	.2 991	988	985	982	978	974	970	966	961	956	3 - 5
.2	951	945	939	933	927	920	913	906	898	890	6 - 8
.3	882	874	865	856	847	837	828	818	807	797	8 - 11
.4	786	775	764	752	740	728	715	703	690	677	11 - 14
.5	663	650	636	622	607	593	578	563	547	532	13 - 16
.6	516	500	484	467	451	434	416	399	381	364	16 - 18
.7	346	327	309	290	271	252	233	214	194	174	18 - 20
.8	154	134	113	093	072	051	030	009	987	965	20 - 22
.9	.1 944	922	899	877	855	832	809	786	763	740	22 - 23
8.0	717	693	669	645	622	597	573	549	524	500	23 - 25
.1	475	450	425	400	375	350	325	299	274	248	25 - 26
.2	222	196	170	144	118	092	066	039	013	987	26 - 27
.3	.0 960	933	907	880	853	826	800	773	746	719	26 - 27
.4	692	664	637	610	583	556	529	501	474	447	27 - 28
.5	419	392	365	337	310	283	255	228	201	174	27 - 28
.6	146	119	092	064	037	010	017	044	071	098	27 - 28
.7	-.0 125	152	179	206	233	259	286	313	339	366	26 - 27
.8	392	419	445	471	497	523	549	575	601	627	26 - 27
.9	653	678	704	729	754	779	804	829	854	879	24 - 26
9.0	903	928	952	976	000	024	048	072	096	119	23 - 25
.1	-.1 142	166	189	211	234	257	279	302	324	346	21 - 24
.2	367	389	411	432	453	474	495	516	536	556	20 - 22
.3	577	597	616	636	655	674	694	712	731	749	18 - 20
.4	768	786	804	821	839	856	873	890	907	923	16 - 18
.5	939	955	971	987	002	017	032	047	061	076	14 - 16
.6	-.2 090	104	117	131	144	157	169	182	194	206	12 - 14
.7	218	230	241	252	263	273	284	294	304	313	9 - 12
.8	323	332	341	350	358	366	374	382	389	396	7 - 9
.9	403	410	417	423	429	434	440	445	450	455	4 - 7

$$J_0(x)$$

x	0	1	2	3	4	5	6	7	8	9	Diff.
10.0	-.2 459	464	468	471	475	478	481	484	486	488	2 - 5
.1	490	492	493	495	496	496	497	497	497	497	0 - 2
.2	496	495	494	493	492	490	488	485	483	480	1 - 3
.3	477	474	470	467	463	458	454	449	444	439	3 - 5
.4	434	428	422	416	410	403	396	389	382	374	6 - 8
.5	366	358	350	342	333	324	315	306	296	286	8 - 10
.6	276	266	256	245	234	223	212	200	188	177	10 - 13
.7	164	152	140	127	114	101	087	074	060	046	12 - 14
.8	032	018	003	989	974	959	943	928	912	897	14 - 16
.9	-.1 881	865	848	832	815	798	781	764	747	730	16 - 18
11.0	712	694	676	658	640	622	603	584	566	547	18 - 19
.1	528	508	489	470	450	430	411	391	370	350	19 - 21
.2	330	309	289	268	247	227	206	185	163	142	20 - 22
.3	121	099	078	056	034	012	991	969	946	924	21 - 23
.4	-.0 902	880	858	835	813	790	767	745	722	699	22 - 23
.5	677	654	631	608	585	562	539	516	493	469	23 - 24
.6	446	423	400	376	353	330	307	283	260	237	23 - 24
.7	213	190	167	143	120	097	073	050	027	004	23 - 24
.8	.0 020	043	066	089	112	135	159	182	205	228	22 - 24
.9	250	273	296	319	342	364	387	410	432	455	22 - 23
12.0	477	499	521	544	566	588	610	632	653	675	21 - 23
.1	697	718	740	761	782	803	824	845	866	887	21 - 22
.2	908	928	949	969	989	009	029	049	069	088	19 - 21
.3	.1 108	127	147	166	185	203	222	241	259	277	18 - 20
.4	296	314	331	349	367	384	401	418	435	452	17 - 18
.5	469	485	502	518	534	550	565	581	596	611	15 - 17
.6	626	641	655	670	684	698	712	726	739	753	13 - 15
.7	766	779	792	804	817	829	841	853	864	876	11 - 13
.8	887	898	909	920	930	940	950	960	970	979	9 - 11
.9	988	997	006	015	023	031	039	047	055	062	7 - 9
13.0	.2 069	076	083	089	096	102	108	113	119	124	5 - 7
.1	129	134	138	143	147	151	154	158	161	164	3 - 5
.2	167	169	172	174	176	178	179	180	182	182	0 - 3
.3	183	183	184	184	183	183	182	181	180	179	0 - 2
.4	177	175	173	171	169	166	163	160	157	154	2 - 4
.5	150	146	142	138	133	128	123	118	113	107	4 - 6
.6	101	095	089	083	076	069	062	055	048	040	6 - 8
.7	032	024	016	008	999	990	981	972	963	953	8 - 10
.8	.1 943	933	923	913	903	892	881	870	859	847	10 - 12
.9	836	824	812	800	788	775	763	750	737	724	12 - 13
14.0	711	697	684	670	656	642	628	613	599	584	13 - 15
.1	570	555	539	524	509	493	478	462	446	430	15 - 16
.2	414	397	381	364	348	331	314	297	280	262	16 - 18
.3	245	227	210	192	174	156	138	120	102	083	17 - 19
.4	065	046	028	009	990	971	952	933	914	895	18 - 20
.5	.0 875	856	837	817	798	778	758	738	719	699	19 - 20
.6	679	659	639	618	598	578	558	538	517	497	20 - 21
.7	476	456	436	415	394	374	353	333	312	291	20 - 21
.8	271	250	229	209	188	167	147	126	105	085	20 - 21
.9	064	043	023	002	019	039	060	081	101	122	20 - 21
	-.0										

$J_0(x)$

x	0	1	2	3	4	5	6	7	8	9	Diff.
15.0	-.0 142	163	183	204	224	244	265	285	305	325	20 - 21
.1	346	366	386	406	426	446	465	485	505	525	19 - 20
.2	544	564	583	603	622	641	660	679	698	717	19 - 20
.3	736	755	773	792	811	829	847	865	883	901	18 - 19
.4	919	937	955	972	990	0̅0̅7̅	0̅2̅4̅	0̅4̅2̅	0̅5̅9̅	0̅7̅6̅	16 - 18
.5	-.1 092	109	126	142	158	174	190	206	222	238	15 - 17
.6	253	269	284	299	314	329	343	358	372	387	14 - 16
.7	401	415	428	442	456	469	482	495	508	521	12 - 14
.8	533	546	558	570	582	594	605	617	628	639	11 - 13
.9	650	660	671	681	692	702	711	721	731	740	9 - 11
16.0	749	758	767	775	784	792	800	808	815	823	7 - 9
.1	830	837	844	851	858	864	870	876	882	887	6 - 7
.2	893	898	903	908	912	917	921	925	929	933	3 - 5
.3	936	939	942	945	948	950	953	955	957	958	1 - 3
.4	960	961	962	963	964	964	965	965	965	964	0 - 1
.5	964	963	962	961	960	958	957	955	953	951	1 - 3
.6	948	946	943	940	937	933	930	926	922	918	2 - 5
.7	913	909	904	899	894	889	883	878	872	866	4 - 6
.8	860	853	847	840	833	826	819	811	804	796	6 - 8
.9	788	780	771	763	754	745	736	727	718	708	8 - 10
17.0	699	689	679	669	658	648	637	626	615	604	10 - 11
.1	593	581	570	558	546	534	522	510	497	485	11 - 13
.2	472	459	446	433	420	406	393	379	365	351	13 - 14
.3	337	323	308	294	279	265	250	235	220	205	14 - 15
.4	190	174	159	143	127	112	096	080	064	047	15 - 17
.5	031	015	9̅9̅8̅	9̅8̅2̅	9̅6̅5̅	9̅4̅8̅	9̅3̅1̅	9̅1̅5̅	8̅9̅8̅	8̅8̅0̅	16 - 18
.6	-.0 863	846	829	811	794	776	759	741	723	706	17 - 18
.7	688	670	652	634	616	598	580	561	543	525	18 - 19
.8	506	488	470	451	433	414	396	377	358	340	18 - 19
.9	321	302	284	265	246	227	209	190	171	152	18 - 19
18.0	134	115	096	077	058	040	021	002	0̅1̅7̅	0̅3̅6̅	18 - 19
.1	.0 054	073	092	110	129	148	166	185	203	222	18 - 19
.2	241	259	277	296	314	332	351	369	387	405	18 - 19
.3	423	441	459	477	495	513	531	548	566	584	17 - 18
.4	601	618	636	653	670	687	704	721	738	755	17 - 18
.5	772	788	805	821	838	854	870	886	902	918	16 - 17
.6	934	949	965	980	996	0̅1̅1̅	0̅2̅6̅	0̅4̅1̅	0̅5̅6̅	0̅7̅1̅	15 - 16
.7	.1 086	100	115	129	143	157	171	185	199	212	13 - 15
.8	226	239	252	265	278	291	304	316	329	341	12 - 13
.9	353	365	377	389	400	412	423	434	445	456	10 - 12
19.0	466	477	487	497	507	517	527	537	546	555	9 - 11
.1	564	573	582	591	599	607	615	623	631	639	7 - 9
.2	646	653	660	667	674	681	687	693	699	705	6 - 7
.3	711	717	722	727	732	737	742	746	751	755	4 - 6
.4	759	762	766	770	773	776	779	781	784	786	2 - 4
.5	789	791	792	794	795	797	798	799	799	800	0 - 2
.6	800	801	801	800	800	800	799	798	797	796	0 - 2
.7	794	793	791	789	787	784	782	779	776	773	1 - 3
.8	770	767	763	760	756	752	747	743	738	734	3 - 5
.9	729	724	718	713	707	702	696	690	683	677	5 - 7
20.0	670										

$$J_1(x) \qquad = -J_0'(x)$$

x	0	1	2	3	4	5	6	7	8	9	Diff.
.0	.0 000	050	100	150	200	250	300	350	400	450	49 - 50
.1	499	549	599	649	698	748	797	847	896	946	49 - 50
.2	995	044	093	142	191	240	289	338	386	435	48 - 49
.3	.1 483	531	580	628	676	723	771	819	866	913	47 - 49
.4	960	007	054	101	147	194	240	286	332	377	45 - 47
.5	.2 423	468	513	558	603	647	692	736	780	823	43 - 45
.6	867	910	953	996	039	081	124	166	207	249	41 - 43
.7	.3 290	331	372	412	452	492	532	572	611	650	38 - 41
.8	688	727	765	803	840	878	915	951	988	024	35 - 39
.9	.4 059	095	130	165	200	234	268	302	335	368	33 - 36
1.0	401	433	465	497	528	559	590	620	650	680	29 - 32
.1	709	738	767	795	823	850	878	904	931	957	26 - 29
.2	983	008	033	058	082	106	130	153	176	198	22 - 25
.3	.5 220	242	263	284	305	325	344	364	383	401	18 - 22
.4	419	437	455	472	488	504	520	536	551	565	14 - 18
.5	579	593	607	620	632	644	656	667	678	689	10 - 14
.6	699	709	718	727	735	743	751	758	765	772	6 - 10
.7	778	783	788	793	798	802	805	808	811	813	2 - 5
.8	815	817	818	818	819	818	818	817	816	814	0 - 2
.9	812	809	806	803	799	794	790	785	779	773	3 - 6
2.0	767	761	754	746	738	730	721	712	703	693	6 - 10
.1	683	672	661	650	638	626	614	601	587	574	11 - 14
.2	560	545	530	515	500	484	468	451	434	416	15 - 18
.3	399	381	362	343	324	305	285	265	244	223	18 - 21
.4	202	180	158	136	113	091	067	044	020	996	22 - 25
.5	.4 971	946	921	895	870	843	817	790	763	736	25 - 28
.6	708	680	652	624	595	566	536	507	477	446	28 - 31
.7	416	385	354	323	291	260	228	195	163	130	31 - 33
.8	097	064	030	997	963	928	894	859	825	790	33 - 36
.9	.3 754	719	683	647	611	575	538	502	465	428	36 - 37
3.0	391	353	316	278	240	202	164	125	087	048	37 - 39
.1	009	970	931	892	852	813	773	733	694	654	39 - 41
.2	.2 613	573	533	492	452	411	370	330	289	248	40 - 41
.3	207	165	124	083	042	000	959	917	876	834	41 - 42
.4	.1 792	751	709	667	625	583	541	500	458	416	41 - 42
.5	374	332	290	248	206	164	122	080	038	996	41 - 42
.6	.0 955	913	871	829	788	746	704	663	621	580	41 - 42
.7	538	497	456	414	373	332	291	250	210	169	40 - 42
.8	128	088	047	007	033	074	114	153	193	233	39 - 41
.9	-.0 272	312	351	390	429	468	507	546	584	622	38 - 40
4.0	660	698	736	774	811	849	886	923	960	996	36 - 38
.1	-.1 033	069	105	141	177	212	247	282	317	352	34 - 36
.2	386	421	455	489	522	556	589	622	654	687	32 - 35
.3	719	751	783	814	845	876	907	938	968	998	30 - 32
.4	-.2 028	057	086	115	144	173	201	229	256	284	27 - 29
.5	311	337	364	390	416	442	467	492	517	541	24 - 27
.6	566	589	613	636	659	682	704	726	748	770	21 - 24
.7	791	812	832	852	872	892	911	930	949	967	18 - 21
.8	985	003	020	037	054	070	086	102	117	132	15 - 18
.9	-.3 147	161	175	189	202	216	228	241	253	264	11 - 14

$$J_1(x) \qquad = -J_0{}'(x)$$

x	0	1	2	3	4	5	6	7	8	9	Diff.
5.0	-.3 276	287	298	308	318	328	337	346	355	363	8 - 11
.1	371	379	386	393	400	406	412	417	423	428	4 - 8
.2	432	436	440	444	447	450	453	455	457	458	1 - 4
.3	460	460	461	461	461	461	460	459	457	456	0 - 3
.4	453	451	448	445	442	438	434	430	425	420	2 - 6
.5	414	409	403	396	390	383	376	368	360	352	5 - 9
.6	343	335	325	316	306	296	286	275	264	253	8 - 12
.7	241	230	218	205	192	179	166	153	139	125	11 - 15
.8	110	096	081	065	050	034	018	002	9̅8̅5̅	9̅6̅9̅	14 - 18
.9	-.2 951	934	917	899	881	862	844	825	806	786	17 - 20
6.0	767	747	727	707	686	666	645	623	602	580	20 - 22
.1	559	537	514	492	469	446	423	400	377	353	22 - 24
.2	329	305	281	257	232	207	182	157	132	106	24 - 26
.3	081	055	029	003	9̅7̅7̅	9̅5̅0̅	9̅2̅4̅	8̅9̅7̅	8̅7̅0̅	8̅4̅3̅	26 - 27
.4	-.1 816	789	762	734	707	679	651	623	595	567	27 - 29
.5	538	510	481	453	424	395	366	337	308	279	28 - 29
.6	250	220	191	162	132	102	073	043	013	9̅8̅3̅	29 - 30
.7	-.0 953	923	893	863	833	803	773	743	713	682	30 - 31
.8	652	622	592	561	531	501	470	440	410	379	30 - 31
.9	349	319	288	258	228	198	167	137	107	077	30 - 31
7.0	047	017	0̅1̅3̅	0̅4̅3̅	0̅7̅3̅	1̅0̅3̅	1̅3̅3̅	1̅6̅3̅	1̅9̅2̅	2̅2̅2̅	29 - 30
.1	.0 252	281	310	340	369	398	428	457	486	514	28 - 30
.2	543	572	601	629	658	686	714	742	770	798	28 - 29
.3	826	853	881	908	935	963	990	0̅1̅6̅	0̅4̅3̅	0̅7̅0̅	26 - 28
.4	.1 096	123	149	175	201	226	252	277	302	328	24 - 27
.5	352	377	402	426	450	475	498	522	546	569	23 - 25
.6	592	615	638	660	683	705	727	749	771	792	21 - 23
.7	813	834	855	875	896	916	936	956	975	994	19 - 21
.8	.2 014	032	051	069	088	106	123	141	158	175	17 - 19
.9	192	208	225	241	257	272	287	303	317	332	14 - 17
8.0	346	360	374	388	401	414	427	440	452	464	12 - 14
.1	476	488	499	510	521	531	542	552	561	571	9 - 12
.2	580	589	598	606	614	622	630	637	644	651	6 - 9
.3	657	664	670	675	681	686	691	696	700	704	4 - 7
.4	708	711	715	718	720	723	725	727	729	730	1 - 4
.5	731	732	733	733	733	733	732	731	730	729	0 - 1
.6	728	726	724	721	719	716	713	709	705	701	2 - 4
.7	697	693	688	683	678	672	666	660	654	648	4 - 7
.8	641	634	626	619	611	603	595	586	577	568	7 - 9
.9	559	550	540	530	519	509	498	487	476	465	9 - 12
9.0	453	441	429	417	404	391	378	365	352	338	12 - 14
.1	324	310	296	281	267	252	237	221	206	190	14 - 16
.2	174	158	142	125	108	091	074	057	040	022	16 - 18
.3	004	9̅8̅6̅	9̅6̅8̅	9̅5̅0̅	9̅3̅1̅	9̅1̅2̅	893	8̅7̅4̅	8̅5̅5̅	8̅3̅6̅	18 - 20
.4	.1 816	797	777	757	737	716	696	675	655	634	19 - 21
.5	613	591	570	549	527	506	484	462	440	418	21 - 23
.6	395	373	350	328	305	282	259	236	213	190	22 - 24
.7	166	143	119	096	072	048	025	001	9̅7̅7̅	9̅5̅3̅	23 - 25
.8	.0 928	904	880	856	831	807	782	758	733	708	24 - 25
.9	684	659	634	609	584	560	535	510	485	460	24 - 25

$$J_1(x) \qquad = -J_0{}'(x)$$

x	0	1	2	3	4	5	6	7	8	9	Diff.
10.0	.0 435	410	385	360	334	309	284	259	234	209	25 - 26
.1	184	159	134	109	084	059	034	009	0̄1̄6̄	0̄4̄1̄	25
.2	-.0 066	091	116	141	165	190	215	240	264	289	24 - 25
.3	313	338	362	386	411	435	459	483	507	531	24 - 25
.4	555	578	602	626	649	673	696	719	742	766	23 - 24
.5	789	811	834	857	879	902	924	946	968	990	22 - 23
.6	-.1 012	034	056	077	099	120	141	162	183	203	20 - 22
.7	224	244	265	285	305	325	344	364	383	403	19 - 21
.8	422	441	459	478	496	515	533	551	568	586	17 - 19
.9	603	621	638	655	671	688	704	720	736	752	16 - 18
11.0	768	783	798	814	828	843	857	872	886	900	13 - 16
.1	913	927	940	953	966	979	991	0̄0̄3̄	0̄1̄5̄	0̄2̄7̄	12 - 14
.2	-.2 039	050	061	072	083	093	104	114	123	133	9 - 11
.3	143	152	161	169	178	186	194	202	210	217	7 - 9
.4	225	231	238	245	251	257	263	268	274	279	5 - 7
.5	284	288	293	297	301	305	308	312	315	317	2 - 5
..6	320	322	324	326	328	329	331	332	332	333	0 - 2
.7	333	333	333	332	332	331	330	328	327	325	0 - 2
.8	323	321	318	315	312	309	306	302	298	294	3 - 4
.9	290	285	281	276	270	265	259	253	247	241	4 - 7
12.0	234	228	221	214	206	199	191	183	175	166	6 - 9
.1	157	149	140	130	121	111	101	091	081	070	8 - 11
.2	060	049	038	027	015	004	9̄9̄2̄	9̄8̄0̄	9̄6̄8̄	9̄5̄5̄	11 - 13
.3	-.1 943	930	917	904	891	877	863	850	836	821	13 - 15
.4	807	793	778	763	748	733	718	702	687	671	14 - 16
.5	655	639	623	606	590	573	556	539	522	505	16 - 18
.6	487	470	452	435	417	399	380	362	344	325	17 - 19
.7	307	288	269	250	231	212	192	173	154	134	19 - 20
.8	114	095	075	055	035	014	9̄9̄4̄	9̄7̄4̄	9̄5̄4̄	9̄3̄5̄	19 - 21
.9	-.0 912	892	871	850	830	809	788	767	746	724	20 - 22
13.0	703	682	661	639	618	596	575	553	532	510	21 - 22
.1	489	467	445	423	402	380	358	336	314	293	21 - 22
.2	271	249	227	205	183	161	139	117	096	074	21 - 22
.3	052	030	008	0̄1̄4̄	0̄3̄6̄	0̄5̄7̄	0̄7̄9̄	1̄0̄1̄	1̄2̄3̄	1̄4̄4̄	21 - 22
.4	.0 166	188	209	231	252	274	295	317	338	359	21 - 22
.5	380	402	423	444	465	486	507	528	548	569	20 - 22
.6	590	610	631	651	671	692	712	732	752	772	20 - 21
.7	791	811	831	850	870	889	908	927	946	965	19 - 20
.8	984	0̄0̄3̄	0̄2̄1̄	0̄4̄0̄	0̄5̄8̄	0̄7̄6̄	0̄9̄4̄	1̄1̄2̄	1̄3̄0̄	1̄4̄8̄	17 - 19
.9	.1 165	183	200	217	234	251	268	285	301	318	16 - 18
14.0	334	350	366	382	397	413	428	443	458	473	15 - 16
.1	488	502	517	531	545	559	573	586	600	613	13 - 15
.2	626	639	652	664	677	689	701	713	724	736	11 - 13
.3	747	758	769	780	791	801	811	821	831	841	9 - 11
.4	850	860	869	878	886	895	903	911	919	927	7 - 10
.5	934	942	949	956	962	969	975	981	987	993	6 - 8
.6	999	0̄0̄4̄	0̄0̄9̄	0̄1̄4̄	0̄1̄9̄	0̄2̄3̄	0̄2̄7̄	0̄3̄1̄	0̄3̄5̄	0̄3̄9̄	4 - 5
.7	.2 043	046	049	052	054	057	059	061	063	065	1 - 3
.8	066	067	068	069	070	070	070	070	070	069	0 - 1
.9	069	068	067	066	064	062	061	058	056	054	1 - 3

$J_1(x) \quad = -J_o'(x)$

					3	4	5	6	7	8	9	Diff.
[illegible]	[illegible]	[illegible]	[illegible]	[illegible]	[illegible]	038	035	031	027	022	018	3 - 5
[illegible]	[illegible]	[illegible]	[illegible]	[illegible]	[illegible]	$\overline{992}$	$\overline{987}$	$\overline{981}$	$\overline{975}$	$\overline{969}$	$\overline{962}$	5 - 7
[illegible]	[illegible]	[illegible]	[illegible]	[illegible]	[illegible]	927	919	912	904	896	887	6 - 9
[illegible]	[illegible]	[illegible]	[illegible]	[illegible]	[illegible]	843	834	824	814	804	794	9 - 10
[illegible]	[illegible]	[illegible]	[illegible]	[illegible]	[illegible]	741	730	719	707	696	684	10 - 12
[illegible]	[illegible]	[illegible]	[illegible]	[illegible]	[illegible]	623	610	597	584	571	558	12 - 14
[illegible]	[illegible]	[illegible]	[illegible]	[illegible]	[illegible]	489	475	461	446	432	417	13 - 15
[illegible]	[illegible]	[illegible]	[illegible]	[illegible]	[illegible]	342	326	310	295	279	263	15 - 16
[illegible]	[illegible]	[illegible]	[illegible]	[illegible]	[illegible]	182	165	148	131	114	097	16 - 17
[illegible]	[illegible]	[illegible]	[illegible]	[illegible]	[illegible]	011	$\overline{993}$	$\overline{976}$	$\overline{958}$	$\overline{940}$	$\overline{922}$	17 - 18
[illegible]	[illegible]	[illegible]	[illegible]	[illegible]	[illegible]	831	813	794	776	757	739	18 - 19
[illegible]	[illegible]	[illegible]	[illegible]	[illegible]	[illegible]	644	625	606	587	568	549	19
[illegible]	[illegible]	[illegible]	[illegible]	[illegible]	[illegible]	452	433	413	394	374	355	19 - 20
[illegible]	[illegible]	[illegible]	[illegible]	[illegible]	[illegible]	257	237	218	198	178	159	19 - 20
[illegible]	[illegible]	[illegible]	[illegible]	[illegible]	[illegible]	060	041	021	001	$\overline{018}$	$\overline{038}$	19 - 20
[illegible]	[illegible]	[illegible]	[illegible]	[illegible]	[illegible]	136	155	175	194	214	233	19 - 20
[illegible]	[illegible]	252	272	291	310	329	349	368	387	406	425	19 - 20
.7		444	462	481	500	519	537	556	574	593	611	18 - 19
.8		629	647	666	684	702	719	737	755	773	790	17 - 19
.9		807	825	842	859	876	893	910	927	944	960	16 - 18
17.0		977	993	$\overline{009}$	$\overline{025}$	$\overline{041}$	$\overline{057}$	$\overline{073}$	$\overline{089}$	$\overline{104}$	$\overline{120}$	15 - 16
.1	-.1	135	150	165	180	195	210	225	239	253	267	14 - 15
.2		281	295	309	323	336	350	363	376	389	402	12 - 14
.3		414	427	439	451	463	475	487	498	510	521	11 - 13
.4		532	543	554	564	575	585	595	605	615	625	9 - 11
.5		634	643	653	662	670	679	687	696	704	712	7 - 10
.6		719	727	734	742	749	755	762	769	775	781	6 - 8
.7		787	793	798	804	809	814	819	824	828	833	4 - 6
.8		837	841	844	848	851	854	857	860	863	865	2 - 4
.9		868	870	872	873	875	876	877	878	879	880	0 - 2
18.0		880	880	880	880	880	879	878	877	876	875	0 - 1
.1		874	872	870	868	866	863	861	858	855	852	2 - 4
.2		848	845	841	837	833	829	825	820	815	810	3 - 5
.3		805	800	794	789	783	777	771	764	758	751	5 - 7
.4		744	737	730	723	715	707	700	691	683	675	7 - 9
.5		666	658	649	640	631	621	612	602	592	582	8 - 10
.6		572	562	552	541	530	519	508	497	486	475	10 - 12
.7		463	451	439	428	415	403	391	378	366	353	11 - 13
.8		340	327	314	300	287	273	260	246	232	218	13 - 14
.9		204	190	176	161	147	132	117	102	087	072	14 - 15
19.0		057	042	026	011	$\overline{995}$	$\overline{980}$	$\overline{964}$	$\overline{948}$	$\overline{932}$	$\overline{916}$	15 - 16
.1	-.0	900	884	868	852	835	819	802	786	769	752	16 - 17
.2		735	718	701	684	667	650	633	616	599	581	17 - 18
.3		564	546	529	511	494	476	459	441	423	406	17 - 18
.4		388	370	352	334	316	299	281	263	245	227	17 - 18
.5		209	191	173	155	137	119	101	083	065	047	18
.6		029	011	$\overline{007}$	$\overline{025}$	$\overline{043}$	$\overline{061}$	$\overline{079}$	$\overline{097}$	$\overline{115}$	$\overline{133}$	18
.7	.0	151	169	187	204	222	240	258	275	293	311	17 - 18
.8		328	346	363	381	398	415	433	450	467	484	17 - 18
.9		501	518	535	552	569	586	602	619	635	652	16 - 17
20.0		668										

Acknowledgment is made to the Royal Society, London, England, for the Tables of $J_0(x)$ and $J_1(x)$ which are abridged from "Bessel Functions," Part I, Vol. VI of British Association Mathematical Tables, published by Cambridge University Press, London, Eng., 1937.

$J_2(x)$

x	0	1	2	3	4	5	6	7	8	9	Diff.
.0	.0 000	000	000	001	002	003	004	006	008	010	0 - 2
.1	012	015	018	021	024	028	032	036	040	045	3 - 5
.2	050	055	060	066	072	078	084	091	097	104	5 - 8
.3	112	119	127	135	143	152	160	169	178	188	7 - 10
.4	197	207	217	228	238	249	260	271	283	294	10 - 12
.5	306	318	330	343	356	369	382	395	409	423	12 - 14
.6	437	451	465	480	495	510	525	540	556	572	14 - 16
.7	588	604	620	637	654	671	688	705	723	740	16 - 18
.8	758	776	794	813	831	850	869	888	907	926	18 - 20
.9	946	966	985	0̅0̅5̅	0̅2̅5̅	0̅4̅6̅	0̅6̅6̅	0̅8̅7̅	1̅0̅7̅	1̅2̅8̅	19 - 21
1.0	.1 149	170	191	213	234	256	278	299	321	343	21 - 23
.1	366	388	410	433	456	478	501	524	547	570	22 - 23
.2	593	617	640	664	687	711	735	758	782	806	23 - 24
.3	830	854	878	903	927	951	976	0̅0̅0̅	0̅2̅4̅	0̅4̅9̅	24 - 25
.4	.2 074	098	123	147	172	197	222	246	271	296	24 - 25
.5	321	346	371	395	420	445	470	495	520	545	24 - 25
.6	570	595	619	644	669	694	719	743	768	793	24 - 25
.7	817	842	867	891	916	940	964	989	0̅1̅3̅	0̅3̅7̅	24 - 25
.8	.3 061	086	110	134	157	181	205	229	252	276	23 - 25
.9	299	323	346	369	392	415	438	461	483	506	22 - 24
2.0	528	551	573	595	617	639	661	682	704	725	21 - 23
.1	746	767	788	809	830	850	871	891	911	931	20 - 21
.2	951	970	990	0̅0̅9̅	0̅2̅8̅	0̅4̅7̅	0̅6̅6̅	0̅8̅4̅	1̅0̅3̅	1̅2̅1̅	18 - 20
.3	.4 139	157	175	192	210	227	244	261	277	294	16 - 18
.4	310	326	342	357	373	388	403	418	432	446	14 - 16
.5	461	475	488	502	515	528	541	553	566	578	12 - 14
.6	590	601	613	624	635	646	656	666	676	686	10 - 12
.7	696	705	714	723	731	739	747	755	763	770	7 - 9
.8	777	784	790	796	802	808	813	818	823	828	4 - 7
.9	832	836	840	844	847	850	853	855	857	859	2 - 4
3.0	861	862	863	864	865	865	865	865	864	863	0 - 1
.1	862	861	859	857	855	852	849	846	843	839	1 - 4
.2	835	831	827	822	817	811	806	800	794	787	4 - 7
.3	780	773	766	758	750	742	734	725	716	707	7 - 10
.4	697	687	677	667	656	645	634	622	611	599	10 - 13
.5	586	574	561	548	534	521	507	492	478	463	12 - 15
.6	448	433	417	401	385	369	352	335	318	301	15 - 18
.7	283	265	247	229	210	191	172	153	133	113	18 - 20
.8	093	073	052	031	010	9̅8̅9̅	9̅6̅7̅	9̅4̅5̅	9̅2̅3̅	9̅0̅1̅	20 - 22
.9	.3 879	856	833	810	786	763	739	715	690	666	23 - 25
4.0	641	616	591	566	540	515	489	463	436	410	25 - 27
.1	383	356	329	302	274	246	219	191	162	134	27 - 29
.2	105	077	048	019	9̅8̅9̅	9̅6̅0̅	9̅3̅0̅	9̅0̅1̅	8̅7̅1̅	8̅4̅1̅	28 - 30
.3	.2 811	780	750	719	688	657	626	595	564	532	30 - 32
.4	501	469	437	405	373	341	309	276	244	211	32 - 33
.5	178	146	113	080	047	013	9̅8̅0̅	9̅4̅7̅	9̅1̅3̅	8̅8̅0̅	32 - 34
.6	.1 846	812	778	745	711	677	643	608	574	540	33 - 35
.7	506	471	437	403	368	334	299	264	230	195	34 - 35
.8	161	126	091	056	022	9̅8̅7̅	9̅5̅2̅	9̅1̅7̅	8̅8̅2̅	8̅4̅8̅	34 - 35
.9	.0 813	778	743	709	674	639	604	570	535	500	34 - 35

The tables of $J_2(x)$ to $J_5(x)$, inclusive, are adapted from the large tables in the volumes "Tables of the Bessel Functions of the First Kind," published by the Staff of the Computation Laboratory, Harvard University, H. H. Aiken, Director, Harvard University Press, 1947.

$$J_2(x)$$

x	0	1	2	3	4	5	6	7	8	9	Diff.
5.0	.0 466	431	396	362	327	293	259	224	190	156	34 - 35
.1	121	087	053	019	015	049	083	116	150	184	33 - 34
.2	-.0 217	251	284	317	350	384	417	449	482	515	32 - 34
.3	547	580	612	645	677	709	741	772	804	836	31 - 33
.4	867	898	929	960	991	022	052	083	113	143	30 - 31
.5	-.1 173	203	233	262	291	321	350	378	407	435	28 - 30
.6	464	492	520	548	575	603	630	657	684	710	26 - 28
.7	737	763	789	815	840	866	891	916	941	965	24 - 26
.8	990	014	038	061	085	108	131	154	176	199	22 - 24
.9	-.2 221	243	264	286	307	328	348	369	389	409	20 - 22
6.0	429	448	467	486	505	523	542	560	577	595	17 - 19
.1	612	629	645	662	678	694	709	725	740	754	15 - 17
.2	769	783	797	811	824	837	850	863	875	887	12 - 14
.3	899	910	921	932	943	953	963	973	983	992	9 - 11
.4	-.3 001	009	018	026	034	041	048	055	062	068	6 - 9
.5	074	080	086	091	096	100	105	109	112	116	3 - 6
.6	119	122	125	127	129	131	132	133	134	135	0 - 3
.7	135	135	135	134	134	133	131	129	128	125	0 - 3
.8	123	120	117	114	110	106	102	097	093	087	3 - 6
.9	082	077	071	065	058	052	045	037	030	022	5 - 8
7.0	014	006	997	989	979	970	961	951	941	930	8 - 11
.1	-.2 920	909	898	886	875	863	851	858	826	813	11 - 13
.2	800	786	773	759	745	731	716	702	687	671	13 - 16
.3	656	640	624	608	592	576	559	542	525	507	16 - 18
.4	490	472	454	436	417	399	380	361	342	322	18 - 20
.5	303	283	263	243	223	202	181	161	140	118	20 - 22
.6	097	076	054	032	010	988	965	943	920	898	21 - 23
.7	-.1 875	852	828	805	782	758	734	710	686	662	23 - 24
.8	638	613	589	564	539	515	490	465	439	414	24 - 26
.9	389	363	338	312	286	260	234	208	182	156	25 - 26
8.0	130	104	077	051	024	998	971	944	917	891	26 - 27
.1	-.0 864	837	810	783	756	729	702	675	647	620	27 - 28
.2	593	566	538	511	484	456	429	402	374	347	27 - 28
.3	320	292	265	238	210	183	156	129	101	074	27 - 28
.4	047	020	007	035	062	089	116	143	170	196	26 - 28
.5	.0 223	250	277	303	330	356	383	409	436	462	26 - 27
.6	488	514	540	566	592	618	643	669	695	720	25 - 26
.7	745	770	796	821	845	870	895	920	944	968	24 - 26
.8	993	017	041	064	088	112	135	158	182	205	23 - 24
.9	.1 228	250	273	295	318	340	362	384	406	427	21 - 23
9.0	448	470	491	512	532	553	573	594	614	634	19 - 22
.1	653	673	692	711	730	749	768	786	804	822	18 - 20
.2	840	858	875	892	910	926	943	959	976	992	16 - 18
.3	.2 008	023	039	054	069	084	098	112	127	140	13 - 16
.4	154	168	181	194	207	219	232	244	256	267	11 - 14
.5	279	290	301	312	322	333	343	352	362	371	9 - 11
.6	380	389	398	406	415	422	430	438	445	452	6 - 9
.7	458	465	471	477	483	488	494	499	503	508	4 - 7
.8	512	516	520	524	527	530	533	535	538	540	2 - 4
.9	542	543	544	546	546	547	547	547	547	547	0 - 2

$$J_2(x)$$

x	0	1	2	3	4	5	6	7	8	9	Diff.
10.0	.2 546	545	544	543	541	540	537	535	533	530	1 - 3
.1	527	523	520	516	512	508	503	499	494	489	3 - 6
.2	483	478	472	466	459	453	446	439	432	424	5 - 8
.3	416	408	400	392	383	374	365	356	347	337	8 - 10
.4	327	317	307	296	285	274	263	252	240	228	10 - 12
.5	216	204	192	179	166	153	140	127	113	099	12 - 14
.6	085	071	057	042	028	013	998	982	967	951	14 - 16
.7	.1 936	920	904	887	871	854	837	821	803	786	16 - 18
.8	769	751	733	716	698	679	661	643	624	605	17 - 19
.9	586	567	548	529	510	490	470	451	431	411	19 - 21
11.0	390	370	350	329	309	288	267	246	225	204	20 - 21
.1	183	162	140	119	097	075	054	032	010	988	21 - 22
.2	.0 966	944	922	899	877	854	832	809	787	764	22 - 23
.3	741	719	696	673	650	627	604	581	558	535	22 - 23
.4	512	489	466	442	419	396	373	349	326	303	23 - 24
.5	279	256	233	209	186	163	139	116	093	069	23 - 24
.6	046	023	000	024	047	070	093	116	139	162	23 - 24
.7	-.0 185	208	231	254	277	300	323	346	368	391	22 - 23
.8	413	436	458	481	503	525	547	569	592	613	21 - 23
.9	635	657	679	700	722	743	765	786	807	828	21 - 22
12.0	849	870	891	912	932	953	973	993	013	033	20 - 21
.1	-.1 053	073	093	112	132	151	170	189	208	227	18 - 20
.2	245	264	282	300	318	336	354	372	389	407	17 - 19
.3	424	441	458	474	491	507	524	540	556	571	15 - 17
.4	587	603	618	633	648	663	677	691	706	720	14 - 16
.5	734	747	761	774	787	800	813	826	838	850	12 - 14
.6	862	874	886	897	908	919	930	941	951	962	10 - 12
.7	972	982	991	001	010	019	028	036	045	053	8 - 10
.8	-.2 061	069	077	084	091	098	105	111	118	124	6 - 8
.9	130	136	141	146	151	156	161	165	170	174	3 - 6
13.0	177	181	184	188	190	193	196	198	200	202	1 - 4
.1	203	205	206	207	208	208	209	209	209	208	0 - 2
.2	208	207	206	205	204	202	200	198	196	193	1 - 3
.3	191	188	185	181	178	174	170	166	162	157	3 - 5
.4	152	148	142	137	131	126	120	113	107	100	4 - 7
.5	094	087	079	072	064	057	049	040	032	023	7 - 9
.6	015	006	997	987	978	968	958	948	938	927	9 - 11
.7	-.1 917	906	895	884	872	861	849	837	825	813	11 - 12
.8	801	788	776	763	750	736	723	710	696	682	12 - 14
.9	668	654	640	625	611	596	581	566	551	536	14 - 16
14.0	520	505	489	473	457	441	425	408	392	375	15 - 17
.1	358	342	325	308	290	273	256	238	220	203	16 - 18
.2	185	167	149	130	112	094	075	057	038	019	18 - 19
.3	001	982	963	944	924	905	886	866	847	827	19 - 20
.4	-.0 808	788	768	749	729	709	689	669	649	629	19 - 20
.5	609	588	568	548	528	507	487	466	446	425	20 - 21
.6	405	384	364	343	323	302	281	261	240	219	20 - 21
.7	199	178	157	136	116	095	074	054	033	012	20 - 21
.8	.0 008	029	050	070	091	111	132	152	173	193	20 - 21
.9	214	234	255	275	295	315	335	356	376	396	20 - 21

$$J_2(x)$$

x	0	1	2	3	4	5	6	7	8	9	Diff.
15.0	.0 416	436	456	475	495	515	534	554	573	593	19 - 20
.1	612	632	651	670	689	708	727	746	764	783	18 - 20
.2	802	820	838	857	875	893	911	929	946	964	17 - 19
.3	982	999	016	034	051	068	085	101	118	135	16 - 18
.4	.1 151	167	183	200	215	231	247	262	278	293	15 - 17
.5	308	323	338	353	367	381	396	410	424	438	13 - 15
.6	451	465	478	491	504	517	530	543	555	567	12 - 14
.7	579	591	603	615	626	637	648	659	670	681	10 - 12
.8	691	701	711	721	731	741	750	759	768	777	9 - 10
.9	786	794	802	810	818	826	834	841	848	855	7 - 8
16.0	862	869	875	881	887	893	899	904	910	915	5 - 7
.1	920	924	929	933	937	941	945	949	952	955	3 - 5
.2	958	961	964	966	968	970	972	974	975	976	1 - 3
.3	977	978	979	979	979	979	979	979	978	978	0 - 1
.4	977	976	974	973	971	969	967	965	962	960	1 - 3
.5	957	954	951	947	944	940	936	932	927	923	3 - 5
.6	918	913	908	903	897	891	886	879	873	867	5 - 7
.7	860	854	847	840	832	825	817	809	801	793	6 - 8
.8	785	776	768	759	750	741	731	722	712	702	8 - 10
.9	692	682	672	661	651	640	629	618	607	595	10 - 12
17.0	584	572	560	548	536	524	511	499	486	473	12 - 13
.1	460	447	434	420	407	393	379	365	351	337	13 - 14
.2	323	308	294	279	265	250	235	220	204	189	14 - 16
.3	174	158	142	127	111	095	079	062	046	030	15 - 17
.4	013	997	980	964	947	930	913	896	879	862	16 - 18
.5	.0 844	827	810	792	775	757	739	721	704	686	17 - 18
.6	668	650	632	614	596	577	559	541	523	504	18 - 19
.7	486	467	449	430	412	393	375	356	337	319	18 - 19
.8	300	281	263	244	225	206	188	169	150	131	18 - 19
.9	112	094	075	056	037	018	000	019	038	057	18 - 19
18.0	-.0 075	094	113	131	150	169	187	206	224	243	18 - 19
.1	261	280	298	316	335	353	371	389	408	426	18 - 19
.2	444	462	480	497	515	533	551	568	586	603	17 - 18
.3	621	638	655	672	690	707	724	740	757	774	16 - 18
.4	791	807	824	840	856	872	888	904	920	936	16 - 17
.5	952	967	983	998	013	029	044	059	073	088	14 - 16
.6	-.1 103	117	132	146	160	174	188	202	215	229	13 - 15
.7	242	255	268	281	294	307	320	332	344	356	12 - 13
.8	368	380	392	404	415	426	437	448	459	470	11 - 12
.9	481	491	501	511	521	531	541	550	559	569	9 - 10
19.0	578	586	595	604	612	620	628	636	644	651	7 - 9
.1	658	666	673	680	686	693	699	705	711	717	6 - 8
.2	723	728	733	739	744	748	753	757	762	766	4 - 6
.3	770	773	777	780	783	786	789	792	794	797	2 - 4
.4	799	801	802	804	805	807	808	808	809	810	0 - 2
.5	810	810	810	810	809	809	808	807	806	805	0 - 2
.6	803	802	800	798	796	793	791	788	785	782	1 - 3
.7	779	776	772	768	764	760	756	751	747	742	3 - 5
.8	737	732	727	721	716	710	704	698	691	685	5 - 7
.9	678	672	665	658	650	643	635	628	620	612	6 - 9
20.0	603										

$$J_3(x)$$

x	0	1	2	3	4	5	6	7	8	9	Diff.
.0	.00 000	000	000	000	000	000	000	001	001	002	0 - 1
.1	002	003	004	005	006	007	009	010	012	014	1 - 3
.2	017	019	022	025	029	032	036	041	046	051	2 - 5
.3	056	062	068	074	081	089	096	105	113	122	6 - 10
.4	132	142	153	164	175	187	200	213	227	241	10 - 15
.5	256	272	288	305	322	340	359	378	398	419	16 - 21
.6	440	462	485	508	532	557	583	609	636	664	22 - 29
.7	693	722	753	784	816	848	882	916	952	988	29 - 37
.8	.01 025	063	101	141	181	223	265	308	352	397	38 - 46
.9	443	490	538	587	637	688	739	792	846	901	47 - 55
1.0	.0 196	201	207	213	219	225	231	237	244	250	5 - 7
.1	257	264	270	277	284	292	299	306	314	321	6 - 8
.2	329	337	344	352	360	369	377	385	394	403	7 - 9
.3	411	420	429	438	447	457	466	476	485	495	9 - 10
.4	505	515	525	535	546	556	566	577	588	599	10 - 11
.5	610	621	632	643	655	666	678	689	701	713	11 - 12
.6	725	737	750	762	774	787	800	813	825	838	12 - 13
.7	851	865	878	891	905	919	932	946	960	974	13 - 14
.8	988	002	017	031	045	060	075	089	104	119	14 - 15
.9	.1 134	149	165	180	195	211	226	242	258	274	15 - 16
2.0	289	305	321	338	354	370	387	403	419	436	16 - 17
.1	453	470	486	503	520	537	554	571	589	606	16 - 18
.2	623	641	658	676	693	711	729	746	764	782	17 - 18
.3	800	818	836	854	872	890	908	926	945	963	18 - 19
.4	981	999	018	036	055	073	092	110	129	147	18 - 19
.5	.2 166	185	203	222	241	259	278	297	315	334	18 - 19
.6	353	372	390	409	428	447	465	484	503	522	18 - 19
.7	540	559	578	597	615	634	653	671	690	708	18 - 19
.8	727	746	764	783	801	819	838	856	874	893	18 - 19
.9	911	929	947	965	983	001	019	037	055	073	18
3.0	.3 091	108	126	143	161	178	196	213	230	247	18 - 17
.1	264	281	298	315	332	349	365	382	398	414	17 - 16
.2	431	447	463	479	495	510	526	542	557	572	16 - 15
.3	588	603	618	633	648	662	677	691	706	720	15 - 14
.4	734	748	762	775	789	802	816	829	842	855	14 - 13
.5	868	880	893	905	917	929	941	953	965	976	13 - 11
.6	988	999	010	021	031	042	052	063	073	083	11 - 9
.7	.4 092	102	111	120	130	138	147	156	164	172	10 - 8
.8	180	188	196	203	211	218	225	231	238	244	8 - 6
.9	250	256	262	268	273	279	284	288	293	297	6 - 4
4.0	302	306	310	313	317	320	323	326	328	331	4 - 2
.1	333	335	337	339	340	341	342	343	343	344	2 - 0
.2	344	344	344	343	342	341	340	339	337	335	0 - 2
.3	333	331	329	326	323	320	317	313	309	305	2 - 4
.4	301	297	292	287	282	277	271	266	260	253	4 - 7
.5	247	240	234	226	219	212	204	196	188	179	6 - 9
.6	171	162	153	143	134	124	114	104	094	083	9 - 11
.7	072	061	050	038	027	015	003	990	978	965	11 - 13
.8	.3 952	939	925	912	898	884	870	855	841	826	13 - 15
.9	811	795	780	764	748	732	716	699	682	665	15 - 17

$$J_3(x)$$

x	0	1	2	3	4	5	6	7	8	9	Diff.
5.0	.3 648	631	613	596	578	560	541	523	504	485	17 - 19
.1	466	447	427	408	388	368	348	327	307	286	19 - 21
.2	265	244	223	201	180	158	136	114	092	069	21 - 23
.3	046	024	001	9̄78	9̄54	9̄31	9̄07	8̄83	8̄60	8̄35	22 - 25
.4	.2 811	787	762	738	713	688	663	638	612	587	24 - 26
.5	561	535	510	483	457	431	405	378	351	325	25 - 27
.6	298	271	244	216	189	162	134	106	079	051	27 - 28
.7	023	9̄95	9̄67	9̄38	9̄10	8̄82	8̄53	8̄24	7̄96	7̄67	28 - 29
.8	.1 738	709	680	651	622	593	564	534	505	475	29 - 30
.9	446	416	387	357	327	297	267	238	208	178	29 - 30
6.0	148	118	088	057	027	9̄97	9̄67	9̄37	9̄07	8̄76	30 - 31
.1	.0 846	816	785	755	725	694	664	634	603	573	30 - 31
.2	543	513	482	452	422	391	361	331	301	271	30 - 31
.3	240	210	180	150	120	090	060	030	000	0̄29	30 - 29
.4	-.0 059	089	118	148	178	207	236	266	295	324	30 - 29
.5	353	383	412	440	469	498	527	555	584	612	30 - 28
.6	641	669	697	725	753	781	809	836	864	891	28 - 27
.7	918	946	973	0̄00	0̄26	0̄53	0̄80	1̄06	1̄32	1̄59	28 - 26
.8	-.1 185	211	236	262	288	313	338	363	388	413	26 - 25
.9	438	462	487	511	535	559	582	606	629	653	25 - 23
7.0	676	698	721	744	766	788	810	832	854	875	23 - 21
.1	896	918	938	959	980	0̄00	0̄20	0̄40	0̄60	0̄79	22 - 19
.2	-.2 099	118	137	156	174	192	211	229	246	264	19 - 17
.3	281	298	315	332	348	364	380	396	412	427	17 - 15
.4	442	457	472	486	500	514	528	541	555	568	15 - 13
.5	581	593	606	618	630	641	653	664	675	685	13 - 10
.6	696	706	716	726	735	744	753	762	771	779	10 - 8
.7	787	795	802	810	817	823	830	836	842	848	8 - 5
.8	853	859	864	869	873	877	881	885	889	892	6 - 3
.9	895	898	900	903	905	906	908	909	910	911	3 - 0
8.0	911	912	912	911	911	910	909	908	906	905	0 - 2
.1	903	900	898	895	892	889	886	882	878	874	2 - 5
.2	869	865	860	854	849	843	837	831	825	818	4 - 7
.3	811	804	797	790	782	774	765	757	748	739	7 - 9
.4	730	721	711	701	691	681	670	660	649	638	9 - 12
.5	626	615	603	591	578	566	553	540	527	514	11 - 13
.6	501	487	473	459	445	430	415	400	385	370	14 - 15
.7	355	339	323	307	291	274	258	241	224	207	16 - 17
.8	190	172	1̄54	1̄37	119	101	082	064	045	026	17 - 19
.9	007	9̄88	9̄69	9̄49	9̄30	9̄10	8̄90	8̄70	8̄50	8̄30	19 - 21
9.0	-.1 809	789	768	747	726	705	684	662	641	619	20 - 22
.1	598	576	554	532	509	487	465	442	420	397	22 - 23
.2	374	351	328	305	282	258	235	212	188	164	23 - 24
.3	141	117	093	069	045	021	9̄97	9̄73	9̄48	9̄24	24 - 25
.4	-.0 900	875	851	826	802	777	752	728	703	678	24 - 25
.5	653	628	603	578	554	529	504	479	453	428	24 - 26
.6	403	378	353	328	303	278	253	228	203	178	25
.7	153	128	103	077	052	028	003	0̄22	0̄47	0̄72	26 - 24
.8	.0 097	122	147	171	196	221	245	270	294	319	26 - 25
.9	343	368	392	416	440	464	488	512	536	560	26 - 25

$$J_3(x)$$

x	0	1	2	3	4	5	6	7	8	9	Diff.
10.0	.0 584	607	631	655	678	701	725	748	771	794	24 - 23
.1	817	840	862	885	907	930	952	974	996	018	23 - 22
.2	.1 040	062	083	105	126	147	168	189	210	231	22 - 21
.3	252	272	292	313	333	352	372	392	411	431	21 - 19
.4	450	469	488	506	525	543	561	580	597	615	19 - 17
.5	633	650	667	685	701	718	735	751	767	783	18 - 16
.6	799	815	830	846	861	876	890	905	919	934	16 - 14
.7	948	961	975	988	002	015	027	040	053	065	14 - 12
.8	.2 077	089	100	112	123	134	145	155	166	176	12 - 10
.9	186	195	205	214	223	232	241	249	258	266	10 - 7
11.0	273	281	288	296	303	309	316	322	328	334	8 - 6
.1	340	345	350	355	360	364	369	373	376	380	5 - 3
.2	383	387	390	392	395	397	399	401	403	404	4 - 1
.3	405	406	407	407	407	407	407	407	406	405	1 - 0
.4	404	403	401	399	398	395	393	390	387	384	1 - 3
.5	381	377	374	370	366	361	357	352	347	341	3 - 6
.6	336	330	324	318	312	305	299	292	285	277	6 - 8
.7	270	262	254	246	237	229	220	211	202	192	8 - 10
.8	183	173	163	153	142	132	121	110	099	088	10 - 12
.9	076	065	053	041	028	016	003	991	978	965	11 - 14
12.0	.1 951	938	924	910	897	882	868	854	839	824	13 - 15
.1	809	794	779	764	748	732	716	700	684	668	15 - 17
.2	651	635	618	601	584	567	550	533	515	497	16 - 18
.3	480	462	444	425	407	389	370	352	333	314	18 - 19
.4	295	276	257	238	218	199	179	160	140	120	19 - 20
.5	100	080	060	040	019	999	979	958	938	917	20 - 21
.6	.0 896	875	855	834	813	792	771	749	728	707	20 - 22
.7	686	664	643	621	600	578	557	535	514	492	21 - 22
.8	470	448	427	405	383	361	340	318	296	274	21 - 22
.9	252	230	208	186	164	143	121	099	077	055	21 - 22
13.0	033	011	010	032	054	076	098	119	141	163	21 - 22
.1	-.0 184	206	227	249	270	292	313	335	356	377	21 - 22
.2	398	420	441	462	483	504	524	545	566	587	22 - 20
.3	607	628	648	668	689	709	729	749	769	789	21 - 20
.4	809	828	848	867	887	906	925	944	963	982	20 - 19
.5	-.1 001	019	038	056	075	093	111	129	147	165	19 - 17
.6	182	200	217	234	251	268	285	302	318	335	18 - 16
.7	351	367	383	399	415	430	446	461	476	491	16 - 15
.8	506	521	535	549	564	578	591	605	619	632	15 - 13
.9	645	658	671	684	696	709	721	733	745	757	13 - 11
14.0	768	779	791	802	812	823	833	844	854	864	12 - 9
.1	873	883	892	901	910	919	927	936	944	952	10 - 8
.2	960	967	975	982	989	996	003	009	015	021	8 - 6
.3	-.2 027	033	039	044	049	053	058	063	067	071	6 - 4
.4	075	078	082	085	088	091	094	096	098	100	4 - 2
.5	102	104	105	106	108	108	109	109	110	110	2 - 0
.6	109	109	108	108	107	106	104	103	101	099	0 - 2
.7	097	094	092	089	086	083	079	076	072	068	2 - 4
.8	064	059	055	050	045	040	035	029	023	017	4 - 6
.9	011	005	999	992	985	978	971	963	956	948	6 - 8
	-.1										

$J_3(x)$

x	0	1	2	3	4	5	6	7	8	9	Diff.
15.0	-.1 940	932	924	915	907	898	889	880	870	861	8 - 10
.1	851	841	831	821	810	800	789	778	767	756	10 - 11
.2	745	733	721	709	697	685	673	660	648	635	12 - 13
.3	622	609	596	582	569	555	542	528	514	499	13 - 15
.4	485	471	456	441	426	411	396	381	366	350	14 - 16
.5	335	319	303	287	271	255	239	222	206	189	16 - 17
.6	172	155	139	122	104	087	070	053	035	017	16 - 18
.7	000	982	964	946	928	910	892	874	856	837	18 - 19
.8	-.0 819	800	782	763	744	726	707	688	669	650	18 - 19
.9	631	612	593	574	555	535	516	497	477	458	19 - 20
16.0	438	419	400	380	360	341	321	302	282	263	19 - 20
.1	243	223	204	184	164	145	125	105	085	066	19 - 20
.2	046	026	007	013	032	052	072	091	111	130	19 - 20
.3	.0 150	169	189	208	228	247	266	286	305	324	19 - 20
.4	343	362	381	400	419	438	457	476	495	513	19 - 18
.5	532	551	569	588	606	624	642	661	679	697	19 - 18
.6	715	732	750	768	785	803	820	838	855	872	18 - 17
.7	889	906	923	940	956	973	989	006	022	038	17 - 16
.8	.1 054	070	086	102	117	133	148	163	178	193	16 - 15
.9	208	223	237	252	266	280	294	308	322	336	15 - 13
17.0	349	363	376	389	402	415	427	440	452	465	14 - 12
.1	477	489	500	512	524	535	546	557	568	579	12 - 10
.2	589	600	610	620	630	639	649	658	668	677	11 - 9
.3	686	694	703	711	719	728	735	743	751	758	9 - 7
.4	765	772	779	786	792	798	805	810	816	822	7 - 5
.5	827	832	837	842	847	851	856	860	864	868	5 - 3
.6	871	875	878	881	884	886	889	891	893	895	4 - 2
.7	897	898	900	901	902	903	903	904	904	904	2 - 0
.8	904	904	903	903	902	901	900	898	897	895	0 - 2
.9	893	891	888	886	883	880	877	874	871	867	2 - 4
18.0	863	859	855	851	846	842	837	832	827	821	4 - 6
.1	816	810	804	798	792	785	779	772	765	758	6 - 7
.2	751	744	736	728	720	712	704	696	687	678	7 - 9
.3	670	661	651	642	633	623	613	603	593	583	9 - 11
.4	572	562	551	540	529	518	507	496	484	472	1C - 12
.5	461	449	437	424	412	399	387	374	361	348	12 - 13
.6	335	322	308	295	281	268	254	240	226	212	13 - 14
.7	197	183	168	154	139	124	109	094	079	064	14 - 15
.8	049	033	018	002	987	971	955	939	923	907	15 - 16
.9	.0 891	874	858	842	825	809	792	775	759	742	16 - 17
19.0	725	708	691	674	657	640	622	605	588	570	17 - 18
.1	553	535	518	500	483	465	447	430	412	394	17 - 18
.2	376	359	341	323	305	287	269	251	233	215	17 - 18
.3	197	179	161	143	125	107	089	071	053	035	18
.4	017	001	019	037	055	073	091	109	127	145	18
.5	-.0 163	180	198	216	234	251	269	287	304	322	18 - 17
.6	339	357	374	392	409	426	444	461	478	495	18 - 17
.7	512	529	546	563	580	596	613	630	646	663	17 - 16
.8	679	695	712	728	744	760	776	792	807	823	17 - 15
.9	839	854	869	885	900	915	930	945	960	974	16 - 14
20.0	989										

$$J_4(x)$$

x	0	1	2	3	4	5	6	7	8	9	Diff.
.0	.00 000	000	000	000	000	000	000	000	000	000	0
.1	000	000	000	000	000	000	000	000	000	000	0
.2	000	001	001	001	001	001	001	001	002	002	0 - 1
.3	002	002	003	003	003	004	004	005	005	006	0 - 1
.4	007	007	008	009	010	011	012	013	014	015	0 - 1
.5	016	017	019	020	022	023	025	027	029	031	1 - 2
.6	033	035	038	040	043	046	048	051	054	058	2 - 3
.7	061	065	068	072	076	080	084	089	093	098	3 - 5
.8	103	108	114	119	125	131	137	144	150	157	5 - 7
.9	164	171	179	187	195	203	211	220	229	238	8 - 10
1.0	248	257	268	278	289	299	311	322	334	346	9 - 13
.1	359	372	385	398	412	426	441	456	471	486	13 - 16
.2	502	519	535	552	570	588	606	625	644	663	16 - 20
.3	683	703	724	745	767	789	812	835	858	882	20 - 24
.4	906	931	956	982	$\overline{009}$	$\overline{035}$	$\overline{063}$	$\overline{090}$	$\overline{119}$	$\overline{147}$	25 - 30
.5	.01 177	207	237	268	299	331	364	397	431	465	30 - 35
.6	500	535	571	607	644	682	720	759	798	838	35 - 41
.7	879	920	962	$\overline{005}$	$\overline{048}$	$\overline{091}$	$\overline{136}$	$\overline{181}$	$\overline{226}$	$\overline{273}$	41 - 47
.8	.02 320	367	415	464	$\overline{514}$	$\overline{564}$	$\overline{615}$	667	719	772	47 - 53
.9	825	880	935	990	$\overline{047}$	$\overline{104}$	$\overline{161}$	$\overline{220}$	$\overline{279}$	$\overline{339}$	55 - 61
	.03										
2.0	.0 340	346	352	359	365	371	378	384	391	398	6 - 7
.1	405	411	418	425	432	440	447	454	461	469	6 - 8
.2	476	484	492	500	507	515	523	531	539	548	7 - 9
.3	556	564	573	581	590	599	607	616	625	634	8 - 9
.4	643	652	661	671	680	689	699	709	718	728	9 - 10
.5	738	748	758	768	778	788	798	809	819	830	10 - 11
.6	840	851	861	872	883	894	905	916	927	939	10 - 12
.7	950	961	973	984	996	$\overline{007}$	$\overline{019}$	$\overline{031}$	$\overline{043}$	$\overline{055}$	11 - 12
.8	.1 067	079	091	103	115	128	140	153	165	178	12 - 13
.9	190	203	216	229	242	255	268	281	294	307	13
3.0	320	334	347	361	374	388	401	415	429	442	13 - 14
.1	456	470	484	498	512	526	540	554	569	583	14 - 15
.2	597	612	626	640	655	669	684	699	713	728	14 - 15
.3	743	758	772	787	802	817	832	847	862	877	14 - 15
.4	892	907	922	937	953	968	983	998	$\overline{013}$	$\overline{029}$	15 - 16
.5	.2 044	059	075	090	105	121	136	152	167	183	15 - 16
.6	198	213	229	244	260	275	291	306	322	337	15 - 16
.7	353	368	384	399	415	430	446	461	477	492	15 - 16
.8	507	523	538	554	569	584	600	615	630	645	15 - 16
.9	661	676	691	706	721	736	751	766	781	796	15
4.0	811	826	841	856	871	885	900	915	929	944	15 - 14
.1	958	973	987	$\overline{001}$	$\overline{016}$	$\overline{030}$	$\overline{044}$	$\overline{058}$	$\overline{072}$	$\overline{086}$	15 - 14
.2	.3 100	114	128	142	155	169	183	196	210	223	14 - 13
.3	236	249	262	275	288	301	314	327	339	352	13 - 12
.4	365	377	389	401	413	426	437	449	461	473	13 - 11
.5	484	496	507	518	529	540	551	562	573	584	12 - 10
.6	594	604	615	625	635	645	655	665	674	684	11 - 9
.7	693	702	711	720	729	738	746	755	763	772	9 - 8
.8	780	788	795	803	811	818	825	832	839	846	8 - 7
.9	853	860	866	872	879	885	890	896	902	907	7 - 5

$$J_4(x)$$

x	0	1	2	3	4	5	6	7	8	9	Diff.
5.0	.3 912	917	922	927	932	936	941	945	949	953	5 - 3
.1	956	960	963	967	970	973	975	978	980	983	4 - 2
.2	985	987	989	990	991	993	994	995	995	996	2 - 0
.3	996	996	997	996	996	996	995	994	993	992	0 - 1
.4	991	989	987	985	983	981	979	976	973	970	2 - 3
.5	967	964	960	957	953	949	944	940	935	931	3 - 5
.6	926	921	915	910	904	898	892	886	879	873	5 - 7
.7	866	859	852	844	837	829	821	813	805	796	7 - 9
.8	788	779	770	761	751	742	732	722	712	702	9 - 11
.9	691	680	670	659	647	636	624	613	601	589	10 - 13
6.0	576	564	551	539	526	512	499	486	472	458	12 - 14
.1	444	430	415	401	386	371	356	341	325	310	14 - 16
.2	294	278	262	246	230	213	196	179	162	145	16 - 17
.3	128	110	092	075	057	038	020	002	$\overline{983}$	$\overline{964}$	17 - 19
.4	.2 945	926	907	888	868	848	829	809	789	768	19 - 21
.5	748	728	707	686	665	644	623	602	580	559	20 - 22
.6	537	515	493	471	449	426	404	381	359	336	22 - 23
.7	313	290	267	243	220	196	173	149	125	101	23 - 24
.8	077	053	029	005	$\overline{980}$	$\overline{956}$	$\overline{931}$	$\overline{907}$	$\overline{882}$	$\overline{857}$	24 - 25
.9	.1 832	807	782	757	731	706	680	655	629	604	25 - 26
7.0	578	552	526	500	474	448	422	396	370	343	26 - 27
.1	317	291	$\underline{264}$	$\underline{238}$	$\underline{211}$	$\underline{185}$	$\underline{158}$	$\underline{131}$	104	078	26 - 27
.2	051	024	997	970	$\underline{943}$	$\underline{916}$	$\underline{889}$	$\underline{862}$	$\underline{835}$	$\underline{808}$	27
.3	.0 781	754	727	700	673	646	618	591	564	537	27 - 28
.4	510	482	455	428	401	374	347	320	292	265	27 - 28
.5	238	211	184	157	130	103	076	049	022	$\overline{004}$	27 - 26
.6	-.0 031	058	085	111	138	165	191	218	244	271	27 - 26
.7	297	323	350	376	402	428	454	480	506	531	27 - 25
.8	557	583	608	634	659	685	710	735	$\underline{760}$	$\underline{785}$	26 - 25
.9	810	835	859	884	909	933	957	982	$\overline{006}$	$\overline{030}$	25 - 24
8.0	-.1 054	077	101	125	148	171	195	218	241	264	24 - 22
.1	286	309	331	354	376	398	420	442	464	485	23 - 21
.2	507	528	549	570	591	611	632	652	673	693	21 - 20
.3	713	732	752	772	791	810	829	848	866	885	20 - 18
.4	903	921	939	957	975	992	$\overline{010}$	$\overline{027}$	$\overline{044}$	$\overline{060}$	18 - 16
.5	-.2 077	093	110	126	141	157	173	188	203	218	17 - 15
.6	233	247	261	276	290	303	317	330	343	356	15 - 13
.7	369	382	394	406	418	430	441	453	464	475	13 - 10
.8	485	496	506	516	526	536	545	554	563	572	11 - 9
.9	581	589	597	605	613	620	628	635	642	648	8 - 6
9.0	655	661	667	673	678	683	689	693	698	702	6 - 4
.1	707	711	714	718	721	724	727	730	732	734	4 - 2
.2	736	738	739	741	742	743	743	744	744	744	2 - 0
.3	743	743	742	741	740	739	737	735	733	731	0 - 3
.4	728	726	723	720	716	713	709	705	700	696	2 - 6
.5	691	686	681	676	670	665	659	652	646	639	5 - 7
.6	633	626	618	611	603	595	587	579	570	562	7 - 9
.7	553	544	534	525	515	505	495	485	474	464	9 - 11
.8	453	442	430	419	407	396	384	371	359	346	11 - 13
.9	334	321	307	294	281	267	253	239	225	211	13 - 15

$$J_4(x)$$

x	0	1	2	3	4	5	6	7	8	9	Diff.
10.0	-.2 196	181	166	151	136	121	105	090	074	058	15 - 16
.1	042	025	009	9̄9̄2̄	9̄7̄5̄	9̄5̄8̄	9̄4̄1̄	9̄2̄4̄	9̄0̄7̄	8̄8̄9̄	16 - 18
.2	-.1 871	854	836	818	799	781	763	744	725	706	17 - 19
.3	687	668	649	630	610	590	571	551	531	511	19 - 20
.4	491	470	450	429	409	388	367	347	326	304	20 - 22
.5	283	262	241	219	198	176	154	133	111	089	21 - 22
.6	067	045	023	001	9̄7̄8̄	9̄5̄6̄	9̄3̄4̄	9̄1̄1̄	8̄8̄9̄	8̄6̄6̄	22 - 23
.7	-.0 844	821	798	775	753	730	707	684	661	638	22 - 23
.8	615	592	569	546	523	499	476	453	430	407	23 - 24
.9	383	360	337	313	290	267	244	220	197	174	23 - 24
11.0	150	127	104	081	057	034	011	0̄1̄2̄	0̄3̄5̄	0̄5̄9̄	23 - 24
.1	.0 082	105	128	151	174	197	220	243	265	288	23 - 22
.2	311	334	356	379	401	424	446	469	491	513	23 - 22
.3	536	558	580	602	624	645	667	689	710	732	22 - 21
.4	753	775	796	817	838	859	880	901	922	942	22 - 20
.5	963	983	004	024	044	064	084	103	123	143	21 - 19
.6	.1 162	181	201	220	239	257	276	295	313	331	20 - 18
.7	349	367	385	403	421	438	455	473	490	506	18 - 16
.8	523	540	556	573	589	605	620	636	652	667	17 - 15
.9	682	697	712	727	741	756	770	784	798	811	15 - 13
12.0	825	838	852	864	877	890	902	915	927	939	14 - 11
.1	950	962	973	985	996	0̄0̄6̄	0̄1̄7̄	0̄2̄7̄	0̄3̄8̄	0̄4̄8̄	12 - 10
.2	.2 058	067	077	086	095	104	113	121	130	138	10 - 8
.3	146	153	161	168	175	182	189	195	202	208	8 - 6
.4	214	219	225	230	235	240	245	249	254	258	6 - 4
.5	262	265	269	272	275	278	281	283	285	287	4 - 2
.6	289	291	292	293	294	295	295	296	296	296	2 - 0
.7	296	295	294	294	292	291	290	288	286	284	0 - 2
.8	282	279	276	273	270	267	263	260	256	251	3 - 5
.9	247	243	238	233	228	222	217	211	205	199	4 - 6
13.0	193	186	180	173	166	158	151	143	135	127	6 - 8
.1	119	111	102	093	084	075	066	056	047	037	8 - 10
.2	027	017	006	9̄9̄6̄	9̄8̄5̄	9̄7̄4̄	9̄6̄3̄	9̄5̄2̄	9̄4̄0̄	9̄2̄9̄	10 - 12
.3	.1 917	905	893	881	868	856	843	830	817	804	12 - 14
.4	790	777	763	749	736	721	707	693	678	664	13 - 15
.5	649	634	619	603	588	573	557	541	525	509	15 - 16
.6	493	477	460	444	427	410	394	377	360	342	16 - 18
.7	325	308	290	272	255	237	219	201	183	164	17 - 19
.8	146	128	109	090	072	053	034	015	9̄9̄6̄	9̄7̄7̄	18 - 19
.9	.0 958	939	919	900	881	861	841	822	802	782	19 - 20
14.0	762	743	723	703	683	662	642	622	602	582	19 - 21
.1	561	541	521	500	480	459	439	418	398	377	20 - 21
.2	357	336	315	295	274	253	233	212	191	171	20 - 21
.3	150	129	109	088	067	047	026	005	0̄1̄5̄	0̄3̄6̄	20 - 21
.4	-.0 057	077	098	118	139	159	180	200	221	241	20 - 21
.5	261	282	302	322	342	362	382	402	422	442	21 - 20
.6	462	482	502	521	541	560	580	599	619	638	20 - 19
.7	657	676	695	714	733	752	771	790	808	827	19 - 18
.8	845	863	882	900	918	936	953	971	989	0̄0̄6̄	19 - 17
.9	-.1 024	041	058	075	092	109	126	143	159	176	17 - 16

$$J_4(x)$$

x	0	1	2	3	4	5	6	7	8	9	Diff.
15.0	-.1 192	208	224	240	256	271	287	302	318	333	16 - 15
.1	348	363	377	392	406	421	435	449	463	477	15 - 13
.2	490	504	517	530	543	556	569	581	594	606	14 - 12
.3	618	630	641	653	664	676	687	698	709	719	12 - 10
.4	730	740	750	760	770	779	789	798	807	816	10 - 9
.5	825	833	842	850	858	866	873	881	888	895	9 - 7
.6	902	909	915	922	928	934	940	946	951	956	7 - 5
.7	961	966	971	976	980	984	988	992	995	999	5 - 3
.8	-.2 002	005	008	011	013	015	017	019	021	022	3 - 1
.9	024	025	026	027	027	027	028	028	027	027	1 - 0
16.0	026	026	025	024	022	021	019	017	015	013	0 - 3
.1	010	008	005	002	9̄9̄8̄	9̄9̄5̄	9̄9̄1̄	9̄8̄8̄	9̄8̄4̄	9̄8̄0̄	2 - 5
.2	-.1 975	971	966	961	956	951	945	940	934	928	4 - 6
.3	922	916	909	903	896	889	882	874	867	859	6 - 8
.4	851	843	835	827	818	809	800	791	782	773	8 - 10
.5	763	754	744	734	724	713	703	692	682	671	9 - 11
.6	660	648	637	625	614	602	590	578	566	553	11 - 13
.7	541	528	515	502	489	476	463	449	436	422	13 - 14
.8	408	394	380	366	352	337	323	308	293	278	14 - 15
.9	263	248	233	218	202	187	171	155	139	123	15 - 16
17.0	107	091	075	059	042	026	009	9̄9̄2̄	9̄7̄6̄	9̄5̄9̄	16 - 17
.1	-.0 942	925	908	891	873	856	839	821	804	786	17 - 18
.2	769	751	733	715	697	679	661	643	625	607	18
.3	589	571	552	534	516	497	479	460	442	423	18 - 19
.4	405	386	368	349	330	312	293	274	255	237	18 - 19
.5	218	199	1̄8̄0̄	162	143	124	105	086	068	049	18 - 19
.6	030	011	0̄0̄8̄	0̄2̄6̄	0̄4̄5̄	0̄6̄4̄	0̄8̄3̄	1̄0̄1̄	1̄2̄0̄	1̄3̄9̄	18 - 19
.7	.0 157	176	194	213	231	250	268	287	305	323	18 - 19
.8	342	360	378	396	414	433	451	468	486	504	19 - 17
.9	522	540	557	575	593	610	627	645	662	679	18 - 17
18.0	696	713	730	747	764	781	797	814	831	847	17 - 16
.1	863	879	896	912	927	943	959	975	990	0̄0̄6̄	17 - 15
.2	.1 021	036	051	066	081	096	111	125	140	154	15 - 14
.3	168	182	196	210	224	237	251	264	277	290	14 - 13
.4	303	316	329	341	354	366	378	390	402	414	13 - 11
.5	425	437	448	459	470	481	492	503	513	523	12 - 10
.6	533	543	553	563	572	582	591	600	609	618	10 - 8
.7	626	635	643	651	659	667	674	682	689	696	9 - 7
.8	703	710	716	723	729	735	741	747	753	758	7 - 5
.9	763	768	773	778	783	787	791	795	799	803	5 - 3
19.0	806	810	813	816	819	822	824	826	828	830	4 - 2
.1	832	834	835	836	838	838	839	840	840	840	2 - 0
.2	840	840	840	839	839	838	837	835	834	833	0 - 2
.3	831	829	827	825	822	820	817	814	811	807	2 - 4
.4	804	800	796	793	788	784	780	775	770	765	3 - 5
.5	760	755	749	744	738	732	726	719	713	706	5 - 7
.6	699	692	685	678	671	663	655	648	639	631	7 - 9
.7	623	614	606	597	588	579	570	560	551	541	8 - 10
.8	531	521	511	501	491	480	470	459	448	437	10 - 11
.9	426	414	403	391	380	368	356	344	331	319	11 - 13
20.0	307										

$$J_5(x)$$

x	0	1	2	3	4	5	6	7	8	9	Diff.
.0											
.1											
.2											
.3											
.4	.00 000	000	000	000	000	000	001	001	001	001	0 - 1
.5	001	001	001	001	001	001	001	002	002	002	0 - 1
.6	002	002	002	003	003	003	003	003	004	004	0 - 1
.7	004	005	005	005	006	006	006	007	007	008	0 - 1
.8	008	009	009	010	011	011	012	013	013	014	0 - 1
.9	015	016	017	017	018	019	020	022	023	024	0 - 2
1.0	025	026	028	029	030	032	033	035	036	038	1 - 2
.1	040	042	044	045	047	050	052	054	056	059	1 - 3
.2	061	064	066	069	072	074	077	080	084	087	2 - 4
.3	090	093	097	101	104	108	112	116	120	125	3 - 5
.4	129	134	138	143	148	153	158	163	169	174	4 - 6
.5	180	186	192	198	204	211	217	224	231	238	6 - 7
.6	245	253	260	268	276	284	292	301	310	318	7 - 9
.7	327	337	346	356	366	376	386	397	407	418	9 - 11
.8	429	441	452	464	476	489	501	514	527	540	11 - 14
.9	554	568	582	596	611	626	641	656	672	688	14 - 16
2.0	704	721	737	754	772	790	808	826	845	864	16 - 19
.1	883	902	922	943	963	984	$\overline{005}$	$\overline{027}$	$\overline{049}$	$\overline{071}$	19 - 23
.2	.01 094	117	140	164	188	212	237	262	288	313	23 - 27
.3	340	366	393	421	449	477	506	535	564	594	26 - 30
.4	624	655	$\underline{686}$	$\underline{717}$	$\underline{749}$	782	815	$\underline{848}$	$\underline{881}$	$\underline{916}$	31 - 35
.5	950	985	021	057	093	130	167	205	243	$\overline{282}$	35 - 39
.6	.02 321	360	400	441	482	524	566	608	651	695	39 - 44
.7	739	783	828	874	920	966	$\overline{013}$	$\overline{061}$	$\overline{109}$	$\overline{158}$	44 - 49
.8	.03 207	257	307	357	409	$\underline{461}$	$\underline{513}$	566	619	673	50 - 55
.9	728	783	838	894	951	008	066	$\overline{124}$	$\overline{183}$	$\overline{243}$	55 - 60
3.0	.04 .0 430	436	442	449	455	461	467	474	480	487	6 - 7
.1	493	500	507	514	520	527	534	541	548	555	6 - 7
.2	562	570	577	584	592	599	607	614	622	629	7 - 8
.3	637	645	653	661	669	677	685	693	701	710	8 - 9
.4	718	726	735	743	752	760	769	778	787	796	8 - 9
.5	804	813	822	832	841	850	859	868	878	887	9 - 10
.6	897	906	916	926	935	945	955	965	975	985	9 - 10
.7	995	$\overline{005}$	$\overline{015}$	$\overline{025}$	$\overline{036}$	$\overline{046}$	$\overline{056}$	$\overline{067}$	$\overline{077}$	$\overline{088}$	10 - 11
.8	.1 098	109	120	130	141	152	163	174	185	196	10 - 11
.9	207	218	230	241	252	263	275	286	298	309	11 - 12
4.0	321	332	344	356	368	379	391	403	415	427	11 - 12
.1	439	451	463	475	488	500	512	524	537	549	12 - 13
.2	561	574	586	599	611	624	636	649	662	674	12 - 13
.3	687	700	713	726	738	751	764	777	790	803	12 - 13
.4	816	829	842	855	868	881	894	908	921	934	13 - 14
.5	947	960	974	987	$\overline{000}$	$\overline{013}$	$\overline{027}$	$\overline{040}$	$\overline{053}$	$\overline{067}$	13 - 14
.6	.2 080	093	107	120	133	147	160	173	187	200	13 - 14
.7	214	227	240	254	267	280	294	307	321	334	13 - 14
.8	347	361	374	387	401	414	427	440	454	467	13 - 14
.9	480	493	507	520	533	546	559	572	585	598	13 - 14

$J_5(x)$

x	0	1	2	3	4	5	6	7	8	9	Diff.
5.0	.2 611	624	637	650	663	676	689	702	715	727	13 - 12
.1	740	753	765	778	791	803	816	828	840	853	13 - 12
.2	865	877	890	902	914	926	938	950	962	974	13 - 12
.3	986	997	009	021	032	044	055	067	078	089	12 - 11
.4	.3 101	112	123	134	145	156	167	177	188	199	11 - 10
.5	209	220	230	240	251	261	271	281	291	301	11 - 9
.6	310	320	330	339	348	358	367	376	385	394	10 - 9
.7	403	412	420	429	437	446	454	462	470	478	9 - 8
.8	486	494	502	509	517	524	531	538	545	552	8 - 7
.9	559	566	572	579	585	591	598	604	609	615	7 - 5
6.0	621	626	632	637	642	647	652	657	662	666	6 - 4
.1	671	675	679	683	687	691	694	698	701	705	4 - 3
.2	708	711	713	716	719	721	723	726	728	730	3 - 1
.3	731	733	734	736	737	738	739	739	740	740	2 - 0
.4	741	741	741	741	740	740	739	739	738	737	0 - 1
.5	736	734	733	731	729	727	725	723	721	718	1 - 3
.6	716	713	710	706	703	700	696	692	688	684	3 - 4
.7	680	676	671	666	661	656	651	646	640	635	4 - 6
.8	629	623	617	610	604	597	590	584	576	569	6 - 8
.9	562	554	546	539	531	522	514	505	497	488	7 - 9
7.0	479	470	461	451	441	432	422	412	401	391	9 - 11
.1	380	370	359	348	337	325	314	302	290	278	10 - 12
.2	266	254	242	229	216	204	191	177	164	151	12 - 14
.3	137	123	109	095	081	067	052	038	023	008	14 - 15
.4	.2 993	978	962	947	931	916	900	884	867	851	15 - 17
.5	835	818	801	785	768	750	733	716	698	681	16 - 18
.6	663	645	627	609	591	572	554	535	516	497	18 - 19
.7	478	459	440	421	401	382	362	342	322	302	19 - 20
.8	282	262	241	221	200	180	159	138	117	096	20 - 21
.9	075	053	032	011	989	967	946	924	902	880	21 - 22
8.0	.1 858	836	813	791	768	746	723	701	678	655	22 - 23
.1	632	609	586	563	540	517	493	470	446	423	23 - 24
.2	399	376	352	328	305	281	257	233	209	185	23 - 24
.3	161	137	112	088	064	040	015	991	966	942	24 - 25
.4	.0 918	893	868	844	819	795	770	745	721	696	24 - 25
.5	671	647	622	597	572	548	523	498	473	448	24 - 25
.6	424	399	374	349	325	300	275	250	226	201	24 - 25
.7	176	151	127	102	077	053	028	004	021	045	24 - 25
.8	-.0 070	094	119	143	167	192	216	240	264	288	24 - 25
.9	313	337	361	384	408	432	456	480	503	527	24 - 23
9.0	550	574	597	621	644	667	690	713	736	759	24 - 23
.1	782	805	827	850	872	895	917	939	961	983	23 - 22
.2	-.1 005	027	049	071	092	114	135	156	177	198	22 - 21
.3	219	240	261	281	302	322	343	363	383	403	21 - 19
.4	422	442	462	481	500	519	538	557	576	595	20 - 18
.5	613	632	650	668	686	704	721	739	756	773	19 - 17
.6	790	807	824	841	857	874	890	906	922	937	17 - 15
.7	953	968	983	999	013	028	043	057	071	085	16 - 14
.8	-.2 099	113	127	140	153	166	179	192	204	217	14 - 12
.9	229	241	253	264	276	287	298	309	320	330	12 - 10

$$J_5(x)$$

x	0	1	2	3	4	5	6	7	8	9	Diff.
10.0	-.2 341	351	361	371	380	390	399	408	417	425	10 - 8
.1	434	442	450	458	466	473	481	488	495	501	8 - 6
.2	508	514	520	526	532	537	543	548	553	558	6 - 4
.3	562	566	571	574	578	582	585	588	591	594	5 - 2
.4	596	599	601	603	604	606	607	608	609	610	3 - 1
.5	611	611	611	611	611	610	609	608	607	606	0 - 2
.6	604	603	601	599	596	594	591	588	585	582	1 - 4
.7	578	575	571	567	562	558	553	548	543	538	3 - 6
.8	532	527	521	515	508	502	495	489	482	474	5 - 8
.9	467	459	452	444	436	427	419	410	401	392	7 - 9
11.0	383	373	364	354	344	334	324	313	303	292	9 - 11
.1	281	270	258	247	235	223	211	199	187	174	11 - 13
.2	161	149	136	122	109	096	082	068	054	040	12 - 14
.3	026	011	997	982	967	952	937	922	907	891	14 - 16
.4	-.1 875	860	844	827	811	795	778	762	745	728	15 - 17
.5	711	694	677	659	642	624	607	589	571	553	17 - 19
.6	534	516	498	479	461	442	423	404	385	366	18 - 19
.7	347	328	308	289	269	250	230	210	190	170	19 - 20
.8	150	130	110	089	069	049	028	007	987	966	20 - 21
.9	-.0 945	925	904	883	862	841	820	798	777	756	20 - 22
12.0	735	713	692	671	649	628	606	585	563	541	21 - 22
.1	520	498	476	455	433	411	389	368	346	324	21 - 22
.2	302	280	259	237	215	193	171	149	128	106	21 - 22
.3	084	062	040	019	003	025	046	068	090	111	21 - 22
.4	.0 133	155	176	198	219	241	262	283	305	326	21 - 22
.5	347	369	390	411	432	453	474	495	516	536	22 - 20
.6	557	578	598	619	639	660	680	700	720	740	21 - 20
.7	760	780	800	820	840	859	879	898	917	937	20 - 19
.8	956	975	994	013	031	050	068	087	105	123	19 - 18
.9	.1 142	160	177	195	213	230	248	265	282	299	18 - 17
13.0	316	333	350	366	383	399	415	431	447	463	17 - 15
.1	478	494	509	524	539	554	569	584	598	613	16 - 14
.2	627	641	655	668	682	695	709	722	735	747	14 - 12
.3	760	773	785	797	809	821	833	844	855	866	13 - 11
.4	877	888	899	909	920	930	940	950	959	969	11 - 9
.5	978	987	996	005	013	021	030	038	045	053	9 - 7
.6	.2 060	068	075	082	088	095	101	107	113	119	8 - 6
.7	125	130	135	140	145	150	154	159	163	167	5 - 3
.8	170	174	177	180	183	186	188	191	193	195	4 - 2
.9	197	198	200	201	202	203	203	204	204	204	2 - 0
14.0	204	203	203	202	201	200	199	197	196	194	0 - 2
.1	192	189	187	184	182	179	175	172	168	165	2 - 4
.2	161	157	152	148	143	138	133	128	122	117	4 - 6
.3	111	105	099	093	086	079	073	065	058	051	6 - 8
.4	043	036	028	020	011	003	994	985	976	967	7 - 9
.5	.1 958	949	939	929	919	909	899	889	878	867	9 - 11
.6	856	845	834	823	811	799	788	776	764	751	11 - 13
.7	739	726	714	701	688	675	661	648	634	621	12 - 14
.8	607	593	579	565	550	536	521	507	492	477	14 - 15
.9	462	447	431	416	400	385	369	353	337	321	15 - 16

$$J_5(x)$$

x	0	1	2	3	4	5	6	7	8	9	Diff.
15.0	.1 305	288	272	255	239	222	205	188	171	154	16 - 17
.1	137	120	102	085	067	050	032	014	$\overline{996}$	$\overline{978}$	17 - 18
.2	.0 960	942	924	906	887	869	851	832	814	795	18 - 19
.3	776	757	739	720	701	682	663	644	625	606	18 - 19
.4	587	567	548	529	509	490	471	451	432	412	19 - 20
.5	393	373	354	334	315	295	275	256	236	216	19 - 20
.6	197	177	158	138	118	099	079	059	040	020	19 - 20
.7	-.0 000	019	039	058	078	098	117	137	156	175	19 - 20
.8	195	214	234	253	272	292	311	330	349	$\overline{368}$	19 - 20
.9	387	406	425	444	463	482	500	519	538	556	19 - 18
16.0	575	593	612	630	648	666	684	702	720	738	19 - 18
.1	756	774	791	809	826	$\underline{844}$	861	878	895	912	18 - 17
.2	929	946	963	980	996	$\overline{012}$	$\overline{029}$	$\overline{045}$	$\overline{061}$	$\overline{077}$	17 - 16
.3	-.1 093	109	125	140	156	171	186	201	217	231	16 - 14
.4	246	261	275	290	304	318	332	346	360	373	15 - 13
.5	387	400	414	427	440	452	465	478	490	502	14 - 12
.6	514	526	538	550	561	573	584	595	606	617	12 - 10
.7	627	638	648	658	668	678	688	697	707	716	11 - 9
.8	725	734	742	751	759	768	776	783	791	799	9 - 7
.9	806	813	820	827	834	840	847	853	859	865	7 - 5
17.0	870	876	881	886	891	896	901	905	909	913	6 - 4
.1	917	921	925	928	931	934	937	940	942	944	4 - 2
.2	947	949	950	952	953	955	956	956	957	958	2 - 0
.3	958	958	958	958	957	957	956	955	954	953	0 - 2
.4	951	950	948	946	944	941	939	936	933	930	1 - 3
.5	927	923	920	916	912	908	904	899	895	890	3 - 5
.6	885	880	874	869	863	857	851	845	839	833	5 - 7
.7	826	819	812	805	798	790	783	775	767	759	7 - 9
.8	750	742	734	725	716	707	698	688	679	669	8 - 10
.9	659	650	639	629	619	608	598	587	576	565	9 - 11
18.0	554	542	531	519	507	496	484	471	459	447	11 - 13
.1	434	422	409	396	383	370	356	343	330	316	12 - 14
.2	302	288	274	260	246	232	218	203	188	174	14 - 15
.3	159	144	129	114	099	084	068	053	037	021	15 - 16
.4	006	$\overline{990}$	$\overline{974}$	$\overline{958}$	$\overline{942}$	$\overline{926}$	$\overline{910}$	$\overline{893}$	$\overline{877}$	$\overline{861}$	16 - 17
.5	-.0 844	828	811	794	777	761	744	727	710	693	16 - 17
.6	676	658	641	624	607	589	572	554	537	519	17 - 18
.7	502	484	466	449	431	413	395	378	360	342	17 - 18
.8	324	306	288	270	252	234	216	198	180	162	18
.9	144	126	108	090	072	054	036	018	000	$\overline{018}$	18
19.0	.0 036	054	072	090	107	125	143	161	179	197	18 - 17
.1	215	232	250	268	285	303	320	338	356	373	18 - 17
.2	390	408	425	442	460	477	494	511	528	545	18 - 17
.3	562	579	595	612	629	645	662	678	694	711	17 - 16
.4	727	743	759	775	791	807	822	838	854	869	16 - 15
.5	885	900	915	930	945	960	975	990	$\overline{004}$	$\overline{019}$	15 - 14
.6	.1 033	047	062	076	090	104	117	131	145	158	15 - 13
.7	171	184	198	211	223	236	249	261	274	286	14 - 12
.8	298	310	322	333	345	356	368	379	390	401	12 - 11
.9	412	422	433	443	453	463	473	483	493	502	11 - 9
20.0	512										

x	$J_1{}'(x)$	x	$J_1{}'(x)$	x	$J_1{}'(x)$
.00	.5	2.0	-.064 471 62	6.0	.196 759 23
.01	.499 981 25	2.1	-.104 008 32	6.1	.219 236 47
.02	.499 925 00	2.2	-.142 348 21	6.2	.239 314 41
.03	.499 831 26	2.3	-.179 187 40	6.3	.256 841 68
.04	.499 700 03	2.4	-.214 236 18	6.4	.271 691 47
.05	.499 531 33	2.5	-.247 221 42	6.5	.283 762 50
.06	.499 325 17	2.6	-.277 888 90	6.6	.292 979 75
.07	.499 081 56	2.7	-.306 005 44	6.7	.299 294 90
.08	.498 800 53	2.8	-.331 360 76	6.8	.302 686 58
.09	.498 482 10	2.9	-.353 769 30	6.9	.303 160 31
.10	.498 126 30	3.0	-.373 071 61	7.0	.300 748 25
.11	.497 733 16	3.1	-.389 135 68	7.1	.295 508 67
.12	.497 302 70	3.2	-.401 857 93	7.2	.287 525 22
.13	.496 834 97	3.3	-.411 163 97	7.3	.276 905 93
.14	.496 330 00	3.4	-.417 009 08	7.4	.263 782 03
.15	.495 787 84	3.5	-.419 378 46	7.5	.248 306 53
.16	.495 208 53	3.6	-.418 287 19	7.6	.230 652 65
.17	.494 592 12	3.7	-.413 779 93	7.7	.211 012 03
.18	.493 938 66	3.8	-.405 930 36	7.8	.189 592 82
.19	.493 248 20	3.9	-.394 840 36	7.9	.166 617 62
.2	.492 520 81	4.0	-.380 638 98	8.0	.142 321 26
.3	.483 230 19				
.4	.470 331 78	4.1	-.363 481 08	8.1	.116 948 59
.5	.453 932 89	4.2	-.343 545 88	8.2	.090 752 06
.6	.434 169 88	4.3	-.321 035 17	8.3	.063 989 32
.7	.411 206 97	4.4	-.296 171 44	8.4	.036 920 80
.8	.385 234 80	4.5	-.269 195 75	8.5	.009 807 26
.9	.356 468 75	4.6	-.240 365 46	8.6	-.017 092 69
1.0	.325 147 10	4.7	-.209 951 91	8.7	-.043 524 92
		4.8	-.178 237 86	8.8	-.069 242 18
1.1	.291 528 93	4.9	-.145 514 93	8.9	-.094 006 32
1.2	.255 891 86				
1.3	.218 529 65	5.0	-.112 080 94	9.0	-.117 590 48
1.4	.179 749 61	5.1	-.078 237 26	9.1	-.139 781 07
1.5	.139 870 00	5.2	-.044 286 02	9.2	-.160 379 75
1.6	.099 217 21	5.3	-.010 527 48	9.3	-.179 205 07
1.7	.058 122 96	5.4	.022 742 64	9.4	-.196 094 15
1.8	.016 921 44	5.5	.055 235 81	9.5	-.210 903 95
1.9	-.024 053 58	5.6	.086 673 18	9.6	-.223 512 55
		5.7	.116 788 02	9.7	-.233 820 08
		5.8	.145 328 04	9.8	-.241 749 51
		5.9	.172 057 50	9.9	-.247 247 15
				10.0	-.250 283 04

Jour. of Math. and Phys., 1946, p. 93.

x	$J_2{}'(x)$	x	$J_2{}'(x)$	x	$J_2{}'(x)$
.00	0	2.0	.223 890 78	6.0	-.195 726 12
.01	.002 500 0	2.1	.211 507 73	6.1	-.170 231 49
.02	.004 999 7	2.2	.196 818 79	6.2	-.143 599 92
.03	.007 498 9	2.3	.179 946 80	6.3	-.116 064 29
.04	.009 997 3	2.4	.161 035 23	6.4	-.087 864 91
.05	.012 495	2.5	.140 246 86	6.5	-.059 247 34
.06	.014 991	2.6	.117 762 23	6.6	-.030 460 12
.07	.017 486	2.7	.093 778 04	6.7	-.001 752 54
.08	.019 979	2.8	.068 505 32	6.8	.026 627 68
.09	.022 470	2.9	.042 167 45	6.9	.054 436 62
.10	.024 958	3.0	.014 998 12	7.0	.081 436 38
.11	.027 445	3.1	-.012 760 81	7.1	.107 397 20
.12	.029 928	3.2	-.040 861 56	7.2	.132 099 57
.13	.032 409	3.3	-.069 052 72	7.3	.155 336 16
.14	.034 886	3.4	-.097 081 54	7.4	.176 913 70
.15	.037 360	3.5	-.124 696 29	7.5	.196 654 67
.16	.039 830	3.6	-.151 648 56	7.6	.214 398 89
.17	.042 296	3.7	-.177 695 56	7.7	.230 004 90
.18	.044 757	3.8	-.202 602 32	7.8	.243 351 19
.19	.047 215	3.9	-.226 143 89	7.9	.254 337 22
.2	.049 667 3	4.0	-.248 107 40	8.0	.262 884 28
.3	.073 879 7				
		4.1	-.268 293 98	8.1	.268 936 10
.4	.097 353 3	4.2	-.286 520 61	8.2	.272 459 28
.5	.119 852 4	4.3	-.302 621 78	8.3	.273 443 53
.6	.141 150 7				
		4.4	-.316 451 02	8.4	.271 901 59
.7	.161 033 0	4.5	-.327 882 20	8.5	.267 869 08
.8	.179 297 6	4.6	-.336 810 71	8.6	.261 404 06
.9	.195 757 8				
		4.7	-.343 154 37	8.7	.252 586 36
1.0	.210 243 6	4.8	-.346 854 19	8.8	.241 516 76
		4.9	-.347 874 88	8.9	.228 315 99
1.1	.222 603 9				
1.2	.232 707 4	5.0	-.346 205 18	9.0	.213 123 49
1.3	.240 443 7				
		5.1	-.341 857 89	9.1	.196 096 04
1.4	.245 725 0	5.2	-.334 869 77	9.2	.177 406 24
1.5	.248 486 3	5.3	-.325 301 16	9.3	.157 240 82
1.6	.248 686 2				
		5.4	-.313 235 39	9.4	.135 798 86
1.7	.246 307 7	5.5	-.298 778 04	9.5	.113 289 87
1.8	.241 357 5	5.6	-.282 055 88	9.6	.089 931 81
1.9	.233 866 8				
		5.7	-.263 215 74	9.7	.065 949 02
		5.8	-.242 423 08	9.8	.041 570 09
		5.9	-.219 860 53	9.9	.017 025 75
				10.0	-.007 453 32

Jour. of Math. and Phys., 1946, p. 93.

$$Y_O(x) \qquad = N_O(x) \text{ as in Jahnke and Emde}$$

x	$Y_O(x)$	x	$Y_O(x)$
.00	- Infin.	.50	-.4445
.01	-3.0055	.51	-.4299
.02	-2.5640	.52	-.4156
.03	-2.3055	.53	-.4015
.04	-2.1219	.54	-.3876
.05	-1.9793	.55	-.3739
.06	-1.8626	.56	-.3604
.07	-1.7638	.57	-.3472
.08	-1.6780	.58	-.3341
.09	-1.6022	.59	-.3212
.10	-1.5342	.60	-.3085
.11	-1.4726	.61	-.2960
.12	-1.4162	.62	-.2837
.13	-1.3642	.63	-.2715
.14	-1.3159	.64	-.2595
.15	-1.2708	.65	-.2476
.16	-1.2285	.66	-.2359
.17	-1.1886	.67	-.2244
.18	-1.1509	.68	-.2130
.19	-1.1151	.69	-.2018
.20	-1.0811	.70	-.1907
.21	-1.0486	.71	-.1797
.22	-1.0175	.72	-.1689
.23	-.9877	.73	-.1582
.24	-.9591	.74	-.1476
.25	-.9316	.75	-.1372
.26	-.9050	.76	-.1269
.27	-.8794	.77	-.1167
.28	-.8546	.78	-.1066
.29	-.8306	.79	-.0966
.30	-.8073	.80	-.0868
.31	-.7847	.81	-.0771
.32	-.7627	.82	-.0675
.33	-.7414	.83	-.0580
.34	-.7206	.84	-.0486
.35	-.7003	.85	-.0393
.36	-.6806	.86	-.0301
.37	-.6613	.87	-.0210
.38	-.6424	.88	-.0120
.39	-.6240	.89	-.0032
.40	-.6060	.90	.0056
.41	-.5884	.91	.0143
.42	-.5712	.92	.0229
.43	-.5542	.93	.0314
.44	-.5377	.94	.0398
.45	-.5214	.95	.0481
.46	-.5055	.96	.0563
.47	-.4898	.97	.0644
.48	-.4745	.98	.0725
.49	-.4594	.99	.0804

$$Y_0(x) \qquad = N_0(x) \text{ as in Jahnke and Emde}$$

x	0	1	2	3	4	5	6	7	8	9	Diff.
1.0	.0 883	960	037	113	188	262	336	409	480	551	70 - 77
.1	.1 622	691	760	828	895	961	026	091	155	218	63 - 69
.2	.2 281	343	404	464	523	582	640	698	754	810	55 - 62
.3	865	920	974	027	079	131	182	232	282	331	48 - 55
.4	.3 379	427	473	520	565	610	654	698	741	783	41 - 48
.5	824	865	906	945	984	022	060	097	133	169	35 - 41
.6	.4 204	239	273	306	338	370	401	432	462	491	29 - 35
.7	520	548	576	603	629	655	680	705	728	752	22 - 28
.8	774	796	818	839	859	879	898	916	934	951	17 - 22
.9	968	984	000	015	029	043	056	069	081	093	11 - 16
2.0	.5 104	114	124	133	142	150	158	165	172	177	6 - 10
.1	183	188	192	196	199	202	204	206	207	208	0 - 5
.2	208	207	207	205	203	201	198	194	190	186	0 - 5
.3	181	175	169	163	156	148	141	132	123	114	6 - 10
.4	104	094	083	072	060	048	036	022	009	995	10 - 14
.5	.4 981	966	951	935	919	902	885	868	850	832	15 - 19
.6	813	794	775	755	735	714	693	672	650	628	19 - 23
.7	605	582	559	535	511	487	462	437	411	385	23 - 26
.8	359	333	306	279	251	223	195	167	138	109	26 - 30
.9	079	049	019	989	958	927	896	865	833	801	30 - 32
3.0	.3 769	736	703	670	637	603	569	535	500	466	33 - 35
.1	431	396	361	325	289	253	217	181	144	108	35 - 37
.2	071	033	996	958	921	883	845	807	768	730	37 - 39
.3	.2 691	652	613	574	535	495	456	416	376	336	39 - 40
.4	296	256	216	175	135	094	054	013	972	931	40 - 41
.5	.1 890	849	808	767	726	684	643	602	560	519	41 - 42
.6	477	436	394	352	311	269	227	186	144	102	41 - 42
.7	061	019	977	936	894	853	811	769	728	686	41 - 42
.8	.0 645	604	562	521	480	439	397	356	315	275	40 - 42
.9	234	193	152	112	071	031	009	050	090	130	39 - 41
4.0	-.0 169	209	249	288	328	367	406	445	484	522	38 - 40
.1	561	599	638	676	714	751	789	826	864	901	37 - 39
.2	938	974	011	047	083	119	155	191	226	261	35 - 37
.3	-.1 296	331	365	400	434	467	501	535	568	601	32 - 35
.4	633	666	698	730	762	793	825	856	886	917	30 - 33
.5	947	977	007	036	065	094	123	151	179	207	28 - 30
.6	-.2 235	262	289	315	342	368	394	419	444	469	25 - 27
.7	494	518	542	566	589	612	635	658	680	702	21 - 24
.8	723	744	765	786	806	826	845	865	884	902	18 - 21
.9	921	939	956	973	990	007	023	039	055	070	15 - 18
	-.3										

Acknowledgment is made to the Royal Society, London, England, for the Tables of $Y_0(x)$ and $Y_1(x)$ which are abridged from "Bessel Functions," Part I, Vol. VI of British Association Mathematical Tables, published by Cambridge University Press, London, Eng., 1937.

For tables for extended ranges, see "Bessel Functions," Part II, (orders 2 to 20) by W. G. Bickley, L. J. Comrie, J. C. P. Miller, D. H. Sadler and A. J. Thompson, Vol. X of British Association Mathematical Tables, 1952, and "A Short Table for Bessel Functions of Integer Orders and Large Arguments" by L. Fox, No. 3 of the Royal Society Shorter Mathematical Tables, 1954, both published by Cambridge University Press, London, Eng.

$$Y_o(x) \qquad = N_o(x) \text{ as in Jahnke and Emde}$$

x	0	1	2	3	4	5	6	7	8	9	Diff.
5.0	-.3 085	100	114	128	142	155	168	180	193	204	11 - 15
.1	216	227	238	249	259	269	278	287	296	304	8 - 11
.2	313	320	328	335	341	348	354	359	365	370	4 - 8
.3	374	379	383	386	389	392	395	397	399	400	1 - 5
.4	402	403	403	403	403	402	402	400	399	397	0 - 2
.5	395	392	389	386	383	379	375	370	365	360	3 - 6
.6	354	349	342	336	329	322	315	307	299	290	5 - 9
.7	282	273	263	254	244	233	223	212	201	189	9 - 12
.8	177	165	153	140	127	114	101	087	073	058	12 - 15
.9	044	029	013	9̅9̅8̅	9̅8̅2̅	9̅6̅6̅	9̅5̅0̅	9̅3̅3̅	9̅1̅6̅	8̅9̅9̅	15 - 17
6.0	-.2 882	864	846	828	810	791	772	753	734	714	18 - 20
.1	694	674	654	633	613	592	570	549	527	505	20 - 22
.2	483	461	438	415	393	369	346	322	299	275	22 - 24
.3	251	226	202	177	152	127	102	077	051	025	24 - 26
.4	-.1 999	973	947	921	894	868	841	814	787	760	26 - 28
.5	732	705	677	650	622	594	566	538	509	481	27 - 29
.6	452	424	395	366	337	308	279	250	221	191	28 - 30
.7	162	132	103	073	044	014	9̅8̅4̅	9̅5̅4̅	9̅2̅4̅	8̅9̅4̅	29 - 30
.8	-.0 864	834	804	774	744	714	684	653	623	593	30 - 31
.9	563	532	502	472	441	411	381	350	320	290	30 - 31
7.0	259	229	199	169	139	108	078	048	018	0̅1̅2̅	30 - 31
.1	.0 042	072	102	131	161	191	221	250	280	309	30 - 29
.2	339	368	397	426	455	484	513	542	571	599	29 - 28
.3	628	656	684	713	741	769	797	824	852	879	29 - 27
.4	907	934	961	988	0̅1̅5̅	0̅4̅2̅	0̅6̅8̅	0̅9̅5̅	1̅2̅1̅	1̅4̅7̅	27 - 26
.5	.1 173	199	225	250	276	301	326	351	375	400	26 - 24
.6	424	448	472	496	520	543	567	590	613	635	24 - 22
.7	658	680	702	724	746	768	789	810	831	852	22 - 20
.8	872	893	913	932	952	972	991	0̅1̅0̅	0̅2̅8̅	0̅4̅7̅	21 - 18
.9	.2 065	083	101	119	136	153	170	187	203	219	18 - 16
8.0	235	251	266	282	296	311	326	340	354	367	16 - 13
.1	381	394	407	420	432	444	456	468	479	490	13 - 11
.2	501	512	522	532	542	551	561	570	578	587	11 - 8
.3	595	603	611	618	625	632	639	645	651	657	8 - 5
.4	662	667	672	677	681	686	689	693	696	699	5 - 3
.5	702	705	707	709	710	712	713	714	714	715	3 - 0
.6	715	714	714	713	712	711	709	707	705	703	0 - 3
.7	700	697	694	690	687	683	678	674	669	664	3 - 5
.8	659	653	647	641	635	628	621	614	607	599	6 - 8
.9	592	583	575	566	558	549	539	530	520	510	8 - 11
9.0	499	489	478	467	456	444	433	421	408	396	10 - 13
.1	383	371	357	344	331	317	303	289	274	260	12 - 15
.2	245	230	215	199	184	1̅6̅8̅	1̅5̅2̅	1̅3̅6̅	1̅1̅9̅	1̅0̅3̅	15 - 17
.3	086	069	052	034	017	9̅9̅9̅	9̅8̅1̅	9̅6̅3̅	9̅4̅5̅	9̅2̅6̅	17 - 19
.4	.1 907	889	870	851	831	812	792	772	752	732	18 - 20
.5	712	692	671	650	630	609	588	566	545	523	20 - 22
.6	502	480	458	436	414	392	369	347	324	302	22 - 23
.7	279	256	2̅3̅3̅	2̅1̅0̅	1̅8̅6̅	1̅6̅3̅	1̅4̅0̅	1̅1̅6̅	093	069	23 - 24
.8	045	021	9̅9̅8̅	974	9̅4̅9̅	9̅2̅5̅	9̅0̅1̅	8̅7̅7̅	8̅5̅3̅	8̅2̅8̅	23 - 25
.9	.0 804	779	755	730	705	681	656	631	606	582	24 - 25

$Y_o(x)$ = $N_o(x)$ as in Jahnke and Emde

x	0	1	2	3	4	5	6	7	8	9	Diff.
10.0	.0 557	532	507	482	457	432	407	382	357	332	25
.1	307	281	256	231	206	181	156	131	106	081	26 - 25
.2	056	031	006	019	044	069	094	119	143	168	25 - 24
.3	-.0 193	218	242	267	291	316	340	365	389	413	25 - 24
.4	437	462	486	510	534	557	581	605	628	652	25 - 23
.5	675	699	722	745	768	791	814	837	859	882	24 - 22
.6	904	926	949	971	993	015	036	058	079	101	23 - 21
.7	-.1 122	143	164	185	205	226	246	267	287	307	21 - 19
.8	326	346	366	385	404	423	442	461	479	498	20 - 18
.9	516	534	552	569	587	604	622	639	655	672	18 - 16
11.0	688	705	721	737	752	768	783	798	813	828	17 - 15
.1	843	857	871	885	899	913	926	939	952	965	14 - 12
.2	977	990	002	014	025	037	048	059	070	081	13 - 10
.3	-.2 091	101	111	121	130	140	149	158	166	175	10 - 8
.4	183	191	199	206	213	220	227	234	240	246	8 - 6
.5	252	258	263	269	274	278	283	287	291	295	6 - 4
.6	299	302	305	308	311	313	315	317	319	321	3 - 1
.7	322	323	324	324	325	325	324	324	324	323	1 - 0
.8	322	320	319	317	315	313	310	308	305	302	1 - 4
.9	298	295	291	287	283	278	273	269	263	258	3 - 6
12.0	252	247	241	234	228	221	214	207	200	192	5 - 8
.1	184	176	168	160	151	142	133	124	115	105	8 - 10
.2	095	085	075	064	054	043	032	021	009	998	10 - 12
.3	-.1 986	974	962	949	937	924	911	898	885	871	12 - 14
.4	858	844	830	816	802	787	772	758	743	727	14 - 16
.5	712	697	681	665	649	633	617	601	584	567	15 - 17
.6	551	534	517	499	482	464	447	429	411	393	17 - 18
.7	375	357	338	320	301	282	264	245	226	206	18 - 20
.8	187	168	148	129	109	089	069	049	029	009	19 - 20
.9	-.0 989	968	948	927	907	886	866	845	824	803	20 - 21
13.0	782	761	740	719	698	676	655	634	612	591	21 - 22
.1	569	548	526	505	483	461	439	418	396	374	21 - 22
.2	352	331	309	287	265	243	221	199	177	156	21 - 22
.3	134	112	090	068	046	024	002	019	041	063	21 - 22
.4	.0 085	107	128	150	172	193	215	236	258	279	21 - 22
.5	301	322	343	365	386	407	428	449	470	491	21 - 22
.6	512	533	554	574	595	615	636	656	677	697	21 - 20
.7	717	737	757	777	796	816	836	855	875	894	20 - 19
.8	913	932	951	970	989	007	026	044	062	081	19 - 18
.9	.1 099	117	134	152	169	187	204	221	238	255	18 - 17
14.0	272	289	305	321	337	353	369	385	401	416	17 - 16
.1	431	446	461	476	491	505	520	534	548	562	15 - 13
.2	575	589	602	615	628	641	654	666	679	691	14 - 12
.3	703	715	726	738	749	760	771	781	792	802	12 - 10
.4	812	822	832	842	851	860	869	878	886	895	10 - 8
.5	903	911	919	926	934	941	948	955	962	968	8 - 6
.6	974	980	986	992	997	002	007	012	017	021	6 - 4
.7	.2 025	029	033	036	040	043	046	049	051	054	4 - 2
.8	056	058	059	061	062	063	064	065	065	065	2 - 0
.9	065	065	065	064	064	063	061	060	058	057	0 - 2

$$Y_0(x) \qquad = N_0(x) \text{ as in Jahnke and Emde}$$

x	0	1	2	3	4	5	6	7	8	9	Diff.
15.0	.2 055	052	050	047	045	042	038	035	031	027	2 - 4
.1	023	019	015	010	005	000	9̅9̅5̅	9̅9̅0̅	9̅8̅4̅	9̅7̅8̅	4 - 6
.2	.1 972	966	960	953	946	939	932	925	917	910	6 - 8
.3	902	894	885	877	868	860	851	841	832	823	8 - 10
.4	813	803	793	783	772	762	751	740	729	718	10 - 12
.5	706	695	683	671	659	647	635	622	610	597	11 - 13
.6	584	571	557	544	530	517	503	489	475	460	13 - 15
.7	446	431	417	402	387	372	357	341	326	310	14 - 16
.8	295	279	263	247	231	215	198	182	165	148	16 - 17
.9	132	115	098	081	063	046	029	011	9̅9̅4̅	9̅7̅6̅	17 - 18
16.0	.0 958	940	922	904	886	868	850	832	813	795	18 - 19
.1	776	758	739	720	701	683	664	645	626	607	18 - 19
.2	588	569	549	530	511	492	472	453	433	414	19 - 20
.3	394	375	355	336	316	297	277	258	238	218	19 - 20
.4	199	1̲7̲9̲	1̲5̲9̲	1̲4̲0̲	1̲2̲0̲	1̲0̲0̲	080	061	041	021	19 - 20
.5	002	0̲1̲8̲	0̲3̲7̲	0̲5̲7̲	0̲7̲7̲	0̲9̲6̲	1̲1̲6̲	1̲3̲5̲	1̲5̲5̲	1̲7̲4̲	19 - 20
.6	-.0 194	213	233	252	271	290	310	329	348	367	19 - 20
.7	386	405	424	443	462	481	499	518	537	555	19 - 18
.8	574	592	610	629	647	665	683	701	719	737	19 - 17
.9	754	772	789	807	824	842	859	876	893	910	18 - 16
17.0	926	943	960	976	992	0̅0̅9̅	0̅2̅5̅	0̅4̅1̅	0̅5̅7̅	0̅7̅3̅	17 - 15
.1	-.1 088	104	119	135	150	165	180	195	209	224	16 - 14
.2	238	253	267	281	295	308	322	335	349	362	15 - 13
.3	375	388	401	413	426	438	450	462	474	486	13 - 11
.4	497	509	520	531	542	553	563	574	584	594	12 - 10
.5	604	614	623	633	642	651	660	669	678	686	10 - 8
.6	694	702	710	718	725	733	740	747	754	761	8 - 6
.7	767	773	779	785	791	797	802	807	812	817	6 - 5
.8	822	826	830	835	838	842	846	849	852	855	5 - 3
.9	858	861	863	865	867	869	871	872	874	875	3 - 1
18.0	876	876	877	877	877	877	877	877	876	875	0 - 1
.1	874	873	872	870	869	867	865	862	860	857	1 - 3
.2	854	851	848	845	841	838	834	829	825	821	3 - 5
.3	816	811	806	801	796	790	785	779	773	766	5 - 7
.4	760	753	747	740	733	725	718	710	703	695	6 - 8
.5	687	678	670	661	653	644	635	625	616	606	8 - 10
.6	597	587	577	567	556	546	535	525	514	503	10 - 11
.7	492	480	469	457	445	433	421	409	397	385	11 - 13
.8	372	359	346	334	320	307	294	280	267	253	12 - 14
.9	239	225	211	197	183	169	154	140	125	110	14 - 15
19.0	095	080	065	050	035	019	004	9̅8̅8̅	9̅7̅2̅	9̅5̅7̅	15 - 16
.1	-.0 941	925	909	893	877	860	844	828	811	794	16 - 17
.2	778	761	744	728	711	694	677	660	642	625	16 - 17
.3	608	591	573	556	539	521	503	486	468	451	17 - 18
.4	433	415	397	380	362	344	326	308	290	272	17 - 18
.5	255	237	219	201	183	165	147	129	110	092	18 - 19
.6	074	056	038	020	002	0̅1̅6̅	0̅3̅4̅	0̅5̅2̅	0̅7̅0̅	0̅8̅8̅	18 - 17
.7	.0 105	123	141	159	177	195	213	230	248	266	18 - 17
.8	283	301	319	336	354	371	388	406	423	440	18 - 17
.9	458	475	492	509	526	543	560	576	593	610	17 - 16
20.0	626										

$$Y_1(x) \qquad = N_1(x) \text{ as in Jahnke and Emde } = -Y_o'(x)$$

x	$Y_1(x)$		x	$Y_1(x)$
.00	- Infin.		.50	-1.4715
.01	-63.6786		.51	-1.4469
.02	-31.8598		.52	-1.4233
.03	-21.2600		.53	-1.4005
.04	-15.9643		.54	-1.3785
.05	-12.7899		.55	-1.3572
.06	-10.6758		.56	-1.3366
.07	-9.1675		.57	-1.3166
.08	-8.0377		.58	-1.2973
.09	-7.1601		.59	-1.2786
.10	-6.4590		.60	-1.2604
.11	-5.8861		.61	-1.2427
.12	-5.4094		.62	-1.2256
.13	-5.0067		.63	-1.2089
.14	-4.6620		.64	-1.1926
.15	-4.3637		.65	-1.1768
.16	-4.1031		.66	-1.1613
.17	-3.8734		.67	-1.1463
.18	-3.6696		.68	-1.1316
.19	-3.4875		.69	-1.1173
.20	-3.3238		.70	-1.1032
.21	-3.1759		.71	-1.0895
.22	-3.0417		.72	-1.0761
.23	-2.9192		.73	-1.0630
.24	-2.8071		.74	-1.0502
.25	-2.7041		.75	-1.0376
.26	-2.6091		.76	-1.0253
.27	-2.5212		.77	-1.0131
.28	-2.4397		.78	-1.0013
.29	-2.3638		.79	-.9896
.30	-2.2931		.80	-.9781
.31	-2.2270		.81	-.9669
.32	-2.1650		.82	-.9558
.33	-2.1068		.83	-.9449
.34	-2.0520		.84	-.9342
.35	-2.0004		.85	-.9236
.36	-1.9516		.86	-.9132
.37	-1.9055		.87	-.9030
.38	-1.8618		.88	-.8929
.39	-1.8203		.89	-.8829
.40	-1.7809		.90	-.8731
.41	-1.7433		.91	-.8634
.42	-1.7076		.92	-.8539
.43	-1.6734		.93	-.8444
.44	-1.6408		.94	-.8351
.45	-1.6095		.95	-.8258
.46	-1.5796		.96	-.8167
.47	-1.5509		.97	-.8077
.48	-1.5234		.98	-.7988
.49	-1.4969		.99	-.7900

$Y_1(x)$ $= N_1(x)$ as in Jahnke and Emde $= -Y_0'(x)$

x	0	1	2	3	4	5	6	7	8	9	Diff.
1.0	-.7 812	726	640	555	471	388	305	223	142	061	86 - 80
.1	-.6 981	902	823	745	667	590	513	437	361	286	79 - 75
.2	211	137	063	990	916	844	771	699	628	556	74 - 71
.3	-.5 485	415	344	274	204	135	066	997	928	860	71 - 68
.4	-.4 791	724	656	589	521	454	388	321	255	189	68 - 66
.5	123	057	992	927	862	797	732	668	604	540	66 - 64
.6	-.3 476	412	349	285	222	159	096	034	972	909	64 - 62
.7	-.2 847	785	724	662	601	540	479	418	357	297	62 - 60
.8	237	177	117	057	997	938	879	820	761	702	60 - 58
.9	-.1 644	586	528	470	412	355	297	240	184	127	58 - 56
2.0	070	014	958	902	846	791	736	681	626	571	56 - 54
.1	-.0 517	463	409	355	301	248	195	142	090	037	54 - 52
.2	.0 015	067	118	170	221	272	323	373	423	473	52 - 50
.3	523	572	621	670	719	767	815	863	911	958	49 - 47
.4	.1 005	052	098	144	190	236	281	326	371	415	47 - 44
.5	459	503	547	590	633	675	718	760	801	843	44 - 41
.6	884	924	965	005	045	084	123	162	200	239	41 - 37
.7	.2 276	314	351	388	424	460	496	531	566	601	38 - 34
.8	635	669	703	736	769	802	834	866	897	929	34 - 30
.9	959	990	020	050	079	108	136	164	192	220	31 - 27
3.0	.3 247	273	300	326	351	376	401	425	449	473	27 - 23
.1	496	519	542	564	585	607	627	648	668	688	23 - 19
.2	707	726	745	763	780	798	815	831	847	863	19 - 16
.3	879	893	908	922	936	949	962	975	987	999	15 - 11
.4	.4 010	021	032	042	052	061	070	079	087	095	11 - 7
.5	102	109	115	122	127	133	138	142	147	150	7 - 3
.6	154	157	160	162	164	165	166	167	167	167	3 - 0
.7	167	166	165	163	161	159	156	153	149	145	1 - 4
.8	141	137	132	126	120	114	108	101	094	086	4 - 8
.9	078	070	061	052	043	033	023	013	002	991	8 - 12
4.0	.3 979	967	955	943	930	917	903	889	875	861	12 - 15
.1	846	831	815	800	783	767	750	733	716	698	15 - 18
.2	680	662	643	624	605	586	566	546	525	505	18 - 21
.3	484	463	441	420	397	375	353	330	307	283	21 - 24
.4	260	236	212	187	163	138	113	087	062	036	24 - 26
.5	010	984	957	930	904	876	849	821	794	766	26 - 29
.6	.2 737	709	680	652	623	594	564	535	505	475	28 - 30
.7	445	415	384	354	323	292	261	230	199	167	30 - 32
.8	136	104	072	040	008	976	943	911	878	845	32 - 33
.9	.1 812	780	746	713	680	647	613	580	546	512	32 - 34

$Y_1(x)$ $= N_1(x)$ as in Jahnke and Emde $= -Y_0{}'(x)$

x	0	1	2	3	4	5	6	7	8	9	Diff.
5.0	.1 479	445	411	377	343	309	275	240	206	172	34 - 35
.1	137	103	069	034	000	965	930	896	861	827	34 - 35
.2	.0 792	757	723	688	653	619	584	549	515	480	34 - 35
.3	445	411	376	342	307	273	238	204	170	136	34 - 35
.4	101	067	033	001	035	069	103	137	170	204	34 - 33
.5	-.0 238	271	304	338	371	404	437	470	503	535	34 - 32
.6	568	601	633	665	697	729	761	793	824	856	33 - 31
.7	887	918	949	980	011	042	072	102	133	163	31 - 29
.8	-.1 192	222	251	281	310	339	368	396	425	453	30 - 28
.9	481	509	536	564	591	618	645	671	698	724	28 - 26
6.0	750	776	801	827	852	877	902	926	950	974	26 - 24
.1	998	022	045	068	091	114	136	158	180	201	24 - 21
.2	-.2 223	244	265	285	306	326	346	365	385	404	21 - 18
.3	422	441	459	477	495	512	530	547	563	580	19 - 16
.4	596	611	627	642	657	672	686	700	714	728	16 - 13
.5	741	754	767	779	791	803	814	826	836	847	13 - 10
.6	857	868	877	887	896	905	913	922	930	937	11 - 7
.7	945	952	958	965	971	977	983	988	993	997	7 - 4
.8	-.3 002	006	010	013	016	019	022	024	026	028	4 - 1
.9	029	030	031	032	032	032	031	031	030	028	0 - 2
7.0	027	025	023	020	017	014	011	007	003	999	2 - 4
.1	-.2 995	990	985	980	974	968	962	955	949	942	5 - 8
.2	934	927	919	911	902	893	885	875	866	856	7 - 10
.3	846	836	825	814	803	792	780	768	756	744	10 - 13
.4	731	718	705	692	678	664	650	636	621	606	13 - 15
.5	591	576	560	545	529	512	496	479	462	445	15 - 17
.6	428	410	393	375	357	338	320	301	282	263	17 - 20
.7	243	224	204	184	164	143	123	102	081	060	19 - 21
.8	039	017	996	974	952	930	908	885	863	840	21 - 23
.9	-.1 817	794	771	748	724	701	677	653	629	605	23 - 24
8.0	581	556	532	507	482	457	432	407	382	357	24 - 26
.1	331	306	280	255	229	203	177	151	125	099	25 - 27
.2	072	046	020	993	967	940	913	887	860	833	26 - 27
.3	-.0 806	779	752	725	698	671	644	617	589	562	27 - 28
.4	535	508	480	453	426	398	371	344	316	289	27 - 28
.5	262	234	207	180	152	125	098	071	043	016	27 - 28
.6	.0 011	038	065	092	119	146	173	200	227	253	27 - 26
.7	280	307	333	360	386	413	439	465	491	518	27 - 26
.8	544	569	595	621	647	672	698	723	748	774	26 - 25
.9	799	824	849	873	898	922	947	971	995	019	25 - 24
9.0	.1 043	067	091	114	137	161	184	207	229	252	24 - 22
.1	275	297	319	341	363	385	406	428	449	470	22 - 21
.2	491	512	532	553	573	593	613	633	652	671	21 - 19
.3	691	710	728	747	765	783	801	819	837	854	19 - 17
.4	871	888	905	922	938	954	970	986	001	017	17 - 15
.5	.2 032	047	061	076	090	104	118	131	145	158	15 - 13
.6	171	183	196	208	220	232	243	254	265	276	13 - 11
.7	287	297	307	317	326	336	345	354	362	371	10 - 8
.8	379	387	394	402	409	416	423	429	435	441	8 - 6
.9	447	452	458	463	467	472	476	480	484	487	6 - 3

$$Y_1(x) \qquad = N_1(x) \text{ as in Jahnke and Emde} \quad = -Y_0{}'(x)$$

x	0	1	2	3	4	5	6	7	8	9	Diff.
10.0	.2 490	493	496	498	500	502	504	506	507	508	3 - 0
.1	508	509	509	509	509	508	507	506	505	504	0 - 2
.2	502	500	498	495	492	489	486	483	479	475	2 - 4
.3	471	466	462	457	451	446	440	435	428	422	4 - 7
.4	416	409	402	394	387	379	371	363	355	346	7 - 9
.5	337	328	319	309	299	289	279	269	258	247	9 - 11
.6	236	225	214	202	190	178	166	153	140	128	11 - 14
.7	114	101	088	074	060	046	032	017	003	$\overline{988}$	13 - 15
.8	.1 973	958	942	927	911	895	879	863	846	830	15 - 17
.9	813	796	779	762	745	727	709	692	674	655	17 - 19
11.0	637	619	600	581	562	543	524	505	486	466	18 - 20
.1	446	427	407	387	366	346	326	305	285	264	19 - 21
.2	243	222	201	180	159	137	116	095	073	051	21 - 22
.3	029	008	$\overline{986}$	$\overline{964}$	$\overline{941}$	$\overline{919}$	$\overline{897}$	$\overline{875}$	$\overline{852}$	$\overline{830}$	21 - 23
.4	.0 807	785	762	740	717	694	671	648	625	602	22 - 23
.5	579	556	533	510	487	464	441	417	394	371	23 - 24
.6	348	324	301	278	254	231	208	184	161	138	23 - 24
.7	114	091	068	045	021	$\overline{002}$	$\overline{025}$	$\overline{048}$	$\overline{072}$	$\overline{095}$	23 - 24
.8	-.0 118	141	164	187	210	233	256	279	302	324	23 - 22
.9	347	370	392	415	437	460	482	505	527	549	23 - 22
12.0	571	593	615	637	659	680	702	723	745	766	22 - 21
.1	787	809	830	851	871	892	913	933	954	974	22 - 20
.2	994	$\overline{014}$	$\overline{034}$	$\overline{054}$	$\overline{074}$	$\overline{093}$	$\overline{113}$	$\overline{132}$	$\overline{151}$	$\overline{171}$	20 - 18
.3	-.1 189	208	227	246	264	282	300	318	336	354	19 - 17
.4	371	389	406	423	440	457	474	490	506	522	18 - 16
.5	538	554	570	585	601	616	631	645	660	675	16 - 14
.6	689	703	717	730	744	757	771	783	796	809	14 - 12
.7	821	834	846	857	869	880	892	903	914	924	13 - 10
.8	935	945	955	965	975	984	993	$\overline{002}$	$\overline{011}$	$\overline{020}$	10 - 8
.9	-.2 028	036	044	052	060	067	074	081	088	095	8 - 6
13.0	101	107	113	118	124	129	134	139	144	148	6 - 4
.1	152	156	160	163	167	170	172	175	178	180	4 - 2
.2	182	183	185	186	187	188	189	189	190	190	2 - 0
.3	190	189	188	188	187	185	184	182	180	178	0 - 2
.4	176	173	170	167	164	161	157	153	149	145	3 - 5
.5	140	136	131	126	120	115	109	103	097	090	4 - 7
.6	084	077	070	063	056	048	040	032	024	016	7 - 9
.7	007	$\overline{999}$	$\overline{990}$	$\overline{981}$	$\overline{971}$	$\overline{962}$	$\overline{952}$	$\overline{942}$	$\overline{932}$	$\overline{922}$	8 - 10
.8	-.1 912	901	890	879	868	857	845	834	822	810	11 - 12
.9	798	785	773	760	747	734	721	707	694	680	12 - 14
14.0	666	652	638	624	610	595	580	565	550	535	14 - 15
.1	520	504	489	473	457	441	425	409	392	376	15 - 17
.2	359	342	325	308	291	274	257	239	222	204	17 - 18
.3	186	168	150	132	114	096	077	059	040	021	18 - 19
.4	003	$\overline{984}$	$\overline{965}$	$\overline{946}$	$\overline{927}$	$\overline{907}$	$\overline{888}$	$\overline{869}$	$\overline{849}$	$\overline{830}$	19 - 20
.5	-.0 810	791	771	751	732	712	692	672	652	632	19 - 20
.6	612	591	571	551	531	510	490	469	449	428	20 - 21
.7	408	387	367	346	326	305	284	264	243	222	20 - 21
.8	202	181	160	140	119	098	077	057	036	015	20 - 21
.9	.0 005	026	047	067	088	108	129	149	170	190	20 - 21

$Y_1(x)$ $= N_1(x)$ as in Jahnke and Emde $= -Y_0{}'(x)$

x	0	1	2	3	4	5	6	7	8	9	Diff.
15.0	.0 211	231	251	272	292	312	332	353	373	393	21 - 20
.1	413	433	453	472	492	512	531	551	571	590	20 - 19
.2	609	629	648	667	686	705	724	743	761	780	20 - 18
.3	799	817	835	854	872	890	908	926	943	961	19 - 17
.4	979	996	013	031	048	065	082	098	115	131	18 - 16
.5	.1 148	164	180	196	212	228	244	259	274	290	16 - 15
.6	305	320	334	349	363	378	392	406	420	434	15 - 13
.7	447	461	474	487	500	513	526	538	551	563	14 - 12
.8	575	587	599	610	621	633	644	655	665	676	12 - 10
.9	686	696	706	716	726	735	744	754	762	771	10 - 8
16.0	780	788	796	804	812	820	827	835	842	848	8 - 6
.1	855	862	868	874	880	886	891	897	902	907	7 - 5
.2	912	916	921	925	929	933	936	940	943	946	5 - 3
.3	949	952	954	956	958	960	962	963	965	966	3 - 1
.4	967	967	968	968	968	968	968	967	967	966	0 - 1
.5	965	963	962	960	959	956	954	952	949	946	1 - 3
.6	943	940	937	933	929	925	921	917	912	908	3 - 5
.7	903	898	892	887	881	875	869	863	857	850	5 - 7
.8	843	837	829	822	815	807	799	791	783	775	6 - 9
.9	766	758	749	740	731	721	712	702	692	682	8 - 10
17.0	672	662	651	641	630	619	608	596	585	573	10 - 12
.1	562	550	538	526	513	501	488	476	463	450	12 - 13
.2	437	423	410	396	383	369	355	341	327	312	13 - 15
.3	298	283	269	254	239	224	209	193	178	163	14 - 16
.4	147	131	116	100	084	068	051	035	019	002	15 - 17
.5	.0 986	969	952	936	919	902	885	867	850	833	16 - 18
.6	816	798	781	763	745	728	710	692	674	656	17 - 18
.7	638	620	602	584	566	547	529	511	492	474	18 - 19
.8	456	437	419	400	381	363	344	325	307	288	18 - 19
.9	269	251	232	213	194	176	157	138	119	100	18 - 19
18.0	082	063	044	025	006	012	031	050	069	087	18 - 19
.1	-.0 106	125	143	162	181	199	218	236	255	273	18 - 19
.2	292	310	328	346	365	383	401	419	437	455	18 - 19
.3	473	491	509	527	544	562	579	597	614	632	18 - 17
.4	649	666	683	700	717	734	751	768	784	801	17 - 16
.5	817	834	850	866	882	898	914	930	946	961	17 - 15
.6	977	992	008	023	038	053	068	082	097	111	16 - 14
.7	-.1 126	140	154	168	182	196	210	223	236	250	14 - 13
.8	263	276	289	301	314	326	339	351	363	375	13 - 11
.9	386	398	409	421	432	443	454	464	475	485	12 - 10
19.0	496	506	516	525	535	544	554	563	572	581	10 - 8
.1	589	598	606	614	622	630	638	645	653	660	9 - 7
.2	667	674	680	687	693	699	705	711	717	722	7 - 5
.3	727	732	737	742	747	751	755	759	763	767	5 - 3
.4	770	774	777	780	783	785	788	790	792	794	4 - 2
.5	796	797	799	800	801	802	802	803	803	803	2 - 0
.6	803	803	802	802	801	800	799	797	796	794	0 - 2
.7	792	790	788	785	783	780	777	774	771	767	2 - 4
.8	764	760	756	752	747	743	738	733	728	723	4 - 5
.9	718	712	707	701	695	689	682	676	669	662	5 - 7
20.0	655										

x	$Y_2(x)$	x	$Y_2(x)$	x	$Y_2(x)$
.00	-Infin.	2.0	-.617 408 1	6.0	.229 858
.01	-12 732.714	2.1	-.567 511 5	6.1	.203 923
.02	-3 183.417	2.2	-.519 431 7	6.2	.176 606
.03	-1 415.029	2.3	-.472 616 9	6.3	.148 157
.04	-796.094	2.4	-.426 674 0	6.4	.118 836
.05	-509.615	2.5	-.381 335 8	6.5	.088 907
.06	-353.997	2.6	-.336 435 6	6.6	.058 636
.07	-260.164	2.7	-.291 886 9	6.7	.028 293
.08	-199.264	2.8	-.247 669 3	6.8	-.001 856
.09	-157.510	2.9	-.203 815 2	6.9	-.031 549
.10	-127.645	3.0	-.160 400 4	7.0	-.060 527
.11	-105.548	3.1	-.117 535 5	7.1	-.088 542
.12	-88.741 1	3.2	-.075 358 7	7.2	-.115 357
.13	-75.661 8	3.3	-.034 029 6	7.3	-.140 745
.14	-65.283 9	3.4	.006 276 0	7.4	-.164 496
.15	-56.911 7	3.5	.045 371 4	7.5	-.186 414
.16	-50.059 7	3.6	.083 063 2	7.6	-.206 324
.17	-44.381 1	3.7	.119 155 1	7.7	-.224 066
.18	-39.622 5	3.8	.153 451 9	7.8	-.239 505
.19	-35.595 3	3.9	.185 762 6	7.9	-.252 526
.2	-32.157 14	4.0	.215 903 6	8.0	-.263 037
.3	-14.480 09	4.1	.243 701 5	8.1	-.270 968
		4.2	.268 995 4	8.2	-.276 274
.4	-8.298 34	4.3	.291 639 5	8.3	-.278 936
.5	-5.441 371	4.4	.311 504 9	8.4	-.278 956
.6	-3.892 795	4.5	.328 481 6	8.5	-.276 362
.7	-2.961 478	4.6	.342 479 6	8.6	-.271 206
.8	-2.358 558	4.7	.353 430 8	8.7	-.263 560
.9	-1.945 910	4.8	.361 289 3	8.8	-.253 521
1.0	-1.650 683	4.9	.366 032 8	8.9	-.241 208
1.1	-1.431 471	5.0	.367 663	9.0	-.226 756
1.2	-1.263 311	5.1	.366 205	9.1	-.210 322
1.3	-1.130 412	5.2	.361 709	9.2	-.192 078
1.4	-1.022 391	5.3	.354 248	9.3	-.172 213
1.5	-.932 193 8	5.4	.343 919	9.4	-.150 928
1.6	-.854 899 4	5.5	.330 841	9.5	-.128 436
1.7	-.786 999 1	5.6	.315 156	9.6	-.104 960
1.8	-.725 948 2	5.7	.297 026	9.7	-.080 728
1.9	-.669 878 7	5.8	.276 631	9.8	-.055 977
		5.9	.254 170	9.9	-.030 944
				10.0	-.005 868

x	$Y_1'(x)$	x	$Y_1'(x)$	x	$Y_1'(x)$
.00	Infin.	2.0	.563 892	6.0	-.259 026
.01	6 364.854	2.1	.542 903	6.1	-.236 679
.02	1 590.427	2.2	.520 108	6.2	-.212 458
.03	706.362	2.3	.495 346	6.3	-.186 609
.04	396.986	2.4	.468 544	6.4	-.159 392
.05	253.818	2.5	.439 703	6.5	-.131 075
.06	176.067	2.6	.408 883	6.6	-.101 931
.07	129.200	2.7	.376 195	6.7	-.072 242
.08	98.792 8	2.8	.341 793	6.8	-.042 289
.09	77.954 1	2.9	.305 863	6.9	-.012 353
.10	63.055 3	3.0	.268 625	7.0	.017 288
.11	52.037 5	3.1	.230 319	7.1	.046 362
.12	43.662 5	3.2	.191 206	7.2	.074 604
.13	37.148 8	3.3	.151 561	7.3	.101 759
.14	31.984 0	3.4	.111 670	7.4	.127 588
.15	27.820 4	3.5	.071 825	7.5	.151 864
.16	24.415 6	3.6	.032 323	7.6	.174 376
.17	21.596 2	3.7	-.006 540	7.7	.194 934
.18	19.235 8	3.8	-.044 474	7.8	.213 366
.19	17.240 1	3.9	-.081 193	7.9	.229 524
.2	15.538 0	4.0	-.116 422	8.0	.243 279
.3	6.836 41				
		4.1	-.149 898	8.1	.254 529
.4	3.846 16	4.2	-.181 373	8.2	.263 196
.5	2.498 43	4.3	-.210 618	8.3	.269 226
.6	1.792 14				
		4.4	-.237 421	8.4	.272 589
.7	1.385 41	4.5	-.261 593	8.5	.273 264
.8	1.135 88	4.6	-.282 970	8.6	.271 332
.9	.975 769				
		4.7	-.301 409	8.7	.266 780
1.0	.869 470	4.8	-.316 797	8.8	.259 698
		4.9	-.329 044	8.9	.250 182
1.1	.796 817				
1.2	.745 697	5.0	-.338 090	9.0	.238 346
1.3	.708 474				
		5.1	-.343 904	9.1	.224 329
1.4	.680 143	5.2	-.346 480	9.2	.208 286
1.5	.657 321	5.3	-.345 843	9.3	.190 391
1.6	.637 663				
		5.4	-.342 043	9.4	.170 836
1.7	.619 513	5.5	-.335 161	9.5	.149 823
1.8	.601 690	5.6	-.325 300	9.6	.127 570
1.9	.583 349				
		5.7	-.312 592	9.7	.104 302
		5.8	-.297 189	9.8	.080 252
		5.9	-.279 268	9.9	.055 661
				10.0	.030 770

x	$Y_2'(x)$	x	$Y_2'(x)$	x	$Y_2'(x)$
.00	Infin.	2.0	.510 376	6.0	-.251 630
.01	2 546 479	2.1	.488 808	6.1	-.266 672
.02	318 310	2.2	.473 698	6.2	-.279 253
.03	94 314.0	2.3	.463 249	6.3	-.289 284
.04	39 788.7	2.4	.456 051	6.4	-.296 696
.05	20 371.8	2.5	.450 987	6.5	-.301 447
.06	11 789.2	2.6	.447 160	6.6	-.303 516
.07	7 424.10	2.7	.443 845	6.7	-.302 905
.08	4 973.56	2.8	.440 452	6.8	-.299 641
.09	3 493.07	2.9	.436 502	6.9	-.293 773
.10	2 546.44	3.0	.431 608	7.0	-.285 374
.11	1 913.16	3.1	.425 459	7.1	-.274 537
.12	1 473.61	3.2	.417 811	7.2	-.261 379
.13	1 159.02	3.3	.408 477	7.3	-.246 034
.14	927.965	3.4	.397 324	7.4	-.228 657
.15	754.459	3.5	.384 262	7.5	-.209 418
.16	621.643	3.6	.369 246	7.6	-.188 505
.17	518.257	3.7	.352 266	7.7	-.166 119
.18	436.580	3.8	.333 351	7.8	-.142 473
.19	371.200	3.9	.312 557	7.9	-.117 790
.2	318.248	4.0	.289 974	8.0	-.092 301
.3	94.240 9				
		4.1	.265 715	8.1	-.066 243
.4	39.710 8	4.2	.239 920	8.2	-.039 857
.5	20.294 0	4.3	.212 747	8.3	-.013 384
.6	11.715 6				
		4.4	.184 378	8.4	.012 934
.7	7.358 11	4.5	.155 005	8.5	.038 858
.8	4.918 25	4.6	.124 841	8.6	.064 155
.9	3.451 12				
		4.7	.094 105	8.7	.088 599
1.0	2.520 15	4.8	.063 028	8.8	.111 974
		4.9	.031 846	8.9	.134 073
1.1	1.904 56				
1.2	1.484 38	5.0	.000 798	9.0	.154 705
1.3	1.190 58				
		5.1	-.029 873	9.1	.173 690
1.4	.981 411	5.2	-.059 928	9.2	.190 869
1.5	.830 616	5.3	-.089 131	9.3	.206 096
1.6	.721 046				
		5.4	-.117 250	9.4	.219 248
1.7	.641 155	5.5	-.144 064	9.5	.230 219
1.8	.582 944	5.6	-.169 361	9.6	.238 926
1.9	.540 730				
		5.7	-.192 943	9.7	.245 305
		5.8	-.214 624	9.8	.249 317
		5.9	-.234 237	9.9	.250 944
				10.0	.250 189

The tables of $Y_2(x)$, $Y_1'(x)$, and $Y_2'(x)$ are from
Jour. of Math. and Phys., 1946, p. 93.

$$I_0(x)$$

x	0	1	2	3	4	5	6	7	8	9	Diff.
.0	1.0 000	000	001	002	004	006	009	012	016	020	0 - 5
.1	025	030	036	042	049	056	064	072	081	090	5 - 10
.2	100	111	121	133	145	157	170	183	197	211	10 - 15
.3	226	242	258	274	291	309	327	345	364	384	16 - 20
.4	404	425	446	468	490	513	536	560	584	609	21 - 26
.5	635	661	688	715	742	771	800	829	859	889	26 - 31
.6	920	952	984	017	051	084	119	154	190	226	32 - 37
.7	1.1 263	301	339	377	417	456	497	538	580	622	38 - 43
.8	665	709	753	798	843	889	936	984	032	080	44 - 50
.9	1.2 130	180	231	282	334	387	440	494	549	604	50 - 57
1.0	661	718	775	833	892	952	013	074	136	198	57 - 64
.1	1.3 262	326	391	456	523	590	658	726	796	866	64 - 71
.2	937	009	082	155	230	305	381	457	535	613	72 - 80
.3	1.4 693	773	854	936							80 - 88
1.5					019	102	187	272	359	446	
.4	1. 553	562	571	580	590	599	608	618	627	637	9 - 10
.5	647	657	667	677	687	697	707	718	728	739	10 - 11
.6	750	761	772	783	794	806	817	829	840	852	11 - 12
.7	864	876	888	900	913	925	938	951	963	976	12 - 14
.8	990	003	016	030	043	057	071	085	099	113	13 - 15
.9	2. 128	142	157	172	187	202	217	233	248	264	14 - 16
2.0	280	296	312	328	344	361	378	395	412	429	16 - 17
.1	446	464	482	499	517	536	554	573	591	610	17 - 19
.2	629	648	668	687	707	727	747	768	788	809	19 - 21
.3	830	851	872	893	915	937	959	981	004	026	21 - 23
.4	3. 049	072	096	119	143	167	191	215	240	265	23 - 25
.5	290	315	341	366	392	419	445	472	499	526	25 - 27
.6	553	581	609	637	666	694	723	752	782	812	28 - 30
.7	842	872	903	933	965	996	028	060	092	124	30 - 33
.8	4. 157	190	224	258	292	326	361	396	431	467	33 - 36
.9	503	539	576	613	650	688	725	764	802	841	36 - 40
3.0	881	921	961	001	042	083	125	166	209	251	40 - 43
.1	5. 294	338	382	426	471	516	561	607	653	700	44 - 47
.2	747	795	843	891	940	989	039	089	140	191	48 - 52
.3	6. 243	295	347	400	454	508	562	617	672	728	52 - 57
.4	785	842	899	957	016	075	134	195	255	316	57 - 62
.5	7. 378	441	503	567	631	696	761	827	893	960	62 - 68
.6	8. 028	096	165	234	304	375	447	519	591	665	68 - 74
.7	739	813	889	965	041	119	197	276	356	436	74 - 81
.8	9. 517	599	681	764	848	933	019	105	192	280	82 - 89
.9	10. 369	458	549	640	732	825	919	013	108	205	89 - 97
4.0	11. 302	400	499	599	699	801	904	007	112	217	98 - 107
.1	12. 324	431	539	649	759	870	983	096	210	326	107 - 116
.2	13. 442	560	679	798	919	041	164	289	414	540	118 - 128
.3	14. 668	797	927	058	190	324	459	595	732	871	129 - 139
.4	15.										
	16. 010	152	294	438	583	729	877	026	176	328	142 - 153
.5	17. 481	636	792	949	108	268	430	594	758	925	155 - 166
.6	18.										
	19. 093	262	433	606	780	955	133	312	492	675	169 - 183
.7	20. 858										
	21.	044	231	421	611	804	998	194	392	592	186 - 202
.8	22. 794	997									
	23.		202	410	619	830	043	258	475	694	203 - 221
.9	24. 915										
	25.	138	363	590	819	051	284	520	758	998	223 - 242
	26.										

$I_0(x)$

x		0	1	2	3	4	5	6	7	8	9	Diff.
5.0	10× 2.	724	748	773	798	823	849	874	900	926	952	24 - 27
.1		979	006	033	060	088	115	143	172	200	229	27 - 29
.2	10× 3.	258	288	317	347	378	408	439	470	501	533	29 - 32
.3		565	597	630	662	696	729	763	797	831	866	32 - 35
.4		901	936	972	008	044	081	118	155	193	231	35 - 38
.5	10× 4.	269	308	347	387	427	467	508	549	590	632	39 - 42
.6		674	716	759	803	846	890	935	980	025	071	42 - 46
.7	10× 5.	117	164	211	259	306	355	404	453	503	553	47 - 51
.8		604	655	707	759	811	865	918	972	027	082	51 - 56
.9	10× 6.	138	194	251	308	365	424	483	542	602	662	56 - 61
6.0		723	785	847	910	973	037	102	167	233	299	62 - 67
.1	10× 7.	366	434	502	571	641	711	782	853	925	998	68 - 74
.2	10× 8.	072	146	221	297	373	450	528	606	685	765	75 - 81
.3		846	928	010	093	177	261	347	433	520	608	82 - 88
.4	10× 9.	696	786	876	967							90 - 92
	100× 1.					006	015	025	034	044	053	9 - 10
.5		063	073	083	093	103	113	123	134	144	155	10 - 11
.6		165	176	187	198	209	220	232	243	255	266	11 - 12
.7		278	290	302	314	326	338	351	363	376	388	12 - 13
.8		401	414	427	441	454	468	481	495	509	523	13 - 14
.9		537	551	566	580	595	610	625	640	655	670	14 - 16
7.0		686	702	717	733	750	766	782	799	816	832	15 - 18
.1		850	867	884	902	919	937	955	974	992	010	17 - 19
.2	100× 2.	029	048	067	086	106	126	145	165	186	206	19 - 21
.3		227	247	268	290	311	332	354	376	398	421	20 - 23
.4		443	466	489	513	536	560	584	608	632	657	23 - 25
.5		682	707	732	758	783	809	836	862	889	916	25 - 27
.6		943	971	999	027	055	084	113	142	171	201	28 - 30
.7	100× 3.	231	261	292	323	354	385	417	449	481	514	30 - 33
.8		547	580	614	648	682	716	751	786	822	858	33 - 36
.9		894	931	968	005	042	080	119	157	196	236	37 - 40
8.0	100× 4.	276	316	356	397	439	480	522	565	608	651	40 - 44
.1		695	739	784	829	874	920	966	013	060	108	44 - 48
.2	100× 5.	156	204	253	303	353	403	454	506	557	610	48 - 53
.3		663	716	770	824	879	934	990	047	104	161	53 - 58
.4	100× 6.	219	278	337	397	457	518	580	642	705	768	59 - 64
.5		832	896	961	027	093	160	228	296	365	434	64 - 71
.6	100× 7.	505	575	647	719	792	866	940	015	091	167	70 - 77
.7	100× 8.	244	322	401	480	561	642	723	806	889	973	78 - 85
.8	100× 9.	058	144	230	317	406	495	584	675	767	859	86 - 93
.9		952										
9.0	1000× 1.	094	005	014	024	033	043	053	063	073	083	9 - 11
.1		202	213	225	236	248	260	272	284	296	308	10 - 12
.2		321	333	346	359	371	384	398	411	424	438	11 - 13
.3		451	465	479	493	507	522	536	551	565	580	12 - 14
												14 - 15
.4		595	610	626	641	657	673	688	704	721	737	15 - 17
.5		753	770	787	804	821	838	856	874	891	909	17 - 18
.6		927	946	964	983	002	021	040	060	079	099	18 - 20
.7	1000× 2.	119	139	159	180	201	222	243	264	286	307	20 - 22
.8		329	352	374	397	419	442	466	489	513	537	22 - 24
.9		561	585	610	635	660	685	711	737	763	789	24 - 27
10.0		816										

$$I_1(x) = I_0{}'(x)$$

x	0	1	2	3	4	5	6	7	8	9	Diff.
.0	.0 000	050	100	150	200	250	300	350	400	450	50 - 51
.1	501	551	601	651	702	752	803	853	904	954	50 - 51
.2	.1 005	056	107	158	209	260	311	362	414	465	51 - 52
.3	517	569	621	673	725	777	829	882	935	987	52 - 53
.4	.2 040	093	147	200	254	307	361	415	470	524	53 - 55
.5	579	634	689	744	800	855	911	967	024	080	55 - 57
.6	.3 137	194	251	309	367	425	483	542	600	659	57 - 60
.7	719	778	838	899	959	020	081	142	204	266	59 - 63
.8	.4 329	391	454	518	581	646	710	775	840	905	62 - 66
.9	971	038	104	171	239	306	375	443	512	582	66 - 70
1.0	.5 652	722	793	864	935	008	080	153	227	300	70 - 75
.1	.6 375	450	525	601	677	754	832	910	988	067	75 - 80
.2	.7 147	227	308	389	470	553	636	719	803	888	80 - 85
.3	973										
	.8	059	146	233	321	409	498	588	678	769	86 - 92
.4	861	953	046	140	235	330	426	522	620	718	92 - 99
.5	.9 817	916	017	118	220	322	426	530	635	741	99 - 107
.6	1.0 848	956									
	1.1		064	174	284	395	507	620	733	848	108 - 115
.7	1. 196	208	220	232	244	256	268	280	292	305	12 - 13
.8	317	330	343	355	368	381	395	408	421	435	12 - 14
.9	448	462	476	490	504	518	532	547	561	576	14 - 15
2.0	591	606	621	636	651	666	682	698	713	729	15 - 16
.1	745	762	778	795	811	828	845	862	879	897	16 - 18
.2	914	932	950	968	986	004	022	041	060	079	18 - 19
.3	2. 098	117	136	156	176	196	216	236	257	277	19 - 21
.4	298	319	340	362	383	405	427	449	471	494	21 - 23
.5	517	540	563	586	610	633	657	682	706	731	23 - 25
.6	755	780	806	831	857	883	909	935	962	989	25 - 27
.7	3. 016	043	071	099	127	155	184	213	242	271	27 - 30
.8	301	331	361	392	422	453	485	516	548	580	30 - 33
.9	613	645	678	712	745	779	813	848	883	918	32 - 35
3.0	953	989	025	062	098	136	173	211	249	287	36 - 39
.1	4. 326	365	405	445	485	526	567	608	650	692	39 - 42
.2	734	777	820	864	908	953	997	043	088	134	43 - 47
.3	5. 181	228	275	323	371	420	469	519	569	619	47 - 51
.4	670	722	773	826	879	932	986	040	095	150	51 - 56
.5	6. 206	262	319	376	434	493	552	611	671	732	56 - 61
.6	793	854	917	979	043	107	171	237	302	369	61 - 67
.7	7. 436	503	572	640	710	780	851	922	994	067	67 - 73
.8	8. 140	215	289	365	441	518	595	674	753	832	74 - 81
.9	913	994	076	159	242	326	411	497	584	671	81 - 88
4.0	9. 759	848	938	029	121	213	306	400	495	591	89 - 97
.1	10. 688	785	884	983	084	185	287	390	494	600	97 - 106
.2	11. 706	813	921	030	140	251	363	476	590	706	107 - 116
.3	12. 822	939	058	177	298	420	543	667	792	919	117 - 127
	13.										
.4	14. 046	175	305	436	569	702	837	973	111	249	129 - 140
.5	15. 389	530	673	817	962	109	257	406	557	709	141 - 154
.6	16. 863										
	17.	018	174	332	491	652	814	978	144	311	155 - 168
.7	18. 479	649	821	994							170 - 175
	19.				169	345	523	703	885	068	176 - 185
.8	20. 253	439	628	818							186 - 192
	21.				010	203	399	596	795	996	193 - 203
.9	22. 199	404	611	819							207 - 211
	23.				030	243	457	674	892	113	213 - 223
	24.										

BESSEL FUNCTIONS

$$I_1(x) \quad = I_0{}'(x)$$

x		0	1	2	3	4	5	6	7	8	9	Diff.
5.0	10 × 2.	434	456	479	502	525	548	572	595	619	644	22 - 25
.1		668	693	718	743	768	794	820	846	872	899	25 - 27
.2		925	953	980	007	035	063	092	120	149	179	27 - 30
.3	10 × 3.	208	238	268	298	329	359	391	422	454	486	30 - 32
.4		518	551	584	617	651	685	719	753	788	823	33 - 36
.5		859	895	931	967	004	041	079	117	155	194	36 - 39
.6	10 × 4.	233	272	312	352	393	433	475	516	558	601	39 - 43
.7		644	687	730	774	819	864	909	955	001	048	43 - 47
.8	10 × 5.	095	142	190	238	287	337	386	436	487	538	47 - 52
.9		590	642	695	748	802	856	910	966	021	077	52 - 57
6.0	10 × 6.	134	191	249	308	367	426	486	547	608	670	57 - 62
.1		732	795	858	922	987	053	118	185	252	320	63 - 69
.2	10 × 7.	389	458	527	598	669	741	813	886	960	035	69 - 75
.3	10 × 8.	110	186	263	340	418	497	577	657	738	820	76 - 83
.4		903	986	070	155	241	328	415	504	593	683	83 - 91
.5	10 × 9.	774	865	958								91 - 93
	100 × 1.				005	015	024	034	043	053	063	9 - 10
.6		073	083	093	104	114	124	135	146	156	167	10 - 11
.7		178	189	200	212	223	235	246	258	270	282	11 - 12
.8		294	306	318	331	343	356	369	381	394	408	12 - 14
.9		421	434	448	461	475	489	503	517	531	546	13 - 15
7.0		560	575	590	605	620	635	651	666	682	698	15 - 16
.1		714	730	746	763	779	796	813	830	847	865	16 - 18
.2		883	900	918	936	955	973	992	010	029	049	17 - 20
.3	100 × 2.	068	087	107	127	147	167	188	209	229	250	19 - 22
.4		272	293	315	337	359	381	404	426	449	472	21 - 24
.5		496	519	543	567	592	616	641	666	691	717	23 - 26
.6		742	768	794	821	848	874	902	929	957	985	26 - 28
.7	100 × 3.	013	042	070	100	129	159	188	219	249	280	28 - 31
.8		311	342	374	406	438	471	504	537	571	604	31 - 35
.9		639	673	708	743	779	814	851	887	924	961	34 - 38
8.0		999										
	100 × 4.		037	075	114	153	192	232	272	313	354	38 - 41
.1		395	437	479	521	564	607	651	695	740	785	42 - 45
.2		830	876	923	969	017	064	112	161	210	260	46 - 50
.3	100 × 5.	310	360	411	462	514	567	620	673	727	782	50 - 55
.4		837	892	948	005	062	119	178	236	296	356	55 - 60
.5	100 × 6.	416	477	539	601	664	727	791	856	921	987	61 - 67
.6	100 × 7.	054	121	189	257	326	396	467	538	609	682	67 - 73
.7		755	829	904	979	055	132	209	287	366	446	74 - 81
.8	100 × 8.	527	608	690	773	856	941	026	112	199	287	81 - 88
.9	100 × 9.	375	465	555	646	738	831	925				90 - 94
	1000 × 1.								002	012	021	9 - 10
9.0		031	041	051	061	071	081	091	102	112	123	10 - 11
.1		134	144	155	166	178	189	200	212	223	235	10 - 12
.2		247	259	271	283	295	307	320	332	345	358	12 - 13
.3		371	384	397	411	424	438	452	465	479	494	13 - 15
.4		508	522	537	552	566	581	596	612	627	643	14 - 16
.5		658	674	690	707	723	739	756	773	790	807	16 - 19
.6		824	842	859	877	895	913	931	950	969	987	17 - 19
.7	1000 × 2.	006	026	045	065	084	104	125	145	165	186	19 - 21
.8		207	228	250	271	293	315	337	359	382	405	21 - 23
.9		428	451	475	498	522	547	571	596	621	646	23 - 25
10.0		671										

The tables of $I_0(x)$ and $I_1(x)$ are from "Tables of Functions with Formulae and Curves" by E. Jahnke and F. Emde, ($2.00), Dover Publications, New York 10, New York. For extended tables of $I_0(x)$ and $I_1(x)$, see pages 362 - 381, "Table of Bessel Functions for Complex Arguments," by A. N. Lowan, Columbia Univ. Press, New York, 1943.

x	$I_2(x)$	$I_3(x)$	$I_4(x)$
0	0	0	0
.1	.001 251 0	.000 020 846	.000 000 260 55
.2	.005 016 7	.000 167 08	.000 004 175 0
.3	.011 335	.000 565 67	.000 021 189
.4	.020 268	.001 346 7	.000 067 202
.5	.031 906	.002 645 1	.000 164 81
.6	.046 365	.004 602 2	.000 343 62
.7	.063 790	.007 367 4	.000 640 74
.8	.084 353	.011 100	.001 101 3
.9	.108 26	.015 972	.001 779 0
1.0	.135 75	.022 168	.002 737 1
1.1	.167 09	.029 891	.004 049 3
1.2	.202 60	.039 359	.005 800 7
1.3	.242 62	.050 815	.008 088 8
1.4	.287 55	.064 522	.011 026
1.5	.337 83	.080 774	.014 738
1.6	.393 97	.099 892	.019 371
1.7	.456 50	.122 23	.025 089
1.8	.526 04	.148 19	.032 077
1.9	.603 27	.178 20	.040 545
2.0	.688 95	.212 74	.050 729
2.1	.783 90	.252 35	.062 895
2.2	.889 06	.297 63	.077 345
2.3	1.005 4	.349 22	.094 415
2.4	1.134 2	.407 87	.114 48
2.5	1.276 5	.474 37	.137 98
2.6	1.433 7	.549 63	.165 37
2.7	1.607 5	.634 63	.197 21
2.8	1.799 4	.730 48	.234 08
2.9	2.011 3	.838 41	.276 66
3.0	2.245 2	.959 75	.325 71
3.1	2.503 4	1.096 0	.382 05
3.2	2.788 3	1.248 9	.446 65
3.3	3.102 7	1.420 2	.520 54
3.4	3.449 5	1.611 9	.604 90
3.5	3.832 0	1.826 4	.701 05
3.6	4.254 0	2.066 1	.810 46
3.7	4.719 3	2.333 8	.934 75
3.8	5.232 5	2.632 6	1.075 8
3.9	5.798 3	2.965 8	1.235 5
4.0	6.422 2	3.337 3	1.416 3
4.1	7.110 0	3.751 1	1.620 6
4.2	7.868 4	4.212 0	1.851 3
4.3	8.704 3	4.724 9	2.111 5
4.4	9.625 8	5.295 5	2.404 6
4.5	10.642	5.930 1	2.734 7
4.6	11.761	6.635 5	3.106 0
4.7	12.995	7.419 5	3.523 3
4.8	14.355	8.290 3	3.992 1
4.9	15.854	9.257 5	4.518 2
5.0	17.506	10.331	5.108 2
5.1	19.326	11.523	5.769 7
5.2	21.332	12.845	6.510 6
5.3	23.542	14.312	7.340 2
5.4	25.978	15.939	8.268 6
5.5	28.663	17.743	9.307 0
5.6	31.620	19.742	10.468
5.7	34.879	21.959	11.765
5.8	38.470	24.415	13.214
5.9	42.427	27.136	14.831
6.0	46.787	30.151	16.637

x	$I_5(x)$	$I_6(x)$	$I_7(x)$
0	0	0	0
.1	$.26053 \times 10^{-8}$	$.21709 \times 10^{-10}$	$.15506 \times 10^{-12}$
.2	$.83472 \times 10^{-7}$	$.13909 \times 10^{-8}$	$.19866 \times 10^{-10}$
.3	$.63519 \times 10^{-6}$	$.15871 \times 10^{-7}$	$.33996 \times 10^{-9}$
.4	$.26845 \times 10^{-5}$	$.89398 \times 10^{-7}$	$.25524 \times 10^{-8}$
.5	$.82232 \times 10^{-5}$	$.34212 \times 10^{-6}$	$.12205 \times 10^{-7}$
.6	$.20556 \times 10^{-4}$	$.10256 \times 10^{-5}$	$.43883 \times 10^{-7}$
.7	$.44670 \times 10^{-4}$	$.25982 \times 10^{-5}$	$.12963 \times 10^{-6}$
.8	$.87635 \times 10^{-4}$	$.58202 \times 10^{-5}$	$.33164 \times 10^{-6}$
.9	$.15904 \times 10^{-3}$	$.11871 \times 10^{-4}$	$.76039 \times 10^{-6}$
1.0	$.27146 \times 10^{-3}$	$.22489 \times 10^{-4}$	$.15992 \times 10^{-5}$
1.1	$.44101 \times 10^{-3}$	$.40138 \times 10^{-4}$	$.31369 \times 10^{-5}$
1.2	$.68789 \times 10^{-3}$	$.68209 \times 10^{-4}$	$.58093 \times 10^{-5}$
1.3	$.10371 \times 10^{-2}$	$.11124 \times 10^{-3}$	$.10253 \times 10^{-4}$
1.4	$.15191 \times 10^{-2}$	$.17520 \times 10^{-3}$	$.17369 \times 10^{-4}$
1.5	$.21706 \times 10^{-2}$	$.26777 \times 10^{-3}$	$.28406 \times 10^{-4}$
1.6	$.30356 \times 10^{-2}$	$.39874 \times 10^{-3}$	$.45060 \times 10^{-4}$
1.7	$.41665 \times 10^{-2}$	$.58039 \times 10^{-3}$	$.69587 \times 10^{-4}$
1.8	$.56248 \times 10^{-2}$	$.82798 \times 10^{-3}$	$.10495 \times 10^{-3}$
1.9	$.74830 \times 10^{-2}$	$.11603 \times 10^{-2}$	$.15500 \times 10^{-3}$
2.0	$.98257 \times 10^{-2}$	$.16002 \times 10^{-2}$	$.22464 \times 10^{-3}$
2.1	$.12751 \times 10^{-1}$	$.21754 \times 10^{-2}$	$.32011 \times 10^{-3}$
2.2	$.16374 \times 10^{-1}$	$.29195 \times 10^{-2}$	$.44923 \times 10^{-3}$
2.3	$.20825 \times 10^{-1}$	$.38722 \times 10^{-2}$	$.62173 \times 10^{-3}$
2.4	$.26257 \times 10^{-1}$	$.50814 \times 10^{-2}$	$.84966 \times 10^{-3}$
2.5	$.32843 \times 10^{-1}$	$.66033 \times 10^{-2}$	$.11478 \times 10^{-2}$
2.6	$.40786 \times 10^{-1}$	$.85045 \times 10^{-2}$	$.15342 \times 10^{-2}$
2.7	$.50313 \times 10^{-1}$	$.10863 \times 10^{-1}$	$.20306 \times 10^{-2}$
2.8	$.61686 \times 10^{-1}$	$.13772 \times 10^{-1}$	$.26636 \times 10^{-2}$
2.9	$.75204 \times 10^{-1}$	$.17337 \times 10^{-1}$	$.34648 \times 10^{-2}$
3.0	$.91206 \times 10^{-1}$	$.21684 \times 10^{-1}$	$.44721 \times 10^{-2}$
3.1	.11008	$.26957 \times 10^{-1}$	$.57309 \times 10^{-2}$
3.2	.13226	$.33325 \times 10^{-1}$	$.72948 \times 10^{-2}$
3.3	.15825	$.40982 \times 10^{-1}$	$.92274 \times 10^{-2}$
3.4	.18861	$.50153 \times 10^{-1}$	$.11604 \times 10^{-1}$
3.5	.22398	$.61096 \times 10^{-1}$	$.14512 \times 10^{-1}$
3.6	.26509	$.74109 \times 10^{-1}$	$.18055 \times 10^{-1}$
3.7	.31273	$.89532 \times 10^{-1}$	$.22356 \times 10^{-1}$
3.8	.36784	.10776	$.27554 \times 10^{-1}$
3.9	.43145	.12923	$.33815 \times 10^{-1}$
4.0	.50472	.15446	$.41330 \times 10^{-1}$
4.1	.58899	.18404	$.50322 \times 10^{-1}$
4.2	.68571	.21863	$.61048 \times 10^{-1}$
4.3	.79656	.25899	$.73805 \times 10^{-1}$
4.4	.92342	.30598	$.88939 \times 10^{-1}$
4.5	1.0684	.36057	.10684
4.6	1.2338	.42389	.12798
4.7	1.4223	.49719	.15286
4.8	1.6369	.58191	.18210
4.9	1.8809	.67967	.21638
5.0	2.1580	.79229	.25649
5.1	2.4724	.92185	.30334
5.2	2.8288	1.0707	.35796
5.3	3.2324	1.2415	.42152
5.4	3.6690	1.4371	.49538
5.5	4.2052	1.6611	.58106
5.6	4.7884	1.9171	.68031
5.7	5.4466	2.2095	.79511
5.8	6.1890	2.5430	.92771
5.9	7.0259	2.9230	1.0807
6.0	7.9685	3.3558	1.2569

x	$I_8(x)$	$I_9(x)$	$I_{10}(x)$	$I_{11}(x)$
0	0	0	0	0
.1	$.96908 \times 10^{-15}$	$.53836 \times 10^{-17}$	$.26918 \times 10^{-19}$	$.12235 \times 10^{-21}$
.2	$.24829 \times 10^{-12}$	$.27585 \times 10^{-14}$	$.27582 \times 10^{-16}$	$.25073 \times 10^{-18}$
.3	$.63723 \times 10^{-11}$	$.10618 \times 10^{-12}$	$.15923 \times 10^{-14}$	$.21710 \times 10^{-16}$
.4	$.63775 \times 10^{-10}$	$.14166 \times 10^{-11}$	$.28321 \times 10^{-13}$	$.51478 \times 10^{-15}$
.5	$.38108 \times 10^{-9}$	$.10578 \times 10^{-10}$	$.26430 \times 10^{-12}$	$.60041 \times 10^{-14}$
.6	$.16436 \times 10^{-8}$	$.54731 \times 10^{-10}$	$.16406 \times 10^{-11}$	$.44713 \times 10^{-13}$
.7	$.56615 \times 10^{-8}$	$.21987 \times 10^{-9}$	$.76869 \times 10^{-11}$	$.24436 \times 10^{-12}$
.8	$.16545 \times 10^{-7}$	$.73404 \times 10^{-9}$	$.29319 \times 10^{-10}$	$.10649 \times 10^{-11}$
.9	$.42652 \times 10^{-7}$	$.21278 \times 10^{-8}$	$.95576 \times 10^{-10}$	$.39040 \times 10^{-11}$
1.0	$.99606 \times 10^{-7}$	$.55184 \times 10^{-8}$	$.27529 \times 10^{-9}$	$.12490 \times 10^{-10}$
1.1	$.21476 \times 10^{-6}$	$.13080 \times 10^{-7}$	$.71745 \times 10^{-9}$	$.35791 \times 10^{-10}$
1.2	$.43354 \times 10^{-6}$	$.28788 \times 10^{-7}$	$.17216 \times 10^{-8}$	$.93653 \times 10^{-10}$
1.3	$.82818 \times 10^{-6}$	$.59535 \times 10^{-7}$	$.38550 \times 10^{-8}$	$.22707 \times 10^{-9}$
1.4	$.15095 \times 10^{-5}$	$.11678 \times 10^{-6}$	$.81382 \times 10^{-8}$	$.51598 \times 10^{-9}$
1.5	$.26426 \times 10^{-5}$	$.21885 \times 10^{-6}$	$.16331 \times 10^{-7}$	$.11088 \times 10^{-8}$
1.6	$.44666 \times 10^{-5}$	$.39424 \times 10^{-6}$	$.31358 \times 10^{-7}$	$.22696 \times 10^{-8}$
1.7	$.73208 \times 10^{-5}$	$.68593 \times 10^{-6}$	$.57926 \times 10^{-7}$	$.44518 \times 10^{-8}$
1.8	$.11677 \times 10^{-4}$	$.11574 \times 10^{-5}$	$.10341 \times 10^{-6}$	$.84091 \times 10^{-8}$
1.9	$.18180 \times 10^{-4}$	$.19001 \times 10^{-5}$	$.17905 \times 10^{-6}$	$.15359 \times 10^{-7}$
2.0	$.27699 \times 10^{-4}$	$.30442 \times 10^{-5}$	$.30170 \times 10^{-6}$	$.27222 \times 10^{-7}$
2.1	$.41388 \times 10^{-4}$	$.47707 \times 10^{-5}$	$.49600 \times 10^{-6}$	$.46956 \times 10^{-7}$
2.2	$.60761 \times 10^{-4}$	$.73288 \times 10^{-5}$	$.79748 \times 10^{-6}$	$.79029 \times 10^{-7}$
2.3	$.87785 \times 10^{-4}$	$.11056 \times 10^{-4}$	$.12565 \times 10^{-5}$	$.13007 \times 10^{-6}$
2.4	$.12499 \times 10^{-3}$	$.16406 \times 10^{-4}$	$.19436 \times 10^{-5}$	$.20976 \times 10^{-6}$
2.5	$.17560 \times 10^{-3}$	$.23978 \times 10^{-4}$	$.29557 \times 10^{-5}$	$.33199 \times 10^{-6}$
2.6	$.24368 \times 10^{-3}$	$.34560 \times 10^{-4}$	$.44256 \times 10^{-5}$	$.51648 \times 10^{-6}$
2.7	$.33437 \times 10^{-3}$	$.49175 \times 10^{-4}$	$.65319 \times 10^{-5}$	$.79085 \times 10^{-6}$
2.8	$.45403 \times 10^{-3}$	$.69146 \times 10^{-4}$	$.95134 \times 10^{-5}$	$.11933 \times 10^{-5}$
2.9	$.61056 \times 10^{-3}$	$.96163 \times 10^{-4}$	$.13686 \times 10^{-4}$	$.17762 \times 10^{-5}$
3.0	$.81370 \times 10^{-3}$	$.13237 \times 10^{-3}$	$.19464 \times 10^{-4}$	$.26104 \times 10^{-5}$
3.1	$.10754 \times 10^{-2}$	$.18049 \times 10^{-3}$	$.27388 \times 10^{-4}$	$.37913 \times 10^{-5}$
3.2	$.14102 \times 10^{-2}$	$.24391 \times 10^{-3}$	$.38155 \times 10^{-4}$	$.54459 \times 10^{-5}$
3.3	$.18357 \times 10^{-2}$	$.32690 \times 10^{-3}$	$.52660 \times 10^{-4}$	$.77421 \times 10^{-5}$
3.4	$.23734 \times 10^{-2}$	$.43470 \times 10^{-3}$	$.72046 \times 10^{-4}$	$.10900 \times 10^{-4}$
3.5	$.30489 \times 10^{-2}$	$.57384 \times 10^{-3}$	$.97761 \times 10^{-4}$	$.15207 \times 10^{-4}$
3.6	$.38932 \times 10^{-2}$	$.75232 \times 10^{-3}$	$.13163 \times 10^{-3}$	$.21034 \times 10^{-4}$
3.7	$.49431 \times 10^{-2}$	$.97992 \times 10^{-3}$	$.17595 \times 10^{-3}$	$.28859 \times 10^{-4}$
3.8	$.62427 \times 10^{-2}$	$.12686 \times 10^{-2}$	$.23357 \times 10^{-3}$	$.39293 \times 10^{-4}$
3.9	$.78443 \times 10^{-2}$	$.16329 \times 10^{-2}$	$.30805 \times 10^{-3}$	$.53115 \times 10^{-4}$
4.0	$.98099 \times 10^{-2}$	$.20903 \times 10^{-2}$	$.40379 \times 10^{-3}$	$.71308 \times 10^{-4}$
4.1	$.12213 \times 10^{-1}$	$.26620 \times 10^{-2}$	$.52620 \times 10^{-3}$	$.95115 \times 10^{-4}$
4.2	$.15140 \times 10^{-1}$	$.33734 \times 10^{-2}$	$.68194 \times 10^{-3}$	$.12609 \times 10^{-3}$
4.3	$.18692 \times 10^{-1}$	$.42552 \times 10^{-2}$	$.87914 \times 10^{-3}$	$.16618 \times 10^{-3}$
4.4	$.22989 \times 10^{-1}$	$.53438 \times 10^{-2}$	$.11277 \times 10^{-2}$	$.21779 \times 10^{-3}$
4.5	$.28170 \times 10^{-1}$	$.66826 \times 10^{-2}$	$.14397 \times 10^{-2}$	$.28393 \times 10^{-3}$
4.6	$.34400 \times 10^{-1}$	$.83235 \times 10^{-2}$	$.18297 \times 10^{-2}$	$.36829 \times 10^{-3}$
4.7	$.41869 \times 10^{-1}$	$.10328 \times 10^{-1}$	$.23153 \times 10^{-2}$	$.47541 \times 10^{-3}$
4.8	$.50798 \times 10^{-1}$	$.12768 \times 10^{-1}$	$.29178 \times 10^{-2}$	$.61087 \times 10^{-3}$
4.9	$.61448 \times 10^{-1}$	$.15730 \times 10^{-1}$	$.36625 \times 10^{-2}$	$.78148 \times 10^{-3}$
5.0	$.74117 \times 10^{-1}$	$.19316 \times 10^{-1}$	$.45800 \times 10^{-2}$	$.99554 \times 10^{-3}$
5.1	$.89153 \times 10^{-1}$	$.23643 \times 10^{-1}$	$.57069 \times 10^{-2}$	$.12631 \times 10^{-2}$
5.2	$.10696$	$.28852 \times 10^{-1}$	$.70864 \times 10^{-2}$	$.15965 \times 10^{-2}$
5.3	$.12800$	$.35107 \times 10^{-1}$	$.87705 \times 10^{-2}$	$.20104 \times 10^{-2}$
5.4	$.15281$	$.42598 \times 10^{-1}$	$.10820 \times 10^{-1}$	$.25226 \times 10^{-2}$
5.5	$.18202$	$.51550 \times 10^{-1}$	$.13309 \times 10^{-1}$	$.31545 \times 10^{-2}$
5.6	$.21633$	$.62225 \times 10^{-1}$	$.16322 \times 10^{-1}$	$.39319 \times 10^{-2}$
5.7	$.25657$	$.74925 \times 10^{-1}$	$.19961 \times 10^{-1}$	$.48854 \times 10^{-2}$
5.8	$.30367$	$.90004 \times 10^{-1}$	$.24346 \times 10^{-1}$	$.60519 \times 10^{-2}$
5.9	$.35872$	$.10787$	$.29617 \times 10^{-1}$	$.74750 \times 10^{-2}$
6.0	$.42297$	$.12901$	$.35940 \times 10^{-1}$	$.92070 \times 10^{-2}$

Trans. American Institute of Electrical Engineers, 1941, p. 135.

x	$K_o(x)$		x	$K_o(x)$
.00	Infin.		.50	.9244
.01	4.7212		.51	.9081
.02	4.0285		.52	.8921
.03	3.6235		.53	.8766
.04	3.3365		.54	.8614
.05	3.1142		.55	.8466
.06	2.9329		.56	.8321
.07	2.7798		.57	.8180
.08	2.6475		.58	.8042
.09	2.5310		.59	.7907
.10	2.4271		.60	.7775
.11	2.3333		.61	.7646
.12	2.2479		.62	.7520
.13	2.1695		.63	.7397
.14	2.0972		.64	.7277
.15	2.0300		.65	.7159
.16	1.9674		.66	.7043
.17	1.9088		.67	.6930
.18	1.8537		.68	.6820
.19	1.8018		.69	.6711
.20	1.7527		.70	.6605
.21	1.7062		.71	.6501
.22	1.6620		.72	.6399
.23	1.6199		.73	.6300
.24	1.5798		.74	.6202
.25	1.5415		.75	.6106
.26	1.5048		.76	.6012
.27	1.4697		.77	.5920
.28	1.4360		.78	.5829
.29	1.4036		.79	.5740
.30	1.3725		.80	.5653
.31	1.3425		.81	.5568
.32	1.3136		.82	.5484
.33	1.2857		.83	.5402
.34	1.2587		.84	.5321
.35	1.2327		.85	.5242
.36	1.2075		.86	.5165
.37	1.1832		.87	.5088
.38	1.1596		.88	.5013
.39	1.1367		.89	.4940
.40	1.1145		.90	.4867
.41	1.0930		.91	.4796
.42	1.0721		.92	.4727
.43	1.0518		.93	.4658
.44	1.0321		.94	.4591
.45	1.0129		.95	.4524
.46	.9943		.96	.4459
.47	.9761		.97	.4396
.48	.9584		.98	.4333
.49	.9412		.99	.4271

$$K_0(x)$$

x	0	1	2	3	4	5	6	7	8	9	Diff.
1.0	.4 210	151	092	034	977	922	867	813	760	707	59 - 51
.1	.3 656	605	556	507	459	411	365	319	273	229	51 - 44
.2	185	142	100	058	017	976	936	897	858	820	43 - 38
.3	.2 782	746	709	673	638	603	569	535	502	469	37 - 32
.4	437	405	373	342	312	282	252	223	194	166	32 - 28
.5	138	111	083	057	030	004	979	953	928	904	28 - 24
.6	.1 880	856	832	809	786	763	741	719	697	676	24 - 21
.7	655	634	614	593	573	554	534	515	496	478	21 - 18
.8	459	441	423	406	388	371	354	337	321	305	18 - 16
.9	288	273	257	242	226	211	196	182	167	153	16 - 14
2.0	139	125	111	098	084	071	058	045	033	020	14 - 12
.1	.10 078										
	.09	956	836	717	600	484	370	257	145	035	122 - 108
.2	.08 927	820	714	609	506	404	304	204	106	010	107 - 96
.3	.07 914	820	726	634	544	454	365	278	191	106	94 - 84
.4	022	939	856	775	695	616	538	461	384	309	83 - 74
.5	.06 235	161	089	017	946	877	808	739	672	606	74 - 66
.6	.05 540	475	411	348	285	223	162	102	042	984	65 - 58
.7	.04 926	868	811	755	700	645	592	538	485	433	58 - 51
.8	382	331	281	231	182	134	086	039	992	946	51 - 45
.9	.03 901	856	811	767	724	681	638	597	555	514	45 - 40
3.0	474	434	395	356	317	279	241	204	168	131	40 - 36
.1	095	060	025	990	956	922	889	856	824	791	35 - 32
.2	.02 759	728	697	666	636	606	576	547	518	489	31 - 28
.3	461	433	405	378	351	325	298	272	246	221	28 - 25
.4	196	171	146	122	098	074	051	028	005	982	25 - 22
.5	.01 960	938	916	894	873	852	831	810	790	770	22 - 20
.6	750	730	711	692	673	654	635	617	599	581	20 - 18
.7	563	546	528	511	494	477	461	445	428	412	18 - 15
.8	397	381	366	350	335	320	306	291	277	262	16 - 14
.9	248	234	221	207	194	180	167	154	141	129	14 - 12
4.0	.011 160	036									
	.010		913	792	672	553	436	320	205	092	124 - 112
.1	.009 980	869	760	652	545	439	334	231	128	027	111 - 100
.2	.008 927	829	731	634	539	444	351	259	167	077	98 - 89
.3	.007 988	900	813	726	641	557	473	391	309	229	88 - 80
.4	149	070	992	915	839	764	689	616	543	471	79 - 71
.5	.006 400	329	260	191	123	056	989	923	858	794	71 - 64
.6	.005 730	668	605	544	483	423	363	305	246	189	63 - 57
.7	132	076	020	965	911	857	804	751	699	648	56 - 51
.8	.004 597	547	497	448	399	351	304	257	210	164	50 - 45
.9	119	074	030	986	942	899	857	814	773	732	45 - 41
5.	.00 369	331	297	266	238	214	192	172	154	139	
6.	124	112	100	900	808	726	652	586	526	473	
	.000										
7.	425	382	343	308	277	249	224	201	181	163	
8.	146	132	118	107	959	863	776	698	628	565	
	.0000										
9.	509	458	412	371	334	301	271	244	219	197	
10.	178										

x	$K_1(x)$	$=-K_0{}'(x)$	x	$K_1(x)$
.00	Infin.		.50	1.6564
.01	99.9739		.51	1.6149
.02	49.9547		.52	1.5749
.03	33.2715		.53	1.5364
.04	24.9233		.54	1.4994
.05	19.9097		.55	1.4637
.06	16.5637		.56	1.4292
.07	14.1710		.57	1.3960
.08	12.3742		.58	1.3638
.09	10.9749		.59	1.3328
.10	9.8538		.60	1.3028
.11	8.9353		.61	1.2738
.12	8.1688		.62	1.2458
.13	7.5192		.63	1.2186
.14	6.9615		.64	1.1923
.15	6.4775		.65	1.1668
.16	6.0533		.66	1.1420
.17	5.6784		.67	1.1181
.18	5.3447		.68	1.0948
.19	5.0456		.69	1.0722
.20	4.7760		.70	1.0503
.21	4.5317		.71	1.0290
.22	4.3092		.72	1.0083
.23	4.1058		.73	.9882
.24	3.9191		.74	.9686
.25	3.7470		.75	.9496
.26	3.5880		.76	.9311
.27	3.4405		.77	.9130
.28	3.3033		.78	.8955
.29	3.1755		.79	.8784
.30	3.0560		.80	.8618
.31	2.9441		.81	.8456
.32	2.8390		.82	.8298
.33	2.7402		.83	.8144
.34	2.6470		.84	.7993
.35	2.5591		.85	.7847
.36	2.4760		.86	.7704
.37	2.3973		.87	.7564
.38	2.3227		.88	.7428
.39	2.2518		.89	.7295
.40	2.1844		.90	.7165
.41	2.1202		.91	.7039
.42	2.0590		.92	.6915
.43	2.0006		.93	.6794
.44	1.9449		.94	.6675
.45	1.8915		.95	.6560
.46	1.8405		.96	.6447
.47	1.7916		.97	.6336
.48	1.7447		.98	.6228
.49	1.6997		.99	.6122

$$K_1(x) \qquad = -K_0{}'(x)$$

x	0	1	2	3	4	5	6	7	8	9	Diff.
1.0	.6 019	918	819	722	627	534	443	354	267	181	101 - 83
.1	.5 098	016	935	856	779	703	629	556	485	415	82 - 69
.2	.4 346	279	212	147	084	021	960	900	841	782	67 - 57
.3	.3 725	670	615	561	508	455	404	354	305	256	55 - 48
.4	208	161	115	070	026	982	939	897	855	814	47 - 40
.5	.2 774	734	695	657	620	583	546	510	475	440	40 - 34
.6	406	373	340	307	275	244	213	182	152	123	33 - 29
.7	094	065	037	009	982	955	928	902	876	851	29 - 25
.8	.1 826	802	777	754	730	707	684	662	640	618	25 - 21
.9	597	575	555	534	514	494	474	455	436	417	22 - 18
2.0	399	380	362	345	327	310	293	276	260	244	19 - 16
.1	227	212	196	181	166	151	136	121	107	093	16 - 14
.2	.10 790	652	517	383	252	122	993	867	742	620	138 - 122
.3	.09 498	379	261	144	029	916	804	694	586	478	119 - 106
.4	.08 372	268	165	063	963	864	767	670	575	482	104 - 93
.5	.07 389	298	208	119	031	945	859	775	692	609	91 - 81
.6	.06 528	448	369	292	215	139	064	990	917	845	80 - 71
.7	.05 774	704	634	566	498	432	366	301	237	174	70 - 63
.8	111	050	989	929	869	811	753	696	639	584	61 - 55
.9	.04 529	474	421	368	316	264	213	163	113	064	55 - 48
3.0	016	968	921	874	828	782	738	693	649	606	48 - 43
.1	.03 563	521	480	438	398	358	318	279	240	202	42 - 38
.2	164	127	090	054	018	983	948	913	879	845	37 - 33
.3	.02 812	779	746	714	682	651	620	589	559	529	33 - 29
.4	500	471	442	414	385	358	330	303	276	250	29 - 26
.5	224	198	173	147	123	098	074	050	026	003	26 - 23
.6	.01 979	957	934	912	890	868	846	825	804	783	23 - 20
.7	763	743	722	703	683	664	645	626	607	589	21 - 18
.8	571	553	535	517	500	483	466	449	432	416	18 - 16
.9	400	384	368	353	337	322	307	292	277	263	16 - 14
4.0	248	234	220	206	193	179	166	152	139	126	14 - 12
.1	114	101	089	076	064	052	040	028	017	005	13 - 11
.2	.009 938	826	715	605	497	390	284	179	076	973	112 - 101
.3	.008 872	772	674	576	479	384	290	196	104	013	100 - 90
.4	.007 923	834	746	659	573	488	404	321	239	158	89 - 80
.5	078	999	920	843	766	691	616	542	469	397	79 - 72
.6	.006 325	254	185	116	047	980	913	847	782	717	71 - 63
.7	.005 654	591	529	467	406	346	286	228	169	112	63 - 57
.8	055	999	943	889	834	781	727	675	623	572	56 - 51
.9	.004 521	471	421	372	324	276	229	182	136	090	50 - 45
5.	.00 404	362	324	290	260	233	208	187	167	150	
6.	134	120	108								
.000				969	869	780	700	628	564	506	
7.	454	408	366	329	295	265	238	214	192	173	
8.	155	140	126	113	101						
.0000						912	820	737	663	596	
9.	536	482	434	390	351	316	284	256	230	207	
10.	186										

Acknowledgment is made to the Royal Society, London, England, for the tables of K₀(x) and K₁(x) which, for x from 0 to 5, are abridged from "Bessel Functions," Part I, Vol. VI of the British Association Mathematical Tables, published by Cambridge University Press, London, Eng., 1937, and for x from 5 to 10, from the Proceedings of the Royal Society, 1898.

x	ber x	bei x	ber' x	bei' x
0	1.00000	0	0	0
.1	1.00000	.002500	-.0000625	.050000
.2	.99998	.010000	-.0005000	.099999
.3	.99987	.022500	-.0016875	.14999
.4	.99960	.039998	-.004000	.19997
.5	.99902	.062493	-.007812	.24992
.6	.99798	.089980	-.013498	.29980
.7	.99625	.12245	-.021433	.34956
.8	.99360	.15989	-.031989	.39915
.9	.98975	.20227	-.045537	.44846
1.0	.98438	.24957	-.062446	.49740
1.1	.97714	.30173	-.083082	.54581
1.2	.96763	.35870	-.10781	.59352
1.3	.95543	.42041	-.13697	.64034
1.4	.94008	.48673	-.17093	.68601
1.5	.92107	.55756	-.21001	.73025
1.6	.89789	.63273	-.25454	.77274
1.7	.86997	.71204	-.30484	.81310
1.8	.83672	.79526	-.36118	.85093
1.9	.79752	.88212	-.42384	.88574
2.0	.75173	.97229	-.49307	.91701
2.1	.69869	1.0654	-.56906	.94418
2.2	.63769	1.1610	-.65200	.96661
2.3	.56805	1.2585	-.74202	.98361
2.4	.48905	1.3575	-.83920	.99443
2.5	.39997	1.4572	-.94358	.99827
2.6	.30009	1.5569	-1.0551	.99426
2.7	.18871	1.6557	-1.1738	.98149
2.8	.065112	1.7529	-1.2993	.95897
2.9	-.071368	1.8472	-1.4314	.92566
3.0	-.22138	1.9376	-1.5698	.88048
3.1	-.38553	2.0228	-1.7141	.82230
3.2	-.56438	2.1016	-1.8636	.74992
3.3	-.75841	2.1723	-2.0177	.66214
3.4	-.96804	2.2334	-2.1755	.55769
3.5	-1.1936	2.2832	-2.3361	.43530
3.6	-1.4353	2.3199	-2.4983	.29366
3.7	-1.6933	2.3413	-2.6608	.13149
3.8	-1.9674	2.3454	-2.8222	-.052527
3.9	-2.2576	2.3300	-2.9807	-.25965
4.0	-2.5634	2.2927	-3.1347	-.49114
4.1	-2.8843	2.2309	-3.2818	-.74817
4.2	-3.2195	2.1422	-3.4200	-1.0319
4.3	-3.5679	2.0236	-3.5465	-1.3433
4.4	-3.9283	1.8726	-3.6588	-1.6833
4.5	-4.2991	1.6860	-3.7537	-2.0526
4.6	-4.6784	1.4610	-3.8880	-2.4520
4.7	-5.0639	1.1946	-3.8782	-2.8818
4.8	-5.4531	.88366	-3.9006	-3.3422
4.9	-5.8429	.52515	-3.8911	-3.8331

$$\text{ber } x + i \text{ bei } x = J_o(xi^{3/2})$$

where J_o denotes the Bessel function of the
first kind and order zero.

$$\text{ber' } x = \frac{d}{dx} \text{ ber } x$$

x	ber x	bei x	ber' x	bei' x
5.0	-6.2301	.11603	-3.8453	-4.3541
5.1	-6.6107	-.34666	-3.7589	-4.9046
5.2	-6.9803	-.86584	-3.6270	-5.4835
5.3	-7.3344	-1.4443	-3.4445	-6.0892
5.4	-7.6674	-2.0845	-3.2064	-6.7199
5.5	-7.9736	-2.7890	-2.9070	-7.3729
5.6	-8.2466	-3.5597	-2.5410	-8.0454
5.7	-8.4794	-4.3986	-2.1024	-8.7336
5.8	-8.6644	-5.3068	-1.5855	-9.4333
5.9	-8.7937	-6.2854	-.98438	-10.139
6.0	-8.8583	-7.3347	-.29308	-10.846
6.1	-8.8491	-8.4545	.49429	-11.547
6.2	-8.7561	-9.6437	1.3835	-12.235
6.3	-8.5688	-10.901	2.3802	-12.901
6.4	-8.2762	-12.223	3.4899	-13.536
6.5	-7.8669	-13.607	4.7174	-14.129
6.6	-7.3287	-15.047	6.0675	-14.670
6.7	-6.6492	-16.538	7.5442	-15.146
6.8	-5.8155	-18.074	9.1510	-15.543
6.9	-4.8146	-19.644	10.891	-15.847
7.0	-3.6329	-21.239	12.765	-16.041
7.1	-2.2571	-22.848	14.774	-16.109
7.2	-.67370	-24.456	16.918	-16.033
7.3	1.1308	-26.049	19.194	-15.792
7.4	3.1695	-27.609	21.600	-15.367
7.5	5.4550	-29.116	24.130	-14.736
7.6	7.9994	-30.548	26.777	-13.875
7.7	10.814	-31.882	29.532	-12.763
7.8	13.909	-33.092	32.382	-11.373
7.9	17.293	-34.147	35.314	-9.6806
8.0	20.974	-35.017	38.311	-7.6603
8.1	24.957	-35.667	41.353	-5.2855
8.2	29.245	-36.061	44.415	-2.5296
8.3	33.840	-36.159	47.472	.63410
8.4	38.738	-35.920	50.492	4.2318
8.5	43.936	-35.298	53.442	8.2895
8.6	49.423	-34.246	56.281	12.832
8.7	55.187	-32.714	58.967	17.883
8.8	61.210	-30.651	61.451	23.465
8.9	67.469	-28.003	63.682	29.598
9.0	73.936	-24.713	65.601	36.299
9.1	80.576	-20.724	67.145	43.583
9.2	87.350	-15.976	68.246	51.460
9.3	94.208	-10.412	68.831	59.936
9.4	101.10	-3.9693	68.821	69.012
9.5	107.95	3.4106	68.132	78.684
9.6	114.70	11.787	66.674	88.940
9.7	121.26	21.218	64.353	99.763
9.8	127.54	31.758	61.070	111.12
9.9	133.43	43.459	56.720	122.99

BESSEL FUNCTIONS

x	ber x	bei x	ber' x	bei' x
10.0	138.84	56.370	51.195	135.31
10.1	143.63	70.534	44.384	148.03
10.2	147.67	85.987	36.171	161.08
10.3	150.81	102.76	26.438	174.38
10.4	152.90	120.87	15.066	187.82
10.5	153.77	140.32	1.9344	201.30
10.6	153.23	161.12	-13.076	214.69
10.7	151.09	183.25	-30.083	227.85
10.8	147.14	206.68	-49.202	240.59
10.9	141.17	231.35	-70.544	252.75
11.0	132.95	257.21	-94.212	264.12
11.1	122.25	284.14	-120.30	274.46
11.2	108.81	312.06	-148.90	283.54
11.3	92.383	340.80	-180.08	291.07
11.4	72.707	370.21	-213.89	296.76
11.5	49.517	400.08	-250.37	300.29
11.6	22.543	430.18	-289.55	301.32
11.7	-8.4832	460.25	-331.41	299.48
11.8	-43.828	489.97	-375.92	294.37
11.9	-83.753	519.00	-423.01	285.58
12.0	-128.51	546.95	-472.57	272.67
12.1	-178.34	573.38	-524.46	255.18
12.2	-233.48	597.82	-578.51	232.62
12.3	-294.11	619.72	-634.46	204.50
12.4	-360.42	638.51	-692.03	170.30
12.5	-432.56	653.56	-750.87	129.49
12.6	-510.62	664.17	-810.58	81.534
12.7	-594.69	669.61	-870.67	25.889
12.8	-684.75	669.07	-930.59	-37.992
12.9	-780.78	661.72	-989.72	-110.65
13.0	-882.65	646.64	-1047.3	-192.61
13.1	-990.17	622.87	-1102.7	-284.38
13.2	-1103.1	589.42	-1154.8	-386.45
13.3	-1221.0	545.22	-1202.7	-499.28
13.4	-1343.4	489.19	-1245.3	-623.27
13.5	-1469.8	420.18	-1281.5	-758.77
13.6	-1599.5	337.04	-1309.9	-906.08
13.7	-1731.5	238.57	-1329.2	-1065.4
13.8	-1865.0	123.55	-1337.7	-1236.9
13.9	-1998.7	-9.210	-1333.9	-1420.5
14.0	-2131.3	-160.94	-1316.1	-1616.1
14.1	-2261.3	-332.82	-1282.3	-1823.5
14.2	-2387.1	-526.02	-1230.7	-2042.3
14.3	-2506.8	-741.65	-1159.1	-2272.0
14.4	-2618.2	-980.75	-1065.4	-2511.6
14.5	-2719.1	-1244.3	-947.37	-2760.4
14.6	-2806.8	-1533.1	-802.69	-3016.9
14.7	-2878.6	-1847.9	-628.96	-3279.9
14.8	-2931.6	-2189.2	-423.74	-3547.4
14.9	-2962.3	-2557.4	-184.56	-3817.5

x	ber x	bei x	ber' x	bei' x
15.0	-2967.3	-2952.7	91.056	-4087.8
15.1	-2942.8	-3374.9	405.59	-4355.5
15.2	-2884.8	-3823.6	761.47	-4617.5
15.3	-2789.0	-4298.1	1161.1	-4970.4
15.4	-2651.0	-4797.3	1606.6	-5110.3
15.5	-2466.1	-5319.6	2100.3	-5332.7
15.6	-2229.3	-5863.1	2644.1	-5533.0
15.7	-1935.5	-6425.3	3239.6	-5705.8
15.8	-1579.6	-7003.1	3888.3	-5845.4
15.9	-1156.1	-7593.0	4591.3	-5945.6
16.0	-659.50	-8190.7	5349.3	-5999.5
16.1	-84.364	-8791.2	6162.6	-6000.0
16.2	574.85	-9388.7	7030.8	-5939.2
16.3	1323.6	-9976.7	7953.1	-5808.8
16.4	2167.2	-10548	8927.9	-5600.2
16.5	3110.8	-11094	9952.9	-5303.9
16.6	4159.4	-11605	11025	-4910.4
16.7	5317.2	-12072	12140	-4409.5
16.8	6588.5	-12483	13292	-3790.6
16.9	7976.7	-12826	14476	-3043.0
17.0	9484.5	-13087	15683	-2155.5
17.1	11114	-13252	16905	-1116.9
17.2	12866	-13305	18132	84.10
17.3	14740	-13230	19351	1459.0
17.4	16735	-13007	20550	3018.9
17.5	18849	-12619	21711	4774.9
17.6	21076	-12045	22819	6737.5
17.7	23410	-11265	23854	8916.7
17.8	25843	-10255	24795	11322
17.9	28365	-8992.4	25618	13961
18.0	30962	-7454.3	26298	16841
18.1	33619	-5616.0	26807	19968
18.2	36317	-3452.4	27115	23345
18.3	39034	-938.55	27189	26975
18.4	41746	1950.9	26993	30857
18.5	44423	5241.1	26492	34987
18.6	47033	8956.4	25645	39360
18.7	49539	13121	24411	43967
18.8	51901	17757	22745	48793
18.9	54072	22886	20602	53821
19.0	56003	28527	17934	59029
19.1	57640	34697	14691	64390
19.2	58921	41409	10823	69871
19.3	59782	48674	6279.0	75433
19.4	60152	56497	1006.0	81030
19.5	59957	64879	-5048.2	86609
19.6	59115	73816	-11935	92111
19.7	57540	83297	-19706	97468
19.8	55143	93303	-28411	102600
19.9	51826	103810	-38095	107430
20.0	47489	114780	-48803	111860

$$\text{ber } x + i \text{ bei } x = J_0(xi^{3/2}) = M \ (\ \cos \theta + i \sin \theta \ )$$

x	M	θ degrees	x	M	θ degrees
0	1.0000	0	5.0	6.2312	178.933
.1	1.0000	.143	5.1	6.6197	183.002
.2	1.0000	.573	5.2	7.0338	187.071
.3	1.0001	1.289	5.3	7.4752	191.140
.4	1.0004	2.291	5.4	7.9457	195.209
.5	1.0010	3.579	5.5	8.4473	199.279
.6	1.0020	5.152	5.6	8.9821	203.348
.7	1.0037	7.007	5.7	9.5523	207.418
.8	1.0064	9.141	5.8	10.160	211.487
.9	1.0102	11.550	5.9	10.809	215.556
1.0	1.0155	14.226	6.0	11.501	219.625
1.1	1.0227	17.160	6.1	12.239	223.694
1.2	1.0320	20.340	6.2	13.026	227.762
1.3	1.0438	23.750	6.3	13.865	231.830
1.4	1.0586	27.373	6.4	14.761	235.898
1.5	1.0767	31.188	6.5	15.717	239.965
1.6	1.0984	35.172	6.6	16.737	244.031
1.7	1.1242	39.299	6.7	17.825	248.098
1.8	1.1544	43.545	6.8	18.986	252.163
1.9	1.1892	47.883	6.9	20.225	256.229
2.0	1.2290	52.290	7.0	21.548	260.294
2.1	1.2741	56.743	7.1	22.959	264.358
2.2	1.3246	61.221	7.2	24.466	268.422
2.3	1.3808	65.708	7.3	26.074	272.486
2.4	1.4429	70.188	7.4	27.790	276.549
2.5	1.5111	74.651	7.5	29.622	280.612
2.6	1.5855	79.090	7.6	31.578	284.674
2.7	1.6665	83.498	7.7	33.666	288.736
2.8	1.7541	87.873	7.8	35.896	292.798
2.9	1.8486	92.213	7.9	38.276	296.859
3.0	1.9502	96.518	8.0	40.818	300.920
3.1	2.0593	100.791	8.1	43.531	304.981
3.2	2.1760	105.032	8.2	46.429	309.042
3.3	2.3009	109.245	8.3	49.524	313.102
3.4	2.4342	113.433	8.4	52.829	317.162
3.5	2.5764	117.599	8.5	56.359	321.222
3.6	2.7280	121.745	8.6	60.128	325.282
3.7	2.8894	125.875	8.7	64.155	329.341
3.8	3.0613	129.991	8.8	68.455	333.400
3.9	3.2443	134.096	8.9	73.049	337.459
4.0	3.4391	138.191	9.0	77.956	341.518
4.1	3.6464	142.279	9.1	83.199	345.577
4.2	3.8670	146.361	9.2	88.799	349.635
4.3	4.1018	150.439	9.3	94.782	353.693
4.4	4.3518	154.514	9.4	101.17	357.752
4.5	4.6179	158.586	9.5	108.00	1.810
4.6	4.9012	162.657	9.6	115.30	5.867
4.7	5.2029	166.726	9.7	123.10	9.925
4.8	5.5242	170.795	9.8	131.43	13.983
4.9	5.8665	174.864	9.9	140.33	18.040

ber $x + i$ bei $x = J_o(xi^{3/2}) = M (\cos \theta + i \sin \theta)$

x	M	θ degrees	x	M	θ degrees
10.0	149.85	22.098	15.0	4186.1	224.859
10.1	160.02	26.155	15.1	4477.7	228.913
10.2	170.88	30.212	15.2	4789.8	232.967
10.3	182.49	34.269	15.3	5123.7	237.021
10.4	194.91	38.326	15.4	5481.0	241.075
10.5	208.17	42.382	15.5	5863.4	245.128
10.6	222.35	46.439	15.6	6272.6	249.182
10.7	237.51	50.496	15.7	6710.5	253.236
10.8	253.71	54.552	15.8	7179.1	257.289
10.9	271.02	58.608	15.9	7680.5	261.343
11.0	289.54	62.665	16.0	8217.2	265.397
11.1	309.33	66.721	16.1	8791.6	269.450
11.2	330.48	70.777	16.2	9406.2	273.504
11.3	353.10	74.833	16.3	10064.	277.557
11.4	377.28	78.889	16.4	10768	281.611
11.5	403.13	82.945	16.5	11522	285.664
11.6	430.77	87.000	16.6	12328	289.718
11.7	460.33	91.056	16.7	13191	293.771
11.8	491.93	95.112	16.8	14115	297.824
11.9	525.71	99.167	16.9	15104	301.878
12.0	561.84	103.222	17.0	16163	305.931
12.1	600.48	107.278	17.1	17296	309.984
12.2	641.79	111.333	17.2	18508	314.038
12.3	685.97	115.388	17.3	19806	318.091
12.4	733.21	119.443	17.4	21196	322.144
12.5	783.74	123.499	17.5	22683	326.198
12.6	837.77	127.554	17.6	24275	330.251
12.7	895.56	131.609	17.7	25979	334.304
12.8	957.36	135.663	17.8	27804	338.357
12.9	1023.5	139.718	17.9	29756	342.410
13.0	1094.2	143.773	18.0	31847	346.463
13.1	1169.8	147.828	18.1	34085	350.516
13.2	1250.7	151.883	18.2	36481	354.570
13.3	1337.2	155.937	18.3	39046	358.623
13.4	1429.7	159.992	18.4	41791	2.676
13.5	1528.7	164.046	18.5	44731	6.729
13.6	1634.6	168.101	18.6	47878	10.782
13.7	1747.9	172.155	18.7	51247	14.835
13.8	1869.0	176.210	18.8	54854	18.888
13.9	1998.7	180.264	18.9	58716	22.941
14.0	2137.3	184.318	19.0	62851	26.994
14.1	2285.7	188.373	19.1	67277	31.047
14.2	2444.4	192.427	19.2	72017	35.099
14.3	2614.2	196.481	19.3	77091	39.152
14.4	2795.9	200.535	19.4	82524	43.205
14.5	2990.3	204.589	19.5	88341	47.258
14.6	3198.2	208.643	19.6	94570	51.311
14.7	3420.7	212.697	19.7	101240	55.364
14.8	3658.8	216.751	19.8	108380	59.417
14.9	3913.5	220.805	19.9	116020	63.469
			20.0	124210	67.522

$$\text{ber}'\ x + i\ \text{bei}'\ x = \frac{d}{dx}\ J_0(xi^{3/2}) = M\ (\ \cos\theta + i\sin\theta\ )$$

x	M	θ degrees	x	M	θ degrees
0	0	90	5.0	5.8091	228.551
.1	.050000	90.072	5.1	6.1794	232.534
.2	.10000	90.286	5.2	6.5745	236.518
.3	.15000	90.645	5.3	6.9960	240.504
.4	.20001	91.146	5.4	7.4456	244.492
.5	.25004	91.790	5.5	7.9253	248.481
.6	.30010	92.578	5.6	8.4371	252.472
.7	.35022	93.509	5.7	8.9831	256.465
.8	.40043	94.582	5.8	9.5656	260.459
.9	.45077	95.798	5.9	10.187	264.455
1.0	.50130	97.156	6.0	10.850	268.452
1.1	.55209	98.655	6.1	11.558	272.451
1.2	.60323	100.295	6.2	12.313	276.452
1.3	.65482	102.074	6.3	13.119	280.454
1.4	.70698	103.991	6.4	13.978	284.457
1.5	.75985	106.045	6.5	14.896	288.463
1.6	.81358	108.232	6.6	15.876	292.469
1.7	.86837	110.551	6.7	16.921	296.477
1.8	.92441	112.999	6.8	18.037	300.487
1.9	.98192	115.572	6.9	19.228	304.498
2.0	1.0412	118.266	7.0	20.500	308.510
2.1	1.1024	121.077	7.1	21.858	312.523
2.2	1.1659	124.001	7.2	23.308	316.538
2.3	1.2321	127.030	7.3	24.856	320.554
2.4	1.3012	130.161	7.4	26.509	324.571
2.5	1.3736	133.387	7.5	28.274	328.589
2.6	1.4498	136.701	7.6	30.159	332.608
2.7	1.5300	140.098	7.7	32.171	336.628
2.8	1.6148	143.570	7.8	34.321	340.649
2.9	1.7046	147.110	7.9	36.617	344.670
3.0	1.7999	150.713	8.0	39.070	348.693
3.1	1.9011	154.372	8.1	41.689	352.716
3.2	2.0088	158.080	8.2	44.487	356.740
3.3	2.1236	161.832	8.3	47.476	.765
3.4	2.2458	165.622	8.4	50.669	4.791
3.5	2.3763	169.445	8.5	54.081	8.817
3.6	2.5155	173.296	8.6	57.725	12.844
3.7	2.6640	177.171	8.7	61.619	16.871
3.8	2.8227	181.066	8.8	65.779	20.900
3.9	2.9920	184.978	8.9	70.224	24.928
4.0	3.1729	188.905	9.0	74.974	28.957
4.1	3.3660	192.842	9.1	80.049	32.987
4.2	3.5722	196.790	9.2	85.473	37.017
4.3	3.7924	200.744	9.3	91.269	41.048
4.4	4.0274	204.705	9.4	97.463	45.079
4.5	4.2783	208.671	9.5	104.08	49.111
4.6	4.5460	212.641	9.6	111.16	53.143
4.7	4.8317	216.615	9.7	118.72	57.176
4.8	5.1366	220.591	9.8	126.80	61.208
4.9	5.4619	224.570	9.9	135.44	65.242

$$\text{ber' } x + i \text{ bei' } x = \frac{d}{dx} J_0(xi^{3/2}) = M (\cos \theta + i \sin \theta)$$

x	M	θ degrees	x	M	θ degrees
10.0	144.67	69.275	15.0	4088.8	271.276
10.1	154.54	73.310	15.1	4374.3	275.320
10.2	165.09	77.344	15.2	4679.9	279.364
10.3	176.37	81.379	15.3	5006.9	283.409
10.4	188.42	85.414	15.4	5356.9	287.453
10.5	201.31	89.449	15.5	5731.5	291.497
10.6	215.09	93.485	15.6	6132.3	295.542
10.7	229.82	97.521	15.7	6561.4	299.586
10.8	245.57	101.558	15.8	7020.5	303.631
10.9	262.41	105.594	15.9	7512.0	307.676
11.0	280.42	109.631	16.0	8038.0	311.721
11.1	299.67	113.669	16.1	8601.0	315.766
11.2	320.26	117.706	16.2	9203.6	319.811
11.3	342.27	121.744	16.3	9848.6	323.856
11.4	365.81	125.782	16.4	10539	327.901
11.5	390.98	129.820	16.5	11278	331.947
11.6	417.89	133.859	16.6	12069	335.992
11.7	446.68	137.898	16.7	12916	340.037
11.8	477.46	141.937	16.8	13822	344.083
11.9	510.38	145.976	16.9	14792	348.129
12.0	545.59	150.015	17.0	15831	352.174
12.1	583.25	154.055	17.1	16942	356.220
12.2	623.52	158.095	17.2	18132	.266
12.3	666.60	162.135	17.3	19406	4.312
12.4	712.67	166.175	17.4	20770	8.358
12.5	761.95	170.215	17.5	22230	12.404
12.6	814.67	174.256	17.6	23793	16.450
12.7	871.05	178.297	17.7	25466	20.496
12.8	931.37	182.338	17.8	27258	24.542
12.9	995.89	186.379	17.9	29175	28.588
13.0	1064.9	190.420	18.0	31229	32.635
13.1	1138.7	194.462	18.1	33427	36.681
13.2	1217.7	198.503	18.2	35780	40.727
13.3	1302.2	202.545	18.3	38300	44.774
13.4	1392.6	206.587	18.4	40997	48.820
13.5	1489.3	210.629	18.5	43885	52.867
13.6	1592.8	214.671	18.6	46978	56.914
13.7	1703.5	218.714	18.7	50289	60.960
13.8	1821.9	222.756	18.8	53834	65.007
13.9	1948.6	226.799	18.9	57629	69.054
14.0	2084.2	230.842	19.0	61693	73.101
14.1	2229.2	234.885	19.1	66045	77.148
14.2	2384.5	238.928	19.2	70704	81.195
14.3	2550.5	242.971	19.3	75694	85.242
14.4	2728.2	247.014	19.4	81036	89.289
14.5	2918.4	251.057	19.5	86756	93.336
14.6	3121.9	255.101	19.6	92881	97.383
14.7	3339.6	259.145	19.7	99440	101.430
14.8	3572.6	263.188	19.8	106460	105.477
14.9	3821.9	267.232	19.9	113980	109.525
			20.0	122040	113.572

See "Values of the Bessel Functions ber x and bei x and their Derivatives" by H. B. Dwight, Transactions of the American Institute of Electrical Engineers, v. 58, 1939, p. 787. For x from 0 to 10, with more significant figures, see Report of the British Association for the Advancement of Science, 1912, p. 56, 1916, p. 122, and "Tables of Integrals and other Mathematical Data" by H. B. Dwight, Table 1050.

$$\text{ber}_n\,x + i\,\text{bei}_n\,x = J_n(xi^{3/2}) = i^n I_n(xi^{1/2})$$

$$\text{ber}_n{}'x = \frac{d}{dx}\,\text{ber}_n\,x$$

x	$\text{ber}_1\,x$	$\text{bei}_1\,x$	$\text{ber}_1{}'x$	$\text{bei}_1{}'x$
0	0	0	-.353 553	.353 553
1	-.395 868	.307 557	-.476 664	.212 036
2	-.997 078	.299 775	-.720 532	-.305 845
3	-1.732 64	-.487 45	-.635 99	-1.364 13
4	-1.869 25	-2.563 82	.658 74	-2.792 83
5	.359 78	-5.797 91	4.251 33	-3.327 80
6	7.462 20	-7.876 68	10.206 52	.235 45
7	20.368 9	-2.317 2	14.677 5	12.780 7
8	32.506 9	21.673 5	5.866 4	36.882 2
9	20.719 2	72.054 3	-37.108 0	61.749 0
10	-59.478	131.879	-132.087	45.127

x	$\text{ber}_2\,x$	$\text{bei}_2\,x$	$\text{ber}_2{}'x$	$\text{bei}_2{}'x$
0	0	0	0	0
1	.010 411	-.124 675	.041 623	-.248 047
2	.165 279	-.479 225	.327 788	-.437 789
3	.808 37	-.891 02	1.030 93	-.286 47
4	2.317 85	-.725 36	1.975 73	.853 82
5	4.488 43	1.422 10	2.049 97	3.785 30
6	5.242 91	7.432 44	-1.454 56	8.368 74
7	-.950 35	17.592 4	-12.493 0	11.015 1
8	-22.889 0	25.438 9	-32.589 1	1.300 6
9	-65.869 2	10.134 8	-50.963 2	-38.551 6
10	-111.779	-66.610	-28.840	-121.987

x	$\text{ber}_3\,x$	$\text{bei}_3\,x$	$\text{ber}_3{}'x$	$\text{bei}_3{}'x$
0	0	0	0	0
1	.013 788	.015 629	.039 433	.048 634
2	.085 612	.144 210	.093 575	.239 418
3	.130 44	.565 38	.072 00	.636 27
4	-.282 63	1.437 76	-.914 09	1.073 55
5	-2.094 35	2.454 41	-2.922 76	.695 57
6	-6.430 04	1.901 46	-5.747 81	-2.498 96
7	-12.876 5	-4.407 2	-6.249 2	-11.222 9
8	-15.420 4	-22.575 0	3.979 6	-25.707 4
9	3.166 6	-54.538 7	38.354 6	-35.563 4
10	72.253	-81.423	104.463	-7.513

x	$\text{ber}_4\,x$	$\text{bei}_4\,x$	$\text{ber}_4{}'x$	$\text{bei}_4{}'x$
0	0	0	0	0
1	-.002 601	-.000 130	-.010 395	-.000 781
2	-.040 97	-.008 30	-.080 56	-.024 83
3	-.193 27	-.093 02	-.234 32	-.183 52
4	-.493 10	-.499 85	-.323 71	-.716 65
5	-.628 67	-1.727 62	.248 34	-1.834 36
6	.648 3	-4.230 2	2.770 0	-3.071 1
7	6.083 5	-7.116 9	8.745 2	-1.921 9
8	19.094 7	-5.288 8	17.319 5	7.703 5
9	38.667	14.082	19.140	34.545
10	46.579	70.500	-12.148	80.465

x	$\text{ber}_5\,x$	$\text{bei}_5\,x$	$\text{ber}_5{}'x$	$\text{bei}_5{}'x$
0	0	0	0	0
1	.000 192	-.000 176	.000 973	-.000 866
2	.006 80	-.004 84	.017 84	-.011 00
3	.058 59	-.025 54	.104 78	-.028 32
4	.273 08	-.033 53	.360 76	.046 69
5	.851 04	.211 43	.815 11	.565 64
6	1.830 5	1.475 6	1.007 4	2.220 0
7	2.209 0	5.242 3	-.847 2	5.589 6
8	-1.821 3	12.812 8	-8.623 9	9.233 7
9	-18.619	21.384	-26.955	5.504
10	-58.722	15.193	-53.427	-24.511

x	ker x	kei x	ker' x	kei' x
0	Infin.	-.785 398 2	- Infin.	0
.1	2.420 474 0	-.776 850 6	-9.960 959 3	.145 974 8
.2	1.733 142 7	-.758 124 9	-4.922 948 5	.222 926 8
.3	1.337 218 6	-.733 101 9	-3.219 865 2	.274 292 1
.4	1.062 623 9	-.703 800 2	-2.352 069 9	.309 514 0
.5	.855 905 9	-.671 581 7	-1.819 799 8	.333 203 8
.6	.693 120 7	-.637 449 5	-1.456 538 6	.348 164 4
.7	.561 378 3	-.602 175 5	-1.190 943 3	.356 309 5
.8	.452 882 1	-.566 367 6	-.987 335 1	.359 042 5
.9	.362 514 8	-.530 511 1	-.825 868 7	.357 443 2
1.0	.286 706 2	-.494 994 6	-.694 603 9	.352 369 9
1.1	.222 844 5	-.460 129 5	-.585 905 3	.344 521 0
1.2	.168 945 6	-.426 163 6	-.494 643 2	.334 473 9
1.3	.123 455 4	-.393 291 8	-.417 227 4	.322 711 8
1.4	.085 126 0	-.361 664 8	-.351 055 1	.309 641 6
1.5	.052 934 9	-.331 395 6	-.294 181 6	.295 608 1
1.6	.026 029 9	-.302 565 5	-.245 114 7	.280 903 8
1.7	.003 691 1	-.275 228 8	-.202 681 8	.265 777 2
1.8	-.014 696 1	-.249 417 1	-.165 942 4	.250 438 5
1.9	-.029 661 4	-.225 142 2	-.134 128 2	.235 065 7
2.0	-.041 664 5	-.202 400 1	-.106 601 0	.219 807 9
2.1	-.051 106 5	-.181 172 6	-.082 823 4	.204 789 7
2.2	-.058 338 8	-.161 430 7	-.062 337 3	.190 113 7
2.3	-.063 670 5	-.143 135 7	-.044 747 9	.175 863 8
2.4	-.067 373 5	-.126 241 5	-.029 712 3	.162 106 9
2.5	-.069 688 0	-.110 696 1	-.016 929 8	.148 895 4
2.6	-.070 825 7	-.096 442 9	-.006 135 8	.136 268 9
2.7	-.070 973 6	-.083 421 9	.002 904 3	.124 255 8
2.8	-.070 296 3	-.071 570 7	.010 399 0	.112 874 8
2.9	-.068 939 0	-.060 825 5	.016 534 2	.102 136 2
3.0	-.067 029 2	-.051 121 9	.021 476 2	.092 043 1
3.1	-.064 678 6	-.042 395 5	.025 373 8	.082 592 2
3.2	-.061 984 8	-.034 582 3	.028 360 3	.073 775 2
3.3	-.059 032 9	-.027 619 7	.030 555 4	.065 579 4
3.4	-.055 896 6	-.021 446 3	.032 066 2	.057 988 1
3.5	-.052 639 3	-.016 002 6	.032 988 6	.050 982 1
3.6	-.049 315 6	-.011 231 1	.033 408 7	.044 539 4
3.7	-.045 971 7	-.007 076 7	.033 403 0	.038 636 4
3.8	-.042 646 9	-.003 486 7	.033 040 0	.033 248 0
3.9	-.039 373 61	-.000 410 81	.032 380 46	.028 348 32
4.0	-.036 178 85	.002 198 40	.031 478 49	.023 910 62
4.1	-.033 084 40	.004 385 82	.030 381 79	.019 908 04
4.2	-.030 107 58	.006 193 61	.029 132 42	.016 313 67
4.3	-.027 261 77	.007 661 27	.027 767 30	.013 100 84
4.4	-.024 556 89	.008 825 62	.026 318 68	.010 243 31
4.5	-.021 999 88	.009 720 92	.024 814 54	.007 715 43
4.6	-.019 595 03	.010 378 86	.023 279 08	.005 492 26
4.7	-.017 344 41	.010 828 72	.021 733 00	.003 549 76
4.8	-.015 248 19	.011 097 40	.020 193 91	.001 864 78
4.9	-.013 304 90	.011 209 53	.018 676 61	.000 415 22

x	ker x	kei x	ker' x	kei' x
5.0	-.011 511 73	.011 187 59	.017 193 40	-.000 819 98
5.1	-.009 864 74	.011 052 01	.015 754 36	-.001 860 79
5.2	-.008 359 11	.010 821 28	.014 367 57	-.002 726 05
5.3	-.006 989 28	.010 512 06	.013 039 35	-.003 433 49
5.4	-.005 749 13	.010 139 29	.011 774 46	-.003 999 69
5.5	-.004 632 16	.009 716 31	.010 576 33	-.004 440 16
5.6	-.003 631 56	.009 254 96	.009 447 17	-.004 769 28
5.7	-.002 740 38	.008 765 72	.008 388 18	-.005 000 41
5.8	-.001 951 58	.008 257 74	.007 399 67	-.005 145 84
5.9	-.001 258 12	.007 739 02	.006 481 21	-.005 216 89
6.0	-.000 653 04	.007 216 49	.005 631 71	-.005 223 92
6.1	-.000 129 53	.006 696 06	.004 849 57	-.005 176 37
6.2	.000 319 05	.006 182 75	.004 132 75	-.005 082 83
6.3	.000 699 12	.005 680 77	.003 478 86	-.004 951 05
6.4	.001 016 83	.005 193 58	.002 885 23	-.004 788 03
6.5	.001 278 080	.004 723 992	.002 348 995	-.004 600 032
6.6	.001 488 446	.004 274 219	.001 867 130	-.004 392 632
6.7	.001 653 215	.003 845 947	.001 436 521	-.004 170 782
6.8	.001 777 354	.003 440 398	.001 053 999	-.003 938 849
6.9	.001 865 512	.003 058 385	.000 716 382	-.003 700 651
7.0	.001 922 022	.002 700 365	.000 420 510	-.003 459 509
7.1	.001 950 901	.002 366 486	.000 163 267	-.003 218 285
7.2	.001 955 861	.002 056 629	-.000 058 386	-.002 979 421
7.3	.001 940 312	.001 770 454	-.000 247 403	-.002 744 978
7.4	.001 907 373	.001 507 429	-.000 406 628	-.002 516 671
7.5	.001 859 888	.001 266 868	-.000 538 787	-.002 295 904
7.6	.001 800 431	.001 047 959	-.000 646 478	-.002 083 800
7.7	.001 731 326	.000 849 790	-.000 732 165	-.001 881 234
7.8	.001 654 654	.000 671 373	-.000 798 170	-.001 688 855
7.9	.001 572 275	.000 511 664	-.000 846 677	-.001 507 120
8.0	.001 485 834	.000 369 584	-.000 879 724	-.001 336 313
8.1	.001 396 782	.000 244 032	-.000 899 210	-.001 176 567
8.2	.001 306 386	.000 133 902	-.000 906 891	-.001 027 888
8.3	.001 215 743	.000 038 090	-.000 904 388	-.000 890 168
8.4	.001 125 797	-.000 044 491	-.000 893 190	-.000 763 209
8.5	.001 037 349	-.000 114 902	-.000 874 656	-.000 646 733
8.6	.000 951 070	-.000 174 175	-.000 850 022	-.000 540 398
8.7	.000 867 511	-.000 223 306	-.000 820 407	-.000 443 813
8.8	.000 787 120	-.000 263 248	-.000 786 819	-.000 356 543
8.9	.000 710 249	-.000 294 910	-.000 750 159	-.000 278 127
9.0	.000 637 164	-.000 319 153	-.000 711 231	-.000 208 079
9.1	.000 568 055	-.000 336 788	-.000 670 745	-.000 145 903
9.2	.000 503 046	-.000 348 579	-.000 629 326	-.000 091 093
9.3	.000 442 203	-.000 355 236	-.000 587 517	-.000 043 145
9.4	.000 385 540	-.000 357 420	-.000 545 789	-.000 001 559
9.5	.000 333 029	-.000 355 743	-.000 504 544	.000 034 158
9.6	.000 284 604	-.000 350 768	-.000 464 122	.000 064 485
9.7	.000 240 168	-.000 343 010	-.000 424 806	.000 089 887
9.8	.000 199 598	-.000 332 940	-.000 386 830	.000 110 811
9.9	.000 162 751	-.000 320 983	-.000 350 379	.000 127 684
10.0	.000 129 466	-.000 307 524	-.000 315 597	.000 140 914

Report of the British Association for the Advancement of Science, 1915, page 36.

$$\text{ker}_n\ x + i\ \text{kei}_n\ x\ =\ i^{-n} K_n(x i^{1/2})$$

$$\text{ker}_n'x\ =\ \frac{d}{dx}\ \text{ker}_n\ x$$

x	$\text{ker}_1\ x$	$\text{kei}_1\ x$	$\text{ker}_1'x$	$\text{kei}_1'x$
1	-.740 32	-.242 00	.887 60	.794 74
2	-.230 81	.080 05	.287 98	.073 632
3	-.049 90	.080 27	.100 18	-.038 005
4	.005 351 3	.039 166	.022 690	-.036 928
5	.012 737	.011 578	-.002 318 3	-.018 366
6	.007 676 1	.000 288 35	-.005 920 4	-.005 612 7
7	.002 743 6	-.002 148 9	-.003 660 5	.000 156 61
8	.000 322 86	-.001 567 0	-.001 352 3	.000 985 18
9	-.000 355 78	-.000 650 05	-.000 185 34	.000 748 45
10	-.000 322 80	-.000 123 52	.000 158 19	.000 321 35

x	$\text{ker}_2\ x$	$\text{kei}_2\ x$	$\text{ker}_2'x$	$\text{kei}_2'x$
1	.418 03	1.884 2	-.141 46	-4.120 8
2	.261 47	.309 00	-.154 87	-.528 81
3	.128 39	.036 80	-.107 07	-.116 58
4	.048 134	-.017 938	-.055 546	-.014 942
5	.011 184	-.018 065	-.021 667	.008 046 0
6	-.001 088 3	-.009 093 7	-.005 268 9	.008 255 2
7	-.002 910 5	-.002 820 5	.000 411 05	.004 265 4
8	-.001 819 9	-.000 149 65	.001 334 7	.001 373 7
9	-.000 683 40	.000 477 20	.000 863 10	.000 102 03
10	-.000 101 28	.000 370 64	.000 335 85	-.000 215 04

x	$\text{ker}_3\ x$	$\text{kei}_3\ x$	$\text{ker}_3'x$	$\text{kei}_3'x$
1	4.887 3	-6.269 7	-16.290	17.772
2	.298 02	-.886 82	-.850 42	1.296 6
3	-.036 451	-.236 02	-.080 360	.300 78
4	-.052 071	-.060 518	.017 701	.092 108
5	-.029 283	-.007 685 2	.022 436	.025 293
6	-.011 450	.004 511 5	.012 925	.003 405 0
7	-.002 707 2	.004 464 6	.005 212 6	-.001 977 0
8	.000 267 67	.002 263 3	.001 292 3	-.002 029 8
9	.000 720 5	.000 714 8	-.000 094 4	-.001 059 0
10	.000 456 3	.000 047 3	-.000 327 3	-.000 347 9

x	$\text{ker}_4\ x$	$\text{kei}_4\ x$	$\text{ker}_4'x$	$\text{kei}_4'x$
1	-47.753	3.981 0	191.99	-8.035
2	-2.774 9	.940 03	5.966 1	-1.042 3
3	-.410 62	.348 52	.740 16	-.323 58
4	-.057 09	.137 36	.136 71	-.131 38
5	.007 143	.049 433	.020 426	-.054 819
6	.012 375	.014 000	-.003 344	-.020 620
7	.007 257	.001 780	-.005 361	-.006 088
8	.002 878 3	-.001 192 6	-.003 228 8	-.000 814 8
9	.000 680 7	-.001 153 8	-.001 317 5	.000 516 8
10	-.000 072 2	-.000 584 3	-.000 327 2	.000 522 9

x	$\text{ker}_5\ x$	$\text{kei}_5\ x$	$\text{ker}_5'x$	$\text{kei}_5'x$
1	287.76	253.88	-1407.9	-1306.0
2	10.209	6.076 6	-24.226	-17.818
3	1.467 9	.353 1	-2.402 6	-1.125 3
4	.327 07	-.052 99	-.465 59	-.071 26
5	.077 13	-.056 32	-.117 13	.026 42
6	.012 982	-.029 378	-.029 468	.023 332
7	-.001 719	-.011 767	-.005 162	.011 279
8	-.003 146 2	-.003 455 3	.000 774 4	.005 038 1
9	-.001 873 6	-.000 417 5	.001 375 4	.001 529 2
10	-.000 746 0	.000 324 1	.000 837 2	.000 200 1

Trans. A.I.E.E., 1929, p. 815.

Roots $x_n^{(s)}$ of $J_n(x)Y_n(kx) - J_n(kx)Y_n(x) = 0$

k	$(k-1)x_0^{(1)}$ for 1st root	$(k-1)x_0^{(2)}$ for 2nd root	$(k-1)x_0^{(3)}$ for 3rd root	$(k-1)x_0^{(4)}$ for 4th root	$(k-1)x_0^{(5)}$ for 5th root
1.0	3.1416	6.2832	9.4248	12.5664	15.7080
1.1	3.1412	6.2830	9.4247	12.5663	15.7079
1.2	3.1403	6.2825	9.4243	12.5660	15.7077
1.3	3.1389	6.2818	9.4239	12.5657	15.7074
1.4	3.1371	6.2809	9.4233	12.5652	15.7071
1.5	3.1351	6.2799	9.4226	12.5647	15.7066
1.6	3.1329	6.2787	9.4218	12.5641	15.7062
1.8	3.128	6.276	9.420	12.563	15.705
2.0	3.123	6.273	9.418	12.561	15.704
2.5	3.110	6.266	9.413	12.558	15.701
3.0	3.097	6.258	9.408	12.553	15.697
3.5	3.085	6.250	9.402	12.549	15.694
4.0	3.073	6.243	9.396	12.545	15.690
5	3.053	6.228	9.39		
6	3.035	6.215	9.38		
8	3.006	6.191	9.36		
10	2.983	6.172	9.34		
12	2.963	6.155	9.32		
14	2.947	6.140	9.31		
16	2.934	6.126			
18	2.922	6.114			
20	2.911	6.104			
25	2.89	6.08			
30	2.87	6.06			
35	2.86	6.05			
40	2.85	6.03	Note that $x_0' = x_1$.		
45	2.84	6.02			
50	2.83	6.02			

k	$(k-1)x_1^{(1)}$ for 1st root	$(k-1)x_1^{(2)}$ for 2nd root	$(k-1)x_1^{(3)}$ for 3rd root	$(k-1)x_1^{(4)}$ for 4th root	$(k-1)x_1^{(5)}$ for 5th root
1.0	3.1416	6.2832	9.4248	12.5664	15.7080
1.1	3.1427	6.2837	9.4251	12.5666	15.7082
1.2	3.1455	6.2852	9.4261	12.5674	15.7088
1.3	3.1498	6.2873	9.4275	12.5684	15.7096
1.4	3.1550	6.2900	9.4293	12.5698	15.7107
1.5	3.1609	6.2931	9.4314	12.5713	15.7119
1.6	3.1675	6.2965	9.4337	12.5731	15.7133
1.8	3.182	6.304	9.439	12.577	15.716
2.0	3.197	6.312	9.444	12.581	15.720
2.5	3.235	6.335	9.460	12.593	15.729
3.0	3.271	6.357	9.476	12.605	15.739
3.5	3.305	6.381	9.493	12.619	15.750
4.0	3.336	6.403	9.509	12.631	15.760
5	3.389	6.445	9.541	12.657	15.782
6	3.432	6.482	9.572	12.682	15.802
8	3.498	6.546	9.626	12.728	15.842
10	3.547	6.598	9.673	12.770	15.879
12	3.583	6.639	9.714	12.807	15.913
14	3.611	6.674	9.749	12.840	15.943
16	3.634	6.704	9.780	12.870	15.971
18	3.652	6.728	9.806	12.896	15.997
20	3.667	6.749	9.830	12.920	16.020
25	3.696	6.790	9.88	12.97	16.07
30	3.717	6.820	9.91	13.01	16.11
35	3.732	6.844	9.94	13.04	16.14
40	3.743	6.861	9.96	13.06	16.17
45	3.752	6.875	9.98	13.09	16.19
50	3.760	6.887	9.99	13.10	16.21

k	$(k-1)x_2^{(1)}$ for 1st root	$(k-1)x_2^{(2)}$ for 2nd root	$(k-1)x_2^{(3)}$ for 3rd root	$(k-1)x_2^{(4)}$ for 4th root	$(k-1)x_2^{(5)}$ for 5th root
1.0	3.1416	6.2832	9.4248	12.5664	15.7080
1.1	3.1470	6.2859	9.4266	12.5677	15.7090
1.2	3.1613	6.2931	9.4314	12.5713	15.7119
1.3	3.1822	6.3038	9.4385	12.5767	15.7162
1.4	3.208	6.3170	9.4474	12.5834	15.7216
1.5	3.237	6.3324	9.4578	12.5912	15.7278
1.6	3.27	6.349	9.4693	12.5998	15.7348
1.8	3.36	6.387	9.495	12.619	15.750
2.0	3.4	6.43	9.523	12.640	15.767

k	$(k-1)x_3^{(1)}$ for 1st root	$(k-1)x_3^{(2)}$ for 2nd root	$(k-1)x_3^{(3)}$ for 3rd root	$(k-1)x_3^{(4)}$ for 4th root	$(k-1)x_3^{(5)}$ for 5th root
1.0	3.1416	6.2832	9.4248	12.5664	15.7080
1.1	3.1542	6.2895	9.4290	12.5695	15.7105
1.2	3.1874	6.3063	9.4402	12.5780	15.7172
1.3	3.236	6.3311	9.4568	12.5904	15.7272
1.4	3.294	6.3619	9.4776	12.6061	15.7397
1.5	3.36	6.397	9.5016	12.6242	15.7543
1.6	3.43	6.437	9.5283	12.6443	15.7704
1.8	3.6	6.523	9.587	12.689	15.806
2.0	3.7	6.62	9.652	12.738	15.846
2.5		6.9	9.83	12.874	15.956
3.0			10.0	13.02	16.07
3.5			10.2	13.2	16.19
4.0				13.3	16.3

Roots $x_n'^{(s)}$ of $J_n'(x)Y_n'(kx) - J_n'(kx)Y_n'(x) = 0$

k	$x_1'^{(1)}$ for 1st root	$(k-1)x_1'^{(2)}$ for 2nd root	$(k-1)x_1'^{(3)}$ for 3rd root	$(k-1)x_1'^{(4)}$ for 4th root	$(k-1)x_1'^{(5)}$ for 5th root	$(k-1)x_1'^{(6)}$ for 6th root
1.0	1.000	3.1416	6.2832	9.4248	12.5664	15.7080
1.1	.953	3.1441	6.2845	9.4256	12.5670	15.7085
1.2	.910	3.1509	6.2878	9.4279	12.5687	15.7098
1.3	.872	3.1609	6.2928	9.4312	12.5712	15.7118
1.4	.837	3.174	6.2991	9.4354	12.5743	15.7143
1.5	.805	3.188	6.3064	9.4403	12.5780	15.7172
1.6	.776	3.205	6.3146	9.4457	12.5820	15.7205
1.8	.723	3.241	6.333	9.458	12.591	15.728
2.0	.677	3.282	6.353	9.471	12.601	15.736
2.5	.585	3.396	6.410	9.509	12.629	15.758
3.0	.514	3.516	6.472	9.550	12.660	15.783
3.5	.457	3.636	6.538	9.593	12.692	15.808
4.0	.411	3.753	6.606	9.638	12.725	15.83
5	.341	3.969	6.746	9.732	12.79	15.89
6	.290	4.153	6.887	9.829		
8	.223	4.433	7.152	10.028		
10	.180	4.623	7.379	10.223		
12	.151	4.754	7.562	10.403		
14	.130	4.848	7.707	10.561		
16	.114	4.917	7.820	10.697		
18	.102	4.970	7.910	10.811		
20	.092	5.011	7.982	10.908		
25	.073	5.08	8.11	11.09		
30	.061	5.13	8.19	11.20		
35	.053	5.16	8.25	11.29		
40		5.18	8.29	11.35		
45		5.20	8.32			
50		5.22	8.34			

k	$x_2^{\prime(1)}$ for 1st root	$(k-1)x_2^{\prime(2)}$ for 2nd root	$(k-1)x_2^{\prime(3)}$ for 3rd root	$(k-1)x_2^{\prime(4)}$ for 4th root	$(k-1)x_2^{\prime(5)}$ for 5th root	$(k-1)x_2^{\prime(6)}$ for 6th root
1.0	2.000	3.1416	6.2832	9.4248	12.5664	15.7080
1.1	1.905	3.1485	6.2866	9.4271	12.5681	15.7093
1.2	1.821	3.1669	6.2958	9.4332	12.5727	15.7130
1.3	1.744	3.1942	6.3094	9.4422	12.5795	15.7184
1.4	1.673	3.229	6.3265	9.4536	12.5880	15.7252
1.5	1.608	3.27	6.3464	9.4668	12.5979	15.7332
1.6	1.548	3.32	6.369	9.4816	12.6089	15.7420
1.8	1.438	3.4	6.419	9.515	12.6337	15.7618
2.0	1.341	3.5	6.47	9.552	12.6612	15.7837
2.5	1.137		6.6	9.665	12.739	15.845
3.0	.977		6.8	9.77	12.82	15.912
3.5	.852		7.0	9.89	12.91	15.982
4.0	.752			10.0	13.0	16.06

k	$x_3^{\prime(1)}$ for 1st root	$(k-1)x_3^{\prime(2)}$ for 2nd root	$(k-1)x_3^{\prime(3)}$ for 3rd root	$(k-1)x_3^{\prime(4)}$ for 4th root	$(k-1)x_3^{\prime(5)}$ for 5th root	$(k-1)x_3^{\prime(6)}$ for 6th root
1.0	3.000	3.1416	6.2832	9.4248	12.5664	15.7080
1.1	2.858	3.1557	6.2902	9.4295	12.5699	15.7108
1.2	2.731	3.1933	6.3090	9.4420	12.5793	15.7183
1.3	2.614	3.2489	6.3370	9.4606	12.5932	15.7294
1.4	2.507	3.319	6.3718	9.4839	12.6107	15.7434
1.5	2.407	3.40	6.4125	9.5110	12.6310	15.7597
1.6	2.312	3.49	6.458	9.5412	12.6537	15.7778
1.8	2.138	3.7	6.56	9.609	12.7044	15.8184
2.0	1.979		6.67	9.684	12.761	15.863
2.5	1.643		7.0	9.90	12.92	15.99
3.0	1.388			10.1	13.09	16.13
3.5	1.196				13.3	16.27
4.0	1.048				13.5	16.4

The roots of Bessel Function equations tabulated here are from "Table of Roots for Natural Frequencies in Coaxial Type Cavities," by H. B. Dwight, Jour. of Math. and Phys., Vol. 27, Apr., 1948.

See also the tables of roots in "Tables of Functions" by E. Jahnke and F. Emde, Dover Publications, Inc., New York, where N_n is the same as Y_n in the tables given here.

The roots $x_0^{\prime}$ are not separately tabulated, since $x_0^{\prime} = x_1$. There are no values of $(k-1)x_0^{\prime}$ smaller than 3.1416.

s	$\zeta(s)$	s	$\zeta(s)$
-24.0	0	-18.0	0
-23.9	1 881.735 233	-17.9	-1.228 853 006
-23.8	3 246.186 820	-17.8	-2.180 715 374
-23.7	4 166.598 749	-17.7	-2.879 716 789
-23.6	4 714.946 870	-17.6	-3.353 101 197
-23.5	4 959.598 315	-17.5	-3.629 759 300
-23.4	4 963.676 398	-17.4	-3.739 009 234
-23.3	4 784.016 857	-17.3	-3.709 611 359
-23.2	4 470.608 038	-17.2	-3.568 998 940
-23.1	4 066.416 588	-17.1	-3.342 703 781
-23.0	3 607.510 546	-17.0	-3.053 954 330
-22.9	3 123.402 717	-16.9	-2.723 423 297
-22.8	2 637.548 156	-16.8	-2.369 102 032
-22.7	2 167.940 390	-16.7	-2.006 279 892
-22.6	1 727.760 914	-16.6	-1.647 608 086
-22.5	1 326.045 812	-16.5	-1.303 229 251
-22.4	968.341 470 9	-16.4	-.980 955 836 4
-22.3	657.328 633 0	-16.3	-.686 482 397 9
-22.2	393.400 166 3	-16.2	-.423 618 895 0
-22.1	175.183 135 4	-16.1	-.194 534 087 7
-22.0	0	-16.0	0
-21.9	-135.732 832 4	-15.9	.160 369 806 1
-21.8	-236.168 236 9	-15.8	.287 893 789 5
-21.7	-305.750 559 5	-15.7	.384 612 009 8
-21.6	-348.992 544 4	-15.6	.453 094 640 7
-21.5	-370.301 878 4	-15.5	.496 271 219 9
-21.4	-373.851 717 5	-15.4	.517 281 504 6
-21.3	-363.489 371 9	-15.3	.519 348 026 1
-21.2	-342.677 381 5	-15.2	.505 669 812 9
-21.1	-314.461 458 1	-15.1	.479 336 265 8
-21.0	-281.460 144 9	-15.0	.443 259 803 9
-20.9	-245.871 508 9	-14.9	.400 125 650 2
-20.8	-209.492 694 7	-14.8	.352 356 959 4
-20.7	-173.748 705 6	-14.7	.302 093 419 5
-20.6	-139.727 308 6	-14.6	.251 181 434 9
-20.5	-108.217 475 1	-14.5	.201 174 049 4
-20.4	-79.749 247 61	-14.4	.153 338 840 2
-20.3	-54.633 364 52	-14.3	.108 672 135 4
-20.2	-32.999 364 46	-14.2	.067 918 038 1
-20.1	-14.831 239 48	-14.1	.031 590 894 6
-20.0	0	-14.0	0
-19.9	11.707 237 10	-13.9	-.026 724 502 7
-19.8	20.561 821 00	-13.8	-.048 605 418 0
-19.7	26.871 821 69	-13.7	-.065 792 723 8
-19.6	30.963 861 72	-13.6	-.078 538 818 9
-19.5	33.168 325 78	-13.5	-.087 175 255 9
-19.4	33.807 683 31	-13.4	-.092 091 297 8
-19.3	33.187 616 64	-13.3	-.093 714 536 2
-19.2	31.590 624 87	-13.2	-.092 493 711 1
-19.1	29.271 766 88	-13.1	-.088 883 794 6
-19.0	26.456 212 12	-13.0	-.083 333 333 3
-18.9	23.338 283 64	-12.9	-.076 273 988 9
-18.8	20.081 698 92	-12.8	-.068 112 171 6
-18.7	16.820 741 07	-12.7	-.059 222 629 9
-18.6	13.662 121 68	-12.6	-.049 943 832 9
-18.5	10.687 327 07	-12.5	-.040 574 967 5
-18.4	7.955 269 647	-12.4	-.031 374 362 6
-18.3	5.505 095 299	-12.3	-.022 559 150 0
-18.2	3.359 025 149	-12.2	-.014 305 973 1
-18.1	1.525 135 183	-12.1	-.006 752 561 9
-18.0	0	-12.0	0

s	$\zeta(s)$	s	$\zeta(s)$
-11.9	.005 884 475 3	-5.9	-.000 586 321 3
-11.8	.010 864 289 8	-5.8	-.001 157 636 7
-11.7	.014 930 096 3	-5.7	-.001 702 682 3
-11.6	.018 096 204 5	-5.6	-.002 210 678 4
-11.5	.020 396 978 7	-5.5	-.002 671 458 0
-11.4	.021 883 288 6	-5.4	-.003 075 585 3
-11.3	.022 619 086 8	-5.3	-.003 414 464 5
-11.2	.022 678 169 7	-5.2	-.003 680 438 0
-11.1	.022 141 167 5	-5.1	-.003 866 875 7
-11.0	.021 092 796 1	-5.0	-.003 968 254 0
-10.9	.019 619 393 6	-4.9	-.003 980 227 0
-10.8	.017 806 753 9	-4.8	-.003 899 689 1
-10.7	.015 738 262 2	-4.7	-.003 724 829 9
-10.6	.013 493 330 3	-4.6	-.003 455 183 1
-10.5	.011 146 122 5	-4.5	-.003 091 669 2
-10.4	.008 764 559 2	-4.4	-.002 636 634 5
-10.3	.006 409 581 9	-4.3	-.002 093 885 3
-10.2	.004 134 657 5	-4.2	-.001 468 720 9
-10.1	.001 985 502 1	-4.1	-.000 767 965 6
-10.0	0	-4.0	0
-9.9	-.001 791 707 0	-3.9	.000 825 204 1
-9.8	-.003 366 982 0	-3.8	.001 696 046 4
-9.7	-.004 710 333 2	-3.7	.002 599 255 0
-9.6	-.005 812 951 8	-3.6	.003 519 835 6
-9.5	-.006 672 172 3	-3.5	.004 441 011 3
-9.4	-.007 290 873 2	-3.4	.005 344 150 3
-9.3	-.007 676 837 7	-3.3	.006 208 678 1
-9.2	-.007 842 091 1	-3.2	.007 011 972 1
-9.1	-.007 802 230 0	-3.1	.007 729 233 5
-9.0	-.007 575 757 6	-3.0	.008 333 333 3
-8.9	-.007 183 434 1	-2.9	.008 794 626 8
-8.8	-.006 647 655 6	-2.8	.009 080 729 5
-8.7	-.005 991 865 7	-2.7	.009 156 249 0
-8.6	-.005 240 009 5	-2.6	.008 982 462 4
-8.5	-.004 416 032 9	-2.5	.008 516 928 8
-8.4	-.003 543 430 8	-2.4	.007 713 024 0
-8.3	-.002 644 848 2	-2.3	.006 519 380 5
-8.2	-.001 741 733 0	-2.2	.004 879 212 4
-8.1	-.000 854 042 2	-2.1	.002 729 499 8
-8.0	0	-2.0	0
-7.9	.000 804 093 2	-1.9	-.003 387 956 0
-7.8	.001 544 003 7	-1.8	-.007 522 934 8
-7.7	.002 207 661 1	-1.7	-.012 505 207 9
-7.6	.002 785 213 1	-1.6	-.018 448 986 7
-7.5	.003 269 039 6	-1.5	-.025 485 201 9
-7.4	.003 653 732 1	-1.4	-.033 764 987 7
-7.3	.003 936 040 9	-1.3	-.043 464 082 9
-7.2	.004 114 793 1	-1.2	-.054 788 441 2
-7.1	.004 190 787 3	-1.1	-.067 981 451 7
-7.0	.004 166 666 7	-1.0	-.083 333 333 3
-6.9	.004 046 774 7	-.9	-.101 193 504 0
-6.8	.003 836 997 5	-.8	-.121 987 077 7
-6.7	.003 544 595 5	-.7	-.146 237 191 7
-6.6	.003 178 027 1	-.6	-.174 595 711 9
-6.5	.002 746 767 9	-.5	-.207 886 225 0
-6.4	.002 261 128 2	-.4	-.247 165 460 8
-6.3	.001 732 069 4	-.3	-.293 813 068 1
-6.2	.001 171 023 7	-.2	-.349 666 280 6
-6.1	.000 589 717 5	-.1	-.417 228 040 6
-6.0	0	0	-.5

s	$\zeta(s)$	s	$\zeta(s)$
0	-.5	6.0	1.017 343 062 0
.1	-.603 037 519 9	6.1	1.016 106 205 0
.2	-.733 920 924 9	6.2	1.014 960 945 2
.3	-.904 559 257 2	6.3	1.013 900 097 5
.4	-1.134 797 783 9	6.4	1.012 917 088 6
.5	-1.460 354 508 8	6.5	1.012 005 899 9
.6	-1.952 661 448 2	6.6	1.011 161 014 1
.7	-2.778 388 445 5	6.7	1.010 377 370 5
.8	-4.437 538 415 8	6.8	1.009 650 322 6
.9	-9.430 114 019 4	6.9	1.008 975 600 0
1.0	Infin.	7.0	1.008 349 277 4
1.1	10.584 448 464 9	7.1	1.007 767 741 8
1.2	5.591 582 441 2	7.2	1.007 227 666 5
1.3	3.931 949 211 8	7.3	1.006 725 986 4
1.4	3.105 547 278 0	7.4	1.006 259 876 0
1.5	2.612 375 348 7	7.5	1.005 826 727 5
1.6	2.285 765 665 7	7.6	1.005 424 136 0
1.7	2.054 288 756 8	7.7	1.005 049 879 3
1.8	1.882 229 618 1	7.8	1.004 701 904 8
1.9	1.749 746 435 1	7.9	1.004 378 314 9
2.0	1.644 934 066 8	8.0	1.004 077 356 2
2.1	1.560 216 533 5	8.1	1.003 797 404 6
2.2	1.490 543 256 5	8.2	1.003 536 958 3
2.3	1.432 417 799 3	8.3	1.003 294 626 8
2.4	1.383 342 858 8	8.4	1.003 069 122 2
2.5	1.341 487 257 3	8.5	1.002 859 250 9
2.6	1.305 477 809 1	8.6	1.002 663 907 5
2.7	1.274 264 644 4	8.7	1.002 482 066 7
2.8	1.247 031 422 3	8.8	1.002 312 777 9
2.9	1.223 133 895 3	8.9	1.002 155 159 2
3.0	1.202 056 903 2	9.0	1.002 008 392 8
3.1	1.183 383 652 1	9.1	1.001 871 719 2
3.2	1.166 773 371 0	9.2	1.001 744 433 5
3.3	1.151 944 794 7	9.3	1.001 625 881 5
3.4	1.138 663 775 7	9.4	1.001 515 455 3
3.5	1.126 733 867 3	9.5	1.001 412 590 6
3.6	1.115 989 079 1	9.6	1.001 316 762 8
3.7	1.106 288 241 5	9.7	1.001 227 484 6
3.8	1.097 510 576 5	9.8	1.001 144 303 0
3.9	1.089 552 184 7	9.9	1.001 066 796 9
4.0	1.082 323 233 7	10.0	1.000 994 575 1
4.1	1.075 745 690 3	10.1	1.000 927 273 4
4.2	1.069 751 477 2	10.2	1.000 864 553 4
4.3	1.064 280 964 3	10.3	1.000 806 100 1
4.4	1.059 281 726 0	10.4	1.000 751 620 7
4.5	1.054 707 510 8	10.5	1.000 700 842 6
4.6	1.050 517 382 6	10.6	1.000 653 512 4
4.7	1.046 675 000 2	10.7	1.000 609 394 0
4.8	1.043 148 013 3	10.8	1.000 568 267 8
4.9	1.039 907 544 0	10.9	1.000 529 929 5
5.0	1.036 927 755 1	11.0	1.000 494 188 6
5.1	1.034 185 474 7	11.1	1.000 460 868 1
5.2	1.031 659 876 7	11.2	1.000 429 802 9
5.3	1.029 332 205 7	11.3	1.000 400 839 6
5.4	1.027 185 538 9	11.4	1.000 373 835 0
5.5	1.025 204 580 0	11.5	1.000 348 655 9
5.6	1.023 375 479 2	11.6	1.000 325 178 3
5.7	1.021 685 677 4	11.7	1.000 303 286 6
5.8	1.020 123 768 4	11.8	1.000 282 873 1
5.9	1.018 679 378 7	11.9	1.000 263 837 6

s	$\zeta(s)$	s	$\zeta(s)$	s	$\zeta(s)$
12.0	1.000 246 086 6	16.0	1.000 015 282 3	20.0	1.000 000 954 0
12.1	1.000 229 533 0	16.1	1.000 014 258 0	20.1	1.000 000 890 1
12.2	1.000 214 095 8	16.2	1.000 013 302 4	20.2	1.000 000 830 5
12.3	1.000 199 699 3	16.3	1.000 012 410 9	20.3	1.000 000 774 8
12.4	1.000 186 273 2	16.4	1.000 011 579 1	20.4	1.000 000 722 9
12.5	1.000 173 751 7	16.5	1.000 010 803 1	20.5	1.000 000 674 5
12.6	1.000 162 073 8	16.6	1.000 010 079 2	20.6	1.000 000 629 3
12.7	1.000 151 182 3	16.7	1.000 009 403 7	20.7	1.000 000 587 2
12.8	1.000 141 024 2	16.8	1.000 008 773 6	20.8	1.000 000 547 9
12.9	1.000 131 550 0	16.9	1.000 008 185 7	20.9	1.000 000 511 2
13.0	1.000 122 713 3	17.0	1.000 007 637 2	21.0	1.000 000 476 9
13.1	1.000 114 471 3	17.1	1.000 007 125 5	21.1	1.000 000 445 0
13.2	1.000 106 783 8	17.2	1.000 006 648 0	21.2	1.000 000 415 2
13.3	1.000 099 613 4	17.3	1.000 006 202 6	21.3	1.000 000 387 4
13.4	1.000 092 925 2	17.4	1.000 005 787 0	21.4	1.000 000 361 4
13.5	1.000 086 686 7	17.5	1.000 005 399 3	21.5	1.000 000 337 2
13.6	1.000 080 867 6	17.6	1.000 005 037 6	21.6	1.000 000 314 6
13.7	1.000 075 439 7	17.7	1.000 004 700 1	21.7	1.000 000 293 6
13.8	1.000 070 376 6	17.8	1.000 004 385 2	21.8	1.000 000 273 9
13.9	1.000 065 653 7	17.9	1.000 004 091 4	21.9	1.000 000 255 6
14.0	1.000 061 248 1	18.0	1.000 003 817 3	22.0	1.000 000 238 5
14.1	1.000 057 138 6	18.1	1.000 003 561 6	22.1	1.000 000 222 5
14.2	1.000 053 305 0	18.2	1.000 003 323 0	22.2	1.000 000 207 6
14.3	1.000 049 728 9	18.3	1.000 003 100 4	22.3	1.000 000 193 7
14.4	1.000 046 393 0	18.4	1.000 002 892 7	22.4	1.000 000 180 7
14.5	1.000 043 281 0	18.5	1.000 002 698 9	22.5	1.000 000 168 6
14.6	1.000 040 378 0	18.6	1.000 002 518 1	22.6	1.000 000 157 3
14.7	1.000 037 669 9	18.7	1.000 002 349 4	22.7	1.000 000 146 8
14.8	1.000 035 143 6	18.8	1.000 002 192 0	22.8	1.000 000 136 9
14.9	1.000 032 786 8	18.9	1.000 002 045 2	22.9	1.000 000 127 8
15.0	1.000 030 588 2	19.0	1.000 001 908 2	23.0	1.000 000 119 2
15.1	1.000 028 537 2	19.1	1.000 001 780 4	23.1	1.000 000 111 2
15.2	1.000 026 623 8	19.2	1.000 001 661 1	23.2	1.000 000 103 8
15.3	1.000 024 838 7	19.3	1.000 001 549 9	23.3	1.000 000 096 8
15.4	1.000 023 173 5	19.4	1.000 001 446 1	23.4	1.000 000 090 3
15.5	1.000 021 619 9	19.5	1.000 001 349 2	23.5	1.000 000 084 3
15.6	1.000 020 170 6	19.6	1.000 001 258 8	23.6	1.000 000 078 7
15.7	1.000 018 818 4	19.7	1.000 001 174 5	23.7	1.000 000 073 4
15.8	1.000 017 557 0	19.8	1.000 001 095 8	23.8	1.000 000 068 5
15.9	1.000 016 380 2	19.9	1.000 001 022 4	23.9	1.000 000 063 9
				24.0	1.000 000 059 6

Where s is a real quantity > 1 or where the real part of s is > 1,

$$\zeta(s) = \frac{1}{1^s} + \frac{1}{2^s} + \frac{1}{3^s} + \ldots + \frac{1}{n^s} + \ldots$$

For other values of s, the values of the function are given by analytic continuation.

s	$(s-1)\zeta(s)$	δ^2	δ^4
-2.0	0	136 362 30	-375 43
-1.9	.009 825 072 4	141 407 26	-382 53
-1.8	.021 064 217 4	146 069 89	-386 50
-1.7	.033 764 061 3	150 346 02	-388 62
-1.6	.047 967 365 4	154 233 53	-388 41
-1.5	.063 713 004 8	157 732 63	-386 28
-1.4	.081 035 970 5	160 845 45	-382 30
-1.3	.099 967 390 7	163 575 97	-376 68
-1.2	.120 534 570 6	165 929 81	-369 64
-1.1	.142 761 048 6	167 914 01	-360 93
-1.0	.166 666 666 7	169 537 28	-351 41
-.9	.192 267 657 6	170 809 14	-340 63
-.8	.219 576 739 9	171 740 37	-328 89
-.7	.248 603 225 9	172 342 71	-316 51
-.6	.279 353 139 0	172 628 54	-303 46
-.5	.311 829 337 5	172 610 91	-289 70
-.4	.346 031 645 1	172 303 58	-275 77
-.3	.381 956 988 5	171 720 48	-261 40
-.2	.419 599 536 7	170 875 98	-246 75
-.1	.458 950 844 7	169 784 73	-232 22
0	.5	168 461 252	-217 36
.1	.542 733 767 86	166 920 422	-202 793
.2	.587 136 739 94	165 176 799	-188 153
.3	.633 191 480 01	163 245 023	-173 864
.4	.680 878 670 31	161 139 383	-159 671
.5	.730 177 254 44	158 874 072	-145 810
.6	.781 064 579 29	156 462 951	-132 315
.7	.833 516 533 65	153 919 515	-119 152
.8	.887 507 683 16	151 256 927	-106 411
.9	.943 011 401 94	148 487 928	-94 086
1.0	1.	145 624 843	-82 232
1.1	1.058 444 846 49	142 679 526	-70 854
1.2	1.118 316 488 24	139 663 355	-59 948
1.3	1.179 584 763 54	136 587 236	-49 568
1.4	1.242 218 911 20	133 461 549	-39 670
1.5	1.306 187 674 35	130 296 192	-30 308
1.6	1.371 459 399 42	127 100 527	-21 424
1.7	1.438 002 129 76	123 883 438	-13 110
1.8	1.505 783 694 48	120 653 239	-5 230
1.9	1.574 771 791 59	117 417 810	2 103
2.0	1.644 934 066 80	114 184 484	8 932
2.1	1.716 238 186 85	110 960 090	15 338
2.2	1.788 651 907 80	107 751 034	21 216
2.3	1.862 143 139 09	104 563 194	26 671
2.4	1.936 680 002 32	101 402 025	31 672
2.5	2.012 230 885 80	98 272 528	36 185
2.6	2.088 764 494 56	95 179 216	40 470
2.7	2.166 249 895 48	92 126 374	44 095
2.8	2.244 656 560 14	89 117 627	47 560
2.9	2.323 954 401 07	86 156 440	50 515
3.0	2.404 113 806 40	83 245 768	53 282
3.1	2.485 105 669 41	80 388 378	55 494
3.2	2.566 901 416 20	77 586 482	57 640
3.3	2.649 473 027 81	74 842 226	59 300
3.4	2.732 793 061 68	72 157 270	60 770
3.5	2.816 834 668 25	69 533 084	62 000
3.6	2.901 571 605 66	66 970 898	62 864
3.7	2.986 978 252 05	64 471 576	63 674
3.8	3.073 029 614 20	62 035 928	64 124
3.9	3.159 701 335 63	59 664 404	64 353
4.0	3.246 969 701 10	57 357 233	64 771

See "Tafeln für die Riemannsche Zetafunktion" by
J. P. Gram, p. 313, v. 10, 1925-26, Det Kongelige Danske
Videnskabernes Selskabs Skrifter, Copenhagen.

s	$\zeta'(s)/\zeta(s)$	s	$\zeta'(s)/\zeta(s)$	s	$\zeta'(s)/\zeta(s)$
-6.0	Infin.	-1.0	1.985 0537	4.0	-.063 6698
-5.9	9.904 6250	-.9	1.902 1688	4.1	-.058 3343
-5.8	4.837 6313	-.8	1.838 3194	4.2	-.053 4990
-5.7	3.102 5786	-.7	1.790 4507	4.3	-.049 1100
-5.6	2.198 5342	-.6	1.756 6442	4.4	-.045 1201
-5.5	1.624 4296	-.5	1.735 8261		
-5.4	1.212 3247	-.4	1.727 6200	4.5	-.041 4878
-5.3	.889 2164	-.3	1.732 3010	4.6	-.038 1769
-5.2	.617 3746	-.2	1.750 8402	4.7	-.035 1551
-5.1	.374 2884	-.1	1.785 0507	4.8	-.032 3941
-5.0	.144 3924			4.9	-.029 8686
-4.9	-.085 0983	0	1.837 8771	5.0	-.027 5562
-4.8	-.326 9679	.1	1.913 9193	5.1	-.025 4369
-4.7	-.596 7776	.2	2.020 3814	5.2	-.023 4929
-4.6	-.917 0321	.3	2.168 8583	5.3	-.021 7082
-4.5	-1.325 4519	.4	2.378 9306	5.4	-.020 0683
-4.4	-1.895 0284	.5	2.686 0917	5.5	-.018 5605
-4.3	-2.793 6871	.6	3.161 5813	5.6	-.017 1732
-4.2	-4.522 4781	.7	3.971 9037	5.7	-.015 8957
-4.1	-9.582 3132	.8	5.616 9182	5.8	-.014 7188
-4.0	Infin.	.9	10.596 5024	5.9	-.013 6338
-3.9	10.301 6255	1.0	Infin.	6.0	-.012 6331
-3.8	5.243 8373	1.1	-9.441 0364	6.1	-.011 7095
-3.7	3.518 4697	1.2	-4.458 3372	6.2	-.010 8567
-3.6	2.624 6290	1.3	-2.808 0944	6.3	-.010 0689
-3.5	2.061 2903	1.4	-1.990 3740	6.4	-.009 3407
-3.4	1.660 5620	1.5	-1.505 2354	6.5	-.008 6675
-3.3	1.349 4950	1.6	-1.186 0649	6.6	-.008 0448
-3.2	1.090 4199	1.7	-.961 4822	6.7	-.007 4685
-3.1	.860 8939	1.8	-.795 8164	6.8	-.006 9351
-3.0	.645 4291	1.9	-.669 2656	6.9	-.006 4411
-2.9	.431 3274	2.0	-.569 9610	7.0	-.005 9836
-2.8	.205 9037	2.1	-.490 3595		
-2.7	-.046 2897	2.2	-.425 4406		
-2.6	-.347 6274	2.3	-.371 7353		
-2.5	-.735 6803	2.4	-.326 7714		
-2.4	-1.283 2658	2.5	-.288 7407		
-2.3	-2.158 1066	2.6	-.256 2910		
-2.2	-3.861 0152	2.7	-.228 3918		
-2.1	-8.892 6221	2.8	-.204 2447		
-2.0	Infin.	2.9	-.183 2216		
-1.9	11.056 2164	3.0	-.164 8227		
-1.8	6.035 9888	3.1	-.148 6450		
-1.7	4.352 3471	3.2	-.134 3606		
-1.6	3.505 1363	3.3	-.121 7002		
-1.5	2.994 2574	3.4	-.110 4406		
-1.4	2.652 9977	3.5	-.100 3956		
-1.3	2.409 9332	3.6	-.091 4087		
-1.2	2.229 4069	3.7	-.083 3475		
-1.1	2.091 6903	3.8	-.076 0992		
-1.0	1.985 0537	3.9	-.069 5676		

From "Anschauliches zur Riemannschen Zetafunktion" by A. Walther, Acta Mathematica, v. 48, 1926, p. 400.

For general references, see E. C. Titchmarsh, No. 26, Cambridge Tracts, 1930, and Whittaker and Watson, Modern Analysis, ed. of 1927, p. 265 - 280.

This collection of tables of the Riemann Zeta Function has been kindly contributed by Professor Harold T. Davis of Northwestern University, Evanston, Illinois.

TRIGONOMETRIC FUNCTIONS
of hundredths of degrees

In addition to the advantages pertaining to a decimal system, the arrangement of these tables is compact, which leads to greater convenience. The arrangement used for the tables of sin, cos, tan and cot has been chosen because it requires less than half as many pages as if these functions of a given angle were all placed side by side on the same page, and if no reduction in type size or change in style of type were employed. Difficulty in showing differences has at the same time been avoided.

Where the name of the function is given at the bottom of the page, the degrees for that function are to be read from the right-hand column. The degrees for the function named at the top of the page are to be read from the left-hand column.

As is customary in tables of this kind, 10 is to be subtracted from the tabulated logarithm of any trigonometric function whose natural value is less than 1.

TRIGONOMETRIC FUNCTIONS

SIN

deg.	0	1	2	3	4	5	6	7	8	9	(10)	
0.0	.00 000	017	035	052	070	087	105	122	140	157	175	.9
.1	175	192	209	227	244	262	279	297	314	332	349	.8
.2	349	367	384	401	419	436	454	471	489	506	524	.7
.3	524	541	559	576	593	611	628	646	663	681	698	.6
.4	698	716	733	750	768	785	803	820	838	855	873	.5
.5	873	890	908	925	942	960	977	995	012	030	047	.4
.6	.01 047	065	082	100	117	134	152	169	187	204	222	.3
.7	222	239	257	274	292	309	326	344	361	379	396	.2
.8	396	414	431	449	466	483	501	518	536	553	571	.1
.9	571	588	606	623	641	658	675	693	710	728	745	89.0
1.0	745	763	780	798	815	832	850	867	885	902	920	.9
.1	920	937	955	972	990	007	024	042	059	077	094	.8
.2	.02 094	112	129	147	164	181	199	216	234	251	269	.7
.3	269	286	304	321	339	356	373	391	408	426	443	.6
.4	443	461	478	496	513	530	548	565	583	600	618	.5
.5	618	635	653	670	687	705	722	740	757	775	792	.4
.6	792	810	827	845	862	879	897	914	932	949	967	.3
.7	967	984	002	019	036	054	071	089	106	124	141	.2
.8	.03 141	159	176	193	211	228	246	263	281	298	316	.1
.9	316	333	350	368	385	403	420	438	455	473	490	88.0
2.0	490	507	525	542	560	577	595	612	629	647	664	.9
.1	664	682	699	717	734	752	769	786	804	821	839	.8
.2	839	856	874	891	909	926	943	961	978	996	013	.7
.3	.04 013	031	048	065	083	100	118	135	153	170	188	.6
.4	188	205	222	240	257	275	292	310	327	345	362	.5 Diff.
.5	362	379	397	414	432	449	467	484	501	519	536	.4 17-18
.6	536	554	571	589	606	623	641	658	676	693	711	.3
.7	711	728	746	763	780	798	815	833	850	868	885	.2
.8	885	902	920	937	955	972	990	007	024	042	059	.1
.9	.05 059	077	094	112	129	146	164	181	199	216	234	87.0
3.0	234	251	268	286	303	321	338	356	373	390	408	.9
.1	408	425	443	460	478	495	512	530	547	565	582	.8
.2	582	600	617	634	652	669	687	704	722	739	756	.7
.3	756	774	791	809	826	844	861	878	896	913	931	.6
.4	931	948	965	983	000	018	035	053	070	087	105	.5
.5	.06 105	122	140	157	175	192	209	227	244	262	279	.4
.6	279	296	314	331	349	366	384	401	418	436	453	.3
.7	453	471	488	505	523	540	558	575	593	610	627	.2
.8	627	645	662	680	697	714	732	749	767	784	802	.1
.9	802	819	836	854	871	889	906	923	941	958	976	86.0
4.0	976	993	010	028	045	063	080	098	115	132	150	.9
.1	.07 150	167	185	202	219	237	254	272	289	306	324	.8
.2	324	341	359	376	393	411	428	446	463	480	498	.7
.3	498	515	533	550	567	585	602	620	637	655	672	.6
.4	672	689	707	724	742	759	776	794	811	829	846	.5
.5	846	863	881	898	916	933	950	968	985	002	020	.4
.6	.08 020	037	055	072	089	107	124	142	159	176	194	.3
.7	194	211	229	246	263	281	298	316	333	350	368	.2
.8	368	385	403	420	437	455	472	490	507	524	542	.1
.9	542	559	576	594	611	629	646	663	681	698	716	85.0
	(10)	9	8	7	6	5	4	3	2	1	0	deg.

COS

SIN

deg.	0	1	2	3	4	5	6	7	8	9	(10)	
5.0	.08 716	733	750	768	785	803	820	837	855	872	889	.9
.1	889	907	924	942	959	976	994	0̅1̅1̅	0̅2̅8̅	0̅4̅6̅	0̅6̅3̅	.8
.2	.09 063	081	098	115	133	150	168	185	202	220	237	.7
.3	237	254	272	289	307	324	341	359	376	393	411	.6
.4	411	428	446	463	480	498	515	532	550	567	585	.5
.5	585	602	619	637	654	671	689	706	724	741	758	.4
.6	758	776	793	810	828	845	863	880	897	915	932	.3
.7	932	949	967	984	0̅0̅1̅	0̅1̅9̅	0̅3̅6̅	0̅5̅4̅	0̅7̅1̅	0̅8̅8̅	1̅0̅6̅	.2
.8	.10 106	123	140	158	175	192	210	227	245	262	279	.1
.9	279	297	314	331	349	366	383	401	418	435	453	84.0
6.0	453	470	488	505	522	540	557	574	592	609	626	.9
.1	626	644	661	678	696	713	731	748	765	783	800	.8
.2	800	817	835	852	869	887	904	921	939	956	973	.7
.3	973	991	0̅0̅8̅	0̅2̅5̅	0̅4̅3̅	0̅6̅0̅	0̅7̅8̅	0̅9̅5̅	1̅1̅2̅	1̅3̅0̅	1̅4̅7̅	.6
.4	.11 147	164	182	199	216	234	251	268	286	303	320	.5
.5	320	338	355	372	390	407	424	442	459	476	494	.4
.6	494	511	528	546	563	580	598	615	632	650	667	.3
.7	667	684	702	719	736	754	771	788	806	823	840	.2
.8	840	858	875	892	910	927	944	962	979	996	0̅1̅4̅	.1
.9	.12 014	031	048	066	083	100	118	135	152	170	187	83.0
7.0	187	204	222	239	256	274	291	308	326	343	360	.9
.1	360	377	395	412	429	447	464	481	499	516	533	.8
.2	533	551	568	585	603	620	637	655	672	689	706	.7
.3	706	724	741	758	776	793	810	828	845	862	880	.6
.4	880	897	914	931	949	966	983	0̅0̅1̅	0̅1̅8̅	0̅3̅5̅	0̅5̅3̅	.5
.5	.13 053	070	087	105	122	139	156	174	191	208	226	.4
.6	226	243	260	278	295	312	329	347	364	381	399	.3
.7	399	416	433	451	468	485	502	520	537	554	572	.2
.8	572	589	606	623	641	658	675	693	710	727	744	.1
.9	744	762	779	796	814	831	848	865	883	900	917	82.0
8.0	917	935	952	969	986	0̅0̅4̅	0̅2̅1̅	0̅3̅8̅	0̅5̅6̅	0̅7̅3̅	0̅9̅0̅	.9
.1	.14 090	107	125	142	159	177	194	211	228	246	263	.8
.2	263	280	297	315	332	349	367	384	401	418	436	.7
.3	436	453	470	487	505	522	539	557	574	591	608	.6
.4	608	626	643	660	677	695	712	729	746	764	781	.5
.5	781	798	815	833	850	867	885	902	919	936	954	.4
.6	954	971	988	0̅0̅5̅	0̅2̅3̅	0̅4̅0̅	0̅5̅7̅	0̅7̅4̅	0̅9̅2̅	1̅0̅9̅	1̅2̅6̅	.3
.7	.15 126	143	161	178	195	212	230	247	264	281	299	.2
.8	299	316	333	350	368	385	402	419	437	454	471	.1
.9	471	488	506	523	540	557	574	592	609	626	643	81.0
9.0	643	661	678	695	712	730	747	764	781	799	816	.9
.1	816	833	850	868	885	902	919	936	954	971	988	.8
.2	988	0̅0̅5̅	0̅2̅3̅	0̅4̅0̅	0̅5̅7̅	0̅7̅4̅	0̅9̅1̅	1̅0̅9̅	1̅2̅6̅	1̅4̅3̅	1̅6̅0̅	.7
.3	.16 160	178	195	212	229	246	264	281	298	315	333	.6
.4	333	350	367	384	401	419	436	453	470	488	505	.5
.5	505	522	539	556	574	591	608	625	642	660	677	.4
.6	677	694	711	728	746	763	780	797	815	832	849	.3
.7	849	866	883	901	918	935	952	969	987	0̅0̅4̅	0̅2̅1̅	.2
.8	.17 021	038	055	073	090	107	124	141	159	176	193	.1
.9	193	210	227	244	262	279	296	313	330	348	365	80.0
	(10)	9	8	7	6	5	4	3	2	1	0	deg.

Diff.
17-18

COS

SIN

deg.	0	1	2	3	4	5	6	7	8	9	(10)	
10.0	.17 365	382	399	416	434	451	468	485	502	519	537	.9
.1	537	554	571	588	605	623	640	657	674	691	708	.8
.2	708	726	743	760	777	794	812	829	846	863	880	.7
.3	880	897	915	932	949	966	983	000	018	035	052	.6
.4	.18 052	069	086	103	121	138	155	172	189	206	224	.5
.5	224	241	258	275	292	309	327	344	361	378	395	.4
.6	395	412	429	447	464	481	498	515	532	550	567	.3
.7	567	584	601	618	635	652	670	687	704	721	738	.2
.8	738	755	772	790	807	824	841	858	875	892	910	.1
.9	910	927	944	961	978	995	012	029	047	064	081	79.0
11.0	.19 081	098	115	132	149	167	184	201	218	235	252	.9
.1	252	269	286	304	321	338	355	372	389	406	423	.8
.2	423	441	458	475	492	509	526	543	560	577	595	.7
.3	595	612	629	646	663	680	697	714	732	749	766	.6
.4	766	783	800	817	834	851	868	885	903	920	937	.5
.5	937	954	971	988	005	022	039	056	074	091	108	.4
.6	.20 108	125	142	159	176	193	210	227	245	262	279	.3
.7	279	296	313	330	347	364	381	398	415	433	450	.2
.8	450	467	484	501	518	535	552	569	586	603	620	.1
.9	620	637	655	672	689	706	723	740	757	774	791	78.0
12.0	791	808	825	842	859	877	894	911	928	945	962	.9
.1	962	979	996	013	030	047	064	081	098	115	132	.8
.2	.21 132	150	167	184	201	218	235	252	269	286	303	.7
.3	303	320	337	354	371	388	405	422	439	456	474	.6
.4	474	491	508	525	‚542	559	576	593	610	627	644	.5 Diff.
.5	644	661	678	695	712	729	746	763	780	797	814	.4 16-18
.6	814	831	848	865	882	899	917	934	951	968	985	.3
.7	985	002	019	036	053	070	087	104	121	138	155	.2
.8	.22 155	172	189	206	223	240	257	274	291	308	325	.1
.9	325	342	359	376	393	410	427	444	461	478	495	77.0
13.0	495	512	529	546	563	580	597	614	631	648	665	.9
.1	665	682	699	716	733	750	767	784	801	818	835	.8
.2	835	852	869	886	903	920	937	954	971	988	005	.7
.3	.23 005	022	039	056	073	090	107	124	141	158	175	.6
.4	175	192	209	226	243	260	277	294	311	328	345	.5
.5	345	362	378	395	412	429	446	463	480	497	514	.4
.6	514	531	548	565	582	599	616	633	650	667	684	.3
.7	684	701	718	735	752	769	786	802	819	836	853	.2
.8	853	870	887	904	921	938	955	972	989	006	023	.1
.9	.24 023	040	057	074	091	108	124	141	158	175	192	76.0
14.0	192	209	226	243	260	277	294	311	328	345	362	.9
.1	362	378	395	412	429	446	463	480	497	514	531	.8
.2	531	548	565	581	598	615	632	649	666	683	700	.7
.3	700	717	734	751	768	784	801	818	835	852	869	.6
.4	869	886	903	920	937	954	970	987	004	021	038	.5
.5	.25 038	055	072	089	106	122	139	156	173	190	207	.4
.6	207	224	241	258	274	291	308	325	342	359	376	.3
.7	376	393	410	426	443	460	477	494	511	528	545	.2
.8	545	561	578	595	612	629	646	663	680	696	713	.1
.9	713	730	747	764	781	798	814	831	848	865	882	75.0 deg.
	(10)	9	8	7	6	5	4	3	2	1	0	

COS

SIN

deg.	0	1	2	3	4	5	6	7	8	9	(10)	
15.0	.25 882	899	916	932	949	966	983	000	017	034	050	.9
.1	.26 050	067	084	101	118	135	152	168	185	202	219	.8
.2	219	236	253	269	286	303	320	337	354	370	387	.7
.3	387	404	421	438	455	471	488	505	522	539	556	.6
.4	556	572	589	606	623	640	657	673	690	707	724	.5
.5	724	741	757	774	791	808	825	842	858	875	892	.4
.6	892	909	926	942	959	976	993	010	026	043	060	.3
.7	.27 060	077	094	110	127	144	161	178	194	211	228	.2
.8	228	245	262	278	295	312	329	346	362	379	396	.1
.9	396	413	429	446	463	480	497	513	530	547	564	74.0
16.0	564	581	597	614	631	648	664	681	698	715	731	.9
.1	731	748	765	782	799	815	832	849	866	882	899	.8
.2	899	916	933	949	966	983	000	016	033	050	067	.7
.3	.28 067	083	100	117	134	150	167	184	201	217	234	.6
.4	234	251	268	284	301	318	335	351	368	385	402	.5
.5	402	418	435	452	468	485	502	519	535	552	569	.4
.6	569	586	602	619	636	652	669	686	703	719	736	.3
.7	736	753	769	786	803	820	836	853	870	886	903	.2
.8	903	920	937	953	970	987	003	020	037	054	070	.1
.9	.29 070	087	104	120	137	154	170	187	204	220	237	73.0
17.0	237	254	271	287	304	321	337	354	371	387	404	.9
.1	404	421	437	454	471	487	504	521	537	554	571	.8
.2	571	587	604	621	637	654	671	687	704	721	737	.7
.3	737	754	771	787	804	821	837	854	871	887	904	.6
.4	904	921	937	954	971	987	004	021	037	054	071	.5 Diff.
.5	.30 071	087	104	121	137	154	170	187	204	220	237	.4 16-17
.6	237	254	270	287	304	320	337	353	370	387	403	.3
.7	403	420	437	453	470	486	503	520	536	553	570	.2
.8	570	586	603	619	636	653	669	686	702	719	736	.1
.9	736	752	769	785	802	819	835	852	868	885	902	72.0
18.0	902	918	935	951	968	985	001	018	034	051	068	.9
.1	.31 068	084	101	117	134	151	167	184	200	217	233	.8
.2	233	250	267	283	300	316	333	350	366	383	399	.7
.3	399	416	432	449	466	482	499	515	532	548	565	.6
.4	565	581	598	615	631	648	664	681	697	714	730	.5
.5	730	747	764	780	797	813	830	846	863	879	896	.4
.6	896	912	929	946	962	979	995	012	028	045	061	.3
.7	.32 061	078	094	111	127	144	160	177	194	210	227	.2
.8	227	243	260	276	293	309	326	342	359	375	392	.1
.9	392	408	425	441	458	474	491	507	524	540	557	71.0
19.0	557	573	590	606	623	639	656	672	689	705	722	.9
.1	722	738	755	771	788	804	821	837	854	870	887	.8
.2	887	903	920	936	953	969	986	002	018	035	051	.7
.3	.33 051	068	084	101	117	134	150	167	183	200	216	.6
.4	216	233	249	265	282	298	315	331	348	364	381	.5
.5	381	397	414	430	446	463	479	496	512	529	545	.4
.6	545	562	578	594	611	627	644	660	677	693	710	.3
.7	710	726	742	759	775	792	808	825	841	857	874	.2
.8	874	890	907	923	939	956	972	989	005	022	038	.1
.9	.34 038	054	071	087	104	120	136	153	169	186	202	70.0 deg.
	(10)	9	8	7	6	5	4	3	2	1	0	

COS

SIN

deg.	0	1	2	3	4	5	6	7	8	9	(10)	
20.0	.34 202	218	235	251	268	284	300	317	333	350	366	.9
.1	366	382	399	415	432	448	464	481	497	513	530	.8
.2	530	546	563	579	595	612	628	644	661	677	694	.7
.3	694	710	726	743	759	775	792	808	824	841	857	.6
.4	857	874	890	906	923	939	955	972	988	$\overline{004}$	$\overline{021}$	.5
.5	.35 021	037	053	070	086	102	119	135	151	168	184	.4
.6	184	201	217	233	250	266	282	298	315	331	347	.3
.7	347	364	380	396	413	429	445	462	478	494	511	.2
.8	511	527	543	560	576	592	609	625	641	657	674	.1
.9	674	690	706	723	739	755	772	788	804	821	837	69.0
21.0	837	853	869	886	902	918	935	951	967	983	$\overline{000}$	.9
.1	.36 000	016	032	049	065	081	097	114	130	146	162	.8
.2	162	179	195	211	228	244	260	276	293	309	325	.7
.3	325	341	358	374	390	406	423	439	455	471	488	.6
.4	488	504	520	536	553	569	585	601	618	634	650	.5
.5	650	666	683	699	715	731	748	764	780	796	812	.4
.6	812	829	845	861	877	894	910	926	942	958	975	.3
.7	975	991	$\overline{007}$	$\overline{023}$	$\overline{040}$	$\overline{056}$	$\overline{072}$	$\overline{088}$	$\overline{104}$	$\overline{121}$	$\overline{137}$	.2
.8	.37 137	153	169	185	202	218	234	250	266	283	299	.1
.9	299	315	331	347	364	380	396	412	428	444	461	68.0
22.0	461	477	493	509	525	542	558	574	590	606	622	.9
.1	622	639	655	671	687	703	719	736	752	768	784	.8
.2	784	800	816	833	$\overline{849}$	$\overline{865}$	$\overline{881}$	897	913	929	$\overline{946}$	.7
.3	946	962	978	994	$\overline{010}$	$\overline{026}$	$\overline{042}$	$\overline{059}$	$\overline{075}$	$\overline{091}$	$\overline{107}$	.6
.4	.38 107	123	139	155	172	188	204	220	236	252	268	.5 Diff.
.5	268	284	301	317	333	349	365	381	397	413	430	.4 15-17
.6	430	446	462	478	494	510	526	542	558	575	591	.3
.7	591	607	623	639	655	671	687	703	719	735	752	.2
.8	752	768	784	800	816	832	$\overline{848}$	$\overline{864}$	$\overline{880}$	$\overline{896}$	$\overline{912}$	.1
.9	912	928	945	961	977	993	$\overline{009}$	$\overline{025}$	$\overline{041}$	$\overline{057}$	$\overline{073}$	67.0
23.0	.39 073	089	105	121	137	153	169	186	202	218	234	.9
.1	234	250	266	282	298	314	330	346	362	378	394	.8
.2	394	410	426	442	458	474	490	506	522	539	555	.7
.3	555	571	587	603	619	635	651	667	683	699	715	.6
.4	715	731	747	763	779	795	811	827	$\overline{843}$	$\overline{859}$	$\overline{875}$	.5
.5	875	891	907	923	939	955	971	987	$\overline{003}$	$\overline{019}$	$\overline{035}$	.4
.6	.40 035	051	067	083	099	115	131	147	163	179	195	.3
.7	195	211	227	243	259	275	291	307	323	339	355	.2
.8	355	370	386	402	418	434	450	466	482	498	514	.1
.9	514	530	546	562	578	594	610	626	642	658	674	66.0
24.0	674	690	706	721	737	753	769	785	801	817	833	.9
.1	833	$\overline{849}$	$\overline{865}$	$\overline{881}$	897	913	929	945	960	976	992	.8
.2	992	$\overline{008}$	$\overline{024}$	$\overline{040}$	$\overline{056}$	$\overline{072}$	$\overline{088}$	$\overline{104}$	$\overline{120}$	$\overline{136}$	$\overline{151}$	.7
.3	.41 151	167	183	199	215	231	247	263	279	295	310	.6
.4	310	326	342	358	374	390	406	422	438	453	469	.5
.5	469	485	501	517	533	549	565	580	596	612	628	.4
.6	628	644	660	676	692	707	723	739	755	771	787	.3
.7	787	803	818	834	850	866	882	898	914	929	945	.2
.8	945	961	977	993	$\overline{009}$	$\overline{024}$	$\overline{040}$	$\overline{056}$	$\overline{072}$	$\overline{088}$	$\overline{104}$	.1
.9	.42 104	119	135	151	167	183	199	214	230	246	262	65.0
(10)	9	8	7	6	5	4	3	2	1	0		deg.

COS

deg.	0	1	2	3	SIN 4	5	6	7	8	9	(10)	
25.0	.42 262	278	293	309	325	341	357	373	388	404	420	.9
.1	420	436	452	467	483	499	515	531	546	562	578	.8
.2	578	594	610	625	641	657	673	688	704	720	736	.7
.3	736	752	767	783	799	815	830	846	862	878	894	.6
.4	894	909	925	941	957	972	988	004	020	035	051	.5
.5	.43 051	067	083	098	114	130	146	161	177	193	209	.4
.6	209	224	240	256	272	287	303	319	334	350	366	.3
.7	366	382	397	413	429	445	460	476	492	507	523	.2
.8	523	539	555	570	586	602	617	633	649	664	680	.1
.9	680	696	712	727	743	759	774	790	806	821	837	64.0
26.0	837	853	868	884	900	916	931	947	963	978	994	.9
.1	994	010	025	041	057	072	088	104	119	135	151	.8
.2	.44 151	166	182	198	213	229	245	260	276	291	307	.7
.3	307	323	338	354	370	385	401	417	432	448	464	.6
.4	464	479	495	510	526	542	557	573	589	604	620	.5
.5	620	635	651	667	682	698	713	729	745	760	776	.4
.6	776	792	807	823	838	854	870	885	901	916	932	.3
.7	932	947	963	979	994	010	025	041	057	072	088	.2
.8	.45 088	103	119	134	150	166	181	197	212	228	243	.1
.9	243	259	275	290	306	321	337	352	368	383	399	63.0
27.0	399	415	430	446	461	477	492	508	523	539	554	.9
.1	554	570	586	601	617	632	648	663	679	694	710	.8
.2	710	725	741	756	772	787	803	818	834	849	865	.7
.3	865	880	896	911	927	942	958	973	989	004	020	.6
.4	.46 020	035	051	066	082	097	113	128	144	159	175	.5 Diff. 15-16
.5	175	190	206	221	237	252	268	283	299	314	330	.4
.6	330	345	361	376	391	407	422	438	453	469	484	.3
.7	484	500	515	531	546	561	577	592	608	623	639	.2
.8	639	654	670	685	700	716	731	747	762	778	793	.1
.9	793	808	824	839	855	870	886	901	916	932	947	62.0
28.0	947	963	978	993	009	024	040	055	070	086	101	.9
.1	.47 101	117	132	147	163	178	194	209	224	240	255	.8
.2	255	270	286	301	317	332	347	363	378	393	409	.7
.3	409	424	440	455	470	486	501	516	532	547	562	.6
.4	562	578	593	608	624	639	655	670	685	701	716	.5
.5	716	731	747	762	777	793	808	823	839	854	869	.4
.6	869	885	900	915	930	946	961	976	992	007	022	.3
.7	.48 022	038	053	068	084	099	114	129	145	160	175	.2
.8	175	191	206	221	237	252	267	282	298	313	328	.1
.9	328	344	359	374	389	405	420	435	450	466	481	61.0
29.0	481	496	511	527	542	557	573	588	603	618	634	.9
.1	634	649	664	679	695	710	725	740	755	771	786	.8
.2	786	801	816	832	847	862	877	893	908	923	938	.7
.3	938	953	969	984	999	014	030	045	060	075	090	.6
.4	.49 090	106	121	136	151	166	182	197	212	227	242	.5
.5	242	258	273	288	303	318	333	349	364	379	394	.4
.6	394	409	425	440	455	470	485	500	516	531	546	.3
.7	546	561	576	591	606	622	637	652	667	682	697	.2
.8	697	713	728	743	758	773	788	803	819	834	849	.1
.9	.50 849	864	879	894	909	924	940	955	970	985	000	60.0 deg.
	(10)	9	8	7	6	5	4	3	2	1	0	

COS

SIN

deg.	0	1	2	3	4	5	6	7	8	9	(10)	
30.0	.50 000	015	030	045	060	076	091	106	121	136	151	.9
.1	151	166	181	196	211	227	242	257	272	287	302	.8
.2	302	317	332	347	362	377	392	408	423	438	453	.7
.3	453	468	483	498	513	528	543	558	573	588	603	.6
.4	603	618	633	649	664	679	694	709	724	739	754	.5
.5	754	769	784	799	814	829	844	859	874	889	904	.4
.6	904	919	934	949	964	979	994	009	024	039	054	.3
.7	.51 054	069	084	099	114	129	144	159	174	189	204	.2
.8	204	219	234	249	264	279	294	309	324	339	354	.1
.9	354	369	384	399	414	429	444	459	474	489	504	59.0
31.0	504	519	534	549	564	579	594	608	623	638	653	.9
.1	653	668	683	698	713	728	743	758	773	788	803	.8
.2	803	818	833	847	862	877	892	907	922	937	952	.7
.3	952	967	982	997	012	026	041	056	071	086	101	.6
.4	.52 101	116	131	146	161	175	190	205	220	235	250	.5
.5	250	265	280	294	309	324	339	354	369	384	399	.4
.6	399	413	428	443	458	473	488	503	517	532	547	.3
.7	547	562	577	592	607	621	636	651	666	681	696	.2
.8	696	710	725	740	755	770	785	799	814	829	844	.1
.9	844	859	873	888	903	918	933	948	962	977	992	58.0
32.0	992	007	022	036	051	066	081	095	110	125	140	.9
.1	.53 140	155	169	184	199	214	229	243	258	273	288	.8
.2	288	302	317	332	347	361	376	391	406	420	435	.7
.3	435	450	465	479	494	509	524	538	553	568	583	.6
.4	583	597	612	627	642	656	671	686	701	715	730	.5 Diff.
.5	730	745	759	774	789	804	818	833	848	862	877	.4 14-15
.6	877	892	906	921	936	951	965	980	995	009	024	.3
.7	.54 024	039	053	068	083	097	112	127	141	156	171	.2
.8	171	185	200	215	229	244	259	273	288	303	317	.1
.9	317	332	347	361	376	391	405	420	435	449	464	57.0
33.0	464	479	493	508	522	537	552	566	581	596	610	.9
.1	610	625	639	654	669	683	698	713	727	742	756	.8
.2	756	771	786	800	815	829	844	859	873	888	902	.7
.3	902	917	931	946	961	975	990	004	019	034	048	.6
.4	.55 048	063	077	092	106	121	135	150	165	179	194	.5
.5	194	208	223	237	252	266	281	296	310	325	339	.4
.6	339	354	368	383	397	412	426	441	455	470	484	.3
.7	484	499	513	528	543	557	572	586	601	615	630	.2
.8	630	644	659	673	688	702	717	731	746	760	775	.1
.9	775	789	803	818	832	847	861	876	890	905	919	56.0
34.0	919	934	948	963	977	992	006	021	035	049	064	.9
.1	.56 064	078	093	107	122	136	151	165	179	194	208	.8
.2	208	223	237	252	266	280	295	309	324	338	353	.7
.3	353	367	381	396	410	425	439	453	468	482	497	.6
.4	497	511	525	540	554	569	583	597	612	626	641	.5
.5	641	655	669	684	698	713	727	741	756	770	784	.4
.6	784	799	813	827	842	856	871	885	899	914	928	.3
.7	928	942	957	971	985	000	014	028	043	057	071	.2
.8	.57 071	086	100	114	129	143	157	172	186	200	215	.1
.9	215	229	243	258	272	286	300	315	329	343	358	55.0 deg.
(10)		9	8	7	6	5	4	3	2	1	0	

COS

SIN

deg.	0	1	2	3	4	5	6	7	8	9	(10)	
35.0	.57 358	372	386	401	415	429	443	458	472	486	501	.9
.1	501	515	529	543	558	572	586	600	615	629	643	.8
.2	643	657	672	686	700	715	729	743	757	772	786	.7
.3	786	800	814	828	843	857	871	885	900	914	928	.6
.4	928	942	957	971	985	999	0̄1̄3̄	0̄2̄8̄	0̄4̄2̄	0̄5̄6̄	0̄7̄0̄	.5
.5	.58 070	085	099	113	127	141	156	170	184	198	212	.4
.6	212	226	241	255	269	283	297	312	326	340	354	.3
.7	354	368	382	397	411	425	439	453	467	482	496	.2
.8	496	510	524	538	552	567	581	595	609	623	637	.1
.9	637	651	666	680	694	708	722	736	750	764	779	54.0
36.0	779	793	807	821	835	849	863	877	891	906	920	.9
.1	920	934	948	962	976	990	0̄0̄4̄	0̄1̄8̄	0̄3̄2̄	0̄4̄6̄	0̄6̄1̄	.8
.2	.59 061	075	089	103	117	131	145	159	173	187	201	.7
.3	201	215	229	244	258	272	286	300	314	328	342	.6
.4	342	356	370	384	398	412	426	440	454	468	482	.5
.5	482	496	510	524	538	552	566	580	594	608	622	.4
.6	622	636	651	665	679	693	707	721	735	749	763	.3
.7	763	777	790	804	818	832	846	860	874	888	902	.2
.8	902	916	930	944	958	972	986	0̄0̄0̄	0̄1̄4̄	0̄2̄8̄	0̄4̄2̄	.1
.9	.60 042	056	070	084	098	112	126	140	154	168	182	53.0
37.0	182	195	209	223	237	251	265	279	293	307	321	.9
.1	321	335	349	363	376	390	404	418	432	446	460	.8
.2	460	474	488	502	516	529	543	557	571	585	599	.7
.3	599	613	627	640	654	668	682	696	710	724	738	.6
.4	738	751	765	779	793	807	821	835	848	862	876	.5 Diff.
.5	876	890	904	918	932	945	959	973	987	0̄0̄1̄	0̄1̄5̄	.4 13-15
.6	.61 015	028	042	056	070	084	097	111	125	139	153	.3
.7	153	167	180	194	208	222	236	249	263	277	291	.2
.8	291	304	318	332	346	360	373	387	401	415	429	.1
.9	429	442	456	470	484	497	511	525	539	552	566	52.0
38.0	566	580	594	607	621	635	649	662	676	690	704	.9
.1	704	717	731	745	759	772	786	800	813	827	841	.8
.2	841	855	868	882	896	909	923	937	951	964	978	.7
.3	978	992	0̄0̄5̄	0̄1̄9̄	0̄3̄3̄	0̄4̄6̄	0̄6̄0̄	0̄7̄4̄	0̄8̄7̄	1̄0̄1̄	1̄1̄5̄	.6
.4	.62 115	128	142	156	169	183	197	210	224	238	251	.5
.5	251	265	279	292	306	320	333	347	361	374	388	.4
.6	388	402	415	429	443	456	470	483	497	511	524	.3
.7	524	538	552	565	579	592	606	620	633	647	660	.2
.8	660	674	688	701	715	728	742	756	769	783	796	.1
.9	796	810	823	837	851	864	878	891	905	918	932	51.0
39.0	932	946	959	973	986	0̄0̄0̄	0̄1̄3̄	0̄2̄7̄	0̄4̄0̄	0̄5̄4̄	0̄6̄8̄	.9
.1	.63 068	081	095	108	122	135	149	162	176	189	203	.8
.2	203	216	230	243	257	271	284	298	311	325	338	.7
.3	338	352	365	379	392	406	419	433	446	460	473	.6
.4	473	487	500	514	527	540	554	567	581	594	608	.5
.5	608	621	635	648	662	675	689	702	715	729	742	.4
.6	742	756	769	783	796	810	823	836	850	863	877	.3
.7	877	890	904	917	930	944	957	971	984	998	0̄1̄1̄	.2
.8	.64 011	024	038	051	065	078	091	105	118	132	145	.1
.9	145	158	172	185	199	212	225	239	252	265	279	50.0
	(10)	9	8	7	6	5	4	3	2	1	0	

COS

SIN

deg.	0	1	2	3	4	5	6	7	8	9	(10)	
40.0	.64 279	292	305	319	332	346	359	372	386	399	412	.9
.1	412	426	439	452	466	479	492	506	519	532	546	.8
.2	546	559	572	586	599	612	626	639	652	666	679	.7
.3	679	692	706	719	732	746	759	772	785	799	812	.6
.4	812	825	839	852	865	878	892	905	918	932	945	.5
.5	945	958	971	985	998	0̄11	0̄24	0̄38	0̄51	0̄64	0̄77	.4
.6	.65 077	091	104	117	130	144	157	170	183	197	210	.3
.7	210	223	236	250	263	276	289	302	316	329	342	.2
.8	342	355	368	382	395	408	421	434	448	461	474	.1
.9	474	487	500	514	527	540	553	566	580	593	606	49.0
41.0	606	619	632	645	659	672	685	698	711	724	738	.9
.1	738	751	764	777	790	803	816	830	843	856	869	.8
.2	869	882	895	908	921	935	948	961	974	987	0̄00	.7
.3	.66 000	013	026	039	053	066	079	092	105	118	131	.6
.4	131	144	157	170	184	197	210	223	236	249	262	.5
.5	262	275	288	301	314	327	340	353	367	380	393	.4
.6	393	406	419	432	445	458	471	484	497	510	523	.3
.7	523	536	549	562	575	588	601	614	627	640	653	.2
.8	653	666	679	692	705	718	731	744	757	770	783	.1
.9	783	796	809	822	835	848	861	874	887	900	913	48.0
42.0	913	926	939	952	965	978	991	0̄04	0̄17	0̄30	0̄43	.9
.1	.67 043	056	069	082	094	107	120	133	146	159	172	.8
.2	172	185	198	211	224	237	250	263	275	288	301	.7
.3	301	314	327	340	353	366	379	392	404	417	430	.6
.4	430	443	456	469	482	495	508	520	533	546	559	.5 Diff.
.5	559	572	585	598	610	623	636	649	662	675	688	.4 12-14
.6	688	700	713	726	739	752	765	777	790	803	816	.3
.7	816	829	842	854	867	880	893	906	919	931	944	.2
.8	944	957	970	983	995	0̄08	0̄21	0̄34	0̄47	0̄59	0̄72	.1
.9	.68 072	085	098	110	123	136	149	162	174	187	200	47.0
43.0	200	213	225	238	251	264	276	289	302	315	327	.9
.1	327	340	353	366	378	391	404	417	429	442	455	.8
.2	455	467	480	493	506	518	531	544	556	569	582	.7
.3	582	595	607	620	633	645	658	671	683	696	709	.6
.4	709	721	734	747	759	772	785	797	810	823	835	.5
.5	835	848	861	8̄73	886	899	9̄11	924	937	949	962	.4
.6	962	975	987	0̄00	0̄12	0̄25	0̄38	0̄50	0̄63	0̄76	0̄88	.3
.7	.69 088	101	113	126	139	151	164	177	189	202	214	.2
.8	214	227	240	252	265	277	290	302	315	328	340	.1
.9	340	353	365	378	390	403	416	428	441	453	466	46.0
44.0	466	478	491	503	516	529	541	554	566	579	591	.9
.1	591	604	616	629	641	654	666	679	691	704	717	.8
.2	717	729	742	754	767	779	792	804	817	829	842	.7
.3	842	854	867	879	891	904	916	929	941	954	966	.6
.4	966	979	991	0̄04	0̄16	0̄29	0̄41	0̄54	0̄66	0̄78	0̄91	.5
.5	.70 091	103	116	128	141	153	166	178	190	203	215	.4
.6	215	228	240	253	265	277	290	302	315	327	339	.3
.7	339	352	364	377	389	401	414	426	439	451	463	.2
.8	463	476	488	501	513	525	538	550	562	575	587	.1
.9	587	600	612	624	637	649	661	674	686	698	711	45.0 deg.
(10)	9	8	7	6	5	4	3	2	1	0		

COS

SIN

deg.	0	1	2	3	4	5	6	7	8	9	(10)	
45.0	.70 711	723	735	748	760	772	785	797	809	822	834	.9
.1	834	846	859	871	883	896	908	920	932	945	957	.8
.2	957	969	982	994	006	019	031	043	055	068	080	.7
.3	.71 080	092	104	117	129	141	154	166	178	190	203	.6
.4	203	215	227	239	252	264	276	288	301	313	325	.5
.5	325	337	350	362	374	386	398	411	423	435	447	.4
.6	447	459	472	484	496	508	520	533	545	557	569	.3
.7	569	581	594	606	618	630	642	655	667	679	691	.2
.8	691	703	715	728	740	752	764	776	788	800	813	.1
.9	813	825	837	849	861	873	885	898	910	922	934	44.0
46.0	934	946	958	970	982	995	007	019	031	043	055	.9
.1	.72 055	067	079	091	104	116	128	140	152	164	176	.8
.2	176	188	200	212	224	236	248	261	273	285	297	.7
.3	297	309	321	333	345	357	369	381	393	405	417	.6
.4	417	429	441	453	465	477	489	501	513	525	537	.5
.5	537	549	561	573	585	597	609	621	633	645	657	.4
.6	657	669	681	693	705	717	729	741	753	765	777	.3
.7	777	789	801	813	825	837	849	861	873	885	897	.2
.8	897	909	921	933	945	957	969	980	992	004	016	.1
.9	.73 016	028	040	052	064	076	088	100	112	123	135	43.0
47.0	135	147	159	171	183	195	207	219	231	242	254	.9
.1	254	266	278	290	302	314	326	337	349	361	373	.8
.2	373	385	397	409	420	432	444	456	468	480	491	.7
.3	491	503	515	527	539	551	562	574	586	598	610	.6
.4	610	622	633	645	657	669	681	692	704	716	728	.5 Diff.
.5	728	740	751	763	775	787	798	810	822	834	846	.4 11-13
.6	846	857	869	881	893	904	916	928	940	951	963	.3
.7	963	975	987	998	010	022	034	045	057	069	080	.2
.8	.74 080	092	104	116	127	139	151	162	174	186	198	.1
.9	198	209	221	233	244	256	268	279	291	303	314	42.0
48.0	314	326	338	350	361	373	385	396	408	419	431	.9
.1	431	443	454	466	478	489	501	513	524	536	548	.8
.2	548	559	571	582	594	606	617	629	641	652	664	.7
.3	664	675	687	699	710	722	733	745	757	768	780	.6
.4	780	791	803	815	826	838	849	861	872	884	896	.5
.5	896	907	919	930	942	953	965	976	988	000	011	.4
.6	.75 011	023	034	046	057	069	080	092	103	115	126	.3
.7	126	138	149	161	172	184	195	207	218	230	241	.2
.8	241	253	264	276	287	299	310	322	333	345	356	.1
.9	356	368	379	391	402	414	425	437	448	460	471	41.0
49.0	471	482	494	505	517	528	540	551	562	574	585	.9
.1	585	597	608	620	631	642	654	665	677	688	700	.8
.2	700	711	722	734	745	756	768	779	791	802	813	.7
.3	813	825	836	848	859	870	882	893	904	916	927	.6
.4	927	938	950	961	973	984	995	007	018	029	041	.5
.5	.76 041	052	063	075	086	097	109	120	131	143	154	.4
.6	154	165	176	188	199	210	222	233	244	256	267	.3
.7	267	278	289	301	312	323	335	346	357	368	380	.2
.8	380	391	402	413	425	436	447	458	470	481	492	.1
.9	492	503	515	526	537	548	560	571	582	593	604	40.0 deg.
	(10)	9	8	7	6	5	4	3	2	1	0	

COS

SIN

deg.	0	1	2	3	4	5	6	7	8	9	(10)	
50.0	.76 604	616	627	638	649	661	672	683	694	705	717	.9
.1	717	728	739	750	761	772	784	795	806	817	828	.8
.2	828	840	851	862	873	884	895	906	918	929	940	.7
.3	940	951	962	973	985	996	007	018	029	040	051	.6
.4	.77 051	062	074	085	096	107	118	129	140	151	162	.5
.5	162	174	185	196	207	218	229	240	251	262	273	.4
.6	273	284	296	307	318	329	340	351	362	373	384	.3
.7	384	395	406	417	428	439	450	461	472	483	494	.2
.8	494	505	517	528	539	550	561	572	583	594	605	.1
.9	605	616	627	638	649	660	671	682	693	704	715	39.0
51.0	715	726	737	748	759	769	780	791	802	813	824	.9
.1	824	835	846	857	868	879	890	901	912	923	934	.8
.2	934	945	956	967	978	988	999	010	021	032	043	.7
.3	.78 043	054	065	076	087	098	108	119	130	141	152	.6
.4	152	163	174	185	196	206	217	228	239	250	261	.5
.5	261	272	283	293	304	315	326	337	348	359	369	.4
.6	369	380	391	402	413	424	434	445	456	467	478	.3
.7	478	488	499	510	521	532	542	553	564	575	586	.2
.8	586	596	607	618	629	640	650	661	672	683	694	.1
.9	694	704	715	726	737	747	758	769	780	790	801	38.0
52.0	801	812	823	833	844	855	866	876	887	898	908	.9
.1	908	919	930	941	951	962	973	983	994	005	016	.8
.2	.79 016	026	037	048	058	069	080	090	101	112	122	.7
.3	122	133	144	154	165	176	186	197	208	218	229	.6
.4	229	240	250	261	272	282	293	303	314	325	335	.5
.5	335	346	357	367	378	388	399	410	420	431	441	.4
.6	441	452	463	473	484	494	505	516	526	537	547	.3
.7	547	558	568	579	590	600	611	621	632	642	653	.2
.8	653	664	674	685	695	706	716	727	737	748	758	.1
.9	758	769	779	790	800	811	822	832	843	853	864	37.0
53.0	864	874	885	895	906	916	927	937	948	958	968	.9
.1	968	979	989	000	010	021	031	042	052	063	073	.8
.2	.80 073	084	094	104	115	125	136	146	157	167	178	.7
.3	178	188	198	209	219	230	240	251	261	271	282	.6
.4	282	292	303	313	323	334	344	355	365	375	386	.5
.5	386	396	406	417	427	438	448	458	469	479	489	.4
.6	489	500	510	520	531	541	551	562	572	582	593	.3
.7	593	603	613	624	634	644	655	665	675	686	696	.2
.8	696	706	717	727	737	748	758	768	778	789	799	.1
.9	799	809	820	830	840	850	861	871	881	891	902	36.0
54.0	902	912	922	932	943	953	963	973	984	994	004	.9
.1	.81 004	014	025	035	045	055	066	076	086	096	106	.8
.2	106	117	127	137	147	157	168	178	188	198	208	.7
.3	208	219	229	239	249	259	269	280	290	300	310	.6
.4	310	320	330	341	351	361	371	381	391	401	412	.5
.5	412	422	432	442	452	462	472	482	493	503	513	.4
.6	513	523	533	543	553	563	573	583	594	604	614	.3
.7	614	624	634	644	654	664	674	684	694	704	714	.2
.8	714	725	735	745	755	765	775	785	795	805	815	.1
.9	815	825	835	845	855	865	875	885	895	905	915	35.0
												deg.
	(10)	9	8	7	6	5	4	3	2	1	0	

Diff.
10-12

COS

SIN

deg.	0	1	2	3	4	5	6	7	8	9	(10)	
55.0	.81 915	925	935	945	955	965	975	985	995	005̄	015̄	.9
.1	.82 015	025	035	045	055	065	075	085	095	105	115	.8
.2	115	125	135	145	155	165	175	185	195	204	214	.7
.3	214	224	234	244	254	264	274	284	294	304	314	.6
.4	314	324	333	343	353	363	373	383	393	403	413	.5
.5	413	423	432	442	452	462	472	482	492	501	511	.4
.6	511	521	531	541	551	561	570	580	590	600	610	.3
.7	610	620	629	639	649	659	669	679	688	698	708	.2
.8	708	718	728	737	747	757	767	777	786	796	806	.1
.9	806	816	826	835	845	855	865	874	884	894	904	34.0
56.0	904	914	923	933	943	953	962	972	982	991	001̄	.9
.1	.83 001	011	021	030	040	050	060	069	079	089	098	.8
.2	098	108	118	128	137	147	157	166	176	186	195	.7
.3	195	205	215	224	234	244	253	263	273	282	292	.6
.4	292	302	311	321	331	340	350	360	369	379	389	.5
.5	389	398	408	417	427	437	446	456	466	475	485	.4
.6	485	494	504	514	523	533	542	552	562	571	581	.3
.7	581	590	600	609	619	629	638	648	657	667	676	.2
.8	676	686	696	705	715	724	734	743	753	762	772	.1
.9	772	781	791	800	810	819	829	839	848	858	867	33.0
57.0	867	877	886	896	905	915	924	934	943	953	962	.9
.1	962	971	981	990	000̄	009̄	019̄	028̄	038̄	047̄	057̄	.8
.2	.84 057	066	076	085	094	104	113	123	132	142	151	.7
.3	151	161	170	179	189	198	208	217	226	236	245	.6
.4	245	255	264	273	283	292	302	311	320	330	339	.5 Diff.
.5	339	349	358	367	377	386	395	405	414	423	433	.4 8-10
.6	433	442	451	461	470	480	489	498	508	517	526	.3
.7	526	536	545	554	563	573	582	591	601	610	619	.2
.8	619	629	638	647	656	666	675	684	694	703	712	.1
.9	712	721	731	740	749	759	768	777	786	796	805	32.0
58.0	805	814	823	833	842	851	860	869	879	888	897	.9
.1	897	906	916	925	934	943	952	962	971	980	989	.8
.2	989	998	008̄	017̄	026̄	035̄	044̄	054̄	063̄	072̄	081̄	.7
.3	.85 081	090	099	109	118	127	136	145	154	164	173	.6
.4	173	182	191	200	209	218	228	237	246	255	264	.5
.5	264	273	282	291	300	310	319	328	337	346	355	.4
.6	355	364	373	382	391	401	410	419	428	437	446	.3
.7	446	455	464	473	482	491	500	509	518	527	536	.2
.8	536	545	555	564	573	582	591	600	609	618	627	.1
.9	627	636	645	654	663	672	681	690	699	708	717	31.0
59.0	717	726	735	744	753	762	771	780	789	798	806	.9
.1	806	815	824	833	842	851	860	869	878	887	896	.8
.2	896	905	914	923	932	941	950	958	967	976	985	.7
.3	985	994	003̄	012̄	021̄	030̄	039̄	048̄	056̄	065̄	074̄	.6
.4	.86 074	083	092	101	110	119	127	136	145	154	163	.5
.5	163	172	181	189	198	207	216	225	234	243	251	.4
.6	251	260	269	278	287	295	304	313	322	331	340	.3
.7	340	348	357	366	375	384	392	401	410	419	427	.2
.8	427	436	445	454	463	471	480	489	498	506	515	.1
.9	515	524	533	541	550	559	568	576	585	594	603	30.0
												deg.
	(10)	9	8	7	6	5	4	3	2	1	0	

COS

SIN

deg.	0	1	2	3	4	5	6	7	8	9	(10)	
60.0	.86 603	611	620	629	637	646	655	664	672	681	690	.9
.1	690	698	707	716	724	733	742	751	759	768	777	.8
.2	777	785	794	803	811	820	829	837	846	855	863	.7
.3	863	872	880	889	898	906	915	924	932	941	949	.6
.4	949	958	967	975	984	993	001	010	018	027	036	.5
.5	.87 036	044	053	061	070	079	087	096	104	113	121	.4
.6	121	130	139	147	156	164	173	181	190	198	207	.3
.7	207	215	224	233	241	250	258	267	275	284	292	.2
.8	292	301	309	318	326	335	343	352	360	369	377	.1
.9	377	386	394	403	411	420	428	437	445	454	462	29.0
61.0	462	470	479	487	496	504	513	521	530	538	546	.9
.1	546	555	563	572	580	589	597	605	614	622	631	.8
.2	631	639	647	656	664	673	681	689	698	706	715	.7
.3	715	723	731	740	748	756	765	773	782	790	798	.6
.4	798	807	815	823	832	840	848	857	865	873	882	.5
.5	882	890	898	907	915	923	932	940	948	957	965	.4
.6	965	973	981	990	998	006	015	023	031	039	048	.3
.7	.88 048	056	064	073	081	089	097	106	114	122	130	.2
.8	130	139	147	155	163	172	180	188	196	204	213	.1
.9	213	221	229	237	246	254	262	270	278	287	295	28.0
62.0	295	303	311	319	328	336	344	352	360	368	377	.9
.1	377	385	393	401	409	417	426	434	442	450	458	.8
.2	458	466	474	483	491	499	507	515	523	531	539	.7
.3	539	547	556	564	572	580	588	596	604	612	620	.6
.4	620	628	637	645	653	661	669	677	685	693	701	.5 Diff.
.5	701	709	717	725	733	741	749	757	765	774	782	.4 7-9
.6	782	790	798	806	814	822	830	838	846	854	862	.3
.7	862	870	878	886	894	902	910	918	926	934	942	.2
.8	942	950	958	966	974	981	989	997	005	013	021	.1
.9	.89 021	029	037	045	053	061	069	077	085	093	101	27.0
63.0	101	109	116	124	132	140	148	156	164	172	180	.9
.1	180	188	196	203	211	219	227	235	243	251	259	.8
.2	259	266	274	282	290	298	306	314	321	329	337	.7
.3	337	345	353	361	368	376	384	392	400	408	415	.6
.4	415	423	431	439	447	454	462	470	478	486	493	.5
.5	493	501	509	517	525	532	540	548	556	563	571	.4
.6	571	579	587	594	602	610	618	625	633	641	649	.3
.7	649	656	664	672	680	687	695	703	710	718	726	.2
.8	726	734	741	749	757	764	772	780	787	795	803	.1
.9	803	810	818	826	833	841	849	856	864	872	879	26.0
64.0	879	887	895	902	910	918	925	933	941	948	956	.9
.1	956	963	971	979	986	994	001	009	017	024	032	.8
.2	.90 032	039	047	055	062	070	077	085	093	100	108	.7
.3	108	115	123	130	138	146	153	161	168	176	183	.6
.4	183	191	198	206	213	221	228	236	243	251	259	.5
.5	259	266	274	281	289	296	304	311	319	326	334	.4
.6	334	341	348	356	363	371	378	386	393	401	408	.3
.7	408	416	423	431	438	446	453	460	468	475	483	.2
.8	483	490	498	505	512	520	527	535	542	549	557	.1
.9	557	564	572	579	586	594	601	609	616	623	631	25.0
												deg.
(10)	9	8	7	6	5	4	3	2	1	0		

COS

SIN

deg.	0	1	2	3	4	5	6	7	8	9	(10)	Diff.	
65.0	.90 631	638	646	653	660	668	675	682	690	697	704	.9	7-8
.1	704	712	719	726	734	741	748	756	763	770	778	.8	
.2	778	785	792	800	807	814	822	829	836	844	851	.7	
.3	851	858	865	873	880	887	895	902	909	916	924	.6	
.4	924	931	938	945	953	960	967	974	982	989	996	.5	
.5	996	003	011	018	025	032	040	047	054	061	068	.4	
.6	.91 068	076	083	090	097	104	112	119	126	133	140	.3	
.7	140	148	155	162	169	176	183	191	198	205	212	.2	
.8	212	219	226	233	241	248	255	262	269	276	283	.1	
.9	283	291	298	305	312	319	326	333	340	347	355	24.0	
66.0	355	362	369	376	383	390	397	404	411	418	425	.9	
.1	425	432	440	447	454	461	468	475	482	489	496	.8	
.2	496	503	510	517	524	531	538	545	552	559	566	.7	
.3	566	573	580	587	594	601	608	615	622	629	636	.6	7
.4	636	643	650	657	664	671	678	685	692	699	706	.5	
.5	706	713	720	727	734	741	748	755	762	769	775	.4	
.6	775	782	789	796	803	810	817	824	831	838	845	.3	
.7	845	852	858	865	872	879	886	893	900	907	914	.2	
.8	914	920	927	934	941	948	955	962	968	975	982	.1	
.9	982	989	996	003	010	016	023	030	037	044	050	23.0	
67.0	.92 050	057	064	071	078	085	091	098	105	112	119	.9	
.1	119	125	132	139	146	152	159	166	173	180	186	.8	
.2	186	193	200	207	213	220	227	234	240	247	254	.7	
.3	254	261	267	274	281	287	294	301	308	314	321	.6	
.4	321	328	334	341	348	355	361	368	375	381	388	.5	
.5	388	395	401	408	415	421	428	435	441	448	455	.4	
.6	455	461	468	475	481	488	494	501	508	514	521	.3	
.7	521	528	534	541	547	554	561	567	574	580	587	.2	
.8	587	594	600	607	613	620	627	633	640	646	653	.1	
.9	653	659	666	673	679	686	692	699	705	712	718	22.0	
68.0	718	725	731	738	745	751	758	764	771	777	784	.9	
.1	784	790	797	803	810	816	823	829	836	842	849	.8	6-7
.2	849	855	862	868	874	881	887	894	900	907	913	.7	
.3	913	920	926	933	939	945	952	958	965	971	978	.6	
.4	978	984	990	997	003	010	016	023	029	035	042	.5	
.5	.93 042	048	055	061	067	074	080	086	093	099	106	.4	
.6	106	112	118	125	131	137	144	150	156	163	169	.3	
.7	169	175	182	188	194	201	207	213	220	226	232	.2	
.8	232	239	245	251	258	264	270	276	283	289	295	.1	
.9	295	302	308	314	320	327	333	339	346	352	358	21.0	
69.0	358	364	371	377	383	389	396	402	408	414	420	.9	
.1	420	427	433	439	445	452	458	464	470	476	483	.8	
.2	483	489	495	501	507	514	520	526	532	538	544	.7	
.3	544	551	557	563	569	575	581	588	594	600	606	.6	
.4	606	612	618	624	630	637	643	649	655	661	667	.5	
.5	667	673	679	686	692	698	704	710	716	722	728	.4	
.6	728	734	740	746	753	759	765	771	777	783	789	.3	
.7	789	795	801	807	813	819	825	831	837	843	849	.2	
.8	849	855	861	867	873	879	885	891	897	903	909	.1	6
.9	909	915	921	927	933	939	945	951	957	963	969	20.0 deg.	
	(10)	9	8	7	6	5	4	3	2	1	0		

COS

SIN

deg.	0	1	2	3	4	5	6	7	8	9	(10)	Diff.
70.0	.93 969	975	981	987	993	999	005̄	011̄	017̄	023̄	029̄	.9 6
.1	.94 029	035	041	047	053	058	064	070	076	082	088	.8
.2	088	094	100	106	112	118	123	129	135	141	147	.7
.3	147	153	159	165	171	176	182	188	194	200	206	.6
.4	206	212	217	223	229	235	241	247	252	258	264	.5
.5	264	270	276	282	287	293	299	305	311	316	322	.4
.6	322	328	334	340	345	351	357	363	369	374	380	.3
.7	380	386	392	397	403	409	415	420	426	432	438	.2
.8	438	443	449	455	461	466	472	478	483	489	495	.1
.9	495	501	506	512	518	523	529	535	540	546	552	19.0
71.0	552	558	563	569	575	580	586	592	597	603	609	.9
.1	609	614	620	625	631	637	642	648	654	659	665	.8
.2	665	671	676	682	687	693	699	704	710	715	721	.7
.3	721	727	732	738	743	749	755	760	766	771	777	.6
.4	777	782	788	794	799	805	810	816	821	827	832	.5
.5	832	838	843	849	854	860	866	871	877	882	888	.4 5-6
.6	888	893	899	904	910	915	921	926	932	937	943	.3
.7	943	948	954	959	964	970	975	981	986	992	997	.2
.8	997	003̄	008̄	014̄	019̄	024̄	030̄	035̄	041̄	046̄	052̄	.1
.9	.95 052	057	062	068	073	079	084	089	095	100	106	18.0
72.0	106	111	116	122	127	133	138	143	149	154	159	.9
.1	159	165	170	176	181	186	192	197	202	208	213	.8
.2	213	218	224	229	234	240	245	250	256	261	266	.7
.3	266	271	277	282	287	293	298	303	309	314	319	.6
.4	319	324	330	335	340	345	351	356	361	366	372	.5
.5	372	377	382	387	393	398	403	408	414	419	424	.4
.6	424	429	434	440	445	450	455	460	466	471	476	.3
.7	476	481	486	492	497	502	507	512	518	523	528	.2
.8	528	533	538	543	548	554	559	564	569	574	579	.1
.9	579	584	590	595	600	605	610	615	620	625	630	17.0
73.0	630	636	641	646	651	656	661	666	671	676	681	.9
.1	681	686	691	697	702	707	712	717	722	727	732	.8
.2	732	737	742	747	752	757	762	767	772	777	782	.7
.3	782	787	792	797	802	807	812	817	822	827	832	.6 5
.4	832	837	842	847	852	857	862	867	872	877	882	.5
.5	882	887	892	897	902	907	912	917	922	926	931	.4
.6	931	936	941	946	951	956	961	966	971	976	981	.3
.7	981	985	990	995	000̄	005̄	010̄	015̄	020̄	024̄	029̄	.2
.8	.96 029	034	039	044	049	054	059	063	068	073	078	.1
.9	078	083	088	092	097	102	107	112	117	121	126	16.0
74.0	126	131	136	141	145	150	155	160	165	169	174	.9
.1	174	179	184	188	193	198	203	208	212	217	222	.8
.2	222	227	231	236	241	246	250	255	260	264	269	.7
.3	269	274	279	283	288	293	297	302	307	312	316	.6
.4	316	321	326	330	335	340	344	349	354	358	363	.5
.5	363	368	372	377	382	386	391	396	400	405	410	.4
.6	410	414	419	423	428	433	437	442	447	451	456	.3
.7	456	460	465	470	474	479	483	488	492	497	502	.2
.8	502	506	511	515	520	524	529	534	538	543	547	.1
.9	547	552	556	561	565	570	574	579	584	588	593	15.0 4-5
	(10)	9	8	7	6	5	4	3	2	1	0	deg.

COS

SIN

deg.	0	1	2	3	4	5	6	7	8	9	(10)	Diff.	
75.0	.96 593	597	602	606	611	615	620	624	629	633	638	.9	4-5
.1	638	642	647	651	656	660	664	669	673	678	682	.8	
.2	682	687	691	696	700	705	709	713	718	722	727	.7	
.3	727	731	736	740	744	749	753	758	762	767	771	.6	
.4	771	775	780	784	788	793	797	802	806	810	815	.5	
.5	815	819	823	828	832	837	841	845	850	854	858	.4	
.6	858	863	867	871	876	880	884	889	893	897	902	.3	
.7	902	906	910	914	919	923	927	932	936	940	945	.2	
.8	945	949	953	957	962	966	970	974	979	983	987	.1	
.9	987	991	996	000	004	008	013	017	021	025	030	14.0	
76.0	.97 030	034	038	042	046	051	055	059	063	067	072	.9	
.1	072	076	080	084	088	093	097	101	105	109	113	.8	
.2	113	118	122	126	130	134	138	142	147	151	155	.7	
.3	155	159	163	167	171	176	180	184	188	192	196	.6	
.4	196	200	204	208	212	217	221	225	229	233	237	.5	
.5	237	241	245	249	253	257	261	265	269	274	278	.4	
.6	278	282	286	290	294	298	302	306	310	314	318	.3	
.7	318	322	326	330	334	338	342	346	350	354	358	.2	4
.8	358	362	366	370	374	378	382	386	390	394	398	.1	
.9	398	402	406	409	413	417	421	425	429	433	437	13.0	
77.0	437	441	445	449	453	457	461	464	468	472	476	.9	
.1	476	480	484	488	492	496	499	503	507	511	515	.8	
.2	515	519	523	527	530	534	538	542	546	550	553	.7	
.3	553	557	561	565	569	573	576	580	584	588	592	.6	
.4	592	595	599	603	607	611	614	618	622	626	630	.5	
.5	630	633	637	641	645	648	652	656	660	663	667	.4	
.6	667	671	675	678	682	686	690	693	697	701	705	.3	
.7	705	708	712	716	719	723	727	731	734	738	742	.2	
.8	742	745	749	753	756	760	764	767	771	775	778	.1	
.9	778	782	786	789	793	797	800	804	807	811	815	12.0	
78.0	815	818	822	826	829	833	836	840	844	847	851	.9	
.1	851	854	858	862	865	869	872	876	880	883	887	.8	
.2	887	890	894	897	901	905	908	912	915	919	922	.7	
.3	922	926	929	933	936	940	943	947	951	954	958	.6	
.4	958	961	965	968	972	975	979	982	986	989	992	.5	3-4
.5	992	996	999	003	006	010	013	017	020	024	027	.4	
.6	.98 027	031	034	037	041	044	048	051	055	058	061	.3	
.7	061	065	068	072	075	079	082	085	089	092	096	.2	
.8	096	099	102	106	109	112	116	119	123	126	129	.1	
.9	129	133	136	139	143	146	149	153	156	159	163	11.0	
79.0	163	166	169	173	176	179	183	186	189	193	196	.9	
.1	196	199	202	206	209	212	216	219	222	225	229	.8	
.2	229	232	235	239	242	245	248	252	255	258	261	.7	
.3	261	265	268	271	274	277	281	284	287	290	294	.6	
.4	294	297	300	303	306	310	313	316	319	322.	325	.5	
.5	325	329	332	335	338	341	345	348	351	354	357	.4	
.6	357	360	363	367	370	373	376	379	382	385	389	.3	
.7	389	392	395	398	401	404	407	410	413	416	420	.2	
.8	420	423	426	429	432	435	438	441	444	447	450	.1	
.9	450	453	456	459	463	466	469	472	475	478	481	10.0	3
	(10)	9	8	7	6	5	4	3	2	1	0	deg.	

COS

SIN

deg.	0	1	2	3	4	5	6	7	8	9	(10)	Diff.
80.0	.98 481	484	487	490	493	496	499	502	505	508	511	.9
.1	511	514	517	520	523	526	529	532	535	538	541	.8 3
.2	541	544	547	550	553	556	559	562	564	567	570	.7
.3	570	573	576	579	582	585	588	591	594	597	600	.6
.4	600	603	605	608	611	614	617	620	623	626	629	.5
.5	629	631	634	637	640	643	646	649	652	654	657	.4
.6	657	660	663	666	669	671	674	677	680	683	686	.3
.7	686	688	691	694	697	700	702	705	708	711	714	.2
.8	714	716	719	722	725	728	730	733	736	739	741	.1
.9	741	744	747	750	752	755	758	761	763	766	769	9.0
81.0	769	772	774	777	780	782	785	788	791	793	796	.9
.1	796	799	801	804	807	809	812	815	817	820	823	.8
.2	823	826	828	831	833	836	839	841	844	847	849	.7
.3	849	852	855	857	860	863	865	868	870	873	876	.6
.4	876	878	881	883	886	889	891	894	896	899	902	.5
.5	902	904	907	909	912	914	917	920	922	925	927	.4
.6	927	930	932	935	937	940	942	945	948	950	953	.3
.7	953	955	958	960	963	965	968	970	973	975	978	.2 2-3
.8	978	980	983	985	988	990	993	995	997	000	002	.1
.9	.99 002	005	007	010	012	015	017	020	022	024	027	8.0
82.0	027	029	032	034	036	039	041	044	046	049	051	.9
.1	051	053	056	058	061	063	065	068	070	072	075	.8
.2	075	077	080	082	084	087	089	091	094	096	098	.7
.3	098	101	103	105	108	110	112	115	117	119	122	.6
.4	122	124	126	128	131	133	135	138	140	142	144	.5
.5	144	147	149	151	154	156	158	160	163	165	167	.4
.6	167	169	172	174	176	178	181	183	185	187	189	.3
.7	189	192	194	196	198	200	203	205	207	209	211	.2
.8	211	214	216	218	220	222	225	227	229	231	233	.1
.9	233	235	238	240	242	244	246	248	250	252	255	7.0
83.0	255	257	259	261	263	265	267	269	272	274	276	.9
.1	276	278	280	282	284	286	288	290	292	294	297	.8
.2	297	299	301	303	305	307	309	311	313	315	317	.7
.3	317	319	321	323	325	327	329	331	333	335	337	.6
.4	337	339	341	343	345	347	349	351	353	355	357	.5 2
.5	357	359	361	363	365	367	369	371	373	375	377	.4
.6	377	379	381	383	385	386	388	390	392	394	396	.3
.7	396	398	400	402	404	406	408	409	411	413	415	.2
.8	415	417	419	421	423	424	426	428	430	432	434	.1
.9	434	436	437	439	441	443	445	447	449	450	452	6.0
84.0	452	454	456	458	459	461	463	465	467	468	470	.9
.1	470	472	474	476	477	479	481	483	485	486	488	.8
.2	488	490	492	493	495	497	499	500	502	504	506	.7
.3	506	507	509	511	512	514	516	518	519	521	523	.6
.4	523	524	526	528	530	531	533	535	536	538	540	.5
.5	540	541	543	545	546	548	550	551	553	555	556	.4
.6	556	558	559	561	563	564	566	568	569	571	572	.3
.7	572	574	576	577	579	580	582	584	585	587	588	.2
.8	588	590	592	593	595	596	598	599	601	603	604	.1
.9	604	606	607	609	610	612	613	615	616	618	619	5.0 1-2
	(10)	9	8	7	6	5	4	3	2	1	0	deg.

COS

SIN

deg.	0	1	2	3	4	5	6	7	8	9	(10)	Diff.
85.0	.99 619	621	623	624	626	627	629	630	632	633	635	.9 1-2
.1	635	636	638	639	640	642	643	645	646	648	649	.8
.2	649	651	652	654	655	657	658	659	661	662	664	.7
.3	664	665	667	668	669	671	672	674	675	676	678	.6
.4	678	679	681	682	683	685	686	688	689	690	692	.5
.5	692	693	694	696	697	699	700	701	703	704	705	.4
.6	705	707	708	709	711	712	713	715	716	717	719	.3
.7	719	720	721	722	724	725	726	728	729	730	731	.2
.8	731	733	734	735	737	738	739	740	742	743	744	.1
.9	744	745	747	748	749	750	752	753	754	755	756	4.0
86.0	.99 756	758	759	760	761	762	764	765	766	767	768	.9
.1	768	770	771	772	773	774	775	777	778	779	780	.8
.2	780	781	782	784	785	786	787	788	789	790	792	.7
.3	792	793	794	795	796	797	798	799	800	802	803	.6
.4	803	804	805	806	807	808	809	810	811	812	813	.5
.5	813	815	816	817	818	819	820	821	822	823	824	.4
.6	824	825	826	827	828	829	830	831	832	833	834	.3
.7	834	835	836	837	838	839	840	841	842	843	844	.2 1
.8	844	845	846	847	848	849	850	851	852	853	854	.1
.9	854	855	856	856	857	858	859	860	861	862	863	3.0
87.0	.99 863	864	865	866	867	867	868	869	870	871	872	.9
.1	872	873	874	875	875	876	877	878	879	880	881	.8
.2	881	881	882	883	884	885	886	887	887	888	889	.7
.3	889	890	891	891	892	893	894	895	895	896	897	.6
.4	897	898	899	899	900	901	902	903	903	904	905	.5
.5	905	906	906	907	908	909	909	910	911	912	912	.4
.6	912	913	914	914	915	916	917	917	918	919	919	.3
.7	919	920	921	922	922	923	924	924	925	926	926	.2
.8	926	927	928	928	929	930	930	931	932	932	933	.1
.9	933	933	934	935	935	936	937	937	938	938	939	2.0
88.0	.99 939	940	940	941	941	942	943	943	944	944	945	.9
.1	945	946	946	947	947	948	948	949	950	950	951	.8
.2	951	951	952	952	953	953	954	954	955	955	956	.7
.3	956	957	957	958	958	959	959	960	960	961	961	.6
.4	961	961	962	962	963	963	964	964	965	965	966	.5
.5	966	966	967	967	968	968	968	969	969	970	970	.4
.6	970	971	971	971	972	972	973	973	973	974	974	.3
.7	974	975	975	975	976	976	977	977	977	978	978	.2
.8	978	978	979	979	980	980	980	981	981	981	982	.1
.9	982	982	982	983	983	983	984	984	984	984	985	1.0
89.0	.99 985	985	985	986	986	986	987	987	987	987	988	.9
.1	988	988	988	988	989	989	989	990	990	990	990	.8
.2	990	990	991	991	991	991	992	992	992	992	993	.7
.3	993	993	993	993	993	994	994	994	994	994	995	.6
.4	995	995	995	995	995	995	996	996	996	996	996	.5
.5	996	996	996	997	997	997	997	997	997	997	998	.4
.6	998	998	998	998	998	998	998	998	998	999	999	.3
.7	999	999	999	999	999	999	999	999	999	999	999	.2
.8	999	999	000	000	000	000	000	000	000	000	000	.1
.9	1.00 000	000	000	000	000	000	000	000	000	000	000	0.0 deg.
90.0	1.00 000											
	(10)	9	8	7	6	5	4	3	2	1	0	

COS

TAN

deg.	0	1	2	3	4	5	6	7	8	9	(10)	
0.0	.00 000	017	035	052	070	087	105	122	140	157	175	.9
.1	175	192	209	227	244	262	279	297	314	332	349	.8
.2	349	367	384	401	419	436	454	471	489	506	524	.7
.3	524	541	558	576	593	611	628	646	663	681	698	.6
.4	698	716	733	751	768	785	803	820	838	855	873	.5
.5	873	890	908	925	943	960	977	995	012	030	047	.4
.6	.01 047	065	082	100	117	135	152	169	187	204	222	.3
.7	222	239	257	274	292	309	327	344	361	379	396	.2
.8	396	414	431	449	466	484	501	519	536	553	571	.1
.9	571	588	606	623	641	658	676	693	711	728	746	89.0
1.0	746	763	780	798	815	833	850	868	885	903	920	.9
.1	920	938	955	972	990	007	025	042	060	077	095	.8
.2	.02 095	112	130	147	165	182	199	217	234	252	269	.7
.3	269	287	304	322	339	357	374	392	409	426	444	.6
.4	444	461	479	496	514	531	549	566	584	601	619	.5
.5	619	636	654	671	688	706	723	741	758	776	793	.4
.6	793	811	828	846	863	881	898	916	933	950	968	.3
.7	968	985	003	020	038	055	073	090	108	125	143	.2
.8	.03 143	160	178	195	213	230	247	265	282	300	317	.1
.9	317	335	352	370	387	405	422	440	457	475	492	88.0
2.0	492	510	527	545	562	579	597	614	632	649	667	.9
.1	667	684	702	719	737	754	772	789	807	824	842	.8
.2	842	859	877	894	912	929	946	964	981	999	016	.7
.3	.04 016	034	051	069	086	104	121	139	156	174	191	.6
.4	191	209	226	244	261	279	296	314	331	349	366	.5 Diff.
.5	366	384	401	419	436	454	471	489	506	523	541	.4 17-18
.6	541	558	576	593	611	628	646	663	681	698	716	.3
.7	716	733	751	768	786	803	821	838	856	873	891	.2
.8	891	908	926	943	961	978	996	013	031	048	066	.1
.9	.05 066	083	101	118	136	153	171	188	206	223	241	87.0
3.0	241	258	276	293	311	328	346	363	381	398	416	.9
.1	416	433	451	468	486	503	521	538	556	573	591	.8
.2	591	608	626	643	661	678	696	713	731	748	766	.7
.3	766	783	801	818	836	854	871	889	906	924	941	.6
.4	941	959	976	994	011	029	046	064	081	099	116	.5
.5	.06 116	134	151	169	186	204	221	239	256	274	291	.4
.6	291	309	327	344	362	379	397	414	432	449	467	.3
.7	467	484	502	519	537	554	572	589	607	624	642	.2
.8	642	660	677	695	712	730	747	765	782	800	817	.1
.9	817	835	852	870	887	905	923	940	958	975	993	86.0
4.0	993	010	028	045	063	080	098	115	133	151	168	.9
.1	.07 168	186	203	221	238	256	273	291	308	326	344	.8
.2	344	361	379	396	414	431	449	466	484	501	519	.7
.3	519	537	554	572	589	607	624	642	659	677	695	.6
.4	695	712	730	747	765	782	800	817	835	853	870	.5
.5	870	888	905	923	940	958	976	993	011	028	046	.4
.6	.08 046	063	081	099	116	134	151	169	186	204	221	.3
.7	221	239	257	274	292	309	327	345	362	380	397	.2
.8	397	415	432	450	468	485	503	520	538	555	573	.1
.9	573	591	608	626	643	661	679	696	714	731	749	85.0 deg.
	(10)	9	8	7	6	5	4	3	2	1	0	

COT

TAN

deg.	0	1	2	3	4	5	6	7	8	9	(10)	Diff.
5.0	.08 749	766	784	802	819	837	854	872	890	907	925	.9 17_
.1	925	942	960	978	995	013	030	048	066	083	101	.8 18
.2	.09 101	118	136	154	171	189	206	224	242	259	277	.7
.3	277	294	312	330	347	365	382	400	418	435	453	.6
.4	453	470	488	506	523	541	558	576	594	611	629	.5
.5	629	647	664	682	699	717	735	752	770	787	805	.4
.6	805	823	840	858	876	893	911	928	946	964	981	.3
.7	981	999	017	034	052	069	087	105	122	140	158	.2
.8	.10 158	175	193	211	228	246	263	281	299	316	334	.1
.9	334	352	369	387	405	422	440	457	475	493	510	84.0
6.0	510	528	546	563	581	599	616	634	652	669	687	.9
.1	687	705	722	740	758	775	793	811	828	846	863	.8
.2	863	881	899	916	934	952	969	987	005	022	040	.7
.3	.11 040	058	075	093	111	128	146	164	181	199	217	.6
.4	217	234	252	270	287	305	323	341	358	376	394	.5
.5	394	411	429	447	464	482	500	517	535	553	570	.4
.6	570	588	606	623	641	659	677	694	712	730	747	.3
.7	747	765	783	800	818	836	853	871	889	907	924	.2
.8	924	942	960	977	995	013	031	048	066	084	101	.1
.9	.12 101	119	137	154	172	190	208	225	243	261	278	83.0
7.0	278	296	314	332	349	367	385	402	420	438	456	.9
.1	456	473	491	509	527	544	562	580	597	615	633	.8
.2	633	651	668	686	704	722	739	757	775	793	810	.7
.3	810	828	846	864	881	899	917	934	952	970	988	.6
.4	988	005	023	041	059	076	094	112	130	147	165	.5
.5	.13 165	183	201	219	236	254	272	290	307	325	343	.4
.6	343	361	378	396	414	432	449	467	485	503	521	.3
.7	521	538	556	574	592	609	627	645	663	681	698	.2
.8	698	716	734	752	769	787	805	823	841	858	876	.1
.9	876	894	912	930	947	965	983	001	018	036	054	82.0
8.0	.14 054	072	090	107	125	143	161	179	196	214	232	.9
.1	232	250	268	286	303	321	339	357	375	392	410	.8
.2	410	428	446	464	481	499	517	535	553	571	588	.7
.3	588	606	624	642	660	678	695	713	731	749	767	.6
.4	767	785	802	820	838	856	874	892	909	927	945	.5
.5	945	963	981	999	016	034	052	070	088	106	124	.4
.6	.15 124	141	159	177	195	213	231	249	266	284	302	.3
.7	302	320	338	356	374	391	409	427	445	463	481	.2
.8	481	499	517	534	552	570	588	606	624	642	660	.1
.9	660	677	695	713	731	749	767	785	803	821	838	81.0
9.0	838	856	874	892	910	928	946	964	982	000	017	.9
.1	.16 017	035	053	071	089	107	125	143	161	179	196	.8
.2	196	214	232	250	268	286	304	322	340	358	376	.7
.3	376	394	411	429	447	465	483	501	519	537	555	.6
.4	555	573	591	609	627	645	663	680	698	716	734	.5
.5	734	752	770	788	806	824	842	860	878	896	914	.4
.6	914	932	950	968	986	004	021	039	057	075	093	.3
.7	.17 093	111	129	147	165	183	201	219	237	255	273	.2
.8	273	291	309	327	345	363	381	399	417	435	453	.1
.9	453	471	489	507	525	543	561	579	597	615	633	80.0 18
	(10)	9	8	7	6	5	4	3	2	1	0	deg.

COT

TAN

deg.	0	1	2	3	4	5	6	7	8	9	(10)	Diff.
10.0	.17 633	651	669	687	705	723	741	759	777	795	813	.9 18
.1	813	831	849	867	885	903	921	939	957	975	993	.8
.2	993	011	029	047	065	083	101	119	137	155	173	.7
.3	.18 173	191	209	227	245	263	281	299	317	335	353	.6
.4	353	371	390	408	426	444	462	480	498	516	534	.5
.5	534	552	570	588	606	624	642	660	678	696	714	.4
.6	714	733	751	769	787	805	823	841	859	877	895	.3
.7	895	913	931	949	968	986	004	022	040	058	076	.2
.8	.19 076	094	112	130	148	166	185	203	221	239	257	.1
.9	257	275	293	311	329	347	366	384	402	420	438	79.0
11. 0	438	456	474	492	510	529	547	565	583	601	619	.9
.1	619	637	655	674	692	710	728	746	764	782	801	.8
.2	801	819	837	855	873	891	909	928	946	964	982	.7
.3	982	000	018	036	055	073	091	109	127	145	164	.6
.4	.20 164	182	200	218	236	254	273	291	309	327	345	.5
.5	345	363	382	400	418	436	454	472	491	509	527	.4
.6	527	545	563	582	600	618	636	654	673	691	709	.3
.7	709	727	745	764	782	800	818	836	855	873	891	.2
.8	891	909	928	946	964	982	000	019	037	055	073	.1
.9	.21 073	092	110	128	146	164	183	201	219	237	256	78.0
12.0	256	274	292	310	329	347	365	383	402	420	438	.9
.1	438	456	475	493	511	529	548	566	584	602	621	.8
.2	621	639	657	676	694	712	730	749	767	785	804	.7
.3	804	822	840	858	877	895	913	932	950	968	986	.6
.4	986	005	023	041	060	078	096	115	133	151	169	.5
.5	.22 169	188	206	224	243	261	279	298	316	334	353	.4
.6	353	371	389	408	426	444	463	481	499	518	536	.3
.7	536	554	573	591	609	628	646	664	683	701	719	.2
.8	719	738	756	775	793	811	830	848	866	885	903	.1
.9	903	921	940	958	977	995	013	032	050	068	087	77.0
13.0	.23 087	105	124	142	160	179	197	216	234	252	271	.9
.1	271	289	308	326	344	363	381	400	418	436	455	.8
.2	455	473	492	510	528	547	565	584	602	621	639	.7
.3	639	657	676	694	713	731	750	768	786	805	823	.6
.4	823	842	860	879	897	916	934	953	971	989	008	.5
.5	.24 008	026	045	063	082	100	119	137	156	174	193	.4
.6	193	211	229	248	266	285	303	322	340	359	377	.3
.7	377	396	414	433	451	470	488	507	525	544	562	.2 18-
.8	562	581	599	618	636	655	673	692	710	729	748	.1 19
.9	747	766	785	803	822	840	859	877	896	914	933	76.0
14.0	933	951	970	988	007	026	044	063	081	100	118	.9
.1	.25 118	137	155	174	192	211	230	248	267	285	304	.8
.2	304	322	341	360	378	397	415	434	453	471	490	.7
.3	490	508	527	545	564	583	601	620	638	657	676	.6
.4	676	694	713	731	750	769	787	806	825	843	862	.5
.5	862	880	899	918	936	955	974	992	011	029	048	.4
.6	.26 048	067	085	104	123	141	160	179	197	216	235	.3
.7	235	253	272	290	309	328	346	365	384	402	421	.2
.8	421	440	458	477	496	515	533	552	571	589	608	.1
.9	608	627	645	664	683	701	720	739	758	776	795	75.0
	(10)	9	8	7	6	5	4	3	2	1	0	deg.

COT

TAN

deg.	0	1	2	3	4	5	6	7	8	9	(10)	Diff.	
15.0	.26 795	814	832	851	870	888	907	926	945	963	982	.9	
.1	982	001	020	038	057	076	094	113	132	151	169	.8	
.2	.27 169	188	207	226	244	263	282	301	319	338	357	.7	
.3	357	376	394	413	432	451	469	488	507	526	545	.6	
.4	545	563	582	601	620	638	657	676	695	714	732	.5	
.5	732	751	770	789	808	826	845	864	883	902	921	.4	
.6	921	939	958	977	996	015	033	052	071	090	109	.3	
.7	.28 109	128	146	165	184	203	222	241	259	278	297	.2	
.8	297	316	335	354	373	391	410	429	448	467	486	.1	
.9	486	505	523	542	561	580	599	618	637	656	675	74.0	
16.0	675	693	712	731	750	769	788	807	826	845	864	.9	
.1	864	882	901	920	939	958	977	996	015	034	053	.8	
.2	.29 053	072	091	109	128	147	166	185	204	223	242	.7	
.3	242	261	280	299	318	337	356	375	394	413	432	.6	
.4	432	451	470	489	507	526	545	564	583	602	621	.5	
.5	621	640	659	678	697	716	735	754	773	792	811	.4	19
.6	811	830	849	868	887	906	925	944	963	982	001	.3	
.7	.30 001	020	039	059	078	097	116	135	154	173	192	.2	
.8	192	211	230	249	268	287	306	325	344	363	382	.1	
.9	382	401	420	440	459	478	497	516	535	554	573	73.0	
17.0	573	592	611	630	649	669	688	707	726	745	764	.9	
.1	764	783	802	821	840	860	879	898	917	936	955	.8	
.2	955	974	993	013	032	051	070	089	108	127	147	.7	
.3	.31 147	166	185	204	223	242	261	281	300	319	338	.6	
.4	338	357	376	396	415	434	453	472	492	511	530	.5	
.5	530	549	568	587	607	626	645	664	683	703	722	.4	
.6	722	741	760	780	799	818	837	856	876	895	914	.3	
.7	914	933	953	972	991	010	029	049	068	087	106	.2	
.8	.32 106	126	145	164	184	203	222	241	261	280	299	.1	
.9	299	318	338	357	376	396	415	434	453	473	492	72.0	
18.0	492	511	531	550	569	588	608	627	646	666	685	.9	
.1	685	704	724	743	762	782	801	820	840	859	878	.8	
.2	878	898	917	936	956	975	994	014	033	052	072	.7	
.3	.33 072	091	111	130	149	169	188	207	227	246	266	.6	
.4	266	285	304	324	343	363	382	401	421	440	460	.5	
.5	460	479	498	518	537	557	576	595	615	634	654	.4	
.6	654	673	693	712	731	751	770	790	809	829	848	.3	
.7	848	868	887	907	926	945	965	984	004	023	043	.2	
.8	.34 043	062	082	101	121	140	160	179	199	218	238	.1	
.9	238	257	277	296	316	335	355	374	394	413	433	71.0	
19.0	433	452	472	491	511	530	550	569	589	609	628	.9	
.1	628	648	667	687	706	726	745	765	785	804	824	.8	
.2	824	843	863	882	902	922	941	961	980	000	020	.7	
.3	.35 020	039	059	078	098	118	137	157	176	196	216	.6	
.4	216	235	255	274	294	314	333	353	373	392	412	.5	
.5	412	432	451	471	490	510	530	549	569	589	608	.4	
.6	608	628	648	667	687	707	726	746	766	785	805	.3	
.7	805	825	845	864	884	904	923	943	963	983	002	.2	
.8	.36 002	022	042	061	081	101	121	140	160	180	199	.1	
.9	199	219	239	259	278	298	318	338	357	377	397	70.0	20
												deg.	
(10)		9	8	7	6	5	4	3	2	1	0		

COT

TRIGONOMETRIC FUNCTIONS

TAN

deg.	0	1	2	3	4	5	6	7	8	9	(10)	Diff.	
20.0	.36 397	417	437	456	476	496	516	535	555	575	595	.9	
.1	595	615	634	654	674	694	714	733	753	773	793	.8	
.2	793	813	832	852	872	892	912	932	951	971	991	.7	
.3	991	011	031	051	071	090	110	130	150	170	190	.6	
.4	.37 190	210	229	249	269	289	309	329	349	369	388	.5	
.5	388	408	428	448	468	488	508	528	548	568	588	.4	
.6	588	607	627	647	667	687	707	727	747	767	787	.3	
.7	787	807	827	847	867	887	907	927	946	966	986	.2	
.8	986	006	026	046	066	086	106	126	146	166	186	.1	20
.9	.38 186	206	226	246	266	286	306	326	346	366	386	69.0	
21.0	386	406	426	446	467	487	507	527	547	567	587	.9	
.1	587	607	627	647	667	687	707	727	747	767	787	.8	
.2	787	808	828	848	868	888	908	928	948	968	988	.7	
.3	988	008	029	049	069	089	109	129	149	169	190	.6	
.4	.39 190	210	230	250	270	290	310	331	351	371	391	.5	
.5	391	411	431	452	472	492	512	532	552	573	593	.4	
.6	593	613	633	653	674	694	714	734	754	775	795	.3	
.7	795	815	835	856	876	896	916	936	957	977	997	.2	
.8	997	017	038	058	078	098	119	139	159	179	200	.1	
.9	.40 200	220	240	261	281	301	321	342	362	382	403	68.0	
22.0	403	423	443	464	484	504	524	545	565	585	606	.9	
.1	606	626	646	667	687	707	728	748	769	789	809	.8	
.2	809	830	850	870	891	911	931	952	972	993	013	.7	
.3	.41 013	033	054	074	095	115	135	156	176	197	217	.6	
.4	217	237	258	278	299	319	340	360	380	401	421	.5	
.5	421	442	462	483	503	524	544	565	585	606	626	.4	
.6	626	646	667	687	708	728	749	769	790	810	831	.3	
.7	831	851	872	892	913	933	954	975	995	016	036	.2	
.8	.42 036	057	077	098	118	139	159	180	201	221	242	.1	
.9	242	262	283	303	324	345	365	386	406	427	447	67.0	
23.0	447	468	489	509	530	551	571	592	612	633	654	.9	
.1	654	674	695	716	736	757	777	798	819	839	860	.8	
.2	860	881	901	922	943	963	984	005	025	046	067	.7	
.3	.43 067	087	108	129	150	170	191	212	232	253	274	.6	
.4	274	295	315	336	357	378	398	419	440	460	481	.5	
.5	481	502	523	544	564	585	606	627	647	668	689	.4	
.6	689	710	731	751	772	793	814	834	855	876	897	.3	
.7	897	918	939	959	980	001	022	043	064	084	105	.2	
.8	.44 105	126	147	168	189	210	230	251	272	293	314	.1	
.9	314	335	356	377	397	418	439	460	481	502	523	66.0	
24.0	523	544	565	586	607	627	648	669	690	711	732	.9	
.1	732	753	774	795	816	837	858	879	900	921	942	.8	
.2	942	963	984	005	026	047	068	089	110	131	152	.7	21
.3	.45 152	173	194	215	236	257	278	299	320	341	362	.6	
.4	362	383	404	425	446	467	488	509	530	552	573	.5	
.5	573	594	615	636	657	678	699	720	741	762	784	.4	
.6	784	805	826	847	868	889	910	931	953	974	995	.3	
.7	995	016	037	058	079	101	122	143	164	185	206	.2	
.8	.46 206	228	249	270	291	312	334	355	376	397	418	.1	
.9	418	440	461	482	503	525	546	567	588	610	631	65.0	
												deg.	
	(10)	9	8	7	6	5	4	3	2	1	0		

COT

TAN

deg.	0	1	2	3	4	5	6	7	8	9	(10)	Diff.	
25.0	.46 631	652	673	695	716	737	758	780	801	822	843	.9	
.1	843	865	886	907	929	950	971	992	014	035	056	.8	
.2	.47 056	078	099	120	142	163	184	206	227	248	270	.7	
.3	270	291	312	334	355	377	398	419	441	462	483	.6	
.4	483	505	526	548	569	590	612	633	655	676	698	.5	
.5	698	719	740	762	783	805	826	848	869	891	912	.4	
.6	912	933	955	976	998	019	041	062	084	105	127	.3	
.7	.48 127	148	170	191	213	234	256	277	299	320	342	.2	
.8	342	363	385	407	428	450	471	493	514	536	557	.1	
.9	557	579	601	622	644	665	687	708	730	752	773	64.0	
26.0	773	795	816	838	860	881	903	925	946	968	989	.9	
.1	989	011	033	054	076	098	119	141	163	184	206	.8	
.2	.49 206	228	249	271	293	315	336	358	380	401	423	.7	
.3	423	445	467	488	510	532	553	575	597	619	640	.6	
.4	640	662	684	706	727	749	771	793	815	836	858	.5	
.5	858	880	902	924	945	967	989	011	033	054	076	.4	
.6	.50 076	098	120	142	164	185	207	229	251	273	295	.3	
.7	295	317	339	360	382	404	426	448	470	492	514	.2	
.8	514	536	557	579	601	623	645	667	689	711	733	.1	
.9	733	755	777	799	821	843	865	887	909	931	953	63.0	
27.0	953	975	997	019	041	063	085	107	129	151	173	.9	22
.1	.51 173	195	217	239	261	283	305	327	349	371	393	.8	
.2	393	415	437	459	481	503	525	548	570	592	614	.7	
.3	614	636	658	680	702	724	747	769	791	813	835	.6	
.4	835	857	879	902	924	946	968	990	012	035	057	.5	
.5	.52 057	079	101	123	145	168	190	212	234	257	279	.4	
.6	279	301	323	345	368	390	412	434	457	479	501	.3	
.7	501	523	546	568	590	613	635	657	679	702	724	.2	
.8	724	746	769	791	813	836	858	880	903	925	947	.1	
.9	947	970	992	014	037	059	081	104	126	149	171	62.0	
28.0	.53 171	193	216	238	261	283	305	328	350	373	395	.9	
.1	395	417	440	462	485	507	530	552	575	597	620	.8	
.2	620	642	664	687	709	732	754	777	799	822	844	.7	
.3	844	867	889	912	935	957	980	002	025	047	070	.6	
.4	.54 070	092	115	137	160	183	205	228	250	273	296	.5	
.5	296	318	341	363	386	409	431	454	476	499	522	.4	
.6	522	544	567	590	612	635	658	680	703	726	748	.3	
.7	748	771	794	816	839	862	885	907	930	953	975	.2	
.8	975	998	021	044	066	089	112	135	157	180	203	.1	
.9	.55 203	226	249	271	294	317	340	362	385	408	431	61.0	
29.0	431	454	477	499	522	545	568	591	614	636	659	.9	
.1	659	682	705	728	751	774	797	819	842	865	888	.8	
.2	888	911	934	957	980	003	026	049	071	094	117	.7	
.3	.56 117	140	163	186	209	232	255	278	301	324	347	.6	
.4	347	370	393	416	439	462	485	508	531	554	577	.5	23
.5	577	600	623	646	669	693	716	739	762	785	808	.4	
.6	808	831	854	877	900	923	947	970	993	016	039	.3	
.7	.57 039	062	085	108	132	155	178	201	224	247	271	.2	
.8	271	294	317	340	363	386	410	433	456	479	503	.1	
.9	503	526	549	572	595	619	642	665	688	712	735	60.0 deg.	
(10)	9	8	7	6	5	4	3	2	1	0			

COT

TAN

deg.	0	1	2	3	4	5	6	7	8	9	(10)	Diff.	
30.0	.57 735	758	782	805	828	851	875	898	921	945	968	.9	
.1	968	991	015	038	061	085	108	131	155	178	201	.8	
.2	.58 201	225	248	272	295	318	342	365	388	412	435	.7	
.3	435	459	482	506	529	552	576	599	623	646	670	.6	
.4	670	693	717	740	764	787	811	834	857	881	905	.5	
.5	905	928	952	975	999	022	046	069	093	116	140	.4	
.6	.59 140	163	187	211	234	258	281	305	328	352	376	.3	
.7	376	399	423	446	470	494	517	541	565	588	612	.2	
.8	612	636	659	683	707	730	754	778	801	825	849	.1	
.9	849	872	896	920	944	967	991	015	039	062	086	59.0	
31.0	.60 086	110	134	157	181	205	229	252	276	300	324	.9	
.1	324	348	371	395	419	443	467	491	514	538	562	.8	
.2	562	586	610	634	658	681	705	729	753	777	801	.7	
.3	801	825	849	873	897	921	944	968	992	016	040	.6	
.4	.61 040	064	088	112	136	160	184	208	232	256	280	.5	24
.5	280	304	328	352	376	400	424	448	472	496	520	.4	
.6	520	544	569	593	617	641	665	689	713	737	761	.3	
.7	761	785	809	834	858	882	906	930	954	978	003	.2	
.8	.62 003	027	051	075	099	124	148	172	196	220	245	.1	
.9	245	269	293	317	341	366	390	414	438	463	487	58.0	
32.0	487	511	535	560	584	608	633	657	681	706	730	.9	
.1	730	754	779	803	827	852	876	900	925	949	973	.8	
.2	973	998	022	047	071	095	120	144	169	193	217	.7	
.3	.63 217	242	266	291	315	340	364	389	413	437	462	.6	
.4	462	486	511	535	560	584	609	633	658	682	707	.5	
.5	707	732	756	781	805	830	854	879	903	928	953	.4	
.6	953	977	002	026	051	076	100	125	150	174	199	.3	
.7	.64 199	224	248	273	297	322	347	372	396	421	446	.2	
.8	446	470	495	520	544	569	594	619	643	668	693	.1	
.9	693	718	742	767	792	817	842	866	891	916	941	57.0	
33.0	941	966	990	015	040	065	090	115	139	164	189	.9	
.1	.65 189	214	239	264	289	314	339	363	388	413	438	.8	
.2	438	463	488	513	538	563	588	613	638	663	688	.7	
.3	688	713	738	763	788	813	838	863	888	913	938	.6	25
.4	938	963	988	013	038	063	088	113	138	163	189	.5	
.5	.66 189	214	239	264	289	314	339	364	390	415	440	.4	
.6	440	465	490	515	541	566	591	616	641	666	692	.3	
.7	692	717	742	767	793	818	843	868	894	919	944	.2	
.8	944	969	995	020	045	071	096	121	147	172	197	.1	
.9	.67 197	223	248	273	299	324	349	375	400	425	451	56.0	
34.0	451	476	502	527	552	578	603	629	654	680	705	.9	
.1	705	731	756	781	807	832	858	883	909	934	960	.8	
.2	960	985	011	036	062	088	113	139	164	190	215	.7	
.3	.68 215	241	267	292	318	343	369	395	420	446	471	.6	
.4	471	497	523	548	574	600	625	651	677	702	728	.5	
.5	728	754	780	805	831	857	882	908	934	960	985	.4	
.6	985	011	037	063	088	114	140	166	192	217	243	.3	
.7	.69 243	269	295	321	347	372	398	424	450	476	502	.2	
.8	502	528	554	579	605	631	657	683	709	735	761	.1	26
.9	761	787	813	839	865	891	917	943	969	995	021	55.0	
	.70											deg.	
(10)	9	8	7	6	5	4	3	2	1	0			

COT

TAN

deg.		0	1	2	3	4	5	6	7	8	9	(10)	Diff.	
35.0	.70	021	047	073	099	125	151	177	203	229	255	281	.9	26
.1		281	307	333	359	386	412	438	464	490	516	542	.8	
.2		542	568	595	621	647	673	699	725	752	778	804	.7	
.3		804	830	856	883	909	935	961	988	014	040	066	.6	
.4	.71	066	093	119	145	171	198	224	250	277	303	329	.5	
.5		329	356	382	408	435	461	487	514	540	567	593	.4	
.6		593	619	646	672	699	725	751	778	804	831	857	.3	
.7		857	884	910	937	963	990	016	043	069	096	122	.2	
.8	.72	122	149	175	202	228	255	282	308	335	361	388	.1	
.9		388	415	441	468	494	521	548	574	601	628	654	54.0	
36.0		654	681	708	734	761	788	814	841	868	895	921	.9	
.1		921	948	975	001	028	055	082	109	135	162	189	.8	
.2	.73	189	216	243	269	296	323	350	377	404	430	457	.7	
.3		457	484	511	538	565	592	619	646	672	699	726	.6	
.4		726	753	780	807	834	861	888	915	942	969	996	.5	27
.5		996	023	050	077	104	131	158	185	212	239	267	.4	
.6	.74	267	294	321	348	375	402	429	456	483	511	538	.3	
.7		538	565	592	619	646	674	701	728	755	782	810	.2	
.8		810	837	864	891	918	946	973	000	028	055	082	.1	
.9	.75	082	109	137	164	191	219	246	273	301	328	355	53.0	
37.0		355	383	410	438	465	492	520	547	575	602	629	.9	
.1		629	657	684	712	739	767	794	822	849	877	904	.8	
.2		904	932	959	987	014	042	069	097	124	152	180	.7	
.3	.76	180	207	235	262	290	318	345	373	400	428	456	.6	
.4		456	483	511	539	566	594	622	650	677	705	733	.5	
.5		733	760	788	816	844	871	899	927	955	983	010	.4	
.6	.77	010	038	066	094	122	149	177	205	233	261	289	.3	
.7		289	317	345	372	400	428	456	484	512	540	568	.2	
.8		568	596	624	652	680	708	736	764	792	820	848	.1	28
.9		848	876	904	932	960	988	016	044	072	100	129	52.0	
38.0	.78	129	157	185	213	241	269	297	325	354	382	410	.9	
.1		410	438	466	495	523	551	579	607	636	664	692	.8	
.2		692	721	749	777	805	834	862	890	919	947	975	.7	
.3		975	004	032	060	089	117	145	174	202	231	259	.6	
.4	.79	259	287	316	344	373	401	430	458	487	515	544	.5	
.5		544	572	601	629	658	686	715	743	772	800	829	.4	
.6		829	858	886	915	943	972	001	029	058	086	115	.3	
.7	.80	115	144	172	201	230	258	287	316	345	373	402	.2	
.8		402	431	460	488	517	546	575	603	632	661	690	.1	
.9		690	719	747	776	805	834	863	892	921	950	978	51.0	
39.0		978	007	036	065	094	123	152	181	210	239	268	.9	
.1	.81	268	297	326	355	384	413	442	471	500	529	558	.8	29
.2		558	587	616	645	674	703	733	762	791	820	849	.7	
.3		849	878	907	937	966	995	024	053	082	112	141	.6	
.4	.82	141	170	199	229	258	287	316	346	375	404	434	.5	
.5		434	463	492	522	551	580	610	639	668	698	727	.4	
.6		727	757	786	815	845	874	904	933	963	992	022	.3	
.7	.83	022	051	081	110	140	169	199	228	258	287	317	.2	
.8		317	346	376	406	435	465	494	524	554	583	613	.1	
.9		613	643	672	702	732	761	791	821	850	880	910	50.0 deg.	
	(10)	9	8	7		6	5	4	3	2	1	0		

COT

TAN

deg.		0	1	2	3	4	5	6	7	8	9	(10)	Diff.
40.0	.83	910	940	969	999	029	059	089	118	148	178	208	.9
.1	.84	208	238	267	297	327	357	387	417	447	477	507	.8
.2		507	536	566	596	626	656	686	716	746	776	806	.7
.3		806	836	866	896	926	956	986	016	046	077	107	.6
.4	.85	107	137	167	197	227	257	287	318	348	378	408	.5
.5		408	438	468	499	529	559	589	620	650	680	710	.4
.6		710	741	771	801	832	862	892	923	953	983	014	.3
.7	.86	014	044	074	105	135	166	196	226	257	287	318	.2
.8		318	348	379	409	440	470	501	531	562	592	623	.1
.9		623	653	684	714	745	776	806	837	867	898	929	49.0
41.0		929	959	990	021	051	082	113	143	174	205	236	.9
.1	.87	236	266	297	328	359	389	420	451	482	513	543	.8
.2		543	574	605	636	667	698	729	759	790	821	852	.7
.3		852	883	914	945	976	007	038	069	100	131	162	.6
.4	.88	162	193	224	255	286	317	348	379	410	441	473	.5
.5		473	504	535	566	597	628	659	691	722	753	784	.4
.6		784	815	847	878	909	940	972	003	034	065	097	.3
.7	.89	097	128	159	191	222	253	285	316	348	379	410	.2
.8		410	442	473	505	536	567	599	630	662	693	725	.1
.9		725	756	788	819	851	883	914	946	977	009	040	48.0
42.0	.90	040	072	104	135	167	199	230	262	294	325	357	.9
.1		357	389	420	452	484	516	547	579	611	643	674	.8
.2		674	706	738	770	802	834	865	897	929	961	993	.7
.3		993	026	057	089	121	153	185	217	249	281	313	.6
.4	.91	313	345	377	409	441	473	505	537	569	601	633	.5
.5		633	665	697	729	762	794	826	858	890	923	955	.4
.6		955	987	019	051	084	116	148	180	213	245	277	.3
.7	.92	277	310	342	374	407	439	471	504	536	569	601	.2
.8		601	633	666	698	731	763	796	828	861	893	926	.1
.9		926	958	991	023	056	088	121	154	186	219	252	47.0
43.0	.93	252	284	317	349	382	415	447	480	513	546	578	.9
.1		578	611	644	677	709	742	775	808	841	873	906	.8
.2		906	939	972	005	038	071	104	136	169	202	235	.7
.3	.94	235	268	301	334	367	400	433	466	499	532	565	.6
.4		565	598	631	665	698	731	764	797	830	863	896	.5
.5		896	930	963	996	029	062	096	129	162	195	229	.4
.6	.95	229	262	295	329	362	395	429	462	495	529	562	.3
.7		562	595	629	662	696	729	763	796	830	863	897	.2
.8		897	930	964	997	031	064	098	131	165	199	232	.1
.9	.96	232	266	299	333	367	400	434	468	501	535	569	46.0
44.0		569	603	636	670	704	738	771	805	839	873	907	.9
.1		907	941	974	008	042	076	110	144	178	212	246	.8
.2	.97	246	280	314	348	382	416	450	484	518	552	586	.7
.3		586	620	654	688	722	756	791	825	859	893	927	.6
.4		927	961	996	030	064	098	133	167	201	235	270	.5
.5	.98	270	304	338	373	407	441	476	510	545	579	613	.4
.6		613	648	682	717	751	786	820	855	889	924	958	.3
.7		958	993	027	062	097	131	166	200	235	270	304	.2
.8	.99	304	339	374	408	443	478	512	547	582	617	652	.1
.9		652	686	721	756	791	826	860	895	930	965	000	45.0
	1.00												deg.
		(10)	9	8	7	6	5	4	3	2	1	0	

Diff. values at right: 30, 31, 32, 33, 34

COT

TAN

deg.		0	1	2	3	4	5	6	7	8	9	(10)	Diff.
45.0	1.0	000	003	007	010	014	017	021	024	028	031	035	.9 3-4
.1		035	038	042	045	049	052	056	060	063	067	070	.8
.2		070	074	077	081	084	088	091	095	098	102	105	.7
.3		105	109	112	116	119	123	126	130	134	137	141	.6
.4		141	144	148	151	155	158	162	165	169	173	176	.5
.5		176	180	183	187	190	194	197	201	205	208	212	.4
.6		212	215	219	222	226	230	233	237	240	244	247	.3
.7		247	251	255	258	262	265	269	272	276	280	283	.2
.8		283	287	290	294	298	301	305	308	312	316	319	.1
.9		319	323	326	330	334	337	341	344	348	352	355	44.0
46.0		355	359	363	366	370	373	377	381	384	388	392	.9
.1		392	395	399	402	406	410	413	417	421	424	428	.8
.2		428	432	435	439	442	446	450	453	457	461	464	.7
.3		464	468	472	475	479	483	486	490	494	497	501	.6
.4		501	505	508	512	516	519	523	527	530	534	538	.5
.5		538	541	545	549	553	556	560	564	567	571	575	.4
.6		575	578	582	586	590	593	597	601	604	608	612	.3
.7		612	615	619	623	627	630	634	638	641	645	649	.2
.8		649	653	656	660	664	668	671	675	679	682	686	.1
.9		686	690	694	697	701	705	709	712	716	720	724	43.0
47.0		724	727	731	735	739	742	746	750	754	758	761	.9
.1		761	765	769	773	776	780	784	788	791	795	799	.8
.2		799	803	807	810	814	818	822	826	829	833	837	.7
.3		837	841	844	848	852	856	860	863	867	871	875	.6
.4		875	879	883	886	890	894	898	902	905	909	913	.5
.5		913	917	921	925	928	932	936	940	944	948	951	.4
.6		951	955	959	963	967	971	974	978	982	986	990	.3
.7		990	994	998	001	005	009	013	017	021	025	028	.2
.8	1.1	028	032	036	040	044	048	052	056	059	063	067	.1
.9		067	071	075	079	083	087	091	094	098	102	106	42.0
48.0		106	110	114	118	122	126	130	133	137	141	145	.9
.1		145	149	153	157	161	165	169	173	177	180	184	.8
.2		184	188	192	196	200	204	208	212	216	220	224	.7
.3		224	228	232	236	240	243	247	251	255	259	263	.6
.4		263	267	271	275	279	283	287	291	295	299	303	.5
.5		303	307	311	315	319	323	327	331	335	339	343	.4
.6		343	347	351	355	359	363	367	371	375	379	383	.3 4
.7		383	387	391	395	399	403	407	411	415	419	423	.2
.8		423	427	431	435	439	443	447	451	455	459	463	.1
.9		463	467	471	475	479	483	487	492	496	500	504	41.0
49.0		504	508	512	516	520	524	528	532	536	540	544	.9
.1		544	548	552	557	561	565	569	573	577	581	585	.8
.2		585	589	593	597	601	606	610	614	618	622	626	.7
.3		626	630	634	638	643	647	651	655	659	663	667	.6
.4		667	671	675	680	684	688	692	696	700	704	708	.5
.5		708	713	717	721	725	729	733	738	742	746	750	.4
.6		750	754	758	762	767	771	775	779	783	787	792	.3
.7		792	796	800	804	808	812	817	821	825	829	833	.2
.8		833	838	842	846	850	854	859	863	867	871	875	.1
.9		875	880	884	888	892	896	901	905	909	913	918	40.0 deg.
	(10)	9	8	7	6	5	4	3	2	1	0		

COT

TAN

deg.		0	1	2	3	4	5	6	7	8	9	(10)	Diff.
50.0	1.1	918	922	926	930	934	939	943	947	951	956	960	.9
.1		960	964	968	973	977	981	985	990	994	998	002	.8
.2	1.2	002	007	011	015	019	024	028	032	037	041	045	.7
.3		045	049	054	058	062	066	071	075	079	084	088	.6
.4		088	092	097	101	105	109	114	118	122	127	131	.5
.5		131	135	140	144	148	153	157	161	166	170	174	.4
.6		174	179	183	187	192	196	200	205	209	213	218	.3
.7		218	222	226	231	235	239	244	248	252	257	261	.2
.8		261	266	270	274	279	283	287	292	296	301	305	.1
.9		305	309	314	318	323	327	331	336	340	345	349	39.0
51.0		349	353	358	362	367	371	375	380	384	389	393	.9
.1		393	398	402	406	411	415	420	424	429	433	437	.8
.2		437	442	446	451	455	460	464	469	473	478	482	.7
.3		482	487	491	495	500	504	509	513	518	522	527	.6
.4		527	531	536	540	545	549	554	558	563	567	572	.5 4-5
.5		572	576	581	585	590	594	599	603	608	612	617	.4
.6		617	621	626	630	635	640	644	649	653	658	662	.3
.7		662	667	671	676	680	685	689	694	699	703	708	.2
.8		708	712	717	721	726	731	735	740	744	749	753	.1
.9		753	758	763	767	772	776	781	786	790	795	799	38.0
52.0		799	804	809	813	818	822	827	832	836	841	846	.9
.1		846	850	855	859	864	869	873	878	883	887	892	.8
.2		892	897	901	906	911	915	920	924	929	934	938	.7
.3		938	943	948	952	957	962	967	971	976	981	985	.6
.4		985	990	995	999	004	009	013	018	023	028	032	.5
.5	1.3	032	037	042	046	051	056	061	065	070	075	079	.4
.6		079	084	089	094	098	103	108	113	117	122	127	.3
.7		127	132	136	141	146	151	155	160	165	170	175	.2
.8		175	179	184	189	194	198	203	208	213	218	222	.1
.9		222	227	232	237	242	246	251	256	261	266	270	37.0
53.0		270	275	280	285	290	295	299	304	309	314	319	.9
.1		319	324	328	333	338	343	348	353	358	362	367	.8
.2		367	372	377	382	387	392	397	401	406	411	416	.7
.3		416	421	426	431	436	440	445	450	455	460	465	.6
.4		465	470	475	480	485	490	495	499	504	509	514	.5
.5		514	519	524	529	534	539	544	549	554	559	564	.4
.6		564	569	574	579	584	588	593	598	603	608	613	.3
.7		613	618	623	628	633	638	643	648	653	658	663	.2 5
.8		663	668	673	678	683	688	693	698	703	708	713	.1
.9		713	718	723	729	734	739	744	749	754	759	764	36.0
54.0		764	769	774	779	784	789	794	799	804	809	814	.9
.1		814	820	825	830	835	840	845	850	855	860	865	.8
.2		865	870	876	881	886	891	896	901	906	911	916	.7
.3		916	922	927	932	937	942	947	952	958	963	968	.6
.4		968	973	978	983	988	994	999	004	009	014	019	.5
.5	1.4	019	025	030	035	040	045	051	056	061	066	071	.4
.6		071	077	082	087	092	097	103	108	113	118	124	.3
.7		124	129	134	139	144	150	155	160	165	171	176	.2
.8		176	181	186	192	197	202	207	213	218	223	229	.1
.9		229	234	239	244	250	255	260	266	271	276	281	36.0
		(10)	9	8	7	6	5	4	3	2	1	0	deg.

COT

TAN

deg.		0	1	2	3	4	5	6	7	8	9	(10)	Diff.
55.0	1.4	281	287	292	297	303	308	313	319	324	329	335	.9
.1		335	340	345	351	356	361	367	372	377	383	388	.8
.2		388	393	399	404	410	415	420	426	431	436	442	.7
.3		442	447	453	458	463	469	474	480	485	490	496	.6
.4		496	501	507	512	517	523	528	534	539	545	550	.5
.5		550	556	561	566	572	577	583	588	594	599	605	.4
.6		605	610	616	621	627	632	637	643	648	654	659	.3
.7		659	665	670	676	681	687	692	698	704	709	715	.2 5-6
.8		715	720	726	731	737	742	748	753	759	764	770	.1
.9		770	775	781	787	792	798	803	809	814	820	826	34.0
56.0		826	831	837	842	848	854	859	865	870	876	882	.9
.1		882	887	893	898	904	910	915	921	927	932	938	.8
.2		938	943	949	955	960	966	972	977	983	989	994	.7
.3		994	000	006	011	017	023	028	034	040	046	051	.6
.4	1.5	051	057	063	068	074	080	085	091	097	103	108	.5
.5		108	114	120	126	131	137	143	149	154	160	166	.4
.6		166	172	177	183	189	195	200	206	212	218	224	.3
.7		224	229	235	241	247	253	258	264	270	276	282	.2
.8		282	287	293	299	305	311	317	322	328	334	340	.1
.9		340	346	352	358	363	369	375	381	387	393	399	33.0
57.0		399	405	410	416	422	428	434	440	446	452	458	.9
.1		458	464	469	475	481	487	493	499	505	511	517	.8
.2		517	523	529	535	541	547	553	559	565	571	577	.7
.3		577	583	589	595	601	607	613	619	625	631	637	.6 6
.4		637	643	649	655	661	667	673	679	685	691	697	.5
.5		697	703	709	715	721	727	733	739	745	751	757	.4
.6		757	764	770	776	782	788	794	800	806	812	818	.3
.7		818	825	831	837	843	849	855	861	867	874	880	.2
.8		880	886	892	898	904	911	917	923	929	935	941	.1
.9		941	948	954	960	966	972	979	985	991	997	003	32.0
58.0	1.6	003	010	016	022	028	034	041	047	053	059	066	.9
.1		066	072	078	084	091	097	103	110	116	122	128	.8
.2		128	135	141	147	154	160	166	172	179	185	191	.7
.3		191	198	204	210	217	223	229	236	242	248	255	.6
.4		255	261	267	274	280	287	293	299	306	312	319	.5
.5		319	325	331	338	344	351	357	363	370	376	383	.4
.6		383	389	395	402	408	415	421	428	434	441	447	.3
.7		447	454	460	467	473	479	486	492	499	505	512	.2 6-7
.8		512	518	525	531	538	545	551	558	564	571	577	.1
.9		577	584	590	597	603	610	617	623	630	636	643	31.0
59.0		643	649	656	663	669	676	682	689	696	702	709	.9
.1		709	715	722	729	735	742	749	755	762	769	775	.8
.2		775	782	788	795	802	808	815	822	829	835	842	.7
.3		842	849	855	862	869	875	882	889	896	902	909	.6
.4		909	916	923	929	936	943	950	956	963	970	977	.5
.5		977	983	990	997	004	011	017	024	031	038	045	.4
.6	1.7	045	051	058	065	072	079	086	092	099	106	113	.3
.7		113	120	127	134	140	147	154	161	168	175	182	.2
.8		182	189	196	202	209	216	223	230	237	244	251	.1
.9		251	258	265	272	279	286	293	300	307	314	321	30.0 7
		(10)	9	8	7	6	5	4	3	2	1	0	Deg.

COT

TAN

deg.		0	1	2	3	4	5	6	7	8	9	(10)	Diff.
60.0	1.7	321	327	334	341	348	355	362	369	376	384	391	.9 7
.1		391	398	405	412	419	426	433	440	447	454	461	.8
.2		461	468	475	482	489	496	503	511	518	525	532	.7
.3		532	539	546	553	560	567	575	582	589	596	603	.6
.4		603	610	617	625	632	639	646	653	661	668	675	.5
.5		675	682	689	697	704	711	718	725	733	740	747	.4
.6		747	754	762	769	776	783	791	798	805	813	820	.3
.7		820	827	834	842	849	856	864	871	878	886	893	.2
.8		893	900	908	915	922	930	937	944	952	959	966	.1
.9		966	974	981	989	996	003	011	018	026	033	040	29.0
61.0	1.8	040	048	055	063	070	078	085	093	100	107	115	.9
.1		115	122	130	137	145	152	160	167	175	182	190	.8
.2		190	197	205	213	220	228	235	243	250	258	265	.7
.3		265	273	281	288	296	303	311	318	326	334	341	.6
.4		341	349	357	364	372	379	387	395	402	410	418	.5
.5		418	425	433	441	448	456	464	471	479	487	495	.4
.6		495	502	510	518	526	533	541	549	556	564	*572	.3
.7		572	580	588	595	603	611	619	626	634	642	650	.2
.8		650	658	666	673	681	689	697	705	713	720	728	.1
.9		728	736	744	752	760	768	776	784	791	799	807	28.0
62.0		807	815	823	831	839	847	855	863	871	879	887	.9
.1		887	895	903	911	919	927	935	943	951	959	967	.8 8
.2		967	975	983	991	999	007	015	023	031	039	047	.7
.3	1.9	047	055	063	071	080	088	096	104	112	120	128	.6
.4		128	136	145	153	161	169	177	185	193	202	210	.5
.5		210	218	226	234	243	251	259	267	275	284	292	.4
.6		292	300	308	317	325	333	342	350	358	366	375	.3
.7		375	383	391	400	408	416	425	433	441	450	458	.2
.8		458	466	475	483	491	500	508	517	525	533	542	.1
.9		542	550	559	567	575	584	592	601	609	618	626	27.0
63.0		626	635	643	652	660	669	677	686	694	703	711	.9
.1		711	720	728	737	745	754	762	771	779	788	797	.8
.2		797	805	814	822	831	840	848	857	866	874	883	.7
.3		883	891	900	909	917	926	935	943	952	961	970	.6
.4		970	978	987	996	004	013	022	031	039	048	057	.5
.5	2.0	057	066	074	083	092	101	110	118	127	136	145	.4
.6		145	154	163	171	180	189	198	207	216	225	233	.3
.7		233	242	251	260	269	278	287	296	305	314	323	.2
.8		323	332	341	350	359	368	377	386	395	404	413	.1 9
.9		413	422	431	440	449	458	467	476	485	494	503	26.0
64.0		503	512	521	530	539	549	558	567	576	585	594	.9
.1		594	603	612	622	631	640	649	658	668	677	686	.8
.2		686	695	704	714	723	732	741	751	760	769	778	.7
.3		778	788	797	806	816	825	834	844	853	862	872	.6
.4		872	881	890	900	909	918	928	937	947	956	965	.5
.5		965	975	984	994	003	013	022	032	041	050	060	.4
.6	2.1	060	069	079	088	098	107	117	127	136	146	155	.3
.7		155	165	174	184	193	203	213	222	232	241	251	.2
.8		251	261	270	280	290	299	309	319	328	338	348	.1
.9		348	357	367	377	387	396	406	416	426	435	445	25.0
		(10)	9	8	7	6	5	4	3	2	1	0	deg.

COT

TAN

deg.		0	1	2	3	4	5	6	7	8	9	(10)	Diff.	
65.0	2.1	445	455	465	474	484	494	504	514	523	533	543	.9	
.1		543	553	563	573	583	592	602	612	622	632	642	.8	
.2		642	652	662	672	682	692	702	712	722	732	742	.7	
.3		742	752	762	772	782	792	802	812	822	832	842	.6	10
.4		842	852	862	872	882	892	902	913	923	933	943	.5	
.5		943	953	963	973	984	994	004	014	024	035	045	.4	
.6	2.2	045	055	065	076	086	096	106	117	127	137	148	.3	
.7		148	158	168	179	189	199	210	220	230	241	251	.2	
.8		251	261	272	282	293	303	313	324	334	345	355	.1	
.9		355	366	376	387	397	408	418	429	439	450	460	24.0	
66.0		460	471	481	492	503	513	524	534	545	556	566	.9	
.1		566	577	588	598	609	620	630	641	652	662	673	.8	
.2		673	684	694	705	716	727	737	748	759	770	781	.7	
.3		781	791	802	813	824	835	846	856	867	878	889	.6	
.4		889	900	911	922	933	944	955	966	976	987	998	.5	
.5		998	009	020	031	042	053	064	075	087	098	109	.4	11
.6	2.3	109	120	131	142	153	164	175	186	197	209	220	.3	
.7		220	231	242	253	264	276	287	298	309	321	332	.2	
.8		332	343	354	366	377	388	399	411	422	433	445	.1	
.9		445	456	467	479	490	501	513	524	536	547	559	23.0	
67.0		559	570	581	593	604	616	627	639	650	662	673	.9	
.1		673	685	696	708	719	731	743	754	766	777	789	.8	
.2		789	801	812	824	836	847	859	871	882	894	906	.7	
.3		906	917	929	941	953	964	976	988	000	012	023	.6	
.4	2.4	023	035	047	059	071	083	095	106	118	130	142	.5	12
.5		142	154	166	178	190	202	214	226	238	250	262	.4	
.6		262	274	286	298	310	322	334	346	358	370	383	.3	
.7		383	395	407	419	431	443	455	468	480	492	504	.2	
.8		504	516	529	541	553	566	578	590	602	615	627	.1	
.9		627	639	652	664	676	689	701	714	726	738	751	22.0	
68.0		751	763	776	788	801	813	826	838	851	863	876	.9	
.1		876	888	901	913	926	939	951	964	976	989	002	.8	
.2	2.5	002	014	027	040	052	065	078	091	103	116	129	.7	
.3		129	142	154	167	180	193	206	219	231	244	257	.6	
.4		257	270	283	296	309	322	335	348	361	373	386	.5	
.5		386	399	412	426	439	452	465	478	491	504	517	.4	13
.6		517	530	543	556	570	583	596	609	622	635	649	.3	
.7		649	662	675	688	702	715	728	742	755	768	782	.2	
.8		782	795	808	822	835	848	862	875	889	902	916	.1	
.9		916	929	943	956	970	983	997	010	024	037	051	21.0	
69.0	2.6	051	064	078	092	105	119	133	146	160	174	187	.9	
.1		187	201	215	229	242	256	270	284	298	311	325	.8	
.2		325	339	353	367	381	395	408	422	436	450	464	.7	
.3		464	478	492	506	520	534	548	562	576	590	605	.6	14
.4		605	619	633	647	661	675	689	704	718	732	746	.5	
.5		746	760	775	789	803	818	832	846	860	875	889	.4	
.6		889	904	918	932	947	961	976	990	005	019	034	.3	
.7	2.7	034	048	063	077	092	106	121	135	150	165	179	.2	
.8		179	194	209	223	238	253	267	282	297	312	326	.1	
.9		326	341	356	371	386	400	415	430	445	460	475	20.0	
		(10)	9	8	7	6	5	4	3	2	1	0	deg.	

COT

TAN

deg.		0	1	2	3	4	5	6	7	8	9	(10)	Diff.	
70.0	2.7	475	490	505	520	535	550	565	580	595	610	625	.9	15
.1		625	640	655	670	685	700	715	731	746	761	776	.8	
.2		776	791	807	822	837	852	868	883	898	914	929	.7	
.3		929	944	960	975	990	006	021	037	052	068	083	.6	
.4	2.8	083	099	114	130	145	161	177	192	208	223	239	.5	
.5		239	255	270	286	302	318	333	349	365	381	397	.4	
.6		397	412	428	444	460	476	492	508	524	540	556	.3	
.7		556	572	588	604	620	636	652	668	684	700	716	.2	16
.8		716	732	748	765	781	797	813	829	846	862	878	.1	
.9		878	895	911	927	944	960	976	993	009	026	042	19.0	
71.0	2.9	042	059	075	092	108	125	141	158	174	191	208	.9	
.1		208	224	241	258	274	291	308	324	341	358	375	.8	
.2		375	392	408	425	442	459	476	493	510	527	544	.7	
.3		544	561	578	595	612	629	646	663	680	697	714	.6	17
.4		714	732	749	766	783	800	818	835	852	870	887	.5	
.5		887	904	922	939	956	974	991	009	026	044	061	.4	
.6	3.0	061	079	096	114	131	149	167	184	202	220	237	.3	
.7		237	255	273	290	308	326	344	362	379	397	415	.2	
.8		415	433	451	469	487	505	523	541	559	577	595	.1	18
.9		595	613	631	649	668	686	704	722	740	759	777	18.0	
72.0		777	795	813	832	850	868	887	905	924	942	961	.9	
.1		961	979	998	016	035	053	072	090	109	128	146	.8	
.2	3.1	146	165	184	202	221	240	259	278	296	315	334	.7	
.3		334	353	372	391	410	429	448	467	486	505	524	.6	19
.4		524	543	562	581	601	620	639	658	677	697	716	.5	
.5		716	735	755	774	793	813	832	852	871	891	910	.4	
.6		910	930	949	969	988	008	028	047	067	087	106	.3	
.7	3.2	106	126	146	166	185	205	225	245	265	285	305	.2	
.8		305	325	345	365	385	405	425	445	465	485	506	.1	20
.9		506	526	546	566	586	607	627	647	668	688	709	17.0	
73.0		709	729	749	770	790	811	831	852	873	893	914	.9	
.1		914	935	955	976	997	017	038	059	080	101	122	.8	
.2	3.3	122	143	163	184	205	226	247	268	290	311	332	.7	21
.3		332	353	374	395	416	438	459	480	502	523	544	.6	
.4		544	566	587	609	630	652	673	695	716	738	759	.5	
.5		759	781	803	824	846	868	890	912	933	955	977	.4	
.6		977	999	021	043	065	087	109	131	153	175	197	.3	22
.7	3.4	197	220	242	264	286	308	331	353	375	398	420	.2	
.8		420	443	465	488	510	533	555	578	600	623	646	.1	
.9		646	669	691	714	737	760	782	805	828	851	874	16.0	
74.0		874	897	920	943	966	989	012	036	059	082	105	.9	23
.1	3.5	105	129	152	175	199	222	245	269	292	316	339	.8	
.2		339	363	386	410	434	457	481	505	529	552	576	.7	
.3		576	600	624	648	672	696	720	744	768	792	816	.6	24
.4		816	840	864	889	913	937	961	986	010	034	059	.5	
.5	3.6	059	083	108	132	157	181	206	231	255	280	305	.4	
.6		305	330	354	379	404	429	454	479	504	529	554	.3	25
.7		554	579	604	629	654	680	705	730	755	781	806	.2	
.8		806	832	857	882	908	933	959	985	010	036	062	.1	
.9	3.7	062	087	113	139	165	191	217	242	268	294	321	15.0	26
													deg.	
(10)		9	8	7		6	5	4		3	2	1	0		

COT

TAN

deg.		0	1	2	3	4	5	6	7	8	9	(10)	Diff.	
75.0	3.7	321	347	373	399	425	451	477	504	530	556	583	.9	26
.1		583	609	636	662	689	715	742	768	795	822	848	.8	
.2		848	875	902	929	956	983	010	037	064	091	118	.7	27
.3	3.8	118	145	172	199	226	254	281	308	336	363	391	.6	
.4		391	418	446	473	501	528	556	584	612	639	667	.5	
.5		667	695	723	751	779	807	835	863	891	919	947	.4	28
.6		947	976	004	032	061	089	117	146	174	203	232	.3	
.7	3.9	232	260	289	318	346	375	404	433	462	491	520	.2	29
.8		520	549	578	607	636	665	694	724	753	782	812	.1	
.9		812	841	871	900	930	959	989	019	048	078	108	14.0	
76.0	4.0	108	138	168	197	227	257	287	318	348	378	408	.9	30
.1		408	438	469	499	529	560	590	621	651	682	713	.8	
.2		713	743	774	805	836	867	898	929	960	991	022	.7	31
.3	4.1	022	053	084	115	146	178	209	241	272	304	335	.6	
.4		335	367	398	430	462	493	525	557	589	621	653	.5	32
.5		653	685	717	749	781	814	846	878	911	943	976	.4	
.6		976	008	041	073	106	139	171	204	237	270	303	.3	33
.7	4.2	303	336	369	402	435	468	502	535	568	602	635	.2	
.8		635	669	702	736	770	803	837	871	905	938	972	.1	
.9		972	006	040	075	109	143	177	212	246	280	315	13.0	34
77.0	4.3	315	349	384	418	453	488	523	557	592	627	662	.9	35
.1		662	697	732	768	803	838	873	909	944	980	015	.8	
.2	4.4	015	051	086	122	158	194	230	265	301	337	373	.7	36
.3		373	410	446	482	518	555	591	628	664	701	737	.6	
.4		737	774	811	848	885	922	959	996	033	070	107	.5	37
.5	4.5	107	144	182	219	257	294	332	369	407	445	483	.4	
.6		483	520	558	596	634	673	711	749	787	826	864	.3	38
.7		864	903	941	980	018	057	096	135	174	213	252	.2	39
.8	4.6	252	291	330	369	409	448	487	527	567	606	646	.1	
.9		646	686	725	765	805	845	885	925	966	006	046	12.0	40
78.0	4.7	046	087	127	168	208	249	290	331	371	412	453	.9	41
.1		453	494	536	577	618	659	701	742	784	826	867	.8	
.2		867	909	951	993	035	077	119	161	203	246	288	.7	42
.3	4.8	288	331	373	416	459	501	544	587	630	673	716	.6	43
.4		716	759	803	846	889	933	977	020	064	108	152	.5	
.5	4.9	152	196	240	284	328	372	416	461	505	550	594	.4	44
.6		594	639	684	729	774	819	864	909	954	000	045	.3	45
.7	5.0	045	091	136	182	228	273	319	365	411	457	504	.2	46
.8		504	550	596	643	689	736	783	830	876	923	970	.1	47
.9		970	018	065	112	159	207	254	302	350	398	446	11.0	
79.0	5.1	446	494	542	590	638	686	735	783	832	880	929	.9	48
.1		929	978	027	076	125	174	224	273	323	372	422	.8	49
.2	5.2	422	472	521	571	621	672	722	772	822	873	924	.7	50
.3		924	974	025	076	127	178	229	280	332	383	435	.6	51
.4	5.3	435	486	538	590	642	694	746	798	850	903	955	.5	52
.5		955	008	060	113	166	219	272	325	379	432	486	.4	53
.6	5.4	486	539	593	647	701	755	809	863	917	972	026	.3	54
.7	5.5	026	081	136	191	246	301	356	411	467	522	578	.2	55
.8		578	633	689	745	801	857	914	970	026	083	140	.1	56
.9	5.6	140	196	253	310	368	425	482	540	597	655	713	10.0	57
													deg.	
(10)		9	8	7	6	5	4	3	2	1	0			

COT

TRIGONOMETRIC FUNCTIONS

TAN

deg.		0	1	2	3	4	5	6	7	8	9	(10)		Diff
80.0	5.6	713	771	829	887	945	004	062	121	180	238	297	.9	
.1	5.7	297	357	416	475	535	594	654	714	774	834	894	.8	
.2		894	954	015	075	136	197	257	319	380	441	502	.7	
.3	5.8	502	564	626	687	749	811	874	936	998	061	124	.6	
.4	5.9	124	186	249	312	376	439	502	566	630	694	758	.5	
.5		758	822	886	950	015	080	144	209	275	340	405	.4	
.6	6.0	405	471	536	602	668	734	800	867	933	000	066	.3	
.7	6.1	066	133	200	267	335	402	470	538	606	674	742	.2	
.8		742	810	879	947	016	085	154	223	293	362	432	.1	
.9	6.2	432	502	572	642	712	783	853	924	995	066	138	9.0	
81.0	6.3	138	209	280	352	424	496	568	641	713	786	859	.9	
.1		859	932	005	078	152	225	299	373	447	522	596	.8	
.2	6.4	596	671	746	821	896	971	047	122	198	274	350	.7	
.3	6.5	350	427	503	580	657	734	811	889	966	044	122	.6	
.4	6.6	122	200	278	357	436	514	594	673	752	832	912	.5	
.5		912	992	072	152	233	313	394	475	557	638	720	.4	
.6	6.7	720	802	884	966	049	131	214	297	380	464	548	.3	
.7	6.8	548	631	715	800	884	969	054	139	224	310	395	.2	
.8	6.9	395	481	567	654	740	827	914	001	088	176	264	.1	
.9	7.0	264	352	440	528	617	706	795	884	974	064	154	0.0	
82.0	7.1	154	244	334	425	516	607	698	790	882	974	066	.9	
.1	7.2	066	159	251	344	438	531	625	719	813	907	002	.8	
.2	7.3	002	097	192	287	383	479	575	671	768	865	962	.7	
.3		962	059	157	254	352	451	549	648	747	847	947	.6	
.4	7.4	947	046	147	247	348	449	550	651	753	855	958	.5	
.5	7.5	958	060	163	266	369	473	577	681	786	891	996	.4	
.6	7.6	996												
	7.7		101	207	313	419	525	632	739	847	954	062	.3	
.7	7.8	062	170	279	388	497	606	716	826	937	047	158	.2	
.8	7.9	158	269	381	493	605	718	830	944	057	171	285	.1	
.9	8.0	285	399	514	629	744	860	976						
	8.1								092	209	326	443	7.0	Diff.
83.0	8.	144	156	168	180	192	204	215	227	239	251	264	.9	11-13
.1		264	276	288	300	312	324	337	349	361	374	386	.8	12-13
.2		386	399	411	424	436	449	462	474	487	500	513	.7	12-13
.3		513	525	538	551	564	577	590	603	616	630	643	.6	12-14
.4		643	656	669	683	696	709	723	736	750	763	777	.5	13-14
.5		777	791	804	818	832	846	859	873	887	901	915	.4	13-15
.6		915	929	943	958	972	986	000	015	029	043	058	.3	14-15
.7	9.	058	072	087	102	116	131	146	160	175	190	205	.2	14-15
.8		205	220	235	250	265	281	296	311	326	342	357	.1	15-16
.9		357	373	388	404	419	435	451	467	483	498	514	6.0	15-16
84.0		514	530	546	563	579	595	611	627	644	660	677	.9	16-17
.1		677	693	710	727	743	760	777	794	811	828	845	.8	16-17
.2		845	862	879	896	914	931	948	966	983	001	019	.7	17-18
.3	10.	019	036	054	072	090	108	126	144	162	180	199	.6	17-19
.4		199	217	236	254	273	291	310	329	348	366	385	.5	18-19
.5		385	404	424	443	462	481	501	520	540	559	579	.4	19-20
.6		579	599	618	638	658	678	698	719	739	759	780	.3	19-21
.7		780	800	821	841	862	883	904	925	946	967	988	.2	20-21
.8		988	009	031	052	074	095	117	139	161	183	205	.1	21-22
.9	11.	205	227	249	271	294	316	339	362	384	407	430	5.0	22-23
													deg.	
	(10)	9	8	7	6	5	4	3	2	1	0			

COT

TAN

deg.	0	1	2	3	4	5	6	7	8	9	(10)	Diff.
85.0	11. 430	453	476	499	523	546	570	593	617	641	664	.9	23-24
.1	664	688	713	737	761	785	810	834	859	884	909	.8	24-25
.2	909	934	959	984	009	035	060	086	111	137	163	.7	25-26
.3	12. 163	189	215	242	268	295	321	348	375	402	429	.6	26-27
.4	429	456	483	511	538	566	594	622	650	678	706	.5	27-28
.5	706	735	763	792	821	850	879	908	937	967	996	.4	28-30
.6	996	026	056	086	116	146	177	207	238	269	300	.3	30-31
.7	13. 300	331	362	393	425	457	488	520	553	585	617	.2	31-33
.8	617	650	683	716	749	782	815	849	883	917	951	.1	33-34
.9	951	985	019	054	089	124	159	194	229	265	301	4.0	34-36
86.0	14. 301	337	373	409	446	482	519	556	593	631	669	.9	36-38
.1	669	706	744	783	821	860	898	937	977	016	056	.8	37-40
.2	15. 056	096	136	176	216	257	298	339	380	422	464	.7	40-42
.3	464	506	548	591	633	676	719	763	806	850	895	.6	42-45
.4	895	939	984	028	074	119	165	211	257	303	350	.5	44-47
.5	16. 350	397	444	492	539	587	636	684	733	782	832	.4	47-50
.6	832	882	932	982	033	084	135	187	238	291	343	.3	50-53
.7	17. 343	396	449	503	556	611	665	720	775	830	886	.2	53-56
.8	886	942	999	056	113	171	229	287	346	405	464	.1	56-59
.9	18. 464	524	585	645	706	768	830	892	955	018	081	3.0	60-63
87.0	19. 081	145	209	274	339	405	471	538	605	672	740	.9	
.1	740	809	878	947	017	087	158	229	301	374	446	.8	
.2	20. 446	520	594	668	743	819	895	972	049	127	205	.7	
.3	21. 205	284	363	444	524	606	688	770	853	937	022	.6	
.4	22. 022	107	193	279	366	454	543	632	722	812	904	.5	
.5	904	996	089	182	277	372	468	564	662	760	859	.4	
.6	23. 859	959	060	162	264	368	472	577	683	790	898	.3	
.7	24. 898	007	116	227	339	452	565		680	796	913		
25.											031	.2	
.8	26. 031	150	270	391	513	637	761	887	014	142	271	.1	
.9	27. 271	402	534	667	801	937							
28.							074	213	352	494	636	2.0 deg.	
(10)	9	8	7	6	5	4	3	2	1	0			

CTN

For 88° and 89° see the following two pages.

For a more extended table of trigonometric functions of decimals of degrees, see "Siebenstellige Werte der Trigonometrischen Funktionen von Tausendstel zu Tausendstel des Grades", by J. Peters.

DEG.	TAN		DEG.	TAN	
88.00	28.636	2.00	88.50	38.188	1.50
.01	28.780	1.99	.51	38.445	.49
.02	28.926	.98	.52	38.705	.48
.03	29.073	.97	.53	38.968	.47
.04	29.221	.96	.54	39.235	.46
.05	29.371	.95	.55	39.506	.45
.06	29.523	.94	.56	39.780	.44
.07	29.676	.93	.57	40.059	.43
.08	29.830	.92	.58	40.341	.42
.09	29.987	.91	.59	40.627	.41
88.10	30.145	1.90	88.60	40.917	1.40
.11	30.304	.89	.61	41.212	.39
.12	30.466	.88	.62	41.511	.38
.13	30.629	.87	.63	41.814	.37
.14	30.793	.86	.64	42.121	.36
.15	30.960	.85	.65	42.433	.35
.16	31.128	.84	.66	42.750	.34
.17	31.299	.83	.67	43.072	.33
.18	31.471	.82	.68	43.398	.32
.19	31.645	.81	.69	43.730	.31
88.20	31.821	1.80	88.70	44.066	1.30
.21	31.998	.79	.71	44.408	.29
.22	32.178	.78	.72	44.755	.28
.23	32.360	.77	.73	45.107	.27
.24	32.544	.76	.74	45.466	.26
.25	32.730	.75	.75	45.829	.25
.26	32.918	.74	.76	46.199	.24
.27	33.109	.73	.77	46.575	.23
.28	33.301	.72	.78	46.957	.22
.29	33.496	.71	.79	47.345	.21
88.30	33.694	1.70	88.80	47.740	1.20
.31	33.893	.69	.81	48.141	.19
.32	34.095	.68	.82	48.549	.18
.33	34.299	.67	.83	48.964	.17
.34	34.506	.66	.84	49.386	.16
.35	34.715	.65	.85	49.816	.15
.36	34.927	.64	.86	50.253	.14
.37	35.141	.63	.87	50.698	.13
.38	35.358	.62	.88	51.150	.12
.39	35.578	.61	.89	51.611	.11
88.40	35.801	1.60	88.90	52.081	1.10
.41	36.026	.59	.91	52.559	.09
.42	36.254	.58	.92	53.045	.08
.43	36.485	.57	.93	53.541	.07
.44	36.719	.56	.94	54.046	.06
.45	36.956	.55	.95	54.561	.05
.46	37.196	.54	.96	55.086	.04
.47	37.439	.53	.97	55.621	.03
.48	37.686	.52	.98	56.166	.02
.49	37.935	1.51	.99	56.723	1.01
	CTN	DEG.		CTN	DEG.

DEG.	TAN		DEG.	TAN	
89.00	57.290	1.00	89.50	114.589	0.50
.01	57.869	0.99	.51	116.927	.49
.02	58.459	.98	.52	119.363	.48
.03	59.062	.97	.53	121.903	.47
.04	59.678	.96	.54	124.553	.46
.05	60.306	.95	.55	127.321	.45
.06	60.947	.94	.56	130.215	.44
.07	61.603	.93	.57	133.243	.43
.08	62.273	.92	.58	136.416	.42
.09	62.957	.91	.59	139.743	.41
89.10	63.657	0.90	89.60	143.237	0.40
.11	64.372	.89	.61	146.910	.39
.12	65.104	.88	.62	150.776	.38
.13	65.852	.87	.63	154.851	.37
.14	66.618	.86	.64	159.153	.36
.15	67.402	.85	.65	163.700	.35
.16	68.204	.84	.66	168.515	.34
.17	69.026	.83	.67	173.622	.33
.18	69.868	.82	.68	179.047	.32
.19	70.731	.81	.69	184.823	.31
89.20	71.615	0.80	89.70	190.984	0.30
.21	72.522	.79	.71	197.570	.29
.22	73.452	.78	.72	204.626	.28
.23	74.406	.77	.73	212.205	.27
.24	75.385	.76	.74	220.367	.26
.25	76.390	.75	.75	229.182	.25
.26	77.422	.74	.76	238.731	.24
.27	78.483	.73	.77	249.111	.23
.28	79.573	.72	.78	260.434	.22
.29	80.694	.71	.79	272.836	.21
89.30	81.847	0.70	89.80	286.478	0.20
.31	83.033	.69	.81	301.56	.19
.32	84.255	.68	.82	318.31	.18
.33	85.512	.67	.83	337.03	.17
.34	86.808	.66	.84	358.10	.16
.35	88.144	.65	.85	381.97	.15
.36	89.521	.64	.86	409.25	.14
.37	90.942	.63	.87	440.74	.13
.38	92.409	.62	.88	477.46	.12
.39	93.924	.61	.89	520.87	.11
89.40	95.489	0.60	89.90	572.96	0.10
.41	97.108	.59	.91	636.62	.09
.42	98.782	.58	.92	716.20	.08
.43	100.516	.57	.93	818.51	.07
.44	102.311	.56	.94	954.93	.06
.45	104.171	.55	.95	1145.92	.05
.46	106.100	.54	.96	1432.4	.04
.47	108.102	.53	.97	1909.9	.03
.48	110.181	.52	.98	2864.8	.02
.49	112.342	0.51	.99	5729.6	.01
			90.00	Infin.	0.00
	CTN	DEG.		CTN	DEG.

TRIGONOMETRIC FUNCTIONS

SEC

deg.	0	1	2	3	4	5	6	7	8	9	(10)	
0.0	1.00 000	000	000	000	000'	000	000	000	000	000	000	.9
.1	000	000	000	000	000	000	000	000	000	001	001	.8
.2	001	001	001	001	001	001	001	001	001	001	001	.7
.3	001	001	002	002	002	002	002	002	002	002	002	.6
.4	002	003	003	003	003	003	003	003	004	004	004	.5
.5	004	004	004	004	004	005	005	005	005	005	005	.4
.6	005	006	006	006	006	006	007	007	007	007	007	.3
.7	007	008	008	008	008	009	009	009	009	010	010	.2
.8	010	010	010	010	011	011	011	012	012	012	012	.1
.9	012	013	013	013	013	014	014	014	015	015	015	89.0
1.0	015	016	016	016	016	017	017	017	018	018	018	.9
.1	018	019	019	019	020	020	020	021	021	022	022	.8
.2	022	022	023	023	023	024	024	025	025	025	026	.7
.3	026	026	027	027	027	028	028	029	029	029	030	.6
.4	030	030	031	031	032	032	032	033	033	034	034	.5
.5	034	035	035	036	036	037	037	038	038	039	039	.4
.6	039	039	040	040	041	041	042	042	043	044	044	.3
.7	044	045	045	046	046	047	047	048	048	049	049	.2
.8	049	050	050	051	052	052	053	053	054	054	055	.1
.9	055	056	056	057	057	058	059	059	060	060	061	88.0
2.0	061	062	062	063	063	064	065	065	066	067	067	.9
.1	067	068	068	069	070	070	071	072	072	073	074	.8
.2	074	074	075	076	076	077	078	079	079	080	081	.7
.3	081	081	082	083	083	084	085	086	086	087	088	.6
.4	088	089	089	090	091	091	092	093	094	095	095	.5
.5	095	096	097	098	098	099	100	101	101	102	103	.4
.6	103	104	105	105	106	107	108	109	109	110	111	.3
.7	111	112	113	114	114	115	116	117	118	119	120	.2
.8	120	120	121	122	123	124	125	126	126	127	128	.1
.9	128	129	130	131	132	133	134	135	135	136	137	87.0
3.0	137	138	139	140	141	142	143	144	145	146	147	.9
.1	147	147	148	149	150	151	152	153	154	155	156	.8
.2	156	157	158	159	160	161	162	163	164	165	166	.7
.3	166	167	168	169	170	171	172	173	174	175	176	.6
.4	176	177	178	179	181	182	183	184	185	186	187	.5
.5	187	188	189	190	191	192	193	194	196	197	198	.4
.6	198	199	200	201	202	203	204	205	207	208	209	.3
.7	209	210	211	212	213	215	216	217	218	219	220	.2
.8	220	222	223	224	225	226	227	229	230	231	232	.1
.9	232	233	235	236	237	238	239	241	242	243	244	86.0
4.0	244	245	247	248	249	250	252	253	254	255	257	.9
.1	257	258	259	260	262	263	264	265	267	268	269	.8
.2	269	271	272	273	274	276	277	278	280	281	282	.7
.3	282	284	285	286	288	289	290	292	293	294	296	.6
.4	296	297	298	300	301	302	304	305	306	308	309	.5
.5	309	311	312	313	315	316	318	319	320	322	323	.4
.6	323	325	326	327	329	330	332	333	335	336	337	.3
.7	337	339	340	342	343	345	346	348	349	350	352	.2
.8	352	353	355	356	358	359	361	362	364	365	367	.1
.9	367	368	370	371	373	374	376	377	379	380	382	85.0
(10)	9	8	7	6	5	4	3	2	1	0		deg.

Diff.
0-2

COSEC

SEC

deg.	0	1	2	3	4	5	6	7	8	9	(10)	
5.0	1.00 382	384	385	387	388	390	391	393	394	396	397	.9
.1	397	399	401	402	404	405	407	408	410	412	413	.8
.2	413	415	416	418	420	421	423	425	426	428	429	.7
.3	429	431	433	434	436	438	439	441	442	444	446	.6
.4	446	447	449	451	452	454	456	457	459	461	463	.5
.5	463	464	466	468	469	471	473	474	476	478	480	.4
.6	480	481	483	485	486	488	490	492	493	495	497	.3
.7	497	499	500	502	504	506	507	509	511	513	515	.2
.8	515	516	518	520	522	524	525	527	529	531	533	.1
.9	533	534	536	538	540	542	543	545	547	549	551	84.0
6.0	551	553	555	556	558	560	562	564	566	568	569	.9
.1	569	571	573	575	577	579	581	583	585	586	588	.8
.2	588	590	592	594	596	598	600	602	604	606	608	.7
.3	608	610	611	613	615	617	619	621	623	625	627	.6
.4	627	629	631	633	635	637	639	641	643	645	647	.5
.5	647	649	651	653	655	657	659	661	663	665	667	.4
.6	667	669	671	673	675	677	679	681	684	686	688	.3
.7	688	690	692	694	696	698	700	702	704	706	708	.2
.8	708	711	713	715	717	719	721	723	725	727	730	.1
.9	730	732	734	736	738	740	742	745	747	749	751	83.0
7.0	751	753	755	757	760	762	764	766	768	771	773	.9
.1	773	775	777	779	782	784	786	788	790	793	795	.8
.2	795	797	799	801	804	806	808	810	813	815	817	.7
.3	817	819	822	824	826	828	831	833	835	838	840	.6
.4	840	842	844	847	849	851	854	856	858	861	863	.5 Diff.
.5	863	865	868	870	872	875	877	879	882	884	886	.4 1-4
.6	886	889	891	893	896	898	900	903	905	908	910	.3
.7	910	912	915	917	919	922	924	927	929	931	934	.2
.8	934	936	939	941	944	946	948	951	953	956	958	.1
.9	958	961	963	965	968	970	973	975	978	980	983	82.0
8.0	983	985	988	990	993	995	998	000	003	005	008	.9
.1	1.01 008	010	013	015	018	020	023	025	028	030	033	.8
.2	033	035	038	041	043	046	048	051	053	056	059	.7
.3	059	061	064	066	069	071	074	077	079	082	084	.6
.4	084	087	090	092	095	097	100	103	105	108	111	.5
.5	111	113	116	119	121	124	126	129	132	134	137	.4
.6	137	140	142	145	148	151	153	156	159	161	164	.3
.7	164	167	169	172	175	178	180	183	186	188	191	.2
.8	191	194	197	199	202	205	208	210	213	216	219	.1
.9	219	221	224	227	230	233	235	238	241	244	247	81.0
9.0	247	249	252	255	258	261	263	266	269	272	275	.9
.1	275	277	280	283	286	289	292	295	297	300	303	.8
.2	303	306	309	312	315	317	320	323	326	329	332	.7
.3	332	335	338	341	344	346	349	352	355	358	361	.6
.4	361	364	367	370	373	376	379	382	385	388	391	.5
.5	391	393	396	399	402	405	408	411	414	417	420	.4
.6	420	423	426	429	432	435	438	441	444	447	450	.3
.7	450	453	456	459	463	466	469	472	475	478	481	.2
.8	481	484	487	490	493	496	499	502	505	508	512	.1
.9	512	515	518	521	524	527	530	533	536	540	543	80.0 deg.
(10)		9	8	7	6	5	4	3	2	1	0	

COSEC

SEC

deg.	0	1	2	3	4	5	6	7	8	9	(10)	Diff.
10.0	1.01 543	546	549	552	555	558	561	565	568	571	574	.9	3
.1	574	577	580	584	587	590	593	596	599	603	606	.8
.2	606	609	612	615	619	622	625	628	631	635	638	.7
.3	638	641	644	648	651	654	657	661	664	667	670	.6
.4	670	674	677	680	683	687	690	693	696	700	703	.5
.5	703	706	710	713	716	720	723	726	729	733	736	.4
.6	736	739	743	746	749	753	756	759	763	766	769	.3
.7	769	773	776	780	783	786	790	793	796	800	803	.2
.8	803	807	810	813	817	820	824	827	830	834	837	.1
.9	837	841	844	848	851	854	858	861	865	868	872	79.0
11.0	872	875	879	882	886	889	892	896	899	903	906	.9
.1	906	910	913	917	920	924	927	931	934	938	941	.8
.2	941	945	949	952	956	959	963	966	970	973	977	.7
.3	977	980	984	988	991	995	998	002	005	009	013	.6
.4	1.02 013	016	020	023	027	031	034	038	041	045	049	.5
.5	049	052	056	060	063	067	070	074	078	081	085	.4
.6	085	089	092	096	100	103	107	111	114	118	122	.3
.7	122	125	129	133	137	140	144	148	151	155	159	.2
.8	159	163	166	170	174	178	181	185	189	193	196	.1
.9	196	200	204	208	211	215	219	223	226	230	234	78.0
12.0	234	238	242	245	249	253	257	261	265	268	272	.9
.1	272	276	280	284	287	291	295	299	303	307	311	.8
.2	311	314	318	322	326	330	334	338	342	345	349	.7
.3	349	353	357	361	365	369	373	377	381	385	388	.6
.4	388	392	396	400	404	408	412	416	420	424	428	.5
.5	428	432	436	440	444	448	452	456	460	464	468	.4	4
.6	468	472	476	480	484	488	492	496	500	504	508	.3
.7	508	512	516	520	524	528	532	536	540	544	548	.2
.8	548	552	557	561	565	569	573	577	581	585	589	.1
.9	589	593	597	602	606	610	614	618	622	626	630	77.0
13.0	630	635	639	643	647	651	655	659	664	668	672	.9
.1	672	676	680	684	689	693	697	701	705	710	714	.8
.2	714	718	722	726	731	735	739	743	748	752	756	.7
.3	756	760	765	769	773	777	782	786	790	794	799	.6
.4	799	803	807	811	816	820	824	829	833	837	842	.5
.5	842	846	850	854	859	863	867	872	876	880	885	.4
.6	885	889	893	898	902	907	911	915	920	924	928	.3
.7	928	933	937	942	946	950	955	959	964	968	972	.2
.8	972	977	981	986	990	994	999	003	008	012	017	.1
.9	1.03 017	021	026	030	035	039	043	048	052	057	061	76.0
14.0	061	066	070	075	079	084	088	093	097	102	106	.9
.1	106	111	115	120	124	129	134	138	143	147	152	.8
.2	152	156	161	165	170	175	179	184	188	193	197	.7
.3	197	202	207	211	216	220	225	230	234	239	244	.6
.4	244	248	253	257	262	267	271	276	281	285	290	.5
.5	290	295	299	304	309	313	318	323	327	332	337	.4
.6	337	342	346	351	356	360	365	370	375	379	384	.3
.7	384	389	393	398	403	408	412	417	422	427	432	.2
.8	432	436	441	446	451	455	460	465	470	475	479	.1
.9	479	484	489	494	499	503	508	513	518	523	528	75.0	5
	(10)	9	8	7	6	5	4	3	2	1	0	deg.

COSEC

SEC

deg.	0	1	2	3	4	5	6	7	8	9	(10)	Diff.	
15.0	1.03 528	532	537	542	547	552	557	562	566	571	576	.9	
.1	576	581	586	591	596	601	606	610	615	620	625	.8	
.2	625	630	635	640	645	650	655	660	665	670	674	.7	
.3	674	679	684	689	694	699	704	709	714	719	724	.6	
.4	724	729	734	739	744	749	754	759	764	769	774	.5	5
.5	774	779	784	789	794	799	804	809	815	820	825	.4	
.6	825	830	835	840	845	850	855	860	865	870	875	.3	
.7	875	881	886	891	896	901	906	911	916	921	927	.2	
.8	927	932	937	942	947	952	957	963	968	973	978	.1	
.9	978	983	988	994	999	004	009	014	020	025	030	74.0	
16.0	1.04 030	035	040	046	051	056	061	066	072	077	082	.9	
.1	082	087	093	098	103	108	114	119	124	130	135	.8	
.2	135	140	145	151	156	161	167	172	177	182	188	.7	
.3	188	193	198	204	209	214	220	225	230	236	241	.6	
.4	241	247	252	257	263	268	273	279	284	290	295	.5	
.5	295	300	306	311	316	322	327	333	338	344	349	.4	
.6	349	354	360	365	371	376	382	387	393	398	403	.3	
.7	403	409	414	420	425	431	436	442	447	453	458	.2	
.8	458	464	469	475	480	486	491	497	502	508	514	.1	
.9	514	519	525	530	536	541	547	552	558	564	569	73.0	
17.0	569	575	580	586	592	597	603	608	614	620	625	.9	
.1	625	631	636	642	648	653	659	665	670	676	682	.8	
.2	682	687	693	699	704	710	716	721	727	733	738	.7	
.3	738	744	750	755	761	767	773	778	784	790	795	.6	
.4	795	801	807	813	818	824	830	836	841	847	853	.5	
.5	853	859	864	870	876	882	888	893	899	905	911	.4	
.6	911	917	922	928	934	940	946	952	957	963	969	.3	
.7	969	975	981	987	992	998	004	010	016	022	028	.2	
.8	1.05 028	034	040	045	051	057	063	069	075	081	087	.1	
.9	087	093	099	105	111	116	122	128	134	140	146	72.0	
18.0	146	152	158	164	170	176	182	188	194	200	206	.9	
.1	206	212	218	224	230	236	242	248	254	260	266	.8	6
.2	266	272	278	284	290	297	303	309	315	321	327	.7	
.3	327	333	339	345	351	357	363	370	376	382	388	.6	
.4	388	394	400	406	412	418	425	431	437	443	449	.5	
.5	449	455	462	468	474	480	486	492	499	505	511	.4	
.6	511	517	523	530	536	542	548	554	561	567	573	.3	
.7	573	579	586	592	598	604	611	617	623	629	636	.2	
.8	636	642	648	655	661	667	673	680	686	692	699	.1	
.9	699	705	711	718	724	730	737	743	749	756	762	71.0	
19.0	762	768	775	781	788	794	800	807	813	819	826	.9	
.1	826	832	839	845	851	858	864	871	877	884	890	.8	
.2	890	896	903	909	916	922	929	935	942	948	955	.7	
.3	955	961	968	974	980	987	993	000	006	013	020	.6	
.4	1.06 020	026	033	039	046	052	059	065	072	078	085	.5	
.5	085	091	098	105	111	118	124	131	137	144	151	.4	
.6	151	157	164	170	177	184	190	197	204	210	217	.3	
.7	217	223	230	237	243	250	257	263	270	277	283	.2	
.8	283	290	297	303	310	317	324	330	337	344	350	.1	
.9	350	357	364	371	377	384	391	398	404	411	418	70.0	7
	(10)	9	8	7	6	5	4	3	2	1	0	deg.	

COSEC

SEC

deg.	0	1	2	3	4	5	6	7	8	9	(10)	Diff.
20.0	1.06 418	425	431	438	445	452	458	465	472	479	486	.9
.1	486	492	499	506	513	520	526	533	540	547	554	.8
.2	554	561	567	574	581	588	595	602	609	616	622	.7
.3	622	629	636	643	650	657	664	671	678	685	691	.6
.4	691	698	705	712	719	726	733	740	747	754	761	.5
.5	761	768	775	782	789	796	803	810	817	824	831	.4
.6	831	838	845	852	859	866	873	880	887	894	901	.3 7
.7	901	908	915	922	929	936	943	951	958	965	972	.2
.8	972	979	986	993	000	007	014	022	029	036	043	.1
.9	1.07 043	050	057	064	072	079	086	093	100	107	114	69.0
21.0	114	122	129	136	143	150	158	165	172	179	186	.9
.1	186	194	201	208	215	223	230	237	244	252	259	.8
.2	259	266	273	281	288	295	303	310	317	324	332	.7
.3	332	339	346	354	361	368	376	383	390	398	405	.6
.4	405	412	420	427	434	442	449	456	464	471	479	.5
.5	479	486	493	501	508	516	523	530	538	545	553	.4
.6	553	560	568	575	582	590	597	605	612	620	627	.3
.7	627	635	642	650	657	665	672	680	687	695	702	.2
.8	702	710	717	725	732	740	747	755	763	770	778	.1
.9	778	785	793	800	808	816	823	831	838	846	853	68.0
22.0	853	861	869	876	884	892	899	907	914	922	930	.9
.1	930	937	945	953	960	968	976	983	991	999	006	.8
.2	1.08 006	014	022	030	037	045	053	060	068	076	084	.7
.3	084	091	099	107	115	122	130	138	146	153	161	.6
.4	161	169	177	185	192	200	208	216	224	231	239	.5
.5	239	247	255	263	271	278	286	294	302	310	318	.4
.6	318	326	333	341	349	357	365	373	381	389	397	.3
.7	397	405	412	420	428	436	444	452	460	468	476	.2
.8	476	484	492	500	508	516	524	532	540	548	556	.1
.9	556	564	572	580	588	596	604	612	620	628	636	67.0 8
23.0	636	644	652	660	668	676	684	692	701	709	717	.9
.1	717	725	733	741	749	757	765	774	782	790	798	.8
.2	798	806	814	822	830	839	847	855	863	871	880	.7
.3	880	888	896	904	912	920	929	937	945	953	962	.6
.4	962	970	978	986	995	003	011	019	028	036	044	.5
.5	1.09 044	052	061	069	077	086	094	102	110	119	127	.4
.6	127	135	144	152	160	169	177	185	194	202	211	.3
.7	211	219	227	236	244	252	261	269	278	286	294	.2
.8	294	303	311	320	328	337	345	353	362	370	379	.1
.9	379	387	396	404	413	421	430	438	447	455	464	66.0
24.0	464	472	481	489	498	506	515	523	532	540	549	.9
.1	549	557	566	575	583	592	600	609	617	626	635	.8
.2	635	643	652	661	669	678	686	695	704	712	721	.7
.3	721	730	738	747	756	764	773	782	790	799	808	.6
.4	808	816	825	834	842	851	860	869	877	886	895	.5
.5	895	904	912	921	930	939	947	956	965	974	982	.4
.6	982	991	000	009	018	026	035	044	053	062	071	.3
.7	1.10 071	079	088	097	106	115	124	133	141	150	159	.2
.8	159	168	177	186	195	204	213	221	230	239	248	.1
.9	248	257	266	275	284	293	302	311	320	329	338	65.0 9
(10)	9	8	7	6	5	4	3	2	1	0		deg.

COSEC

SEC

deg.		0	1	2	3	4	5	6	7	8	9	(10)	Diff.	
25.0	1.10	338	347	356	365	374	383	392	401	410	419	428	.9	9
.1		428	437	446	455	464	473	482	491	500	509	518	.8	
.2		518	527	537	546	555	564	573	582	591	600	609	.7	
.3		609	618	628	637	646	655	664	673	683	692	701	.6	
.4		701	710	719	728	738	747	756	765	774	784	793	.5	
.5		793	802	811	821	830	839	848	858	867	876	885	.4	
.6		885	895	904	913	922	932	941	950	960	969	978	.3	
.7		978	988	997	006	016	025	034	044	053	062	072	.2	
.8	1.11	072	081	091	100	109	119	128	137	147	156	166	.1	
.9		166	175	185	194	203	213	222	232	241	251	260	64.0	
26.0		260	270	279	289	298	308	317	327	336	346	355	.9	
.1		355	365	374	384	393	403	412	422	431	441	451	.8	
.2		451	460	470	479	489	499	508	518	527	537	547	.7	
.3		547	556	566	575	585	595	604	614	624	633	643	.6	
.4		643	653	662	672	682	691	701	711	721	730	740	.5	
.5		740	750	759	769	779	789	798	808	818	828	838	.4	
.6		838	847	857	867	877	886	896	906	916	926	936	.3	
.7		936	945	955	965	975	985	995	004	014	024	034	.2	
.8	1.12	034	044	054	064	074	083	093	103	113	123	133	.1	
.9		133	143	153	163	173	183	193	203	213	223	233	63.0	
27.0		233	243	253	263	273	283	293	303	313	323	333	.9	10
.1		333	343	353	363	373	383	393	403	413	423	433	.8	
.2		433	443	453	464	474	484	494	504	514	524	534	.7	
.3		534	545	555	565	575	585	595	605	616	626	636	.6	
.4		636	646	656	667	677	687	697	707	718	728	738	.5	
.5		738	748	759	769	779	789	800	810	820	831	841	.4	
.6		841	851	861	872	882	892	903	913	923	934	944	.3	
.7		944	954	965	975	986	996	006	017	027	037	048	.2	
.8	1.13	048	058	069	079	090	100	110	121	131	142	152	.1	
.9		152	163	173	184	194	205	215	225	236	246	257	62.0	
28.0		257	268	278	289	299	310	320	331	341	352	362	.9	
.1		362	373	384	394	405	415	426	436	447	458	468	.8	
.2		468	479	490	500	511	521	532	543	553	564	575	.7	
.3		575	585	596	607	617	628	639	650	660	671	682	.6	
.4		682	692	703	714	725	735	746	757	768	779	789	.5	
.5		789	800	811	822	832	843	854	865	876	887	897	.4	
.6		897	908	919	930	941	952	963	973	984	995	006	.3	
.7	1.14	006	017	028	039	050	061	072	082	093	104	115	.2	
.8		115	126	137	148	159	170	181	192	203	214	225	.1	
.9		225	236	247	258	269	280	291	302	313	324	335	61.0	11
29.0		335	346	358	369	380	391	402	413	424	435	446	.9	
.1		446	457	469	480	491	502	513	524	535	547	558	.8	
.2		558	569	580	591	603	614	625	636	647	659	670	.7	
.3		670	681	692	704	715	726	737	749	760	771	782	.6	
.4		782	794	805	816	828	839	850	862	873	884	896	.5	
.5		896	907	918	930	941	952	964	975	987	998	009	.4	
.6	1.15	009	021	032	044	055	066	078	089	101	112	124	.3	
.7		124	135	147	158	170	181	192	204	215	227	239	.2	
.8		239	250	262	273	285	296	308	319	331	342	354	.1	
.9		354	366	377	389	400	412	424	435	447	458	470	60.0 deg.	
		(10)	9	8	7	6	5	4	3	2	1	0		

COSEC

SEC

deg.		0	1	2	3	4	5	6	7	8	9	(10)	Diff.
30.0	1.15	470	482	493	505	517	528	540	552	563	575	587	.9	
.1		587	598	610	622	634	645	657	669	680	692	704	.8
.2		704	716	727	739	751	763	775	786	798	810	822	.7
.3		822	834	845	857	869	881	893	905	916	928	940	.6
.4		940	952	964	976	988	000	012	023	035	047	059	.5
.5	1.16	059	071	083	095	107	119	131	143	155	167	179	.4
.6		179	191	203	215	227	239	251	263	275	287	299	.3	12
.7		299	311	323	335	347	359	371	384	396	408	420	.2
.8		420	432	444	456	468	481	493	505	517	529	541	.1
.9		541	553	566	578	590	602	614	627	639	651	663	59.0
31.0		663	676	688	700	712	725	737	749	761	774	786	.9
.1		786	798	811	823	835	848	860	872	885	897	909	.8
.2		909	922	934	946	959	971	984	996	008	021	033	.7
.3	1.17	033	046	058	070	083	095	108	120	133	145	158	.6
.4		158	170	183	195	208	220	233	245	258	270	283	.5
.5		283	295	308	320	333	346	358	371	383	396	409	.4
.6		409	421	434	446	459	472	484	497	510	522	535	.3
.7		535	548	560	573	586	598	611	624	636	649	662	.2
.8		662	675	687	700	713	726	738	751	764	777	790	.1
.9		790	802	815	828	841	854	866	879	892	905	918	58.0
32.0		918	931	944	956	969	982	995	008	021	034	047	.9
.1	1.18	047	060	073	086	099	111	124	137	150	163	176	.8	13
.2		176	189	202	215	228	241	254	267	280	293	307	.7
.3		307	320	333	346	359	372	385	398	411	424	437	.6
.4		437	451	464	477	490	503	516	529	543	556	569	.5
.5		569	582	595	608	622	635	648	661	675	688	701	.4
.6		701	714	728	741	754	767	781	794	807	821	834	.3
.7		834	847	861	874	887	901	914	927	941	954	967	.2
.8		967	981	994	008	021	034	048	061	075	088	102	.1
.9	1.19	102	115	128	142	155	169	182	196	209	223	236	57.0
33.0		236	250	263	277	290	304	318	331	345	358	372	.9
.1		372	385	399	413	426	440	453	467	481	494	508	.8
.2		508	522	535	549	563	576	590	604	617	631	645	.7
.3		645	659	672	686	700	713	727	741	755	769	782	.6
.4		782	796	810	824	837	851	865	879	893	907	920	.5
.5		920	934	948	962	976	990	004	018	032	045	059	.4
.6	1.20	059	073	087	101	115	129	143	157	171	185	199	.3
.7		199	213	227	241	255	269	283	297	311	325	339	.2	14
.8		339	353	367	381	395	410	424	438	452	466	480	.1
.9		480	494	508	523	537	551	565	579	593	608	622	56.0
34.0		622	636	650	664	679	693	707	721	736	750	764	.9
.1		764	778	793	807	821	836	850	864	879	893	907	.8
.2		907	922	936	950	965	979	993	008	022	037	051	.7
.3	1.21	051	065	080	094	109	123	138	152	166	181	195	.6
.4		195	210	224	239	253	268	282	297	312	326	341	.5
.5		341	355	370	384	399	414	428	443	457	472	487	.4
.6		487	501	516	530	545	560	574	589	604	618	633	.3
.7		633	648	663	677	692	707	722	736	751	766	781	.2
.8		781	795	810	825	840	855	869	884	899	914	929	.1
.9		929	943	958	973	988	003	018	033	048	063	077	55.0	15
	1.22	(10)	9	8	7	6	5	4	3	2	1	0	deg.

COSEC

SEC

deg.	0	1	2	3	4	5	6	7	8	9	(10)	Diff.
35.0	1.22 077	092	107	122	137	152	167	182	197	212	227	.9	
.1	227	242	257	272	287	302	317	332	347	362	377	.8	15
.2	377	392	407	423	438	453	468	483	498	513	528	.7	
.3	528	544	559	574	589	604	619	635	650	665	680	.6	
.4	680	695	711	726	741	756	772	787	802	817	833	.5	
.5	833	848	863	879	894	909	925	940	955	971	986	.4	
.6	986	001	017	032	048	063	078	094	109	125	140	.3	
.7	1.23 140	155	171	186	202	217	233	248	264	279	295	.2	
.8	295	310	326	341	357	373	388	404	419	435	450	.1	
.9	450	466	482	497	513	529	544	560	575	591	607	54.0	
36.0	607	622	638	654	670	685	701	717	732	748	764	.9	
.1	764	780	795	811	827	843	859	874	890	906	922	.8	
.2	922	938	954	969	985	001	017	033	049	065	081	.7	
.3	1.24 081	096	112	128	144	160	176	192	208	224	240	.6	
.4	240	256	272	288	304	320	336	352	368	384	400	.5	16
.5	400	416	432	448	465	481	497	513	529	545	561	.4	
.6	561	577	594	610	626	642	658	675	691	707	723	.3	
.7	723	739	756	772	788	804	821	837	853	870	886	.2	
.8	886	902	918	935	951	967	984	000	017	033	049	.1	
.9	1.25 049	066	082	098	115	131	148	164	181	197	214	53.0	
37.0	214	230	247	263	280	296	313	329	346	362	379	.9	
.1	379	395	412	428	445	462	478	495	511	528	545	.8	
.2	545	561	578	594	611	628	645	661	678	695	711	.7	
.3	711	728	745	761	778	795	812	828	845	862	879	.6	
.4	879	896	912	929	946	963	980	997	013	030	047	.5	
.5	1.26 047	064	081	098	115	132	149	166	183	200	216	.4	
.6	216	233	250	267	284	301	318	335	352	369	387	.3	17
.7	387	404	421	438	455	472	489	506	523	540	557	.2	
.8	557	575	592	609	626	643	660	678	695	712	729	.1	
.9	729	746	764	781	798	815	833	850	867	885	902	52.0	
38.0	902	919	936	954	971	988	006	023	041	058	075	.9	
.1	1.27 075	093	110	128	145	162	180	197	215	232	250	.8	
.2	250	267	285	302	320	337	355	372	390	407	425	.7	
.3	425	442	460	478	495	513	530	548	566	583	601	.6	
.4	601	619	636	654	672	689	707	725	742	760	778	.5	
.5	778	796	813	831	849	867	884	902	920	938	956	.4	
.6	956	974	991	009	027	045	063	081	099	117	134	.3	
.7	1.28 134	152	170	188	206	224	242	260	278	296	314	.2	18
.8	314	332	350	368	386	404	422	440	458	476	495	.1	
.9	495	513	531	549	567	585	603	621	640	658	676	51.0	
39.0	676	694	712	731	749	767	785	803	822	840	858	.9	
.1	858	877	895	913	931	950	968	986	005	023	042	.8	
.2	1.29 042	060	078	097	115	133	152	170	189	207	226	.7	
.3	226	244	263	281	300	318	337	355	374	392	411	.6	
.4	411	429	448	466	485	504	522	541	559	578	597	.5	
.5	597	615	634	653	671	690	709	727	746	765	784	.4	
.6	784	802	821	840	859	877	896	915	934	953	971	.3	
.7	971	990	009	028	047	066	085	104	122	141	160	.2	
.8	1.30 160	179	198	217	236	255	274	293	312	331	350	.1	19
.9	350	369	388	407	426	445	464	483	503	522	541	50.0	
	(10)	9	8	7	6	5	4	3	2	1	0	deg.	

COSEC

SEC

deg.	0	1	2	3	4	5	6	7	8	9	(10)		Diff.
40.0	1.30 541	560	579	598	617	636	656	675	694	713	732	.9	19
.1	732	752	771	790	809	829	848	867	886	906	925	.8	
.2	925	944	964	983	002	022	041	060	080	099	119	.7	
.3	1.31 119	138	157	177	196	216	235	255	274	294	313	.6	
.4	313	333	352	372	391	411	430	450	470	489	509	.5	
.5	509	528	548	568	587	607	626	646	666	686	705	.4	
.6	705	725	745	764	784	804	824	843	863	883	903	.3	
.7	903	923	942	962	982	002	022	042	061	081	101	.2	
.8	1.32 101	121	141	161	181	201	221	241	261	281	301	.1	20
.9	301	321	341	361	381	401	421	441	461	481	501	49.0	
41.0	501	521	542	562	582	602	622	642	662	683	703	.9	
.1	703	723	743	763	784	804	824	845	865	885	905	.8	
.2	905	926	946	966	987	007	027	048	068	089	109	.7	
.3	1.33 109	129	150	170	191	211	232	252	273	293	314	.6	
.4	314	334	355	375	396	416	437	457	478	499	519	.5	
.5	519	540	560	581	602	622	643	664	685	705	726	.4	
.6	726	747	767	788	809	830	850	871	892	913	934	.3	
.7	934	955	975	996	017	038	059	080	101	122	142	.2	
.8	1.34 142	163	184	205	226	247	268	289	310	331	352	.1	21
.9	352	373	394	416	437	458	479	500	521	542	563	48.0	
42.0	563	584	606	627	648	669	690	712	733	754	775	.9	
.1	775	797	818	839	860	882	903	924	946	967	988	.8	
.2	988	010	031	053	074	095	117	138	160	181	203	.7	
.3	1.35 203	224	246	267	289	310	332	353	375	396	418	.6	
.4	418	439	461	483	504	526	547	569	591	612	634	.5	
.5	634	656	678	699	721	743	765	786	808	830	852	.4	
.6	852	873	895	917	939	961	983	005	026	048	070	.3	
.7	1.36 070	092	114	136	158	180	202	224	246	268	290	.2	22
.8	290	312	334	356	378	400	422	444	467	489	511	.1	
.9	511	533	555	577	599	622	644	666	688	710	733	47.0	
43.0	733	755	777	800	822	844	866	889	911	933	956	.9	
.1	956	978	001	023	045	068	090	113	135	158	180	.8	
.2	1.37 180	203	225	248	270	293	315	338	360	383	406	.7	
.3	406	428	451	473	496	519	541	564	587	609	632	.6	
.4	632	655	678	700	723	746	769	791	814	837	860	.5	
.5	860	883	906	928	951	974	997	020	043	066	089	.4	
.6	1.38 089	112	135	158	181	204	227	250	273	296	319	.3	23
.7	319	342	365	388	411	434	458	481	504	527	550	.2	
.8	550	573	597	620	643	666	690	713	736	759	783	.1	
.9	783	806	829	853	876	899	923	946	970	993	016	46.0	
44.0	1.39 016	040	063	087	110	134	157	181	204	228	251	.9	
.1	251	275	298	322	346	369	393	416	440	464	487	.8	
.2	487	511	535	558	582	606	630	653	677	701	725	.7	
.3	725	749	772	796	820	844	868	892	916	939	963	.6	
.4	963	987	011	035	059	083	107	131	155	179	203	.5	24
.5	1.40 203	227	251	275	299	324	348	372	396	420	444	.4	
.6	444	468	493	517	541	565	590	614	638	662	687	.3	
.7	687	711	735	760	784	808	833	857	881	906	930	.2	
.8	930	955	979	004	028	053	077	102	126	151	175	.1	
.9	1.41 175	200	224	249	273	298	323	347	372	397	421	45.0	
	(10)	9	8	7	6	5	4	3	2	1	0	deg.	

COSEC

SEC

deg.	0		1	2	3	4	5	6	7	8	9	(10)	Diff.
45.0	1.41	421	446	471	495	520	545	570	594	619	644	669	.9
.1		669	694	718	743	768	793	818	843	868	893	918	.8
.2		918	943	968	992	017	042	067	093	118	143	168	.7
.3	1.42	168	193	218	243	268	293	318	344	369	394	419	.6	25
.4		419	444	470	495	520	545	571	596	621	646	672	.5
.5		672	697	723	748	773	799	824	850	875	900	926	.4
.6		926	951	977	002	028	053	079	105	130	156	181	.3
.7	1.43	181	207	233	258	284	309	335	361	387	412	438	.2
.8		438	464	490	515	541	567	593	619	644	670	696	.1
.9		696	722	748	774	800	826	852	878	904	930	956	44.0	26
46.0		956	982	008	034	060	086	112	138	164	190	217	.9
.1	1.44	217	243	269	295	321	347	374	400	426	452	479	.8
.2		479	505	531	558	584	610	637	663	690	716	742	.7
.3		742	769	795	822	848	875	901	928	954	981	007	.6
.4	1.45	007	034	061	087	114	141	167	194	221	247	274	.5
.5		274	301	327	354	381	408	435	461	488	515	542	.4
.6		542	569	596	623	649	676	703	730	757	784	811	.3	27
.7		811	838	865	892	919	946	973	001	028	055	082	.2
.8	1.46	082	109	136	164	191	218	245	272	300	327	354	.1
.9		354	382	409	436	464	491	518	546	573	600	628	43.0
47.0		628	655	683	710	738	765	793	820	848	876	903	.9
.1		903	931	958	986	014	041	069	097	124	152	180	.8
.2	1.47	180	207	235	263	291	319	346	374	402	430	458	.7
.3		458	486	514	542	570	598	626	653	682	710	738	.6	28
.4		738	766	794	822	850	878	906	934	962	991	019	.5
.5	1.48	019	047	075	103	132	160	188	216	245	273	301	.4
.6		301	330	358	387	415	443	472	500	529	557	586	.3
.7		586	614	643	671	700	728	757	786	814	843	871	.2
.8		871	900	929	957	986	015	044	072	101	130	159	.1
.9	1.49	159	188	216	245	274	303	332	361	390	419	448	42.0	29
48.0		448	477	506	535	564	593	622	651	680	709	738	.9
.1		738	767	796	826	855	884	913	942	972	001	030	.8
.2	1.50	030	059	089	118	147	177	206	236	265	294	324	.7
.3		324	353	383	412	442	471	501	530	560	590	619	.6
.4		619	649	678	708	738	767	797	827	857	886	916	.5
.5		916	946	976	005	035	065	095	125	155	185	215	.4	30
.6	1.51	215	245	274	304	334	364	394	425	455	485	515	.3
.7		515	545	575	605	635	665	696	726	756	786	817	.2
.8		817	847	877	907	938	968	999	029	059	090	120	.1
.9	1.52	120	151	181	211	242	273	303	334	364	395	425	41.0
49.0		425	456	487	517	548	579	609	640	671	701	732	.9
.1		732	763	794	825	855	886	917	948	979	010	041	.8
.2	1.53	041	072	103	134	165	196	227	258	289	320	351	.7	31
.3		351	382	413	445	476	507	538	569	601	632	663	.6
.4		663	694	726	757	788	820	851	883	914	945	977	.5
.5		977	008	040	071	103	134	166	198	229	261	292	.4
.6	1.54	292	324	356	387	419	451	483	514	546	578	610	.3
.7		610	642	673	705	737	769	801	833	865	897	929	.2	32
.8		929	961	993	025	057	089	121	153	185	218	250	.1
.9	1.55	250	282	314	346	379	411	443	475	508	540	572	40.0
		(10)	9	8	7	6	5	4	3	2	1	0	deg.

COSEC

SEC

deg.		0	1	2	3	4	5	6	7	8	9	(10)		Diff.
50.0	1.55	572	605	637	670	702	734	767	799	832	864	897	.9	
.1		897	929	962	995	027	060	092	125	158	191	223	.8	
.2	1.56	223	256	289	321	354	387	420	453	486	519	551	.7	
.3		551	584	617	650	683	716	749	782	815	848	881	.6	33
.4		881	915	948	981	014	047	080	114	147	180	213	.5	
.5	1.57	213	247	280	313	347	380	413	447	480	514	547	.4	
.6		547	581	614	648	681	715	748	782	816	849	883	.3	
.7		883	917	950	984	018	051	085	119	153	187	221	.2	
.8	1.58	221	254	288	322	356	390	424	458	492	526	560	.1	34
.9		560	594	628	662	696	731	765	799	833	867	902	39.0	
51.0		902	936	970	004	039	073	107	142	176	211	245	.9	
.1	1.59	245	279	314	348	383	418	452	487	521	556	590	.8	
.2		590	625	660	694	729	764	799	833	868	903	938	.7	
.3		938	973	008	043	077	112	147	182	217	252	287	.6	35
.4	1.60	287	322	357	393	428	463	498	533	568	604	639	.5	
.5		639	674	709	745	780	815	851	886	921	957	992	.4	
.6		992	028	063	099	134	170	205	241	277	312	348	.3	
.7	1.61	348	383	419	455	491	526	562	598	634	670	705	.2	
.8		705	741	777	813	849	885	921	957	993	029	065	.1	36
.9	1.62	065	101	137	173	210	246	282	318	354	391	427	38.0	
52.0		427	463	500	536	572	609	645	681	718	754	791	.9	
.1		791	827	864	900	937	974	010	047	083	120	157	.8	
.2	1.63	157	194	230	267	304	341	378	414	451	488	525	.7	
.3		525	562	599	636	673	710	747	784	821	858	895	.6	37
.4		895	933	970	007	044	081	119	156	193	231	268	.5	
.5	1.64	268	305	343	380	418	455	493	530	568	605	643	.4	
.6		643	680	718	756	793	831	869	906	944	982	020	.3	
.7	1.65	020	057	095	133	171	209	247	285	323	361	399	.2	38
.8		399	437	475	513	551	589	627	666	704	742	780	.1	
.9		780	819	857	895	934	972	010	049	087	126	164	37.0	
53.0	1.66	164	203	241	280	318	357	395	434	473	511	550	.9	
.1		550	589	627	666	705	744	783	822	860	899	938	.8	
.2		938	977	016	055	094	133	172	212	251	290	329	.7	39
.3	1.67	329	368	407	447	486	525	564	604	643	683	722	.6	
.4		722	761	801	840	880	919	959	998	038	078	117	.5	
.5	1.68	117	157	197	236	276	316	356	395	435	475	515	.4	
.6		515	555	595	635	675	715	755	795	835	875	915	.3	40
.7		915	955	995	036	076	116	156	197	237	277	318	.2	
.8	1.69	318	358	399	439	479	520	560	601	642	682	723	.1	
.9		723	763	804	845	885	926	967	008	048	089	130	36.0	
54.0	1.70	130	171	212	253	294	335	376	417	458	499	540	.9	41
.1		540	581	622	664	705	746	787	829	870	911	953	.8	
.2		953	994	035	077	118	160	201	243	284	326	368	.7	
.3	1.71	368	409	451	492	534	576	618	659	701	743	785	.6	
.4		785	827	869	911	953	995	037	079	121	163	205	.5	42
.5	1.72	205	247	289	332	374	416	458	501	543	585	628	.4	
.6		628	670	713	755	798	840	883	925	968	010	053	.3	
.7	1.73	053	096	138	181	224	267	309	352	395	438	481	.2	
.8		481	524	567	610	653	696	739	782	825	868	911	.1	43
.9		911	955	998										
	1.74				041	084	128	171	214	258	301	345	35.0	

| | (10) | 9 | 8 | 7 | 6 | 5 | 4 | 3 | 2 | 1 | 0 | | deg. |

COSEC

SEC

deg.	0	1	2	3	4	5	6	7	8	9	(10)	Diff.
55.0	1.74 345	388	432	475	519	562	606	650	693	737	781	.9
.1	781	824	868	912	956	000	043	087	131	175	219	.8 44
.2	1.75 219	263	307	351	395	440	484	528	572	616	661	.7
.3	661	705	749	794	838	882	927	971	016	060	105	.6
.4	1.76 105	149	194	239	283	328	373	417	462	507	552	.5
.5	552	597	641	686	731	776	821	866	911	956	001	.4 45
.6	1.77 001	047	092	137	182	227	273	318	363	409	454	.3
.7	454	500	545	590	636	681	727	773	818	864	910	.2
.8	910	955	001	047	093	138	184	230	276	322	368	.1 46
.9	1.78 368	414	460	506	552	598	644	690	737	783	829	34.0
56.0	829	875	922	968	014	061	107	154	200	247	293	.9
.1	1.79 293	340	387	433	480	527	573	620	667	714	761	.8
.2	761	807	854	901	948	995	042	089	136	184	231	.7 47
.3	1.80 231	278	325	372	420	467	514	562	609	656	704	.6
.4	704	751	799	846	894	942	989	037	085	132	180	.5
.5	1.81 180	228	276	324	371	419	467	515	563	611	659	.4 48
.6	659	707	756	804	852	900	948	997	045	093	142	.3
.7	1.82 142	190	239	287	336	384	433	481	530	579	627	.2
.8	627	676	725	774	822	871	920	969	018	067	116	.1 49
.9	1.83 116	165	214	263	312	362	411	460	509	559	608	33.0
57.0	608	657	707	756	805	855	905	954	004	053	103	.9
.1	1.84 103	153	202	252	302	352	402	451	501	551	601	.8 50
.2	601	651	701	751	801	852	902	952	002	053	103	.7
.3	1.85 103	153	204	254	304	355	405	456	506	557	608	.6
.4	608	658	709	760	811	861	912	963	014	065	116	.5 51
.5	1.86 116	167	218	269	320	371	422	474	525	576	627	.4
.6	627	679	730	782	833	885	936	988	039	091	142	.3
.7	1.87 142	194	246	298	349	401	453	505	557	609	661	.2 52
.8	661	713	765	817	869	921	974	026	078	130	183	.1
.9	1.88 183	235	287	340	392	445	497	550	603	655	708	32.0
58.0	708	761	813	866	919	972	025	078	131	184	237	.9 53
.1	1.89 237	290	343	396	449	503	556	609	662	716	769	.8
.2	769	823	876	930	983	037	090	144	198	251	305	.7
.3	1.90 305	359	413	467	521	575	629	683	737	791	845	.6 54
.4	845	899	953	007	062	116	170	225	279	334	388	.5
.5	1.91 388	443	497	552	606	661	716	771	825	880	935	.4
.6	935	990	045	100	155	210	265	320	375	430	486	.3 55
.7	1.92 486	541	596	652	707	762	818	873	929	985	040	.2
.8	1.93 040	096	151	207	263	319	375	430	486	542	598	.1 56
.9	598	654	710	767	823	879	935	991	048	104	160	31.0
59.0	1.94 160	217	273	330	386	443	499	556	613	670	726	.9
.1	726	783	840	897	954	011	068	125	182	239	296	.8 57
.2	1.95 296	353	411	468	525	583	640	697	755	812	870	.7
.3	870	928	985	043	101	158	216	274	332	390	448	.6
.4	1.96 448	506	564	622	680	738	796	854	913	971	029	.5 58
.5	1.97 029	088	146	205	263	322	380	439	498	557	615	.4
.6	615	674	733	792	851	910	969	028	087	146	205	.3 59
.7	1.98 205	264	324	383	442	502	561	621	680	740	799	.2
.8	799	859	919	978	038	098	158	218	278	338	398	.1 60
.9	1.99 398	458	518	578	638	698	759	819	879	940	000	30.0
2.00	(10)	9	8	7	6	5	4	3	2	1	0	deg.

COSEC

SEC

deg.	0	1	2	3	4	5	6	7	8	9	(10)	Diff.
60.0	2.00 000	060	121	182	242	303	364	424	485	546	607	.9	
.1	607	668	729	790	851	912	973	034	095	156	218	.8	61
.2	2.01 218	279	341	402	463	525	586	648	710	771	833	.7	
.3	833	895	957	019	081	143	205	267	329	391	453	.6	62
.4	2.02 453	515	577	640	702	765	827	889	952	015	077	.5	
.5	2.03 077	140	203	265	328	391	454	517	580	643	706	.4	63
.6	706	769	832	895	959	022	085	149	212	276	339	.3	
.7	2.04 339	403	466	530	594	657	721	785	849	913	977	.2	64
.8	977	041	105	169	233	298	362	426	491	555	619	.1	
.9	2.05 619	684	748	813	878	942	007	072	137	202	267	29.0	
61.0	2.06 267	332	397	462	527	592	657	722	788	853	918	.9	65
.1	918	984	049	115	180	246	312	377	443	509	575	.8	
.2	2.07 575	641	707	773	839	905	971	037	104	170	236	.7	66
.3	2.08 236	303	369	436	502	569	636	702	769	836	903	.6	
.4	903	970	036	103	171	238	305	372	439	507	574	.5	67
.5	2.09 574	641	709	776	844	911	979	047	114	182	250	.4	
.6	2.10 250	318	386	454	522	590	658	726	795	863	931	.3	68
.7	931	000	068	137	205	274	342	411	480	549	617	.2	69
.8	2.11 617	686	755	824	893	963	032	101	170	239	309	.1	
.9	2.12 309	378	448	517	587	657	726	796	866	936	005	28.0	
62.0	2.13 005	075	145	215	286	356	426	496	566	637	707	.9	70
.1	707	778	848	919	989	060	131	202	273	343	414	.8	71
.2	2.14 414	485	556	628	699	770	841	913	984	055	127	.7	
.3	2.15 127	198	270	342	413	485	557	629	701	773	845	.6	72
.4	845	917	989	061	133	206	278	350	423	495	568	.5	
.5	2.16 568	641	713	786	859	932	005	078	151	224	297	.4	73
.6	2.17 297	370	443	517	590	663	737	810	884	958	031	.3	
.7	2.18 031	105	179	253	327	401	475	549	623	697	772	.2	74
.8	772	846	920	995	069	144	218	293	368	442	517	.1	
.9	2.19 517	592	667	742	817	892	968	043	118	194	269	27.0	75
63.0	2.20 269	344	420	496	571	647	723	799	874	950	026	.9	76
.1	2.21 026	102	179	255	331	407	484	560	637	713	790	.8	
.2	790	866	943	020	097	174	251	328	405	482	559	.7	77
.3	2.22 559	636	714	791	868	946	024	101	179	257	334	.6	
.4	2.23 334	412	490	568	646	724	803	881	959	037	116	.5	78
.5	2.24 116	194	273	351	430	509	588	667	745	824	903	.4	79
.6	903	983	062	141	220	300	379	459	538	618	697	.3	
.7	2.25 697	777	857	937	017	097	177	257	337	417	498	.2	80
.8	2.26 498	578	658	739	819	900	981	062	142	223	304	.1	
.9	2.27 304	385	466	547	629	710	791	873	954	036	117	26.0	81
64.0	2.28 117	199	281	362	444	526	608	690	772	855	937	.9	82
.1	937	019	102	184	266	349	432	514	597	680	763	.8	
.2	2.29 763	846	929	012	095	179	262	345	429	512	596	.7	83
.3	2.30 596	680	763	847	931	015	099	183	267	351	436	.6	84
.4	2.31 436	520	604	689	773	858	943	027	112	197	282	.5	
.5	2.32 282	367	452	537	623	708	793	879	964	050	135	.4	85
.6	2.33 135	221	307	393	479	565	651	737	823	910	996	.3	86
.7	996	082	169	255	342	429	516	602	689	776	863	.2	87
.8	2.34 863	951	038	125	212	300	387	475	563	650	738	.1	
.9	2.35 738	826	914										88
	2.36			002	090	178	266	355	443	532	620	25.0	
												deg.	
	(10)	9	8	7	6	5	4	3	2	1	0		

COSEC

SEC

deg.		0	1	2	3	4	5	6	7	8	9	(10)		Diff.
65.0	2.3	662	671	680	689	697	706	715	724	733	742	751	.9	
.1		751	760	769	778	787	796	805	814	823	832	841	.8	9
.2		841	850	859	868	877	886	895	904	913	922	931	.7	
.3		931	940	949	958	967	977	986	995	004	013	022	.6	
.4	2.4	022	031	041	050	059	068	077	087	096	105	114	.5	
.5		114	123	133	142	151	160	170	179	188	198	207	.4	
.6		207	216	226	235	244	254	263	272	282	291	300	.3	
.7		300	310	319	329	338	348	357	366	376	385	395	.2	
.8		395	404	414	423	433	442	452	461	471	480	490	.1	
.9		490	499	509	519	528	538	547	557	567	576	586	24.0	
66.0		586	596	605	615	625	634	644	654	663	673	683	.9	
.1		683	693	702	712	722	731	741	751	761	771	780	.8	
.2		780	790	800	810	820	830	839	849	859	869	879	.7	
.3		879	889	899	909	918	928	938	948	958	968	978	.6	
.4		978	988	998	008	018	028	038	048	058	068	078	.5	10
.5	2.5	078	089	099	109	119	129	139	149	159	169	180	.4	
.6		180	190	200	210	220	230	241	251	261	271	282	.3	
.7		282	292	302	312	323	333	343	354	364	374	384	.2	
.8		384	395	405	415	426	436	447	457	467	478	488	.1	
.9		488	499	509	520	530	540	551	562	572	582	593	23.0	
67.0		593	604	614	625	635	646	656	667	677	688	699	.9	
.1		699	709	720	731	741	752	763	773	784	795	805	.8	
.2		805	816	827	838	848	859	870	881	891	902	913	.7	
.3		913	924	935	946	956	967	978	989	000	011	022	.6	
.4	2.6	022	033	044	054	065	076	087	098	109	120	131	.5	11
.5		131	142	153	164	175	186	197	209	220	231	242	.4	
.6		242	253	264	275	286	298	309	320	331	342	354	.3	
.7		354	365	376	387	398	410	421	432	444	455	466	.2	
.8		466	477	489	500	511	523	534	546	557	568	580	.1	
.9		580	591	603	614	626	637	649	660	672	683	695	22.0	
68.0		695	706	718	729	741	752	764	776	787	799	811	.9	
.1		811	822	834	845	857	869	881	892	904	916	927	.8	
.2		927	939	951	963	975	986	998	010	022	034	046	.7	
.3	2.7	046	057	069	081	093	105	117	129	141	153	165	.6	
.4		165	177	189	201	213	225	237	249	261	273	285	.5	12
.5		285	297	309	321	333	346	358	370	382	394	407	.4	
.6		407	419	431	443	455	468	480	492	504	517	529	.3	
.7		529	541	554	566	579	591	603	616	628	641	653	.2	
.8		653	665	678	690	703	715	728	740	753	766	778	.1	
.9		778	791	803	816	828	841	854	866	879	892	904	21.0	
69.0		904	917	930	942	955	968	981	993	006	019	032	.9	
.1	2.8	032	045	057	070	083	096	109	122	135	148	161	.8	
.2		161	173	186	199	212	225	238	251	264	277	291	.7	13
.3		291	304	317	330	343	356	369	382	396	409	422	.6	
.4		422	435	448	461	475	488	501	515	528	541	555	.5	
.5		555	568	581	595	608	621	635	648	662	675	688	.4	
.6		688	702	715	729	742	756	770	783	797	810	824	.3	
.7		824	837	851	865	878	892	906	919	933	947	960	.2	
.8		960	974	988	002	016	029	043	057	071	085	099	.1	
.9	2.9	099	112	126	140	154	168	182	196	210	224	238	20.0	14
		(10)	9	8	7	6	5	4	3	2	1	0	deg.	

COSEC

SEC

deg.	0	1	2	3	4	5	6	7	8	9	(10)		Diff.
70.0	2.9 238	252	266	280	294	308	322	336	351	365	379	.9	14
.1	379	393	407	422	436	450	464	478	493	507	521	.8	
.2	521	536	550	564	579	593	607	622	636	651	665	.7	
.3	665	680	694	709	723	738	752	767	781	796	811	.6	
.4	811	825	840	854	869	884	899	913	928	943	957	.5	
.5	957	972	987	002	017	031	046	061	076	091	106	.4	
.6	3.0 106	121	136	151	166	181	196	211	226	241	256	.3	15
.7	256	271	286	301	316	331	347	362	377	392	407	.2	
.8	407	423	438	453	469	484	499	514	530	545	561	.1	
.9	561	576	591	607	622	638	653	669	684	700	716	19.0	
71.0	716	731	747	762	778	794	809	825	841	856	872	.9	
.1	872	888	904	919	935	951	967	983	998	014	030	.8	
.2	3.1 030	046	062	078	094	110	126	142	158	174	190	.7	16
.3	190	206	222	239	255	271	287	303	320	336	352	.6	
.4	352	368	384	401	417	433	450	466	483	499	515	.5	
.5	515	532	548	565	581	598	614	631	647	664	681	.4	
.6	681	697	714	731	747	764	781	798	814	831	848	.3	
.7	848	865	882	898	915	932	949	966	983	000	017	.2	
.8	3.2 017	034	051	068	085	102	119	136	153	171	188	.1	17
.9	188	205	222	240	257	274	291	309	326	343	361	18.0	
72.0	361	378	396	413	430	448	465	483	500	518	535	.9	
.1	535	553	571	588	606	624	641	659	677	694	712	.8	
.2	712	730	748	766	784	801	819	837	855	873	891	.7	
.3	891	909	927	945	963	981	000	018	036	054	072	.6	18
.4	3.3 072	090	108	127	145	163	182	200	218	237	255	.5	
.5	255	274	292	310	329	347	366	384	403	422	440	.4	
.6	440	459	477	496	515	534	552	571	590	609	628	.3	
.7	628	646	665	684	703	722	741	760	779	798	817	.2	19
.8	817	836	855	874	894	913	932	951	970	990	009	.1	
.9	3.4 009	028	048	067	086	106	125	145	164	183	203	17.0	
73.0	203	223	242	262	281	301	321	340	360	380	399	.9	
.1	399	419	439	459	479	499	518	538	558	578	598	.8	20
.2	598	618	638	658	678	699	719	739	759	779	799	.7	
.3	799	820	840	860	881	901	921	942	962	983	003	.6	
.4	3.5 003	024	044	065	085	106	127	147	168	189	209	.5	
.5	209	230	251	272	293	313	334	355	376	397	418	.4	21
.6	418	439	460	481	502	523	545	566	587	608	629	.3	
.7	629	651	672	693	715	736	757	779	800	822	843	.2	
.8	843	865	887	908	930	951	973	995	017	038	060	.1	
.9	3.6 060	082	104	126	148	169	191	213	235	257	280	16.0	22
74.0	280	302	324	346	368	390	413	435	457	479	502	.9	
.1	502	524	547	569	591	614	636	659	682	704	727	.8	
.2	727	750	772	795	818	840	863	886	909	932	955	.7	
.3	955	978	001	024	047	070	093	116	139	163	186	.6	23
.4	3.7 186	209	232	256	279	302	326	349	373	396	420	.5	
.5	420	443	467	491	514	538	562	585	609	633	657	.4	
.6	657	681	705	729	752	777	801	825	849	873	897	.3	24
.7	897	921	945	970	994	018	043	067	091	115	140	.2	
.8	3.8 140	165	190	214	239	263	288	313	337	362	387	.1	
.9	387	412	437	462	487	512	537	562	587	612	637	15.0	25
												deg.	
	(10)	9	8	7	6	5	4	3	2	1	0		

COSEC

SEC

deg.		0	1	2	3	4	5	6	7	8	9	(10)	Diff.
75.0	3.8	637	662	687	713	738	763	789	814	840	865	890	.9	
.1		890	916	941	967	993	$\overline{018}$	044	$\overline{070}$	$\overline{096}$	$\overline{121}$	$\overline{147}$	.8
.2	3.9	147	173	199	225	251	277	303	329	355	381	408	.7	26
.3		408	434	460	486	513	539	566	592	619	645	672	.6
.4		672	698	725	751	778	805	832	859	886	912	939	.5
.5		939	966	993	$\overline{020}$	$\overline{047}$	075	102	129	156	183	211	.4	27
.6	4.0	211	238	266	293	320	348	375	403	431	458	486	.3
.7		486	514	541	569	597	625	653	681	709	737	765	.2	28
.8		765	793	822	850	878	906	935	963	991	$\overline{020}$	$\overline{048}$	.1
.9	4.1	048	077	106	134	163	191	220	249	278	307	336	14.0
76.0		336	365	394	423	452	481	510	539	568	598	627	.9	29
.1		627	656	686	715	745	774	804	834	863	893	923	.8
.2		923	953	983	$\overline{012}$	$\overline{042}$	$\overline{072}$	102	132	163	193	223	.7	30
.3	4.2	223	253	283	314	344	375	405	436	466	497	527	.6
.4		527	558	589	620	651	681	712	743	774	806	837	.5	31
.5		837	868	899	930	961	993	$\overline{024}$	$\overline{056}$	$\overline{087}$	119	150	.4
.6	4.3	150	182	214	245	277	309	341	373	405	437	469	.3	32
.7		469	501	533	565	598	630	662	695	727	760	792	.2
.8		792	825	858	890	923	956	989	$\overline{022}$	$\overline{055}$	$\overline{088}$	$\overline{121}$	.1	33
.9	4.4	121	154	187	220	253	287	320	353	387	420	454	13.0
77.0		454	488	521	555	589	623	657	691	725	759	793	.9	34
.1		793	827	861	896	930	964	999	$\overline{033}$	$\overline{068}$	$\overline{102}$	$\overline{137}$	.8
.2	4.5	137	172	206	241	276	311	346	381	416	451	486	.7	35
.3		486	522	557	592	628	663	699	734	770	806	841	.6
.4		841	877	913	949	985	$\overline{021}$	$\overline{057}$	$\overline{093}$	$\overline{130}$	$\overline{166}$	$\overline{202}$	.5	36
.5	4.6	202	239	275	312	348	385	422	458	495	532	569	.4
.6		569	606	643	680	717	755	792	829	867	904	942	.3	37
.7		942	979	$\overline{017}$	$\overline{055}$	$\overline{092}$	$\overline{130}$	$\overline{168}$	$\overline{206}$	$\overline{244}$	$\overline{282}$	$\overline{321}$	.2	38
.8	4.7	321	359	397	435	474	512	551	590	628	667	706	.1
.9		706	745	784	823	862	901	940	979	$\overline{018}$	$\overline{058}$	$\overline{097}$	12.0	39
78.0	4.8	097	137	176	216	256	296	336	375	415	456	496	.9	40
.1		496	536	576	616	657	697	738	778	819	860	901	.8
.2		901	942	983	$\overline{024}$	$\overline{065}$	$\overline{106}$	$\overline{147}$	$\overline{188}$	$\overline{230}$	$\overline{271}$	$\overline{313}$	.7	41
.3	4.9	313	354	396	438	480	521	563	605	647	690	732	.6	42
.4		732	774	817	859	902	944	987	$\overline{030}$	$\overline{073}$	$\overline{116}$	$\overline{159}$	.5	43
.5	5.0	159	202	245	288	331	375	418	462	505	549	593	.4
.6		593	636	680	724	768	813	857	901	945	990	$\overline{034}$	.3	44
.7	5.1	034	079	124	168	213	258	303	348	394	439	484	.2	45
.8		484	530	575	621	666	712	758	804	850	896	942	.1	46
.9		942	988	$\overline{035}$	$\overline{081}$	$\overline{128}$	$\overline{174}$	$\overline{221}$	$\overline{268}$	$\overline{314}$	$\overline{361}$	$\overline{408}$	11.0	47
79.0	5.2	408	456	503	550	597	645	692	740	788	836	883	.9
.1		883	931	979	$\overline{027}$	$\overline{076}$	$\overline{124}$	$\overline{173}$	$\overline{221}$	$\overline{270}$	$\overline{318}$	$\overline{367}$	.8	48
.2	5.3	367	416	465	514	563	612	662	711	761	810	860	.7	49
.3		860	910	960	$\overline{010}$	$\overline{060}$	$\overline{110}$	$\overline{160}$	$\overline{210}$	$\overline{261}$	$\overline{311}$	$\overline{362}$	.6	50
.4	5.4	362	413	464	515	566	617	668	720	771	822	874	.5	51
.5		874	926	978	$\overline{030}$	$\overline{082}$	$\overline{134}$	$\overline{186}$	$\overline{238}$	$\overline{291}$	$\overline{343}$	$\overline{396}$	.4	52
.6	5.5	396	448	501	554	607	660	714	767	820	874	928	.3	53
.7		928	982	$\overline{035}$	$\overline{089}$	$\overline{143}$	$\overline{198}$	$\overline{252}$	$\overline{306}$	$\overline{361}$	$\overline{415}$	$\overline{470}$	.2	54
.8	5.6	470	525	580	635	690	745	801	856	912	967	$\overline{023}$	.1	55
.9	5.7	023	079	135	192	248	304	361	417	474	531	588	10.0	56
													deg.
	(10)	9	8	7	6	5	4	3	2	1	0		

COSEC

SEC

deg.		0	1	2	3	4	5	6	7	8	9	(10)		Diff.
80.0	5.7	588	645	702	759	817	874	932	990	047	105	164	.9	
.1	5.8	164	222	280	338	397	456	515	574	633	692	751	.8	
.2		751	811	870	930	990	049	110	170	230	290	351	.7	
.3	5.9	351	412	472	533	594	656	717	778	840	901	963	.6	
.4		963	025	087	150	212	274	337	400	463	526	589	.5	
.5	6.0	589	652	715	779	842	906	970	034	098	163	227	.4	
.6	6.1	227	292	357	422	487	552	617	683	748	814	880	.3	
.7		880	946	012	078	145	211	278	345	412	479	546	.2	
.8	6.2	546	614	681	749	817	885	953	022	090	159	228	.1	
.9	6.3	228	297	366	435	505	574	644	714	784	854	925	9.0	
81.0		925	995	066	137	208	279	350	422	493	565	637	.9	
.1	6.4	637	709	781	854	926	999	072	145	218	292	366	.8	
.2	6.5	366	439	513	587	662	736	811	886	961	036	111	.7	
.3	6.6	111	186	262	338	414	490	567	643	720	797	874	.6	
.4		874	951	028	106	184	262	340	418	497	576	655	.5	
.5	6.7	655	734	813	893	972	052	132	212	293	373	454	.4	
.6	6.8	454	535	616	698	779	861	943	025	108	190	273	.3	
.7	6.9	273	356	439	523	606	690	774	858	943	027	112	.2	
.8	7.0	112	197	282	368	453	539	625	712	798	885	972	.1	
.9		972	059	146	234	322	410	498	586	675	764	853	8.0	
82.0	7.1	853	942	032	122	212	302	392	483	574	665	757	.9	
.1	7.2	757	848	940	032	125	217	310	403	496	590	684	.8	
.2	7.3	684	778	872	966	061	156	251	347	442	538	635	.7	
.3	7.4	635	731	828	925	022	119	217	315	413	512	611	.6	
.4	7.5	611	710	809	909	008	109	209	309	410	512	613	.5	
.5	7.6	613	715	817	919	021	124	227	331	434	538	642	.4	
.6	7.7	642	747	852	957	062	168	274	380	486	593	700	.3	
.7	7.8	700	807	915	023	131	240	349	458	567	677	787	.2	
.8	7.9	787	898	008	119	231	342	454	567	679	792	905	.1	
.9	8.0	905												
8.1			019	133	247	361	476	591	707	822	939	055	7.0	
8.2														
83.0	8.	206	217	229	241	252	264	276	288	300	312	324	.9	12
.1		324	336	348	360	372	384	397	409	421	433	446	.8	
.2		446	458	470	483	495	508	520	533	546	558	571	.7	
.3		571	584	597	610	622	635	648	661	674	687	700	.6	13
.4		700	714	727	740	753	767	780	793	807	820	834	.5	
.5		834	847	861	874	888	902	916	929	943	957	971	.4	
.6		971	985	999	013	027	041	056	070	084	098	113	.3	14
.7	9.	113	127	142	156	171	186	200	215	230	244	259	.2	
.8		259	274	289	304	319	334	349	365	380	395	411	.1	15
.9		411	426	441	457	472	488	504	519	535	551	567	6.0	
84.0		567	583	599	615	631	647	663	679	696	712	728	.9	16
.1		728	745	761	778	794	811	828	845	862	878	895	.8	17
.2		895	913	930	947	964	981	999	016	033	051	068	.7	
.3	10.	068	086	104	122	139	157	175	193	211	230	248	.6	18
.4		248	266	284	303	321	340	358	377	396	415	433	.5	
.5		433	452	471	490	510	529	548	567	587	606	626	.4	19
.6		626	646	665	685	705	725	745	765	785	806	826	.3	20
.7		826	846	867	887	908	929	950	970	991	012	034	.2	21
.8	11.	034	055	076	097	119	140	162	184	206	227	249	.1	22
.9		249	271	293	316	338	360	383	406	428	451	474	5.0	23
		(10)	9	8	7	6	5	4	3	2	1	0	deg.	

COSEC

SEC

deg.	0	1	2	3	4	5	6	7	8	9	(10)		Diff.
85.0	11. 474	497	520	543	566	589	613	636	660	683	707	.9	23
.1	707	731	755	779	803	828	852	876	901	926	951	.8	24
.2	951	976	001	026	051	076	101	127	153	178	204	.7	25
.3	12. 204	230	256	283	309	335	362	388	415	442	469	.6	26-27
.4	469	496	523	551	578	606	633	661	689	717	745	.5	28
.5	745	774	802	831	860	888	917	946	976	005	035	.4	29
.6	13. 035	064	094	124	154	184	214	245	276	306	337	.3	30
.7	337	368	399	431	462	494	526	557	590	622	654	.2	31-32
.8	654	687	719	752	785	818	852	885	919	953	987	.1	33-34
.9	987	021	055	089	124	159	194	229	264	300	336	4.0	35
86.0	14. 336	371	408	444	480	517	554	590	628	665	703	.9	36-37
.1	703	740	778	816	855	893	932	971	010	049	089	.8	38-39
.2	15. 089	129	169	209	249	290	331	372	413	454	496	.7	40-41
.3	496	538	580	623	665	708	751	794	838	882	926	.6	42-44
.4	926	970	015	060	105	150	196	241	287	334	380	.5	44-47
.5	16. 380	427	474	522	569	618	666	714	763	812	862	.4	47-50
.6	862	911	961	012	062	113	164	216	267	320	372	.3	49-53
.7	17. 372	425	478	531	585	639	693	748	803	858	914	.2	53-56
.8	914	970	027	084	141	198	256	314	373	432	492	.1	56-60
.9	18. 492	551	611	672	733	794	856	918	981	044	107	3.0	59-63
87.0	19. 107	171	235	300	365	431	497	563	630	698	766	.9	
.1	766	834	903	972	042	112	183	254	326	398	471	.8	
.2	20. 471	544	618	692	767	843	919	995	073	150	229	.7	
.3	21. 229	307	387	467	547	629	711	793	876	960	044	.6	
.4	22. 044	130	215	302	389	476	565	654	744	834	926	.5	
.5	926	018	110	204	298	393	489	586	683	781	880	.4	
.6	23. 880	980	081	182	285	388	492	597	703	810	918	.3	
.7	24. 918												
	25.	027	136	247	359	471	585	700	815	932	050	.2	
.8	26. 050	169	289	410	532	655	780	906	033	160	290	.1	
.9	27. 290	420	552	685	820	955							
	28.						092	230	370	511	654	2.0 deg.	
	(10)	9	8	7	6	5	4	3	2	1	0		

COSEC

DEG.	SEC		DEG.	SEC	
88.00	28.654	2.00	88.50	38.202	1.50
.01	28.798	1.99	.51	38.458	.49
.02	28.943	.98	.52	38.718	.48
.03	29.090	.97	.53	38.981	.47
.04	29.238	.96	.54	39.248	.46
.05	29.388	.95	.55	39.519	.45
.06	29.540	.94	.56	39.793	.44
.07	29.693	.93	.57	40.071	.43
.08	29.847	.92	.58	40.353	.42
.09	30.003	.91	.59	40.639	.41
88.10	30.161	1.90	88.60	40.930	1.40
.11	30.321	.89	.61	41.224	.39
.12	30.482	.88	.62	41.523	.38
.13	30.645	.87	.63	41.826	.37
.14	30.810	.86	.64	42.133	.36
.15	30.976	.85	.65	42.445	.35
.16	31.144	.84	.66	42.762	.34
.17	31.314	.83	.67	43.083	.33
.18	31.486	.82	.68	43.410	.32
.19	31.660	.81	.69	43.741	.31
88.20	31.836	1.80	88.70	44.077	1.30
.21	32.014	.79	.71	44.419	.29
.22	32.194	.78	.72	44.766	.28
.23	32.376	.77	.73	45.118	.27
.24	32.560	.76	.74	45.477	.26
.25	32.746	.75	.75	45.840	.25
.26	32.934	.74	.76	46.210	.24
.27	33.124	.73	.77	46.586	.23
.28	33.316	.72	.78	46.967	.22
.29	33.511	.71	.79	47.355	.21
88.30	33.708	1.70	88.80	47.750	1.20
.31	33.908	.69	.81	48.151	.19
.32	34.110	.68	.82	48.559	.18
.33	34.314	.67	.83	48.974	.17
.34	34.520	.66	.84	49.396	.16
.35	34.730	.65	.85	49.826	.15
.36	34.941	.64	.86	50.263	.14
.37	35.156	.63	.87	50.707	.13
.38	35.372	.62	.88	51.160	.12
.39	35.592	.61	.89	51.621	.11
88.40	35.815	1.60	88.90	52.090	1.10
.41	36.040	.59	.91	52.568	.09
.42	36.268	.58	.92	53.055	.08
.43	36.499	.57	.93	53.551	.07
.44	36.733	.56	.94	54.056	.06
.45	36.970	.55	.95	54.570	.05
.46	37.210	.54	.96	55.095	.04
.47	37.453	.53	.97	55.630	.03
.48	37.699	.52	.98	56.175	.02
.49	37.949	1.51	.99	56.731	1.01
	COSEC	DEG.		COSEC	DEG.

DEG.	SEC		DEG.	SEC	
89.00	57.299	1.00	89.50	114.59	0.50
.01	57.877	0.99	.51	116.93	.49
.02	58.468	.98	.52	119.37	.48
.03	59.071	.97	.53	121.91	.47
.04	59.686	.96	.54	124.56	.46
.05	60.314	.95	.55	127.33	.45
.06	60.956	.94	.56	130.22	.44
.07	61.611	.93	.57	133.25	.43
.08	62.281	.92	.58	136.42	.42
.09	62.965	.91	.59	139.75	.41
89.10	63.665	0.90	89.60	143.24	0.40
.11	64.380	.89	.61	146.91	.39
.12	65.111	.88	.62	150.78	.38
.13	65.860	.87	.63	154.85	.37
.14	66.626	.86	.64	159.16	.36
.15	67.409	.85	.65	163.70	.35
.16	68.212	.84	.66	168.52	.34
.17	69.034	.83	.67	173.62	.33
.18	69.875	.82	.68	179.05	.32
.19	70.738	.81	.69	184.83	.31
89.20	71.622	0.80	89.70	190.99	0.30
.21	72.529	.79	.71	197.57	.29
.22	73.458	.78	.72	204.63	.28
.23	74.412	.77	.73	212.21	.27
.24	75.391	.76	.74	220.37	.26
.25	76.397	.75	.75	229.18	.25
.26	77.429	.74	.76	238.73	.24
.27	78.490	.73	.77	249.11	.23
.28	79.580	.72	.78	260.44	.22
.29	80.700	.71	.79	272.84	.21
89.30	81.853	0.70	89.80	286.48	0.20
.31	83.039	.69	.81	301.56	.19
.32	84.260	.68	.82	318.31	.18
.33	85.518	.67	.83	337.03	.17
.34	86.814	.66	.84	358.10	.16
.35	88.149	.65	.85	381.97	.15
.36	89.526	.64	.86	409.26	.14
.37	90.948	.63	.87	440.74	.13
.38	92.414	.62	.88	477.47	.12
.39	93.929	.61	.89	520.87	.11
89.40	95.495	0.60	89.90	572.96	0.10
.41	97.113	.59	.91	636.62	.09
.42	98.787	.58	.92	716.20	.08
.43	100.52	.57	.93	818.51	.07
.44	102.32	.56	.94	954.93	.06
.45	104.18	.55	.95	1145.92	.05
.46	106.10	.54	.96	1432.39	.04
.47	108.11	.53	.97	1909.86	.03
.48	110.19	.52	.98	2864.79	.02
.49	112.35	0.51	.99	5729.58	.01
			90.00	Infin.	0.00
	COSEC	DEG.		COSEC	DEG.

TRIGONOMETRIC FUNCTIONS

DEG.	LOG SIN		DEG.	LOG SIN	
0.00	.....	90.00	0.50	7.94 084	89.50
.01	6.24 188	89.99	.51	7.94 944	.49
.02	6.54 291	.98	.52	7.95 787	.48
.03	6.71 900	.97	.53	7.96 615	.47
.04	6.84 394	.96	.54	7.97 426	.46
.05	6.94 085	.95	.55	7.98 223	.45
.06	7.02 003	.94	.56	7.99 006	.44
.07	7.08 698	.93	.57	7.99 775	.43
.08	7.14 497	.92	.58	8.00 530	.42
.09	7.19 612	.91	.59	8.01 272	.41
0.10	7.24 188	89.90	0.60	8.02 002	89.40
.11	7.28 327	.89	.61	8.02 720	.39
.12	7.32 106	.88	.62	8.03 426	.38
.13	7.35 582	.87	.63	8.04 121	.37
.14	7.38 800	.86	.64	8.04 805	.36
.15	7.41 797	.85	.65	8.05 478	.35
.16	7.44 600	.84	.66	8.06 141	.34
.17	7.47 233	.83	.67	8.06 794	.33
.18	7.49 715	.82	.68	8.07 438	.32
.19	7.52 063	.81	.69	8.08 072	.31
0.20	7.54 291	89.80	0.70	8.08 696	89.30
.21	7.56 410	.79	.71	8.09 312	.29
.22	7.58 430	.78	.72	8.09 920	.28
.23	7.60 360	.77	.73	8.10 519	.27
.24	7.62 209	.76	.74	8.11 110	.26
.25	7.63 982	.75	.75	8.11 693	.25
.26	7.65 685	.74	.76	8.12 268	.24
.27	7.67 324	.73	.77	8.12 836	.23
.28	7.68 903	.72	.78	8.13 396	.22
.29	7.70 427	.71	.79	8.13 949	.21
0.30	7.71 900	89.70	0.80	8.14 495	89.20
.31	7.73 324	.69	.81	8.15 035	.19
.32	7.74 703	.68	.82	8.15 568	.18
.33	7.76 039	.67	.83	8.16 094	.17
.34	7.77 335	.66	.84	8.16 614	.16
.35	7.78 594	.65	.85	8.17 128	.15
.36	7.79 818	.64	.86	8.17 636	.14
.37	7.81 008	.63	.87	8.18 138	.13
.38	7.82 166	.62	.88	8.18 634	.12
.39	7.83 294	.61	.89	8.19 125	.11
0.40	7.84 393	89.60	0.90	8.19 610	89.10
.41	7.85 466	.59	.91	8.20 090	.09
.42	7.86 512	.58	.92	8.20 565	.08
.43	7.87 534	.57	.93	8.21 034	.07
.44	7.88 533	.56	.94	8.21 499	.06
.45	7.89 509	.55	.95	8.21 958	.05
.46	7.90 463	.54	.96	8.22 413	.04
.47	7.91 397	.53	.97	8.22 863	.03
.48	7.92 311	.52	.98	8.23 308	.02
.49	7.93 207	89.51	.99	8.23 749	89.01
	LOG COS	DEG.		LOG COS	DEG.

DEG.	LOG SIN		DEG.	LOG SIN	
1.00	8.24 186	89.00	1.50	8.41 792	88.50
.01	8.24 618	88.99	.51	8.42 080	.49
.02	8.25 045	.98	.52	8.42 367	.48
.03	8.25 469	.97	.53	8.42 652	.47
.04	8.25 889	.96	.54	8.42 935	.46
.05	8.26 304	.95	.55	8.43 216	.45
.06	8.26 716	.94	.56	8.43 495	.44
.07	8.27 124	.93	.57	8.43 772	.43
.08	8.27 528	.92	.58	8.44 048	.42
.09	8.27 928	.91	.59	8.44 322	.41
1.10	8.28 324	88.90	1.60	8.44 594	88.40
.11	8.28 717	.89	.61	8.44 865	.39
.12	8.29 107	.88	.62	8.45 133	.38
.13	8.29 493	.87	.63	8.45 401	.37
.14	8.29 875	.86	.64	8.45 666	.36
.15	8.30 255	.85	.65	8.45 930	.35
.16	8.30 631	.84	.66	8.46 192	.34
.17	8.31 003	.83	.67	8.46 453	.33
.18	8.31 373	.82	.68	8.46 712	.32
.19	8.31 739	.81	.69	8.46 970	.31
1.20	8.32 103	88.80	1.70	8.47 226	88.30
.21	8.32 463	.79	.71	8.47 481	.29
.22	8.32 820	.78	.72	8.47 734	.28
.23	8.33 175	.77	.73	8.47 986	.27
.24	8.33 527	.76	.74	8.48 236	.26
.25	8.33 875	.75	.75	8.48 485	.25
.26	8.34 221	.74	.76	8.48 732	.24
.27	8.34 565	.73	.77	8.48 978	.23
.28	8.34 905	.72	.78	8.49 223	.22
.29	8.35 243	.71	.79	8.49 466	.21
1.30	8.35 578	88.70	1.80	8.49 708	88.20
.31	8.35 911	.69	.81	8.49 948	.19
.32	8.36 241	.68	.82	8.50 188	.18
.33	8.36 569	.67	.83	8.50 425	.17
.34	8.36 894	.66	.84	8.50 662	.16
.35	8.37 217	.65	.85	8.50 897	.15
.36	8.37 538	.64	.86	8.51 131	.14
.37	8.37 856	.63	.87	8.51 364	.13
.38	8.38 171	.62	.88	8.51 596	.12
.39	8.38 485	.61	.89	8.51 826	.11
1.40	8.38 796	88.60	1.90	8.52 055	88.10
.41	8.39 105	.59	.91	8.52 283	.09
.42	8.39 412	.58	.92	8.52 510	.08
.43	8.39 717	.57	.93	8.52 735	.07
.44	8.40 019	.56	.94	8.52 960	.06
.45	8.40 320	.55	.95	8.53 183	.05
.46	8.40 618	.54	.96	8.53 405	.04
.47	8.40 915	.53	.97	8.53 626	.03
.48	8.41 209	.52	.98	8.53 846	.02
.49	8.41 501	88.51	.99	8.54 064	88.01
	LOG COS	DEG.		LOG COS	DEG.

278 TRIGONOMETRIC FUNCTIONS

LOG SIN

deg.	0	1	2	3	4	5	6	7	8	9	(10)	
2.0	8.54 282	498	714	928								
	8.55				142	354	565	775	985	$\overline{193}$	$\overline{400}$	.9
.1	8.56 400	606	811									
	8.57			016	219	421	623	823	$\overline{023}$	$\overline{222}$	$\overline{419}$	.8
.2	8.58 419	616	812									
	8.59			007	201	395	587	779	970	$\overline{160}$	$\overline{349}$	.7
.3	8.60 349	537	725	911								
	8.61				097	282	467	650	833	$\overline{015}$	$\overline{196}$	.6
.4	8.62 196	377	556	735	914	$\overline{091}$	$\overline{268}$	$\overline{444}$	$\overline{619}$	$\overline{794}$	$\overline{968}$	.5
.5	8.63 968											
	8.64		141	314	486	657	827	997	$\overline{166}$	$\overline{335}$	$\overline{503}$	$\overline{670}$	.4
.6	8.65 670	837										
	8.66			003	168	333	497	660	823	985	$\overline{147}$	$\overline{308}$	.3
.7	8.67 308	468	628	788	946	$\overline{104}$	$\overline{262}$	$\overline{419}$	$\overline{575}$	$\overline{731}$	$\overline{886}$	.2
.8	8.68 886											
	8.69		041	195	349	$\overline{502}$	$\overline{654}$	$\overline{806}$	958	$\overline{109}$	$\overline{259}$	$\overline{409}$	.1
.9	8.70 409	558	707	856	$\overline{003}$	$\overline{151}$	$\overline{298}$	$\overline{444}$	$\overline{590}$	$\overline{735}$	$\overline{880}$	87.0
3.0	8.71 880											
	8.72		024	168	312	455	597	739	881	$\overline{022}$	$\overline{163}$	$\overline{303}$	.9
.1	8.73 303	442	582	721	859	997	$\overline{134}$	$\overline{272}$	$\overline{408}$	$\overline{544}$	$\overline{680}$	.8
.2	8.74 680	816	950									
	8.75			085	219	353	486	619	$\overline{751}$	$\overline{883}$	$\overline{015}$	.7
.3	8.76 015	146	277	408	538	667	797	926	$\overline{054}$	$\overline{182}$	$\overline{310}$	.6
.4	8.77 310	438	565	691	$\overline{817}$	$\overline{943}$	$\overline{069}$	$\overline{194}$	$\overline{319}$	$\overline{443}$	$\overline{568}$	.5
.5	8.78 568	691	$\overline{815}$	$\overline{938}$	$\overline{060}$	$\overline{183}$	$\overline{305}$	$\overline{426}$	$\overline{548}$	$\overline{669}$	$\overline{789}$	.4
.6	8.79 789	910	$\overline{030}$	$\overline{149}$	$\overline{269}$	$\overline{388}$	$\overline{506}$	$\overline{625}$	$\overline{743}$	$\overline{860}$	$\overline{978}$	.3
.7	8.80 978											
	8.81		095	212	328	444	560	675	791	905	$\overline{020}$	$\overline{134}$	.2
.8	8.82 134	248	362	475	588	701	814	$\overline{926}$	$\overline{038}$	$\overline{149}$	$\overline{261}$	.1
.9	8.83 261	372	482	593	703	813	923	$\overline{032}$	141	250	$\overline{358}$	86.0
4.0	8.84 358	467	575	682	790	897	$\overline{004}$	$\overline{111}$	$\overline{217}$	$\overline{323}$	$\overline{429}$	.9
.1	8.85 429	535	640	745	850	955	$\overline{059}$	$\overline{163}$	$\overline{267}$	$\overline{370}$	$\overline{474}$	.8
.2	8.86 474	577	680	782	885	987	$\overline{089}$	$\overline{190}$	$\overline{292}$	$\overline{393}$	$\overline{494}$	.7
.3	8.87 494	594	695	795	895	995	$\overline{094}$	$\overline{194}$	$\overline{293}$	$\overline{392}$	$\overline{490}$	.6
.4	8.88 490	589	687	785	883	980	$\overline{077}$	$\overline{174}$	$\overline{271}$	$\overline{368}$	$\overline{464}$	.5
.5	8.89 464	561	657	752	848	943	$\overline{038}$	$\overline{133}$	$\overline{228}$	$\overline{323}$	$\overline{417}$	.4
.6	8.90 417	511	605	699	792	885	978	$\overline{071}$	164	257	$\overline{349}$	.3
.7	8.91 349	441	533	625	716	807	898	989	$\overline{080}$	$\overline{171}$	$\overline{261}$	.2
.8	8.92 261	351	441	531	621	710	799	888	977	$\overline{066}$	$\overline{154}$	.1
.9	8.93 154	243	331	419	507	594	682	769	856	943	$\overline{030}$	85.0
	8.94											deg.
	(10)	9	8	7	6	5	4	3	2	1	0	

LOG COS

LOG SIN

deg.	0	1	2	3	4	5	6	7	8	9	(10)	Diff.
5.0	8.94 030	116	203	289	375	461	546	632	717	802	887	.9 85-87
.1	887	972	057	141	226	310	394	478	562	645	728	.8 83-85
.2	8.95 728	812	895	978	060	143	225	308	390	472	553	.7 81-84
.3	8.96 553	635	716	798	879	960	041	122	202	283	363	.6 80-82
.4	8.97 363	443	523	603	682	762	841	920	000	078	157	.5 78-80
.5	8.98 157	236	314	393	471	549	627	705	782	860	937	.4 77-79
.6	937	015	092	169	245	322	399	475	551	628	704	.3 76-78
.7	8.99 704	779	855	931	006	082	157	232	307	382	456	.2 74-76
.8	9.00 456	531	605	680	754	828	902	976	049	123	196	.1 73-75
.9	9.01 196	269	343	416	489	561	634	707	779	851	923	84.0 72-74
6.0	9.01 923	996	067	139	211	283	354	425	497	568	639	.9 71-73
.1	9.02 639	710	780	851	921	992	062	132	202	272	342	.8 70-71
.2	9.03 342	412	481	551	620	690	759	828	897	966	034	.7 68-70
.3	9.04 034	103	171	240	308	376	444	512	580	648	715	.6 67-69
.4	715	783	850	918	985	052	119	186	253	319	386	.5 66-68
.5	9.05 386	452	519	585	651	717	783	849	915	980	046	.4 65-67
.6	9.06 046	112	177	242	307	372	437	502	567	632	696	.3 64-65
.7	696	761	825	889	954	018	082	145	209	273	337	.2 63-65
.8	9.07 337	400	464	527	590	653	716	779	842	905	968	.1 63-64
.9	968	030	093	155	217	280	342	404	466	528	589	83.0 61-63
7.0	9.08 589	651	713	774	836	897	958	019	080	141	202	.9 61-62
.1	9.09 202	263	324	385	445	506	566	626	686	747	807	.8 60-61
.2	807	867	926	986	046	106	165	225	284	343	402	.7 59-60
.3	9.10 402	462	521	580	638	697	756	815	873	932	990	.6 58-60
.4	990	048	107	165	223	281	339	397	454	512	570	.5 57-59
.5	9.11 570	627	685	742	799	857	914	971	028	085	142	.4 57-58
.6	9.12 142	198	255	312	368	425	481	537	594	650	706	.3 56-57
.7	706	762	818	874	930	985	041	097	152	208	263	.2 55-56
.8	9.13 263	318	373	429	484	539	594	649	703	758	813	.1 54-56
.9	813	867	922	976	031	085	139	193	248	302	356	82.0 54-55
8.0	9.14 356	409	463	517	571	624	678	731	785	838	891	.9 53-54
.1	891	945	998	051	104	157	210	263	315	368	421	.8 52-54
.2	9.15 421	473	526	578	631	683	735	787	840	892	944	.7 52-53
.3	944	995	047	099	151	203	254	306	357	409	460	.6 51-52
.4	9.16 460	511	563	614	665	716	767	818	869	919	970	.5 50-52
.5	970	021	072	122	173	223	273	324	374	424	474	.4 50-51
.6	9.17 474	524	575	624	674	724	774	824	873	923	973	.3 49-51
.7	973	022	072	121	170	220	269	318	367	416	465	.2 49-50
.8	9.18 465	514	563	612	661	709	758	806	855	904	952	.1 48-49
.9	952	000	049	097	145	193	241	289	337	385	433	81.0 48-49
9.0	9.19 433	481	529	577	624	672	719	767	814	862	909	.9 47-48
.1	909	956	004	051	098	145	192	239	286	333	380	.8 47-48
.2	9.20 380	427	473	520	567	613	660	706	752	799	845	.7 46-47
.3	845	891	938	984	030	076	122	168	214	260	306	.6 46-47
.4	9.21 306	351	397	443	488	534	579	625	670	716	761	.5 45-46
.5	761	806	851	897	942	987	032	077	122	167	211	.4 44-46
.6	9.22 211	256	301	346	390	435	480	524	568	613	657	.3 44-45
.7	657	702	746	790	834	878	922	967	011	054	098	.2 43-45
.8	9.23 098	142	186	230	274	317	361	404	448	491	535	.1 43-44
.9	535	578	622	665	708	752	795	838	881	924	967	80.0 43-44
	(10)	9	8	7	6	5	4	3	2	1	0	deg.

LOG COS

LOG SIN

deg.	0	1	2	3	4	5	6	7	8	9	(10)	Diff.
10.0	9.23 967	010	053	096	139	181	224	267	310	352	395	.9 42-43
.1	9.24 395	437	480	522	565	607	649	692	734	776	818	.8 42-43
.2	818	860	902	944	986	028	070	112	154	196	237	.7 41-42
.3	9.25 237	279	321	362	404	445	487	528	570	611	652	.6 41-42
.4	652	694	735	776	817	858	899	940	981	022	063	.5 41-42
.5	9.26 063	104	145	186	227	267	308	349	389	430	470	.4 40-41
.6	470	511	551	592	632	672	713	753	793	833	873	.3 40-41
.7	873	913	954	994	034	073	113	153	193	233	273	.2 39-41
.8	9.27 273	312	352	392	431	471	510	550	589	629	668	.1 39-40
.9	668	707	747	786	825	864	904	943	982	021	060	79.0 39-40
11.0	9.28 060	099	138	177	216	254	293	332	371	409	448	.9 38-39
.1	448	487	525	564	602	641	679	718	756	794	833	.8 38-39
.2	833	871	909	947	985	024	062	100	138	176	214	.7 38-39
.3	9.29 214	252	289	327	365	403	441	478	516	554	591	.6 37-38
.4	591	629	666	704	741	779	816	854	891	928	966	.5 37-38
.5	966	003	040	077	114	151	188	226	263	299	336	.4 36-38
.6	9.30 336	373	410	447	484	521	557	594	631	667	704	.3 36-37
.7	704	741	777	814	850	887	923	960	996	032	068	.2 36-37
.8	9.31 068	105	141	177	213	250	286	322	358	394	430	.1 36-37
.9	430	466	502	538	573	609	645	681	717	752	788	78.0 35-36
12.0	788	824	859	895	930	966	001	037	072	108	143	.9 35-36
.1	9.32 143	178	214	249	284	319	355	390	425	460	495	.8 35-36
.2	495	530	565	600	635	670	705	740	775	809	844	.7 34-35
.3	844	879	914	948	983	018	052	087	121	156	190	.6 34-35
.4	9.33 190	225	259	294	328	362	397	431	465	499	534	.5 34-35
.5	534	568	602	636	670	704	738	772	806	840	874	.4 34
.6	874	908	942	976	010	043	077	111	145	178	212	.3 33-34
.7	9.34 212	246	279	313	346	380	413	447	480	514	547	.2 33-34
.8	547	580	614	647	680	713	747	780	813	846	879	.1 33-34
.9	879	912	945	978	011	044	077	110	143	176	209	77.0 33
13.0	9.35 209	242	274	307	340	373	405	438	471	503	536	.9 32-33
.1	536	568	601	633	666	698	731	763	796	828	860	.8 32-33
.2	860	893	925	957	989	022	054	086	118	150	182	.7 32-33
.3	9.36 182	214	246	278	310	342	374	406	438	470	502	.6 32
.4	502	533	565	597	629	660	692	724	755	787	819	.5 31-32
.5	819	850	882	913	945	976	008	039	070	102	133	.4 31-32
.6	9.37 133	164	196	227	258	289	321	352	383	414	445	.3 31-32
.7	445	476	507	538	569	600	631	662	693	724	755	.2 31
.8	755	786	817	847	878	909	940	970	001	032	062	.1 30-31
.9	9.38 062	093	124	154	185	215	246	276	307	337	368	76.0 30-31
14.0	368	398	428	459	489	519	550	580	610	640	670	.9 30-31
.1	670	701	731	761	791	821	851	881	911	941	971	.8 30-31
.2	971	001	031	061	091	121	150	180	210	240	270	.7 29-30
.3	9.39 270	299	329	359	388	418	448	477	507	536	566	.6 29-30
.4	566	595	625	654	684	713	743	772	801	831	860	.5 29-30
.5	860	889	919	948	977	006	035	065	094	123	152	.4 29-30
.6	9.40 152	181	210	239	268	297	326	355	384	413	442	.3 29
.7	442	471	500	529	557	586	615	644	672	701	730	.2 28-29
.8	730	759	787	816	844	873	902	930	959	987	016	.1 28-29
.9	9.41 016	044	073	101	130	158	186	215	243	271	300	75.0 28-29
(10)	9	8	7	6	5	4	3	2	1	0		deg.

LOG COS

LOG SIN

deg.	0	1	2	3	4	5	6	7	8	9	(10)		Diff.
15.0	9.41 300	328	356	384	413	441	469	497	525	553	582	.9	28-29
.1	582	610	638	666	694	722	750	778	806	834	861	.8	27-28
.2	861	889	917	945	973	001	029	056	084	112	140	.7	27-28
.3	9.42 140	167	195	223	250	278	305	333	361	388	416	.6	27-28
.4	416	443	471	498	526	553	580	608	635	663	690	.5	27-28
.5	690	717	745	772	799	826	854	881	908	935	962	.4	27-28
.6	962	989	017	044	071	098	125	152	179	206	233	.3	27-28
.7	9.43 233	260	287	314	341	367	394	421	448	475	502	.2	26-27
.8	502	528	555	582	609	635	662	689	715	742	769	.1	26-27
.9	769	795	822	848	875	901	928	954	981	007	034	74.0	26-27
16.0	9.44 034	060	087	113	139	166	192	218	245	271	297	.9	26-27
.1	297	324	350	376	402	428	455	481	507	533	559	.8	26-27
.2	559	585	611	637	663	689	715	741	767	793	819	.7	26
.3	819	845	871	897	923	948	974	000	026	052	077	.6	25-26
.4	9.45 077	103	129	155	180	206	232	257	283	309	334	.5	25-26
.5	334	360	385	411	436	462	487	513	538	564	589	.4	25-26
.6	589	615	640	665	691	716	742	767	792	817	843	.3	25-26
.7	843	868	893	918	944	969	994	019	044	069	095	.2	25-26
.8	9.46 095	120	145	170	195	220	245	270	295	320	345	.1	25
.9	345	370	395	420	444	469	494	519	544	569	594	73.0	24-25
17.0	594	618	643	668	693	717	742	767	791	816	841	.9	24-25
.1	841	865	890	915	939	964	988	013	037	062	086	.8	24-25
.2	9.47 086	111	135	160	184	209	233	257	282	306	330	.7	24-25
.3	330	355	379	403	428	452	476	500	525	549	573	.6	24-25
.4	573	597	621	646	670	694	718	742	766	790	814	.5	24-25
.5	814	838	862	886	910	934	958	982	006	030	054	.4	24
.6	9.48 054	078	102	125	149	173	197	221	245	268	292	.3	23-24
.7	292	316	340	363	387	411	434	458	482	505	529	.2	23-24
.8	529	552	576	600	623	647	670	694	717	741	764	.1	23-24
.9	764	788	811	835	858	881	905	928	952	975	998	72.0	23-24
18.0	998	022	045	068	091	115	138	161	184	208	231	.9	23-24
.1	9.49 231	254	277	300	323	347	370	393	416	439	462	.8	23-24
.2	462	485	508	531	554	577	600	623	646	669	692	.7	23
.3	692	715	738	761	783	806	829	852	875	898	920	.6	22-23
.4	920	943	966	989	011	034	057	080	102	125	148	.5	22-23
.5	9.50 148	170	193	216	238	261	283	306	328	351	374	.4	22-23
.6	374	396	419	441	464	486	508	531	553	576	598	.3	22-23
.7	598	620	643	665	688	710	732	755	777	799	821	.2	22-23
.8	821	844	866	888	910	933	955	977	999	021	043	.1	22-23
.9	9.51 043	066	088	110	132	154	176	198	220	242	264	71.0	22-23
19.0	264	286	308	330	352	374	396	418	440	462	484	.9	22
.1	484	506	527	549	571	593	615	637	658	680	702	.8	21-22
.2	702	724	745	767	789	811	832	854	876	897	919	.7	21-22
.3	919	941	962	984	006	027	049	070	092	113	135	.6	21-22
.4	9.52 135	156	178	199	221	242	264	285	307	328	350	.5	21-22
.5	350	371	392	414	435	456	478	499	520	542	563	.4	21-22
.6	563	584	606	627	648	669	690	712	733	754	775	.3	21-22
.7	775	796	818	839	860	881	902	923	944	965	986	.2	21-22
.8	986	007	028	049	071	092	112	133	154	175	196	.1	20-22
.9	9.53 196	217	238	259	280	301	322	343	363	384	405	70.0	20-21
(10)	9	8	7	6	5	4	3	2	1	0		deg.	

LOG COS

TRIGONOMETRIC FUNCTIONS

LOG SIN

deg.	0	1	2	3	4	5	6	7	8	9	(10)		Diff.
20.0	9.53 405	426	447	468	488	509	530	551	571	592	613	.9	20-21
.1	613	634	654	675	696	716	737	758	778	799	819	.8	20-21
.2	819	840	861	881	902	922	943	963	984	004	025	.7	20-21
.3	9.54 025	045	066	086	107	127	148	168	188	209	229	.6	20-21
.4	229	250	270	290	311	331	351	372	392	412	433	.5	20-21
.5	433	453	473	493	514	534	554	574	594	615	635	.4	20-21
.6	635	655	675	695	715	735	756	776	796	816	836	.3	20-21
.7	836	856	876	896	916	936	956	976	996	016	036	.2	20
.8	9.55 036	056	076	096	116	136	155	175	195	215	235	.1	19-20
.9	235	255	275	294	314	334	354	374	393	413	433	69.0	19-20
21.0	433	453	472	492	512	532	551	571	591	610	630	.9	19-20
.1	630	650	669	689	708	728	748	767	787	806	826	.8	19-20
.2	826	845	865	884	904	923	943	962	982	001	021	.7	19-20
.3	9.56 021	040	060	079	098	118	137	157	176	195	215	.6	19-20
.4	215	234	253	273	292	311	330	350	369	388	408	.5	19-20
.5	408	427	446	465	484	504	523	542	561	580	599	.4	19-20
.6	599	619	638	657	676	695	714	733	752	771	790	.3	19-20
.7	790	809	829	848	867	886	905	924	943	961	980	.2	18-20
.8	980	999	018	037	056	075	094	113	132	151	169	.1	18-19
.9	9.57 169	188	207	226	245	264	282	301	320	339	358	68.0	18-19
22.0	358	376	395	414	433	451	470	489	507	526	545	.9	18-19
.1	545	563	582	601	619	638	657	675	694	712	731	.8	18-19
.2	731	749	768	787	805	824	842	861	879	898	916	.7	18-19
.3	916	935	953	972	990	008	027	045	064	082	101	.6	18-19
.4	9.58 101	119	137	156	174	192	211	229	247	266	284	.5	18-19
.5	284	302	321	339	357	375	394	412	430	448	467	.4	18-19
.6	467	485	503	521	539	557	576	594	612	630	648	.3	18-19
.7	648	666	684	702	721	739	757	775	793	811	829	.2	18-19
.8	829	847	865	883	901	919	937	955	973	991	009	.1	18
.9	9.59 009	027	045	063	081	098	116	134	152	170	188	67.0	17-18
23.0	188	206	223	241	259	277	295	313	330	348	366	.9	17-18
.1	366	384	401	419	437	455	472	490	508	526	543	.8	17-18
.2	543	561	579	596	614	632	649	667	684	702	720	.7	17-18
.3	720	737	755	772	790	808	825	843	860	878	895	.6	17-18
.4	895	913	930	948	965	983	000	018	035	053	070	.5	17-18
.5	9.60 070	087	105	122	140	157	174	192	209	227	244	.4	17-18
.6	244	261	279	296	313	331	348	365	382	400	417	.3	17-18
.7	417	434	451	469	486	503	520	538	555	572	589	.2	17-18
.8	589	606	624	641	658	675	692	709	726	744	761	.1	17-18
.9	761	778	795	812	829	846	863	880	897	914	931	66.0	17
24.0	931	948	965	982	999	016	033	050	067	084	101	.9	17
.1	9.61 101	118	135	152	169	186	203	220	236	253	270	.8	16-17
.2	270	287	304	321	338	354	371	388	405	422	438	.7	16-17
.3	438	455	472	489	506	522	539	556	573	589	606	.6	16-17
.4	606	623	639	656	673	689	706	723	739	756	773	.5	16-17
.5	773	789	806	823	839	856	872	889	906	922	939	.4	16-17
.6	939	955	972	988	005	021	038	054	071	087	104	.3	16-17
.7	9.62 104	120	137	153	170	186	203	219	235	252	268	.2	16-17
.8	268	285	301	317	334	350	367	383	399	416	432	.1	16-17
.9	432	448	465	481	497	513	530	546	562	579	595	65.0	16-17
	(10)	9	8	7	6	5	4	3	2	1	0	deg.	

LOG COS

LOG SIN

deg.	0	1	2	3	4	5	6	7	8	9	(10)		Diff.
25.0	9.62 595	611	627	644	660	676	692	708	725	741	757	.9	16-17
.1	757	773	789	806	822	838	854	870	886	902	918	.8	16-17
.2	918	935	951	967	983	999	015	031	047	063	079	.7	16-17
.3	9.63 079	095	111	127	143	159	175	191	207	223	239	.6	16
.4	239	255	271	287	303	319	335	351	367	383	398	.5	15-16
.5	398	414	430	446	462	478	494	510	525	541	557	.4	15-16
.6	557	573	589	604	620	636	652	668	683	699	715	.3	15-16
.7	715	731	746	762	778	794	809	825	841	856	872	.2	15-16
.8	872	888	903	919	935	950	966	982	997	013	028	.1	15-16
.9	9.64 028	044	060	075	091	106	122	138	153	169	184	64.0	15-16
26.0	184	200	215	231	246	262	277	293	308	324	339	.9	15-16
.1	339	355	370	386	401	417	432	447	463	478	494	.8	15-16
.2	494	509	524	540	555	571	586	601	617	632	647	.7	15-16
.3	647	663	678	693	709	724	739	755	770	785	800	.6	15-16
.4	800	816	831	846	861	877	892	907	922	938	953	.5	15-16
.5	953	968	983	998	014	029	044	059	074	089	104	.4	15-16
.6	9.65 104	120	135	150	165	180	195	210	225	240	255	.3	15-16
.7	255	271	286	301	316	331	346	361	376	391	406	.2	15-16
.8	406	421	436	451	466	481	496	511	526	541	556	.1	15
.9	556	571	585	600	615	630	645	660	675	690	705	63.0	14-15
27.0	705	720	734	749	764	779	794	809	823	838	853	.9	14-15
.1	853	868	883	898	912	927	942	957	971	986	001	.8	14-15
.2	9.66 001	016	030	045	060	075	089	104	119	133	148	.7	14-15
.3	148	163	177	192	207	221	236	251	265	280	295	.6	14-15
.4	295	309	324	338	353	368	382	397	411	426	441	.5	14-15
.5	441	455	470	484	499	513	528	542	557	571	586	.4	14-15
-.6	586	600	615	629	644	658	673	687	702	716	731	.3	14-15
.7	731	745	759	774	788	803	817	831	846	860	875	.2	14-15
.8	875	889	903	918	932	946	961	975	989	004	018	.1	14-15
.9	9.67 018	032	047	061	075	090	104	118	132	147	161	62.0	14-15
28.0	161	175	189	204	218	232	246	261	275	289	303	.9	14-15
.1	303	317	332	346	360	374	388	402	417	431	445	.8	14-15
.2	445	459	473	487	501	515	530	544	558	572	586	.7	14-15
.3	586	600	614	628	642	656	670	684	698	712	726	.6	14
.4	726	740	754	768	782	796	810	824	838	852	866	.5	14
.5	866	880	894	908	922	936	950	964	978	992	006	.4	14
.6	9.68 006	020	033	047	061	075	089	103	117	130	144	.3	13-14
.7	144	158	172	186	200	213	227	241	255	269	283	.2	13-14
.8	283	296	310	324	338	351	365	379	393	406	420	.1	13-14
.9	420	434	448	461	475	489	502	516	530	543	557	61.0	13-14
29.0	557	571	584	598	612	625	639	653	666	680	694	.9	13-14
.1	694	707	721	734	748	762	775	789	802	816	829	.8	13-14
.2	829	843	857	870	884	897	911	924	938	951	965	.7	13-14
.3	965	978	992	005	019	032	046	059	073	086	100	.6	13-14
.4	9.69 100	113	127	140	153	167	180	194	207	220	234	.5	13-14
.5	234	247	261	274	287	301	314	328	341	354	368	.4	13-14
.6	368	381	394	408	421	434	448	461	474	487	501	.3	13-14
.7	501	514	527	541	554	567	580	594	607	620	633	.2	13-14
.8	633	647	660	673	686	699	713	726	739	752	765	.1	13-14
.9	765	779	792	805	818	831	844	858	871	884	897	60.0	13-14
	(10)	9	8	7	6	5	4	3	2	1	0	deg.	

LOG COS

LOG SIN

deg.	0	1	2	3	4	5	6	7	8	9	(10)		Diff.
30.0	9.69 897	910	923	936	949	963	976	989	002	015	028	.9	13-14
.1	9.70 028	041	054	067	080	093	106	119	132	145	159	.8	13-14
.2	159	172	185	198	211	224	237	250	263	276	288	.7	12-13
.3	288	301	314	327	340	353	366	379	392	405	418	.6	13
.4	418	431	444	457	470	482	495	508	521	534	547	.5	12-13
.5	547	560	573	585	598	611	624	637	650	662	675	.4	12-13
.6	675	688	701	714	727	739	752	765	778	790	803	.3	12-13
.7	803	816	829	842	854	867	880	892	905	918	931	.2	12-13
.8	931	943	956	969	981	994	007	020	032	045	058	.1	12-13
.9	9.71 058	070	083	096	108	121	133	146	159	171	184	59.0	12-13
31.0	184	197	209	222	234	247	260	272	285	297	310	.9	12-13
.1	310	322	335	348	360	373	385	398	410	423	435	.8	12-13
.2	435	448	460	473	485	498	510	523	535	548	560	.7	12-13
.3	560	573	585	598	610	622	635	647	660	672	685	.6	12-13
.4	685	697	709	722	734	747	759	771	784	796	809	.5	12-13
.5	809	821	833	846	858	870	883	895	907	920	932	.4	12-13
.6	932	944	957	969	981	994	006	018	030	043	055	.3	12-13
.7	9.72 055	067	079	092	104	116	128	141	153	165	177	.2	12-13
.8	177	190	202	214	226	238	251	263	275	287	299	.1	12-13
.9	299	312	324	336	348	360	372	385	397	409	421	58.0	12-13
32.0	421	433	445	457	469	482	494	506	518	530	542	.9	12-13
.1	542	554	566	578	590	602	614	627	639	651	663	.8	12-13
.2	663	675	687	699	711	723	735	747	759	771	783	.7	12
.3	783	795	807	819	831	843	855	867	879	890	902	.6	11-12
.4	902	914	926	938	950	962	974	986	998	010	022	.5	12
.5	9.73 022	034	045	057	069	081	093	105	117	129	140	.4	11-12
.6	140	152	164	176	188	200	211	223	235	247	259	.3	11-12
.7	259	271	282	294	306	318	329	341	353	365	377	.2	11-12
.8	377	388	400	412	424	435	447	459	470	482	494	.1	11-12
.9	494	506	517	529	541	552	564	576	588	599	611	57.0	11-12
33.0	611	623	634	646	658	669	681	692	704	716	727	.9	11-12
.1	727	739	751	762	774	785	797	809	820	832	843	.8	11-12
.2	843	855	867	878	890	901	913	924	936	947	959	.7	11-12
.3	959	971	982	994	005	017	028	040	051	063	074	.6	11-12
.4	9.74 074	086	097	109	120	132	143	155	166	177	189	.5	11-12
.5	189	200	212	223	235	246	258	269	280	292	303	.4	11-12
.6	303	315	326	337	349	360	372	383	394	406	417	.3	11-12
.7	417	428	440	451	463	474	485	497	508	519	531	.2	11-12
.8	531	542	553	565	576	587	598	610	621	632	644	.1	11-12
.9	644	655	666	677	689	700	711	722	734	745	756	56.0	11-12
34.0	756	767	779	790	801	812	824	835	846	857	868	.9	11-12
.1	868	880	891	902	913	924	935	947	958	969	980	.8	11-12
.2	980	991	002	014	025	036	047	058	069	080	091	.7	11-12
.3	9.75 091	103	114	125	136	147	158	169	180	191	202	.6	11-12
.4	202	213	224	236	247	258	269	280	291	302	313	.5	11-12
.5	313	324	335	346	357	368	379	390	401	412	423	.4	11
.6	423	434	445	456	467	478	489	500	511	522	533	.3	11
.7	533	544	554	565	576	587	598	609	620	631	642	.2	10-11
.8	642	653	664	675	685	696	707	718	729	740	751	.1	10-11
.9	751	762	772	783	794	805	816	827	837	848	859	55.0	10-11
	(10)	9	8	7	6	5	4	3	2	1	0	deg.	

LOG COS

LOG SIN

deg.		0	1	2	3	4	5	6	7	8	9	(10)		Diff.
35.0	9.75	859	870	881	892	902	913	924	935	946	956	967	.9	10-11
.1		967	978	989	000	010	021	032	043	053	064	075	.8	10-11
.2	9.76	075	086	096	107	118	129	139	150	161	171	182	.7	10-11
.3		182	193	203	214	225	236	246	257	268	278	289	.6	10-11
.4		289	300	310	321	332	342	353	364	374	385	395	.5	10-11
.5		395	406	417	427	438	448	459	470	480	491	501	.4	10-11
.6		501	512	523	533	544	554	565	575	586	597	607	.3	10-11
.7		607	618	628	639	649	660	670	681	691	702	712	.2	10-11
.8		712	723	733	744	754	765	775	786	796	807	817	.1	10-11
.9		817	828	838	849	859	870	880	891	901	911	922	54.0	10-11
36.0		922	932	943	953	964	974	984	995	005	016	026	.9	10-11
.1	9.77	026	036	047	057	068	078	088	099	109	119	130	.8	10-11
.2		130	140	150	161	171	181	192	202	212	223	233	.7	10-11
.3		233	243	254	264	274	285	295	305	316	326	336	.6	10-11
.4		336	346	357	367	377	387	398	408	418	429	439	.5	10-11
.5		439	449	459	469	480	490	500	510	521	531	541	.4	10-11
.6		541	551	561	572	582	592	602	612	623	633	643	.3	10-11
.7		643	653	663	673	684	694	704	714	724	734	744	.2	10-11
.8		744	755	765	775	785	795	805	815	825	835	846	.1	10-11
.9		846	856	866	876	886	896	906	916	926	936	946	53.0	10
37.0		946	956	966	976	987	997	007	017	027	037	047	.9	10-11
.1	9.78	047	057	067	077	087	097	107	117	127	137	147	.8	10
.2		147	157	167	177	187	197	207	217	227	236	246	.7	9-10
.3		246	256	266	276	286	296	306	316	326	336	346	.6	10
.4		346	356	366	375	385	395	405	415	425	435	445	.5	9-10
.5		445	455	464	474	484	494	504	514	524	533	543	.4	9-10
.6		543	553	563	573	583	592	602	612	622	632	642	.3	9-10
.7		642	651	661	671	681	691	700	710	720	730	739	.2	9-10
.8		739	749	759	769	779	788	798	808	818	827	837	.1	9-10
.9		837	847	856	866	876	886	895	905	915	924	934	52.0	9-10
38.0		934	944	954	963	973	983	992	002	012	021	031	.9	9-10
.1	9.79	031	041	050	060	070	079	089	099	108	118	128	.8	9-10
.2		128	137	147	156	166	176	185	195	204	214	224	.7	9-10
.3		224	233	243	252	262	272	281	291	300	310	319	.6	9-10
.4		319	329	339	348	358	367	377	386	396	405	415	.5	9-10
.5		415	424	434	444	453	463	472	482	491	501	510	.4	9-10
.6		510	520	529	539	548	558	567	576	586	595	605	.3	9-10
.7		605	614	624	633	643	652	662	671	680	690	699	.2	9-10
.8		699	709	718	728	737	746	756	765	775	784	793	.1	9-10
.9		793	803	812	822	831	840	850	859	868	878	887	51.0	9-10
39.0		887	897	906	915	925	934	943	953	962	971	981	.9	9-10
.1		981	990	999	009	018	027	037	046	055	064	074	.8	9-10
.2	9.80	074	083	092	102	111	120	129	139	148	157	166	.7	9-10
.3		166	176	185	194	204	213	222	231	240	250	259	.6	9-10
.4		259	268	277	287	296	305	314	323	333	342	351	.5	9-10
.5		351	360	369	379	388	397	406	415	425	434	443	.4	9-10
.6		443	452	461	470	479	489	498	507	516	525	534	.3	9-10
.7		534	543	553	562	571	580	589	598	607	616	625	.2	9-10
.8		625	635	644	653	662	671	680	689	698	707	716	.1	9-10
.9		716	725	734	743	752	762	771	780	789	798	807	50.0 deg.	9-10
	(10)	9	8	7		6	5	4		3	2	1	0		

LOG COS

LOG SIN

deg.	0	1	2	3	4	5	6	7	8	9	(10)		Diff.
40.0	9.80 807	816	825	834	843	852	861	870	879	888	897	.9	9
.1	897	906	915	924	933	942	951	960	969	978	987	.8	9
.2	987	996	005	014	023	032	041	049	058	067	076	.7	8-9
.3	9.81 076	085	094	103	112	121	130	139	148	157	166	.6	9
.4	166	174	183	192	201	210	219	228	237	246	254	.5	8-9
.5	254	263	272	281	290	299	308	316	325	334	343	.4	8-9
.6	343	352	361	370	378	387	396	405	414	422	431	.3	8-9
.7	431	440	449	458	467	475	484	493	502	510	519	.2	8-9
.8	519	528	537	546	554	563	572	581	589	598	607	.1	8-9
.9	607	616	624	633	642	651	659	668	677	686	694	49.0	8-9
41.0	694	703	712	720	729	738	747	755	764	773	781	.9	8-9
.1	781	790	799	807	816	825	833	842	851	859	868	.8	8-9
.2	868	877	885	894	903	911	920	929	937	946	955	.7	8-9
.3	955	963	972	980	989	998	006	015	023	032	041	.6	8-9
.4	9.82 041	049	058	066	075	084	092	101	109	118	126	.5	8-9
.5	126	135	144	152	161	169	178	186	195	203	212	.4	8-9
.6	212	221	229	238	246	255	263	272	280	289	297	.3	8-9
.7	297	306	314	323	331	340	348	357	365	374	382	.2	8-9
.8	382	391	399	408	416	424	433	441	450	458	467	.1	8-9
.9	467	475	484	492	501	509	517	526	534	543	551	48.0	8-9
42.0	551	560	568	576	585	593	602	610	618	627	635	.9	8-9
.1	635	644	652	660	669	677	685	694	702	711	719	.8	8-9
.2	719	727	736	744	752	761	769	777	786	794	802	.7	8-9
.3	802	811	819	827	836	844	852	861	869	877	885	.6	8-9
.4	885	894	902	910	919	927	935	944	952	960	968	.5	8-9
.5	968	977	985	993	001	010	018	026	034	043	051	.4	8-9
.6	9.83 051	059	067	076	084	092	100	109	117	125	133	.3	8-9
.7	133	141	150	158	166	174	182	191	199	207	215	.2	8-9
.8	215	223	232	240	248	256	264	272	281	289	297	.1	8-9
.9	297	305	313	321	330	338	346	354	362	370	378	47.0	8-9
43.0	378	386	395	403	411	419	427	435	443	451	459	.9	8-9
.1	459	468	476	484	492	500	508	516	524	532	540	.8	8-9
.2	540	548	556	565	573	581	589	597	605	613	621	.7	8-9
.3	621	629	637	645	653	661	669	677	685	693	701	.6	8
.4	701	709	717	725	733	741	749	757	765	773	781	.5	8
.5	781	789	797	805	813	821	829	837	845	853	861	.4	8
.6	861	869	877	885	893	901	909	917	925	932	940	.3	7-8
.7	940	948	956	964	972	980	988	996	004	012	020	.2	8
.8	9.84 020	027	035	043	051	059	067	075	083	091	098	.1	7-8
.9	098	106	114	122	130	138	146	154	161	169	177	46.0	7-8
44.0	177	185	193	201	209	216	224	232	240	248	255	.9	7-8
.1	255	263	271	279	287	295	302	310	318	326	334	.8	7-8
.2	334	341	349	357	365	373	380	388	396	404	411	.7	7-8
.3	411	419	427	435	442	450	458	466	473	481	489	.6	7-8
.4	489	497	504	512	520	528	535	543	551	558	566	.5	7-8
.5	566	574	582	589	597	605	612	620	628	635	643	.4	7-8
.6	643	651	659	666	674	682	689	697	705	712	720	.3	7-8
.7	720	728	735	743	751	758	766	773	781	789	796	.2	7-8
.8	796	804	812	819	827	835	842	850	857	865	873	.1	7-8
.9	873	880	888	895	903	911	918	926	933	941	949	45.0	7-8
	(10)	9	8	7	6	5	4	3	2	1	0	deg.	

LOG COS

LOG SIN

deg.	0	1	2	3	4	5	6	7	8	9	(10)	Diff.
45.0	9.84 949	956	964	971	979	986	994	0̄0̄1̄	0̄0̄9̄	0̄1̄7̄	0̄2̄4̄	.9
.1	9.85 024	032	039	047	054	062	069	077	085	092	100	.8
.2	100	107	115	122	130	137	145	152	160	167	175	.7	7-8
.3	175	182	190	197	205	212	220	227	235	242	250	.6
.4	250	257	265	272	279	287	294	302	309	317	324	.5
.5	324	332	339	347	354	361	369	376	384	391	399	.4
.6	399	406	413	421	428	436	443	450	458	465	473	.3
.7	473	480	487	495	502	510	517	524	532	539	547	.2
.8	547	554	561	569	576	583	591	598	605	613	620	.1
.9	620	627	635	642	649	657	664	671	679	686	693	44.0
46.0	693	701	708	715	723	730	737	745	752	759	766	.9
.1	766	774	781	788	796	803	810	817	825	832	839	.8
.2	839	847	854	861	868	876	883	890	897	905	912	.7
.3	912	919	926	934	941	948	955	962	970	977	984	.6
.4	984	991	999	0̄0̄6̄	0̄1̄3̄	0̄2̄0̄	0̄2̄7̄	0̄3̄5̄	0̄4̄2̄	0̄4̄9̄	0̄5̄6̄	.5
.5	9.86 056	063	071	078	085	092	099	107	114	121	128	.4
.6	128	135	142	150	157	164	171	178	185	192	200	.3
.7	200	207	214	221	228	235	242	250	257	264	271	.2
.8	271	278	285	292	299	306	314	321	328	335	342	.1
.9	342	349	356	363	370	377	384	392	399	406	413	43.0
47.0	413	420	427	434	441	448	455	462	469	476	483	.9
.1	483	490	497	504	511	518	526	533	540	547	554	.8
.2	554	561	568	575	582	589	596	603	610	617	624	.7	7
.3	624	631	638	645	652	659	666	673	680	687	694	.6
.4	694	700	707	714	721	728	735	742	749	756	763	.5
.5	763	770	777	784	791	798	805	812	819	826	832	.4
.6	832	839	846	853	860	867	874	881	888	895	902	.3
.7	902	908	915	922	929	936	943	950	957	963	970	.2
.8	970	977	984	991	998	0̄0̄5̄	0̄1̄2̄	0̄1̄8̄	0̄2̄5̄	0̄3̄2̄	0̄3̄9̄	.1
.9	9.87 039	046	053	060	066	073	080	087	094	101	107	42.0
48.0	107	114	121	128	135	141	148	155	162	169	175	.9
.1	175	182	189	196	203	209	216	223	230	237	243	.8
.2	243	250	257	264	270	277	284	291	298	304	311	.7
.3	311	318	325	331	338	345	351	358	365	372	378	.6
.4	378	385	392	399	405	412	419	425	432	439	446	.5
.5	446	452	459	466	472	479	486	492	499	506	513	.4
.6	513	519	526	533	539	546	553	559	566	573	579	.3
.7	579	586	593	599	606	613	619	626	632	639	646	.2
.8	646	652	659	666	672	679	686	692	699	705	712	.1
.9	712	719	725	732	738	745	752	758	765	771	778	41.0
49.0	778	785	791	798	804	811	817	824	831	837	844	.9
.1	844	850	857	863	870	877	883	890	896	903	909	.8
.2	909	916	922	929	935	942	949	955	962	968	975	.7
.3	975	981	988	994	0̄0̄1̄	0̄0̄7̄	0̄1̄4̄	0̄2̄0̄	0̄2̄7̄	0̄3̄3̄	0̄4̄0̄	.6	6-7
.4	9.88 040	046	053	059	066	072	079	085	092	098	105	.5
.5	105	111	117	124	130	137	143	150	156	163	169	.4
.6	169	176	182	189	195	201	208	214	221	227	234	.3
.7	234	240	246	253	259	266	272	279	285	291	298	.2
.8	298	304	311	317	323	330	336	343	349	355	362	.1
.9	362	368	374	381	387	394	400	406	413	419	425	40.0
												deg.
	(10)	9	8	7	6	5	4	3	2	1	0	

LOG COS

LOG SIN

deg.	0	1	2	3	4	5	6	7	8	9	(10)	Diff.	
50.0	9.88 425	432	438	444	451	457	464	470	476	483	489	.9	6-7
.1	489	495	502	508	514	521	527	533	540	546	552	.8	
.2	552	558	565	571	577	584	590	596	603	609	615	.7	
.3	615	621	628	634	640	647	653	659	665	672	678	.6	
.4	678	684	691	697	703	709	716	722	728	734	741	.5	
.5	741	747	753	759	766	772	778	784	791	797	803	.4	
.6	803	809	815	822	828	834	840	847	853	859	865	.3	
.7	865	871	878	884	890	896	902	909	915	921	927	.2	
.8	927	933	939	946	952	958	964	970	976	983	989	.1	
.9	989	995	001	007	013	020	026	032	038	044	050	39.0	
51.0	9.89 050	056	063	069	075	081	087	093	099	105	112	.9	
.1	112	118	124	130	136	142	148	154	160	166	173	.8	
.2	173	179	185	191	197	203	209	215	221	227	233	.7	
.3	233	239	246	252	258	264	270	276	282	288	294	.6	
.4	294	300	306	312	318	324	330	336	342	348	354	.5	
.5	354	360	366	373	379	385	391	397	403	409	415	.4	
.6	415	421	427	433	439	445	451	457	463	469	475	.3	6
.7	475	481	487	493	499	504	510	516	522	528	534	.2	
.8	534	540	546	552	558	564	570	576	582	588	594	.1	
.9	594	600	606	612	618	624	630	635	641	647	653	38.0	
52.0	653	659	665	671	677	683	689	695	701	706	712	.9	
.1	712	718	724	730	736	742	748	754	759	765	771	.8	
.2	771	777	783	789	795	801	806	812	818	824	830	.7	
.3	830	836	842	847	853	859	865	871	877	883	888	.6	
.4	888	894	900	906	912	918	923	929	935	941	947	.5	
.5	947	952	958	964	970	976	982	987	993	999	005	.4	
.6	9.90 005	011	016	022	028	034	039	045	051	057	063	.3	
.7	063	068	074	080	086	091	097	103	109	114	120	.2	
.8	120	126	132	137	143	149	155	160	166	172	178	.1	
.9	178	183	189	195	201	206	212	218	223	229	235	37.0	
53.0	235	241	246	252	258	263	269	275	280	286	292	.9	
.1	292	298	303	309	315	320	326	332	337	343	349	.8	
.2	349	354	360	366	371	377	383	388	394	400	405	.7	
.3	405	411	417	422	428	434	439	445	450	456	462	.6	
.4	462	467	473	479	484	490	495	501	507	512	518	.5	
.5	518	523	529	535	540	546	551	557	563	568	574	.4	
.6	574	579	585	591	596	602	607	613	618	624	630	.3	
.7	630	635	641	646	652	657	663	669	674	680	685	.2	
.8	685	691	696	702	707	713	718	724	730	735	741	.1	
.9	741	746	752	757	763	768	774	779	785	790	796	36.0	
54.0	796	801	807	812	818	823	829	834	840	845	851	.9	5-6
.1	851	856	862	867	873	878	884	889	895	900	906	.8	
.2	906	911	916	922	927	933	938	944	949	955	960	.7	
.3	960	966	971	976	982	987	993	998	004	009	014	.6	
.4	9.91 014	020	025	031	036	042	047	052	058	063	069	.5	
.5	069	074	079	085	090	096	101	106	112	117	123	.4	
.6	123	128	133	139	144	149	155	160	166	171	176	.3	
.7	176	182	187	192	198	203	209	214	219	225	230	.2	
.8	230	235	241	246	251	257	262	267	273	278	283	.1	
.9	283	289	294	299	305	310	315	321	326	331	336	35.0 deg.	
(10)		9	8	7	6	5	4	3	2	1	0		

LOG COS

LOG SIN

deg.	0	1	2	3	4	5	6	7	8	9	(10)	Diff.	
55.0	9.91 336	342	347	352	358	363	368	374	379	384	389	.9	5-6
.1	389	395	400	405	411	416	421	426	432	437	442	.8	
.2	442	447	453	458	463	469	474	479	484	490	495	.7	
.3	495	500	505	511	516	521	526	531	537	542	547	.6	
.4	547	552	558	563	568	573	579	584	589	594	599	.5	
.5	599	605	610	615	620	625	631	636	641	646	651	.4	
.6	651	657	662	667	672	677	682	688	693	698	703	.3	
.7	703	708	714	719	724	729	734	739	744	750	755	.2	
.8	755	760	765	770	775	781	786	791	796	801	806	.1	
.9	806	811	816	822	827	832	837	842	847	852	857	34.0	
56.0	857	863	868	873	878	883	888	893	898	903	908	.9	
.1	908	914	919	924	929	934	939	944	949	954	959	.8	
.2	959	964	969	975	980	985	990	995	000	005	010	.7	
.3	9.92 010	015	020	025	030	035	040	045	050	055	060	.6	
.4	060	065	070	075	081	086	091	096	101	106	111	.5	
.5	111	116	121	126	131	136	141	146	151	156	161	.4	5
.6	161	166	171	176	181	186	191	196	201	206	211	.3	
.7	211	216	221	226	231	235	240	245	250	255	260	.2	
.8	260	265	270	275	280	285	290	295	300	305	310	.1	
.9	310	315	320	325	330	335	339	344	349	354	359	33.0	
57.0	359	364	369	374	379	384	389	394	398	403	408	.9	
.1	408	413	418	423	428	433	438	443	447	452	457	.8	
.2	457	462	467	472	477	482	486	491	496	501	506	.7	
.3	506	511	516	521	525	530	535	540	545	550	555	.6	
.4	555	559	564	569	574	579	584	588	593	598	603	.5	
.5	603	608	613	617	622	627	632	637	641	646	651	.4	
.6	651	656	661	666	670	675	680	685	690	694	699	.3	
.7	699	704	709	713	718	723	728	733	737	742	747	.2	
.8	747	752	756	761	766	771	776	780	785	790	795	.1	
.9	795	799	804	809	814	818	823	828	833	837	842	32.0	
58.0	842	847	852	856	861	866	870	875	880	885	889	.9	
.1	889	894	899	903	908	913	918	922	927	932	936	.8	
.2	936	941	946	951	955	960	965	969	974	979	983	.7	
.3	983	988	993	997	002	007	011	016	021	025	030	.6	
.4	9.93 030	035	039	044	049	053	058	063	067	072	077	.5	
.5	077	081	086	091	095	100	104	109	114	118	123	.4	
.6	123	128	132	137	141	146	151	155	160	165	169	.3	
.7	169	174	178	183	188	192	197	201	206	211	215	.2	
.8	215	220	224	229	233	238	243	247	252	256	261	.1	
.9	261	265	270	275	279	284	288	293	297	302	307	31.0	
59.0	307	311	316	320	325	329	334	338	343	347	352	.9	
.1	352	357	361	366	370	375	379	384	388	393	397	.8	
.2	397	402	406	411	415	420	424	429	433	438	442	.7	4-5
.3	442	447	451	456	460	465	469	474	478	483	487	.6	
.4	487	492	496	501	505	510	514	519	523	528	532	.5	
.5	532	537	541	545	550	554	559	563	568	572	577	.4	
.6	577	581	585	590	594	599	603	608	612	617	621	.3	
.7	621	625	630	634	639	643	648	652	656	661	665	.2	
.8	665	670	674	678	683	687	692	696	700	705	709	.1	
.9	709	714	718	722	727	731	736	740	744	749	753	30.0	
	(10)	9	8	7	6	5	4	3	2	1	0	deg.	

LOG COS

LOG SIN

deg.	0	1	2	3	4	5	6	7	8	9	(10)	Diff.	
60.0	9.93 753	757	762	766	771	775	779	784	788	792	797	.9	4-5
.1	797	801	805	810	814	819	823	827	832	836	840	.8	
.2	840	845	849	853	858	862	866	871	875	879	884	.7	
.3	884	888	892	897	901	905	909	914	918	922	927	.6	
.4	927	931	935	940	944	948	953	957	961	965	970	.5	
.5	970	974	978	983	987	991	995	000	004	008	012	.4	
.6	9.94 012	017	021	025	030	034	038	042	047	051	055	.3	
.7	055	059	064	068	072	076	081	085	089	093	098	.2	
.8	098	102	106	110	114	119	123	127	131	136	140	.1	
.9	140	144	148	152	157	161	165	169	174	178	182	29.0	
61.0	182	186	190	195	199	203	207	211	215	220	224	.9	
.1	224	228	232	236	241	245	249	253	257	261	266	.8	
.2	266	270	274	278	282	286	291	295	299	303	307	.7	
.3	307	311	315	320	324	328	332	336	340	344	349	.6	
.4	349	353	357	361	365	369	373	377	382	386	390	.5	
.5	390	394	398	402	406	410	415	419	423	427	431	.4	
.6	431	435	439	443	447	451	455	460	464	468	472	.3	
.7	472	476	480	484	488	492	496	500	504	508	513	.2	
.8	513	517	521	525	529	533	537	541	545	549	553	.1	
.9	553	557	561	565	569	573	577	581	585	589	593	28.0	
62.0	593	598	602	606	610	614	618	622	626	630	634	.9	
.1	634	638	642	646	650	654	658	662	666	670	674	.8	4
.2	674	678	682	686	690	694	698	702	706	710	714	.7	
.3	714	718	722	726	730	734	737	741	745	749	753	.6	
.4	753	757	761	765	769	773	777	781	785	789	793	.5	
.5	793	797	801	805	809	813	817	820	824	828	832	.4	
.6	832	836	840	844	848	852	856	860	864	868	871	.3	
.7	871	875	879	883	887	891	895	899	903	907	911	.2	
.8	911	914	918	922	926	930	934	938	942	946	949	.1	
.9	949	953	957	961	965	969	973	976	980	984	988	27.0	
63.0	988	992	996	000	004	007	011	015	019	023	027	.9	
.1	9.95 027	030	034	038	042	046	050	054	057	061	065	.8	
.2	065	069	073	076	080	084	088	092	096	099	103	.7	
.3	103	107	111	115	118	122	126	130	134	137	141	.6	
.4	141	145	149	153	156	160	164	168	172	175	179	.5	
.5	179	183	187	190	194	198	202	206	209	213	217	.4	
.6	217	221	224	228	232	236	239	243	247	251	254	.3	
.7	254	258	262	266	269	273	277	281	284	288	292	.2	
.8	292	295	299	303	307	310	314	318	322	325	329	.1	
.9	329	333	336	340	344	348	351	355	359	362	366	26.0	
64.0	366	370	373	377	381	384	388	392	396	399	403	.9	
.1	403	407	410	414	418	421	425	429	432	436	440	.8	
.2	440	443	447	451	454	458	462	465	469	473	476	.7	
.3	476	480	483	487	491	494	498	502	505	509	513	.6	
.4	513	516	520	523	527	531	534	538	542	545	549	.5	
.5	549	552	556	560	563	567	570	574	578	581	585	.4	
.6	585	588	592	596	599	603	606	610	614	617	621	.3	
.7	621	624	628	632	635	639	642	646	649	653	657	.2	
.8	657	660	664	667	671	674	678	681	685	689	692	.1	
.9	692	696	699	703	706	710	713	717	720	724	728	25.0	3-4
	(10)	9	8	7	6	5	4	3	2	1	0	deg.	

LOG COS

LOG SIN

deg.	0	1	2	3	4	5	6	7	8	9	(10)	Diff.
65.0	9.95 728	731	735	738	742	745	749	752	756	759	763	.9
.1	763	766	770	773	777	780	784	787	791	794	798	.8 3-4
.2	798	801	805	808	812	815	819	822	826	829	833	.7
.3	833	836	840	843	847	850	854	857	861	864	868	.6
.4	868	871	875	878	882	885	888	892	895	899	902	.5
.5	902	906	909	913	916	920	923	926	930	933	937	.4
.6	937	940	944	947	950	954	957	961	964	968	971	.3
.7	971	974	978	981	985	988	992	995	998	002	005	.2
.8	9.96 005	009	012	015	019	022	026	029	032	036	039	.1
.9	039	043	046	049	053	056	060	063	066	070	073	24.0
66.0	073	076	080	083	087	090	093	097	100	103	107	.9
.1	107	110	113	117	120	123	127	130	134	137	140	.8
.2	140	144	147	150	154	157	160	164	167	170	174	.7
.3	174	177	180	184	187	190	193	197	200	203	207	.6
.4	207	210	213	217	220	223	227	230	233	236	240	.5
.5	240	243	246	250	253	256	260	263	266	269	273	.4
.6	273	276	279	282	286	289	292	296	299	302	305	.3
.7	305	309	312	315	318	322	325	328	331	335	338	.2
.8	338	341	344	348	351	354	357	361	364	367	370	.1
.9	370	374	377	380	383	387	390	393	396	399	403	23.0
67.0	403	406	409	412	415	419	422	425	428	432	435	.9
.1	435	438	441	444	447	451	454	457	460	463	467	.8
.2	467	470	473	476	479	483	486	489	492	495	498	.7
.3	498	502	505	508	511	514	517	521	524	527	530	.6
.4	530	533	536	540	543	546	549	552	555	558	562	.5
.5	562	565	568	571	574	577	580	583	587	590	593	.4
.6	593	596	599	602	605	608	612	615	618	621	624	.3
.7	624	627	630	633	636	640	643	646	649	652	655	.2
.8	655	658	661	664	667	670	674	677	680	683	686	.1
.9	686	689	692	695	698	701	704	707	710	714	717	22.0
68.0	717	720	723	726	729	732	735	738	741	744	747	.9
.1	747	750	753	756	759	762	765	768	771	774	778	.8
.2	778	781	784	787	790	793	796	799	802	805	808	.7
.3	808	811	814	817	820	823	826	829	832	835	838	.6 3
.4	838	841	844	847	850	854	856	859	862	865	868	.5
.5	868	871	874	877	880	883	886	889	892	895	898	.4
.6	898	901	904	906	909	912	915	918	921	924	927	.3
.7	927	930	933	936	939	942	945	948	951	954	957	.2
.8	957	960	963	965	968	971	974	977	980	983	986	.1
.9	986	989	992	995	998	001	004	006	009	012	015	21.0
69.0	9.97 015	018	021	024	027	030	033	036	038	041	044	.9
.1	044	047	050	053	056	059	062	064	067	070	073	.8
.2	073	076	079	082	085	087	090	093	096	099	102	.7
.3	102	105	108	110	113	116	119	122	125	127	130	.6
.4	130	133	136	139	142	145	147	150	153	156	159	.5
.5	159	162	164	167	170	173	176	179	181	184	187	.4
.6	187	190	193	195	198	201	204	207	210	212	215	.3
.7	215	218	221	224	226	229	232	235	238	240	243	.2
.8	243	246	249	251	254	257	260	263	265	268	271	.1
.9	271	274	276	279	282	285	288	290	293	296	299	20.0 2-3
(10)	9	8	7	6	5	4	3	2	1	0		deg.

LOG COS

LOG SIN

deg.	0	1	2	3	4	5	6	7	8	9	(10)		Diff.
70.0	9.97 299	301	304	307	310	312	315	318	321	323	326	.9	2-3
.1	326	329	332	334	337	340	343	345	348	351	353	.8	
.2	353	356	359	362	364	367	370	373	375	378	381	.7	
.3	381	383	386	389	392	394	397	400	402	405	408	.6	
.4	408	410	413	416	419	421	424	427	429	432	435	.5	
.5	435	437	440	443	445	448	451	453	456	459	461	.4	
.6	461	464	467	469	472	475	477	480	483	485	488	.3	
.7	488	491	493	496	499	501	504	507	509	512	515	.2	
.8	515	517	520	522	525	528	530	533	536	538	541	.1	
.9	541	543	546	549	551	554	557	559	562	564	567	19.0	
71.0	567	570	572	575	577	580	583	585	588	590	593	.9	
.1	593	596	598	601	603	606	609	611	614	616	619	.8	
.2	619	621	624	627	629	632	634	637	640	642	645	.7	
.3	645	647	650	652	655	657	660	663	665	668	670	.6	
.4	670	673	675	678	680	683	686	688	691	693	696	.5	
.5	696	698	701	703	706	708	711	713	716	718	721	.4	
.6	721	723	726	729	731	734	736	739	741	744	746	.3	
.7	746	749	751	754	756	759	761	764	766	769	771	.2	2-3
.8	771	774	776	779	781	784	786	788	791	793	796	.1	
.9	796	798	801	803	806	808	811	813	816	818	821	18.0	
72.0	821	823	826	828	830	833	835	838	840	843	845	.9	
.1	845	848	850	853	855	857	860	862	865	867	870	.8	
.2	870	872	874	877	879	882	884	887	889	891	894	.7	
.3	894	896	899	901	904	906	908	911	913	916	918	.6	
.4	918	920	923	925	928	930	932	935	937	940	942	.5	
.5	942	944	947	949	951	954	956	959	961	963	966	.4	
.6	966	968	971	973	975	978	980	982	985	987	989	.3	
.7	989	992	994	997	999	001	004	006	008	011	013	.2	
.8	9.98 013	015	018	020	022	025	027	029	032	034	036	.1	
.9	036	039	041	043	046	048	050	053	055	057	060	17.0	
73.0	060	062	064	067	069	071	074	076	078	080	083	.9	
.1	083	085	087	090	092	094	097	099	101	103	106	.8	
.2	106	108	110	113	115	117	119	122	124	126	129	.7	
.3	129	131	133	135	138	140	142	144	147	149	151	.6	
.4	151	153	156	158	160	162	165	167	169	171	174	.5	
.5	174	176	178	180	183	185	187	189	192	194	196	.4	
.6	196	198	201	203	205	207	209	212	214	216	218	.3	
.7	218	221	223	225	227	229	232	234	236	238	240	.2	
.8	240	243	245	247	249	251	254	256	258	260	262	.1	
.9	262	265	267	269	271	273	275	278	280	282	284	16.0	
74.0	284	286	289	291	293	295	297	299	302	304	306	.9	
.1	306	308	310	312	314	317	319	321	323	325	327	.8	
.2	327	329	332	334	336	338	340	342	344	347	349	.7	
.3	349	351	353	355	357	359	361	364	366	368	370	.6	
.4	370	372	374	376	378	381	383	385	387	389	391	.5	
.5	391	393	395	397	399	402	404	406	408	410	412	.4	
.6	412	414	416	418	420	422	425	427	429	431	433	.3	
.7	433	435	437	439	441	443	445	447	449	451	453	.2	
.8	453	456	458	460	462	464	466	468	470	472	474	.1	
.9	474	476	478	480	482	484	486	488	490	492	494	15.0	
	(10)	9	8	7	6	5	4	3	2	1	0	deg.	

LOG COS

LOG SIN

deg.	0	1	2	3	4	5	6	7	8	9	(10)	Diff.
75.0	9.98 494	496	498	500	502	505	507	509	511	513	515	.9 2-3
.1	515	517	519	521	523	525	527	529	531	533	535	.8
.2	535	537	539	541	543	545	547	549	551	553	555	.7 2
.3	555	557	559	561	563	565	567	569	571	573	574	.6
.4	574	576	578	580	582	584	586	588	590	592	594	.5
.5	594	596	598	600	602	604	606	608	610	612	614	.4
.6	614	616	618	620	621	623	625	627	629	631	633	.3
.7	633	635	637	639	641	643	645	647	648	650	652	.2
.8	652	654	656	658	660	662	664	666	668	670	671	.1
.9	671	673	675	677	679	681	683	685	687	689	690	14.0
76.0	690	692	694	696	698	700	702	704	705	707	709	.9
.1	709	711	713	715	717	719	720	722	724	726	728	.8
.2	728	730	732	734	735	737	739	741	743	745	746	.7
.3	746	748	750	752	754	756	758	759	761	763	765	.6
.4	765	767	769	770	772	774	776	778	780	781	783	.5
.5	783	785	787	789	790	792	794	796	798	799	801	.4
.6	801	803	805	807	808	810	812	814	816	817	819	.3
.7	819	821	823	825	826	828	830	832	834	835	837	.2
.8	837	839	841	842	844	846	848	850	851	853	855	.1
.9	855	857	858	860	862	864	865	867	869	871	872	13.0
77.0	872	874	876	878	879	881	883	885	886	888	890	.9
.1	890	892	893	895	897	898	900	902	904	905	907	.8
.2	907	909	911	912	914	916	917	919	921	923	924	.7
.3	924	926	928	929	931	933	934	936	938	940	941	.6
.4	941	943	945	946	948	950	951	953	955	956	958	.5
.5	958	960	962	963	965	967	968	970	972	973	975	.4
.6	975	977	978	980	982	983	985	987	988	990	991	.3
.7	991	993	995	996	998	$\overline{000}$	$\overline{001}$	$\overline{003}$	$\overline{005}$	$\overline{006}$	$\overline{008}$	.2
.8	9.99 008	010	011	013	014	016	018	019	021	023	024	.1
.9	024	026	028	029	031	032	034	036	037	039	040	12.0
78.0	040	042	044	045	047	048	050	052	053	055	056	.9
.1	056	058	060	061	063	064	066	068	069	071	072	.8
.2	072	074	076	077	079	080	082	083	085	087	088	.7
.3	088	090	091	093	094	096	098	099	101	102	104	.6
.4	104	105	107	108	110	112	113	115	116	118	119	.5
.5	119	121	122	124	125	127	128	130	132	133	135	.4
.6	135	136	138	139	141	142	144	145	147	148	150	.3
.7	150	151	153	154	156	157	159	160	162	163	165	.2 1-2
.8	165	166	168	169	171	172	174	175	177	178	180	.1
.9	180	181	183	184	186	187	189	190	192	193	195	11.0
79.0	195	196	198	199	201	202	203	205	206	208	209	.9
.1	209	211	212	214	215	217	218	220	221	222	224	.8
.2	224	225	227	228	230	231	233	234	235	237	238	.7
.3	238	240	241	243	244	245	247	248	250	251	252	.6
.4	252	254	255	257	258	260	261	262	264	265	267	.5
.5	267	268	269	271	272	274	275	276	278	279	281	.4
.6	281	282	283	285	286	288	289	290	292	293	294	.3
.7	294	296	297	299	300	301	303	304	305	307	308	.2
.8	308	310	311	312	314	315	316	318	319	320	322	.1
.9	322	323	324	326	327	328	330	331	332	334	335	10.0
	(10)	9	8	7	6	5	4	3	2	1	0	deg.

LOG COS

LOG SIN

deg.	0	1	2	3	4	5	6	7	8	9	(10)	Diff.
80.0	9.99 335	336	338	339	340	342	343	344	346	347	348	.9 1-2
.1	348	350	351	352	354	355	356	358	359	360	362	.8
.2	362	363	364	366	367	368	369	371	372	373	375	.7
.3	375	376	377	379	380	381	382	384	385	386	388	.6
.4	388	389	390	391	393	394	395	396	398	399	400	.5
.5	400	402	403	404	405	407	408	409	410	412	413	.4
.6	413	414	415	417	418	419	420	422	423	424	425	.3
.7	425	427	428	429	430	432	433	434	435	436	438	.2
.8	438	439	440	441	443	444	445	446	447	449	450	.1
.9	450	451	452	454	455	456	457	458	460	461	462	9.0
81.0	462	463	464	466	467	468	469	470	472	473	474	.9
.1	474	475	476	477	479	480	481	482	483	485	486	.8
.2	486	487	488	489	490	492	493	494	495	496	497	.7
.3	497	499	500	501	502	503	504	505	507	508	509	.6
.4	509	510	511	512	514	515	516	517	518	519	520	.5
.5	520	521	523	524	525	526	527	528	529	530	532	.4
.6	532	533	534	535	536	537	538	539	540	542	543	.3
.7	543	544	545	546	547	548	549	550	552	553	554	.2
.8	554	555	556	557	558	559	560	561	562	563	565	.1
.9	565	566	567	568	569	570	571	572	573	574	575	8.0
82.0	575	576	577	578	580	581	582	583	584	585	586	.9
.1	586	587	588	589	590	591	592	593	594	595	596	.8
.2	596	597	598	599	600	601	603	604	605	606	607	.7
.3	607	608	609	610	611	612	613	614	615	616	617	.6
.4	617	618	619	620	621	622	623	624	625	626	627	.5 1
.5	627	628	629	630	631	632	633	634	635	636	637	.4
.6	637	638	639	640	641	642	643	644	645	646	647	.3
.7	647	648	648	649	650	651	652	653	654	655	656	.2
.8	656	657	658	659	660	661	662	663	664	665	666	.1
.9	666	667	668	669	669	670	671	672	673	674	675	7.0
83.0	675	676	677	678	679	680	681	682	682	683	684	.9
.1	684	685	686	687	688	689	690	691	692	693	693	.8
.2	693	694	695	696	697	698	699	700	701	701	702	.7
.3	702	703	704	705	706	707	708	709	709	710	711	.6
.4	711	712	713	714	715	716	716	717	718	719	720	.5
.5	720	721	722	723	723	724	725	726	727	728	728	.4
.6	728	729	730	731	732	733	734	734	735	736	737	.3
.7	737	738	739	739	740	741	742	743	744	744	745	.2
.8	745	746	747	748	749	749	750	751	752	753	753	.1
.9	753	754	755	756	757	757	758	759	760	761	761	6.0
84.0	761	762	763	764	765	765	766	767	768	769	769	.9
.1	769	770	771	772	772	773	774	775	776	776	777	.8
.2	777	778	779	779	780	781	782	782	783	784	785	.7
.3	785	785	786	787	788	788	789	790	791	791	792	.6
.4	792	793	794	794	795	796	797	797	798	799	800	.5
.5	800	800	801	802	803	803	804	805	805	806	807	.4
.6	807	808	808	809	810	810	811	812	813	813	814	.3
.7	814	815	815	816	817	817	818	819	820	820	821	.2
.8	821	822	822	823	824	824	825	826	826	827	828	.1
.9	828	828	829	830	830	831	832	832	833	834	834	5.0 0-1
(10)	9	8	7	6	5	4	3	2	1	0		deg.

LOG COS

LOG SIN

deg.	0	1	2	3	4	5	6	7	8	9	(10)	Diff.
85.0	9.99 834	835	836	836	837	838	838	839	840	840	841	.9 0-1
.1	841	842	842	843	844	844	845	846	846	847	847	.8
.2	847	848	849	849	850	851	851	852	852	853	854	.7
.3	854	854	855	856	856	857	857	858	859	859	860	.6
.4	860	860	861	862	862	863	864	864	865	865	866	.5
.5	866	867	867	868	868	869	869	870	871	871	872	.4
.6	872	872	873	874	874	875	875	876	876	877	878	.3
.7	878	878	879	879	880	880	881	882	882	883	883	.2
.8	883	884	884	885	885	886	887	887	888	888	889	.1
.9	889	889	890	890	891	891	892	892	893	894	894	4.0
86.0	894	895	895	896	896	897	897	898	898	899	899	.9
.1	899	900	900	901	901	902	902	903	903	904	904	.8
.2	904	905	905	906	906	907	907	908	908	909	909	.7
.3	909	910	910	911	911	912	912	913	913	914	914	.6
.4	914	915	915	916	916	917	917	918	918	918	919	.5
.5	919	919	920	920	921	921	922	922	923	923	923	.4
.6	923	924	924	925	925	926	926	927	927	927	928	.3
.7	928	928	929	929	930	930	931	931	931	932	932	.2
.8	932	933	933	933	934	934	935	935	936	936	936	.1
.9	936	937	937	938	938	938	939	939	940	940	940	3.0
87.0	940	941	941	942	942	942	943	943	944	944	944	.9
.1	944	945	945	945	946	946	947	947	947	948	948	.8
.2	948	948	949	949	950	950	950	951	951	951	952	.7
.3	952	952	952	953	953	954	954	954	955	955	955	.6
.4	955	956	956	956	957	957	957	958	958	958	959	.5
.5	959	959	959	960	960	960	961	961	961	962	962	.4
.6	962	962	963	963	963	963	964	964	964	965	965	.3
.7	965	965	966	966	966	967	967	967	967	968	968	.2
.8	968	968	969	969	969	969	970	970	970	971	971	.1
.9	971	971	971	972	972	972	972	973	973	973	974	2.0
88.0	974	974	974	974	975	975	975	975	976	976	976	.9
.1	976	976	977	977	977	977	978	978	978	978	979	.8
.2	979	979	979	979	980	980	980	980	980	981	981	.7
.3	981	981	981	982	982	982	982	982	983	983	983	.6
.4	983	983	983	984	984	984	984	985	985	985	985	.5
.5	985	985	986	986	986	986	986	986	987	987	987	.4
.6	987	987	987	988	988	988	988	988	988	989	989	.3
.7	989	989	989	989	989	990	990	990	990	990	990	.2
.8	990	991	991	991	991	991	991	992	992	992	992	.1
.9	992	992	992	992	993	993	993	993	993	993	993	1.0
89.0	993	994	994	994	994	994	994	994	994	995	995	.9
.1	995	995	995	995	995	995	995	995	996	996	996	.8
.2	996	996	996	996	996	996	996	996	997	997	997	.7
.3	997	997	997	997	997	997	997	997	997	998	998	.6
.4	998	998	998	998	998	998	998	998	998	998	998	.5
.5	998	998	998	999	999	999	999	999	999	999	999	.4
.6	999	999	999	999	999	999	999	999	999	999	999	.3
.7	999	999	999	0̅0̅0̅	0̅0̅0̅	0̅0̅0̅	0̅0̅0̅	0̅0̅0̅	0̅0̅0̅	0̅0̅0̅	0̅0̅0̅	.2
.8	10.00 000	000	000	000	000	000	000	000	000	000	000	.1
.9	000	000	000	000	000	000	000	000	000	000	000	0.0 0-1
90.0	000											deg.
	(10)	9	8	7	6	5	4	3	2	1	0	

LOG COS

DEG.	LOG TAN		DEG.	LOG TAN	
0.00	.....	90.00	0.50	7.94 086	89.50
.01	6.24 188	89.99	.51	7.94 946	.49
.02	6.54 291	.98	.52	7.95 789	.48
.03	6.71 900	.97	.53	7.96 617	.47
.04	6.84 394	.96	.54	7.97 428	.46
.05	6.94 085	.95	.55	7.98 225	.45
.06	7.02 003	.94	.56	7.99 008	.44
.07	7.08 698	.93	.57	7.99 777	.43
.08	7.14 497	.92	.58	8.00 532	.42
.09	7.19 612	.91	.59	8.01 274	.41
0.10	7.24 188	89.90	0.60	8.02 004	89.40
.11	7.28 327	.89	.61	8.02 722	.39
.12	7.32 106	.88	.62	8.03 429	.38
.13	7.35 582	.87	.63	8.04 124	.37
.14	7.38 801	.86	.64	8.04 808	.36
.15	7.41 797	.85	.65	8.05 481	.35
.16	7.44 600	.84	.66	8.06 144	.34
.17	7.47 233	.83	.67	8.06 797	.33
.18	7.49 715	.82	.68	8.07 441	.32
.19	7.52 063	.81	.69	8.08 075	.31
0.20	7.54 291	89.80	0.70	8.08 700	89.30
.21	7.56 410	.79	.71	8.09 316	.29
.22	7.58 430	.78	.72	8.09 923	.28
.23	7.60 361	.77	.73	8.10 522	.27
.24	7.62 209	.76	.74	8.11 113	.26
.25	7.63 982	.75	.75	8.11 696	.25
.26	7.65 685	.74	.76	8.12 272	.24
.27	7.67 324	.73	.77	8.12 839	.23
.28	7.68 904	.72	.78	8.13 400	.22
.29	7.70 428	.71	.79	8.13 953	.21
0.30	7.71 900	89.70	0.80	8.14 500	89.20
.31	7.73 324	.69	.81	8.15 039	.19
.32	7.74 703	.68	.82	8.15 572	.18
.33	7.76 040	.67	.83	8.16 099	.17
.34	7.77 336	.66	.84	8.16 619	.16
.35	7.78 595	.65	.85	8.17 133	.15
.36	7.79 819	.64	.86	8.17 641	.14
.37	7.81 009	.63	.87	8.18 143	.13
.38	7.82 167	.62	.88	8.18 639	.12
.39	7.83 295	.61	.89	8.19 130	.11
0.40	7.84 394	89.60	0.90	8.19 616	89.10
.41	7.85 467	.59	.91	8.20 096	.09
.42	7.86 513	.58	.92	8.20 570	.08
.43	7.87 535	.57	.93	8.21 040	.07
.44	7.88 534	.56	.94	8.21 504	.06
.45	7.89 510	.55	.95	8.21 964	.05
.46	7.90 464	.54	.96	8.22 419	.04
.47	7.91 398	.53	.97	8.22 869	.03
.48	7.92 313	.52	.98	8.23 315	.02
.49	7.93 208	89.51	.99	8.23 756	89.01
	LOG COT	DEG.		LOG COT	DEG.

DEG.	LOG TAN		DEG.	LOG TAN	
1.00	8.24 192	89.00	1.50	8.41 807	88.50
.01	8.24 624	88.99	.51	8.42 095	.49
.02	8.25 052	.98	.52	8.42 382	.48
.03	8.25 476	.97	.53	8.42 667	.47
.04	8.25 896	.96	.54	8.42 950	.46
.05	8.26 312	.95	.55	8.43 232	.45
.06	8.26 723	.94	.56	8.43 511	.44
.07	8.27 131	.93	.57	8.43 789	.43
.08	8.27 535	.92	.58	8.44 064	.42
.09	8.27 936	.91	.59	8.44 339	.41
1.10	8.28 332	88.90	1.60	8.44 611	88.40
.11	8.28 725	.89	.61	8.44 882	.39
.12	8.29 115	.88	.62	8.45 151	.38
.13	8.29 501	.87	.63	8.45 418	.37
.14	8.29 884	.86	.64	8.45 684	.36
.15	8.30 263	.85	.65	8.45 948	.35
.16	8.30 639	.84	.66	8.46 211	.34
.17	8.31 012	.83	.67	8.46 472	.33
.18	8.31 382	.82	.68	8.46 731	.32
.19	8.31 749	.81	.69	8.46 989	.31
1.20	8.32 112	88.80	1.70	8.47 245	88.30
.21	8.32 473	.79	.71	8.47 500	.29
.22	8.32 830	.78	.72	8.47 754	.28
.23	8.33 185	.77	.73	8.48 006	.27
.24	8.33 537	.76	.74	8.48 256	.26
.25	8.33 886	.75	.75	8.48 505	.25
.26	8.34 232	.74	.76	8.48 753	.24
.27	8.34 575	.73	.77	8.48 999	.23
.28	8.34 916	.72	.78	8.49 244	.22
.29	8.35 254	.71	.79	8.49 487	.21
1.30	8.35 590	88.70	1.80	8.49 729	88.20
.31	8.35 922	.69	.81	8.49 970	.19
.32	8.36 253	.68	.82	8.50 209	.18
.33	8.36 581	.67	.83	8.50 448	.17
.34	8.36 906	.66	.84	8.50 684	.16
.35	8.37 229	.65	.85	8.50 920	.15
.36	8.37 550	.64	.86	8.51 154	.14
.37	8.37 868	.63	.87	8.51 387	.13
.38	8.38 184	.62	.88	8.51 619	.12
.39	8.38 498	.61	.89	8.51 850	.11
1.40	8.38 809	88.60	1.90	8.52 079	88.10
.41	8.39 118	.59	.91	8.52 307	.09
.42	8.39 425	.58	.92	8.52 534	.08
.43	8.39 730	.57	.93	8.52 760	.07
.44	8.40 033	.56	.94	8.52 985	.06
.45	8.40 334	.55	.95	8.53 208	.05
.46	8.40 632	.54	.96	8.53 430	.04
.47	8.40 929	.53	.97	8.53 651	.03
.48	8.41 224	.52	.98	8.53 872	.02
.49	8.41 516	88.51	.99	8.54 091	88.01
	LOG COT	DEG.		LOG COT	DEG.

TRIGONOMETRIC FUNCTIONS

LOG TAN

Deg.		0	1	2	3	4	5	6	7	8	9	(10)	
2.0	8.54	308	525	741	956								
	8.55					169	382	593	804	$\overline{013}$	$\overline{222}$	$\overline{429}$	.9
.1	8.56	429	636	841									
	8.57				046	249	452	654	854	$\overline{054}$	$\overline{253}$	$\overline{451}$	.8
.2	8.58	451	649	845									
	8.59				040	235	428	621	813	$\overline{004}$	$\overline{194}$	$\overline{384}$	.7
.3	8.60	384	572	760	947								
	8.61					133	319	504	687	870	$\overline{053}$	$\overline{234}$	.6
.4	8.62	234	415	595	774	953							
	8.63						131	$\overline{308}$	$\overline{484}$	$\overline{660}$	$\overline{835}$	$\overline{009}$	.5
.5	8.64	009	183	356	528	700	870	$\overline{041}$	$\overline{210}$	$\overline{379}$	$\overline{547}$	$\overline{715}$	.4
.6	8.65	715	882										
	8.66			048	214	379	543	707	870	$\overline{033}$	$\overline{195}$	$\overline{356}$	.3
.7	8.67	356	517	677	837	996	$\overline{154}$	$\overline{312}$	$\overline{470}$	$\overline{626}$	$\overline{783}$	$\overline{938}$	.2
.8	8.68	938											
	8.69		093	248	402	$\overline{555}$	$\overline{708}$	$\overline{860}$	$\overline{012}$	$\overline{164}$	$\overline{314}$	$\overline{465}$	.1
.9	8.70	465	614	764	912	$\overline{061}$	$\overline{208}$	$\overline{356}$	$\overline{502}$	$\overline{649}$	$\overline{794}$	$\overline{940}$	87.0
3.0	8.71	940											
	8.72		084	229	373	516	659	801	943	$\overline{085}$	$\overline{226}$	$\overline{366}$	.9
.1	8.73	366	506	646	785	924	$\overline{063}$	$\overline{201}$	$\overline{338}$	$\overline{475}$	$\overline{612}$	$\overline{748}$	.8
.2	8.74	748	884										
	8.75			019	154	289	423	556	690	823	955	$\overline{087}$	.7
.3	8.76	087	219	350	481	612	742	871	$\overline{001}$	$\overline{130}$	$\overline{258}$	$\overline{387}$	.6
.4	8.77	387	514	642	769	$\overline{896}$	$\overline{022}$	$\overline{148}$	$\overline{274}$	$\overline{399}$	$\overline{524}$	$\overline{649}$	.5
.5	8.78	649	773	897	$\overline{020}$	$\overline{143}$	$\overline{266}$	$\overline{389}$	$\overline{511}$	$\overline{633}$	$\overline{754}$	$\overline{875}$	.4
.6	8.79	875	996										
	8.80			116	237	356	476	595	714	832	950	$\overline{068}$	.3
.7	8.81	068	186	303	420	537	653	769	885	$\overline{000}$	$\overline{115}$	$\overline{230}$	.2
.8	8.82	230	344	458	572	686	799	$\overline{912}$	$\overline{025}$	$\overline{137}$	$\overline{249}$	$\overline{361}$	.1
.9	8.83	361	473	584	695	806	916	$\overline{026}$	$\overline{136}$	$\overline{246}$	$\overline{355}$	$\overline{464}$	86.0
4.0	8.84	464	573	682	790	898	$\overline{006}$	$\overline{113}$	$\overline{220}$	$\overline{327}$	$\overline{434}$	$\overline{540}$	.9
.1	8.85	540	646	752	858	$\overline{963}$	$\overline{069}$	$\overline{173}$	$\overline{278}$	$\overline{383}$	$\overline{487}$	$\overline{591}$	.8
.2	8.86	591	694	798	901	$\overline{004}$	$\overline{106}$	$\overline{209}$	$\overline{311}$	$\overline{413}$	$\overline{515}$	$\overline{616}$	.7
.3	8.87	616	717	819	919	$\overline{020}$	$\overline{120}$	$\overline{220}$	$\overline{320}$	$\overline{420}$	$\overline{519}$	$\overline{618}$	.6
.4	8.88	618	717	816	915	$\overline{013}$	$\overline{111}$	$\overline{209}$	$\overline{307}$	$\overline{404}$	$\overline{501}$	$\overline{598}$	.5
.5	8.89	598	695	792	888	984	$\overline{080}$	$\overline{176}$	$\overline{272}$	$\overline{367}$	$\overline{462}$	$\overline{557}$	.4
.6	8.90	557	652	746	841	935	$\overline{029}$	$\overline{122}$	$\overline{216}$	$\overline{309}$	$\overline{402}$	$\overline{495}$	.3
.7	8.91	495	588	680	773	865	957	$\overline{049}$	$\overline{140}$	$\overline{231}$	$\overline{323}$	$\overline{414}$	.2
.8	8.92	414	504	595	685	776	866	956	$\overline{045}$	$\overline{135}$	$\overline{224}$	$\overline{313}$	.1
.9	8.93	313	402	491	580	668	756	845	932	$\overline{020}$	$\overline{108}$	$\overline{195}$	85.0
	8.94												deg.
	(10)	9	8	7	6	5	4	3	2	1	0		

LOG COT

LOG TAN

deg.	0	1	2	3	4	5	6	7	8	9	(10)		Diff.
5.0	8.94 195	282	369	456	543	630	716	802	888	974	060	.9	86-87
.1	8.95 060	145	231	316	401	486	570	655	739	823	908	.8	84-86
.2	8.95 908	991	075	159	242	325	409	492	574	657	739	.7	82-84
.3	8.96 739	822	904	986	068	150	231	313	394	475	556	.6	81-83
.4	8.97 556	637	717	798	878	959	039	119	199	278	358	.5	79-81
.5	8.98 358	437	516	595	674	753	832	910	989	067	145	.4	78-79
.6	8.99 145	223	301	379	456	534	611	688	765	842	919	.3	77-78
.7	919	995	072	148	225	301	377	452	528	604	679	.2	75-77
.8	9.00 679	755	830	905	980	055	129	204	278	353	427	.1	74-76
.9	9.01 427	501	575	649	722	796	869	943	016	089	162	84.0	73-74
6.0	9.02 162	235	308	380	453	525	597	670	742	813	885	.9	71-73
.1	885	957	028	100	171	242	314	385	455	526	597	.8	70-72
.2	9.03 597	667	738	808	878	948	018	088	158	228	297	.7	69-71
.3	9.04 297	367	436	505	574	643	712	781	850	918	987	.6	68-70
.4	987	055	124	192	260	328	396	463	531	599	666	.5	67-69
.5	9.05 666	733	801	868	935	002	068	135	202	268	335	.4	66-68
.6	9.06 335	401	467	534	600	666	731	797	863	928	994	.3	65-67
.7	994	059	124	190	255	320	385	449	514	579	643	.2	64-66
.8	9.07 643	708	772	836	900	964	028	092	156	220	283	.1	63-65
.9	9.08 283	347	410	474	537	600	663	726	789	852	914	83.0	62-64
7.0	914	977	040	102	164	227	289	351	413	475	537	.9	62-63
.1	9.09 537	598	660	722	783	845	906	967	028	089	150	.8	61-62
.2	9.10 150	211	272	333	394	454	515	575	635	696	756	.7	60-61
.3	756	816	876	936	996	056	115	175	234	294	353	.6	59-60
.4	9.11 353	413	472	531	590	649	708	767	826	884	943	.5	58-60
.5	943	001	060	118	177	235	293	351	409	467	525	.4	58-59
.6	9.12 525	583	640	698	756	813	870	928	985	042	099	.3	57-58
.7	9.13 099	156	213	270	327	384	441	497	554	610	667	.2	56-57
.8	667	723	779	835	892	948	004	060	115	171	227	.1	55-57
.9	9.14 227	283	338	394	449	504	560	615	670	725	780	82.0	55-56
8.0	780	835	890	945	000	054	109	164	218	273	327	.9	54-55
.1	9.15 327	381	435	490	544	598	652	706	760	813	867	.8	53-55
.2	867	921	974	028	081	135	188	241	295	348	401	.7	53-54
.3	9.16 401	454	507	560	613	665	718	771	823	876	928	.6	52-53
.4	928	981	033	085	138	190	242	294	346	398	450	.5	52-53
.5	9.17 450	502	553	605	657	708	760	811	863	914	965	.4	51-52
.6	965	017	068	119	170	221	272	323	374	425	475	.3	50-52
.7	9.18 475	526	577	627	678	728	778	829	879	929	979	.2	50-51
.8	979	029	080	130	179	229	279	329	379	428	478	.1	49-51
.9	9.19 478	528	577	627	676	725	775	824	873	922	971	81.0	49-50
9.0	971	020	069	118	167	216	265	313	362	411	459	.9	48-49
.1	9.20 459	508	556	605	653	701	750	798	846	894	942	.8	48-49
.2	942	990	038	086	134	182	229	277	325	372	420	.7	47-48
.3	9.21 420	467	515	562	610	657	704	751	798	846	893	.6	47-48
.4	893	940	987	034	080	127	174	221	267	314	361	.5	46-47
.5	9.22 361	407	454	500	547	593	639	685	732	778	824	.4	46-47
.6	824	870	916	962	008	054	100	146	191	237	283	.3	45-46
.7	9.23 283	328	374	419	465	510	556	601	646	692	737	.2	45-46
.8	737	782	827	872	917	962	007	052	097	142	186	.1	44-45
.9	9.24 186	231	276	321	365	410	454	499	543	588	632	80.0 deg.	44-45
	(10)	9	8	7	6	5	4	3	2	1	0		

LOG COT

LOG TAN

deg.	0	1	2	3	4	5	6	7	8	9	(10)		Diff.
10.0	9.24 632	676	720	765	809	853	897	941	985	$\overline{029}$	$\overline{073}$	.9	44-45
.1	9.25 073	117	161	205	248	292	336	379	423	466	510	.8	43-44
.2	510	553	597	640	684	727	770	813	857	900	943	.7	43-44
.3	943	986	029	072	115	158	201	243	286	329	372	.6	42-43
.4	9.26 372	414	457	500	542	585	627	670	712	754	797	.5	42-43
.5	797	839	881	923	966	008	050	092	134	176	218	.4	42-43
.6	9.27 218	260	302	343	385	427	469	510	552	594	635	.3	41-42
.7	635	677	718	760	801	842	884	925	966	008	049	.2	41-42
.8	9.28 049	090	131	172	213	254	295	336	377	418	459	.1	41
.9	459	500	540	581	622	662	703	744	784	825	865	79.0	40-41
11.0	865	906	946	986	$\overline{027}$	$\overline{067}$	$\overline{107}$	$\overline{148}$	$\overline{188}$	$\overline{228}$	$\overline{268}$	.9	40-41
.1	9.29 268	308	348	388	428	468	508	548	588	628	668	.8	40
.2	668	707	747	787	827	866	906	945	985	024	064	.7	39-40
.3	9.30 064	103	143	182	221	261	300	339	378	418	457	.6	39-40
.4	457	496	535	574	613	652	691	730	769	807	846	.5	38-39
.5	846	885	924	963	001	040	078	117	156	194	233	.4	38-39
.6	9.31 233	271	310	348	386	425	463	501	540	578	616	.3	38-39
.7	616	654	692	730	768	806	844	882	920	958	996	.2	38
.8	996	034	072	110	147	185	223	260	298	336	373	.1	37-38
.9	9.32 373	411	448	486	523	561	598	636	673	710	747	78.0	37-38
12.0	747	785	822	859	896	933	971	$\overline{008}$	$\overline{045}$	$\overline{082}$	$\overline{119}$	.9	37-38
.1	9.33 119	156	193	230	266	303	340	377	414	450	487	.8	36-37
.2	487	524	560	597	634	670	707	743	780	816	853	.7	36-37
.3	853	889	925	962	998	034	071	107	143	179	215	.6	36-37
.4	9.34 215	252	288	324	360	396	432	468	504	540	576	.5	36-37
.5	576	611	647	683	719	755	790	826	862	897	933	.4	35-36
.6	933	968	004	040	075	111	146	181	217	252	288	.3	35-36
.7	9.35 288	323	358	394	429	464	499	534	570	605	640	.2	35-36
.8	640	675	710	745	780	815	850	885	920	955	989	.1	34-35
.9	989	024	059	094	128	163	198	233	267	302	336	77.0	34-35
13.0	9.36 336	371	406	440	475	509	543	578	612	647	681	.9	34-35
.1	681	715	750	784	818	852	887	921	955	989	$\overline{023}$	.8	34-35
.2	9.37 023	057	091	125	159	193	227	261	295	329	363	.7	34
.3	363	397	431	464	498	532	566	599	633	667	700	.6	33-34
.4	700	734	768	801	835	868	902	935	969	002	$\overline{035}$	.5	33-34
.5	9.38 035	069	102	135	169	202	235	269	302	335	368	.4	33-34
.6	368	401	434	468	501	534	567	600	633	666	699	.3	33-34
.7	699	732	765	797	830	863	896	929	962	994	$\overline{027}$	.2	32-33
.8	9.39 027	060	092	125	158	190	223	256	288	321	353	.1	32-33
.9	353	386	418	451	483	515	548	580	612	645	677	76.0	32-33
14.0	677	709	742	774	806	838	870	903	935	967	999	.9	32-33
.1	999	$\overline{031}$	$\overline{063}$	$\overline{095}$	$\overline{127}$	$\overline{159}$	$\overline{191}$	$\overline{223}$	$\overline{255}$	$\overline{287}$	$\overline{319}$	.8	32
.2	9.40 319	351	382	414	446	478	510	541	573	605	636	.7	31-32
.3	636	668	700	731	763	795	826	858	889	921	952	.6	31-32
.4	952	984	$\overline{015}$	$\overline{046}$	$\overline{078}$	$\overline{109}$	$\overline{141}$	$\overline{172}$	$\overline{203}$	$\overline{235}$	$\overline{266}$	.5	31-32
.5	9.41 266	297	328	360	391	422	453	484	515	546	578	.4	31-32
.6	578	609	640	671	702	733	764	795	825	856	887	.3	30-31
.7	887	918	949	980	$\overline{011}$	$\overline{041}$	$\overline{072}$	$\overline{103}$	$\overline{134}$	$\overline{164}$	$\overline{195}$	.2	30-31
.8	9.42 195	226	256	287	318	348	379	410	440	471	501	.1	30-31
.9	501	532	562	593	623	653	684	714	745	775	805	75.0	30-31
	(10)	9	8	7	6	5	4	3	2	1	0	deg.	

LOG COT

LOG TAN

deg.	0	1	2	3	4	5	6	7	8	9	(10)		Diff.
15.0	9.42 805	836	866	896	926	957	987	017	047	077	108	.9	30-31
.1	9.43 108	138	168	198	228	258	288	318	348	378	408	.8	30
.2	408	438	468	498	528	558	587	617	647	677	707	.7	29-30
.3	707	736	766	796	826	855	885	915	944	974	004	.6	29-30
.4	9.44 004	033	063	092	122	151	181	210	240	269	299	.5	29-30
.5	299	328	358	387	416	446	475	504	534	563	592	.4	29-30
.6	592	622	651	680	709	738	768	797	826	855	884	.3	29-30
.7	884	913	942	971	000	029	058	087	116	145	174	.2	29
.8	9.45 174	203	232	261	290	319	348	376	405	434	463	.1	28-29
.9	463	492	520	549	578	606	635	664	692	721	750	74.0	28-29
16.0	750	778	807	835	864	892	921	950	978	006	035	.9	28-29
.1	9.46 035	063	092	120	149	177	205	234	262	290	319	.8	28-29
.2	319	347	375	403	432	460	488	516	544	573	601	.7	28-29
.3	601	629	657	685	713	741	769	797	825	853	881	.6	28
.4	881	909	937	965	993	021	049	077	105	133	160	.5	27-28
.5	9.47 160	188	216	244	272	299	327	355	383	410	438	.4	27-28
.6	438	466	493	521	549	576	604	632	659	687	714	.3	27-28
.7	714	742	769	797	824	852	879	907	934	961	989	.2	27-28
.8	989	016	044	071	098	126	153	180	208	235	262	.1	27-28
.9	9.48 262	289	317	344	371	398	425	453	480	507	534	73.0	27-28
17.0	534	561	588	615	642	669	696	723	750	777	804	.9	27
.1	804	831	858	885	912	939	966	993	020	046	073	.8	26-27
.2	9.49 073	100	127	154	181	207	234	261	288	314	341	.7	26-27
.3	341	368	394	421	448	474	501	528	554	581	607	.6	26-27
.4	607	634	660	687	713	740	766	793	819	846	872	.5	26-27
.5	872	899	925	951	978	004	031	057	083	110	136	.4	26-27
.6	9.50 136	162	188	215	241	267	293	320	346	372	398	.3	26-27
.7	398	424	451	477	503	529	555	581	607	633	659	.2	26-27
.8	659	685	711	737	763	789	815	841	867	893	919	.1	26
.9	919	945	971	997	023	048	074	100	126	152	178	72.0	25-26
18.0	9.51 178	203	229	255	281	306	332	358	384	409	435	.9	25-26
.1	435	461	486	512	537	563	589	614	640	665	691	.8	25-26
.2	691	717	742	768	793	819	844	870	895	920	946	.7	25-26
.3	946	971	997	022	047	073	098	124	149	174	200	.6	25-26
.4	9.52 200	225	250	275	301	326	351	376	402	427	452	.5	25-26
.5	452	477	502	528	553	578	603	628	653	678	703	.4	25-26
.6	703	728	753	778	804	829	854	879	904	929	953	.3	24-26
.7	953	978	003	028	053	078	103	128	153	178	202	.2	24-25
.8	9.53 202	227	252	277	302	327	351	376	401	426	450	.1	24-25
.9	450	475	500	525	549	574	599	623	648	673	697	71.0	24-25
19.0	697	722	746	771	796	820	845	869	894	918	943	.9	24-25
.1	943	967	992	016	041	065	090	114	139	163	187	.8	24-25
.2	9.54 187	212	236	261	285	309	334	358	382	407	431	.7	24-25
.3	431	455	480	504	528	552	577	601	625	649	673	.6	24-25
.4	673	698	722	746	770	794	818	843	867	891	915	.5	24-25
.5	915	939	963	987	011	035	059	083	107	131	155	.4	24
.6	9.55 155	179	203	227	251	275	299	323	347	371	395	.3	24
.7	395	418	442	466	490	514	538	562	585	609	633	.2	23-24
.8	633	657	680	704	728	752	775	799	823	847	870	.1	23-24
.9	870	894	918	941	965	989	012	036	059	083	107	70.0	23-24
9.56												deg.	
	(10)	9	8	7	6	5	4	3	2	1	0		

LOG COT

LOG TAN

deg.	0	1	2	3	4	5	6	7	8	9	(10)		Diff.
20.0	9.56 107	130	154	177	201	224	248	271	295	318	342	.9	23-24
.1	342	365	389	412	436	459	483	506	530	553	576	.8	23-24
.2	576	600	623	646	670	693	716	740	763	786	810	.7	23-24
.3	810	833	856	880	903	926	949	973	996	019	042	.6	23-24
.4	9.57 042	065	089	112	135	158	181	204	228	251	274	.5	23-24
.5	274	297	320	343	366	389	412	435	458	481	504	.4	23
.6	504	527	550	573	596	619	642	665	688	711	734	.3	23
.7	734	757	780	803	826	849	871	894	917	940	963	.2	22-23
.8	963	986	009	031	054	077	100	122	145	168	191	.1	22-23
.9	9.58 191	213	236	259	282	304	327	350	372	395	418	69.0	22-23
21.0	418	440	463	486	508	531	554	576	599	621	644	.9	22-23
.1	644	666	689	712	734	757	779	802	824	847	869	.8	22-23
.2	869	892	914	937	959	981	004	026	049	071	094	.7	22-23
.3	9.59 094	116	138	161	183	205	228	250	272	295	317	.6	22-23
.4	317	339	362	384	406	429	451	473	495	518	540	.5	22-23
.5	540	562	584	606	629	651	673	695	717	739	762	.4	22-23
.6	762	784	806	828	850	872	894	916	939	961	983	.3	22-23
.7	983	005	027	049	071	093	115	137	159	181	203	.2	22
.8	9.60 203	225	247	269	291	313	335	357	379	400	422	.1	21-22
.9	422	444	466	488	510	532	554	575	597	619	641	68.0	21-22
22.0	641	663	685	706	728	750	772	794	815	837	859	.9	21-22
.1	859	881	902	924	946	967	989	011	033	054	076	.8	21-22
.2	9.61 076	098	119	141	162	184	206	227	249	271	292	.7	21-22
.3	292	314	335	357	378	400	422	443	465	486	508	.6	21-22
.4	508	529	551	572	594	615	637	658	680	701	722	.5	21-22
.5	722	744	765	787	808	830	851	872	894	915	936	.4	21-22
.6	936	958	979	001	022	043	065	086	107	128	150	.3	21-22
.7	9.62 150	171	192	214	235	256	277	299	320	341	362	.2	21-22
.8	362	383	405	426	447	468	489	511	532	553	574	.1	21-22
.9	574	595	616	637	659	680	701	722	743	764	785	67.0	21-22
23.0	785	806	827	848	869	890	912	933	954	975	996	.9	21-22
.1	996	017	038	059	080	101	121	142	163	184	205	.8	20-21
.2	9.63 205	226	247	268	289	310	331	352	373	393	414	.7	20-21
.3	414	435	456	477	498	519	539	560	581	602	623	.6	20-21
.4	623	643	664	685	706	726	747	768	789	809	830	.5	20-21
.5	830	851	872	892	913	934	954	975	996	016	037	.4	20-21
.6	9.64 037	058	078	099	120	140	161	182	202	223	243	.3	20-21
.7	243	264	285	305	326	346	367	387	408	429	449	.2	20-21
.8	449	470	490	511	531	552	572	593	613	634	654	.1	20-21
.9	654	674	695	715	736	756	777	797	818	838	858	66.0	20-21
24.0	858	879	899	919	940	960	981	001	021	042	062	.9	20-21
.1	9.65 062	082	103	123	143	164	184	204	224	245	265	.8	20-21
.2	265	285	306	326	346	366	387	407	427	447	467	.7	20-21
.3	467	488	508	528	548	568	589	609	629	649	669	.6	20-21
.4	669	689	710	730	750	770	790	810	830	850	870	.5	20-21
.5	870	890	911	931	951	971	991	011	031	051	071	.4	20-21
.6	9.66 071	091	111	131	151	171	191	211	231	251	271	.3	20
.7	271	291	311	331	351	371	391	411	430	450	470	.2	19-20
.8	470	490	510	530	550	570	590	609	629	649	669	.1	19-20
.9	669	689	709	729	748	768	788	808	828	847	867	65.0 deg.	19-20
	(10)	9	8	7	6	5	4	3	2	1	0		

LOG COT

LOG TAN

deg.	0	1	2	3	4	5	6	7	8	9	(10)		Diff.
25.0	9.66 867	887	907	927	946	966	986	006	025	045	065	.9	19-20
.1	9.67 065	085	104	124	144	163	183	203	223	242	262	.8	19-20
.2	262	282	301	321	341	360	380	399	419	439	458	.7	19-20
.3	458	478	498	517	537	556	576	596	615	635	654	.6	19-20
.4	654	674	693	713	732	752	772	791	811	830	850	.5	19-20
.5	850	869	889	908	928	947	967	986	005	025	044	.4	19-20
.6	9.68 044	064	083	103	122	142	161	180	200	219	239	.3	19-20
.7	239	258	277	297	316	336	355	374	394	413	432	.2	19-20
.8	432	452	471	490	510	529	548	568	587	606	626	.1	19-20
.9	626	645	664	683	703	722	741	760	780	799	818	64.0	19-20
26.0	818	837	857	876	895	914	934	953	972	991	010	.9	19-20
.1	9.69 010	029	049	068	087	106	125	144	164	183	202	.8	19-20
.2	202	221	240	259	278	298	317	336	355	374	393	.7	19-20
.3	393	412	431	450	469	488	507	526	545	565	584	.6	19-20
.4	584	603	622	641	660	679	698	717	736	755	774	.5	19
.5	774	793	812	831	850	868	887	906	925	944	963	.4	18-19
.6	963	982	001	020	039	058	077	096	114	133	152	.3	18-19
.7	9.70 152	171	190	209	228	247	265	284	303	322	341	.2	18-19
.8	341	360	379	397	416	435	454	473	491	510	529	.1	18-19
.9	529	548	567	585	604	623	642	660	679	698	717	63.0	18-19
27.0	717	735	754	773	792	810	829	848	866	885	904	.9	18-19
.1	904	922	941	960	978	997	016	034	053	072	090	.8	18-19
.2	9.71 090	109	128	146	165	184	202	221	239	258	277	.7	18-19
.3	277	295	314	332	351	370	388	407	425	444	462	.6	18-19
.4	462	481	499	518	537	555	574	592	611	629	648	.5	18-19
.5	648	666	685	703	722	740	759	777	796	814	833	.4	18-19
.6	833	851	869	888	906	925	943	962	980	998	017	.3	18-19
.7	9.72 017	035	054	072	091	109	127	146	164	182	201	.2	18-19
.8	201	219	238	256	274	293	311	329	348	366	384	.1	18-19
.9	384	403	421	439	458	476	494	513	531	549	567	62.0	18-19
28.0	567	586	604	622	641	659	677	695	714	732	750	.9	18-19
.1	750	768	787	805	823	841	859	878	896	914	932	.8	18-19
.2	932	950	969	987	005	023	041	060	078	096	114	.7	18-19
.3	9.73 114	132	150	169	187	205	223	241	259	277	295	.6	18-19
.4	295	314	332	350	368	386	404	422	440	458	476	.5	18-19
.5	476	495	513	531	549	567	585	603	621	639	657	.4	18-19
.6	657	675	693	711	729	747	765	783	801	819	837	.3	18
.7	837	855	873	891	909	927	945	963	981	999	017	.2	18
.8	9.74 017	035	053	071	089	107	125	142	160	178	196	.1	17-18
.9	196	214	232	250	268	286	304	322	339	357	375	61.0	17-18
29.0	375	393	411	429	447	465	482	500	518	536	554	.9	17-18
.1	554	572	589	607	625	643	661	679	696	714	732	.8	17-18
.2	732	750	768	785	803	821	839	856	874	892	910	.7	17-18
.3	910	927	945	963	981	998	016	034	052	069	087	.6	17-18
.4	9.75 087	105	123	140	158	176	193	211	229	247	264	.5	17-18
.5	264	282	300	317	335	353	370	388	406	423	441	.4	17-18
.6	441	459	476	494	511	529	547	564	582	600	617	.3	17-18
.7	617	635	652	670	688	705	723	740	758	776	793	.2	17-18
.8	793	811	828	846	863	881	899	916	934	951	969	.1	17-18
.9	969	986	004	021	039	056	074	091	109	126	144	60.0	17-18
9.76												deg.	
	(10)	9	8	7	6	5	4	3	2	1	0		

LOG COT

LOG TAN

deg.	0	1	2	3	4	5	6	7	8	9	(10)		Diff.
30.0	9.76 144	161	179	196	214	231	249	266	284	301	319	.9	17-18
.1	319	336	354	371	389	406	424	441	458	476	493	.8	17-18
.2	493	511	528	546	563	580	598	615	633	650	668	.7	17-18
.3	668	685	702	720	737	754	772	789	807	824	841	.6	17-18
.4	841	859	876	893	911	928	945	963	980	998	0̄1̄5̄	.5	17-18
.5	9.77 015	032	050	067	084	101	119	136	153	171	188	.4	17-18
.6	188	205	223	240	257	274	292	309	326	344	361	.3	17-18
.7	361	378	395	413	430	447	464	482	499	516	533	.2	17-18
.8	533	551	568	585	602	619	637	654	671	688	706	.1	17-18
.9	706	723	740	757	774	791	809	826	843	860	877	59.0	17-18
31.0	877	895	912	929	946	963	980	997	0̄1̄5̄	0̄3̄2̄	0̄4̄9̄	.9	17-18
.1	9.78 049	066	083	100	117	135	152	169	186	203	220	.8	17-18
.2	220	237	254	271	289	306	323	340	357	374	391	.7	17-18
.3	391	408	425	442	459	476	493	510	528	545	562	.6	17-18
.4	562	579	596	613	630	647	664	681	698	715	732	.5	17
.5	732	749	766	783	800	817	8̲3̲4̲	8̲5̲1̲	8̲6̲8̲	8̲8̲5̲	9̲0̲2̲	.4	17
.6	902	919	936	953	970	987	0̄0̄4̄	0̄2̄1̄	0̄3̄8̄	0̄5̄5̄	0̄7̄2̄	.3	17
.7	9.79 072	089	106	122	139	156	173	190	207	224	241	.2	16-17
.8	241	258	275	292	309	326	343	359	376	393	410	.1	16-17
.9	410	427	444	461	478	495	511	528	545	562	579	58.0	16-17
32.0	579	596	613	630	646	663	680	697	714	731	747	.9	16-17
.1	747	764	781	798	815	832	848	865	882	899	916	.8	16-17
.2	916	932	949	966	983	0̄0̄0̄	0̄1̄6̄	0̄3̄3̄	0̄5̄0̄	0̄6̄7̄	0̄8̄4̄	.7	16-17
.3	9.80 084	100	117	134	151	168	184	201	218	235	251	.6	16-17
.4	251	268	285	302	318	335	352	369	385	402	419	.5	16-17
.5	419	435	452	469	486	502	519	536	552	569	586	.4	16-17
.6	586	603	619	636	653	669	686	703	719	736	753	.3	16-17
.7	753	769	786	803	819	8̲3̲6̲	8̲5̲3̲	8̲6̲9̲	8̲8̲6̲	9̲0̲3̲	9̲1̲9̲	.2	16-17
.8	919	936	953	969	986	0̄0̄3̄	0̄1̄9̄	0̄3̄6̄	0̄5̄2̄	0̄6̄9̄	0̄8̄6̄	.1	16-17
.9	9.81 086	102	119	136	152	169	185	202	219	235	252	57.0	16-17
33.0	252	268	285	302	318	335	351	368	384	401	418	.9	16-17
.1	418	434	451	467	484	500	517	533	550	567	583	.8	16-17
.2	583	600	616	633	649	666	682	699	715	732	748	.7	16-17
.3	748	765	781	798	814	831	847	864	880	897	913	.6	16-17
.4	913	930	946	963	979	996	0̄1̄2̄	0̄2̄9̄	0̄4̄5̄	0̄6̄2̄	0̄7̄8̄	.5	16-17
.5	9.82 078	095	111	128	144	161	177	194	210	226	243	.4	16-17
.6	243	259	276	292	309	325	341	358	374	391	407	.3	16-17
.7	407	424	440	456	473	489	506	522	538	555	571	.2	16-17
.8	571	588	604	620	637	653	670	686	702	719	735	.1	16-17
.9	735	751	768	784	801	817	833	850	866	882	899	56.0	16-17
34.0	899	915	931	948	964	980	997	0̄1̄3̄	0̄2̄9̄	0̄4̄6̄	0̄6̄2̄	.9	16-17
.1	9.83 062	078	095	111	127	144	160	176	193	209	225	.8	16-17
.2	225	242	258	274	290	307	323	339	356	372	388	.7	16-17
.3	388	405	421	437	453	470	486	502	518	535	551	.6	16-17
.4	551	567	583	600	616	632	648	665	681	697	713	.5	16-17
.5	713	730	746	762	778	795	811	827	843	859	876	.4	16-17
.6	876	892	908	924	941	957	973	989	0̄0̄5̄	0̄2̄2̄	0̄3̄8̄	.3	16-17
.7	9.84 038	054	070	086	103	119	135	151	167	183	200	.2	16-17
.8	200	216	232	248	264	280	297	313	329	345	361	.1	16-17
.9	361	377	394	410	426	442	458	474	490	507	523	55.0	16-17
	(10)	9	8	7	6	5	4	3	2	1	0	deg.	

LOG COT

LOG TAN

deg.	0	1	2	3	4	5	6	7	8	9	(10)		Diff.
35.0	9.84 523	539	555	571	587	603	619	636	652	668	684	.9	16-17
.1	684	700	716	732	748	764	781	797	813	829	845	.8	16-17
.2	845	861	877	893	909	925	941	958	974	990	006	.7	16-17
.3	9.85 006	022	038	054	070	086	102	118	134	150	166	.6	16
.4	166	182	198	215	231	247	263	279	295	311	327	.5	16-17
.5	327	343	359	375	391	407	423	439	455	471	487	.4	16
.6	487	503	519	535	551	567	583	599	615	631	647	.3	16
.7	647	663	679	695	711	727	743	759	775	791	807	.2	16
.8	807	823	839	855	871	887	903	919	935	951	967	.1	16
.9	967	983	999	014	030	046	062	078	094	110	126	54.0	15-16
36.0	9.86 126	142	158	174	190	206	222	238	254	269	285	.9	15-16
.1	285	301	317	333	349	365	381	397	413	429	445	.8	16
.2	445	460	476	492	508	524	540	556	572	588	603	.7	15-16
.3	603	619	635	651	667	683	699	715	731	746	762	.6	15-16
.4	762	778	794	810	826	842	857	873	889	905	921	.5	15-16
.5	921	937	953	968	984	000	016	032	048	063	079	.4	15-16
.6	9.87 079	095	111	127	143	158	174	190	206	222	238	.3	15-16
.7	238	253	269	285	301	317	332	348	364	380	396	.2	15-16
.8	396	412	427	443	459	475	490	506	522	538	554	.1	15-16
.9	554	569	585	601	617	633	648	664	680	696	711	53.0	15-16
37.0	711	727	743	759	775	790	806	822	838	853	869	.9	15-16
.1	869	885	901	916	932	948	964	979	995	011	027	.8	15-16
.2	9.88 027	042	058	074	089	105	121	137	152	168	184	.7	15-16
.3	184	200	215	231	247	262	278	294	310	325	341	.6	15-16
.4	341	357	372	388	404	420	435	451	467	482	498	.5	15-16
.5	498	514	529	545	561	577	592	608	624	639	655	.4	15-16
.6	655	671	686	702	718	733	749	765	780	796	812	.3	15-16
.7	812	827	843	859	874	890	906	921	937	953	968	.2	15-16
.8	968	984	000	015	031	046	062	078	093	109	125	.1	15-16
.9	9.89 125	140	156	172	187	203	218	234	250	265	281	52.0	15-16
38.0	281	297	312	328	343	359	375	390	406	422	437	.9	15-16
.1	437	453	468	484	500	515	531	546	562	578	593	.8	15-16
.2	593	609	624	640	656	671	687	702	718	734	749	.7	15-16
.3	749	765	780	796	811	827	843	858	874	889	905	.6	15-16
.4	905	920	936	952	967	983	998	014	029	045	061	.5	15-16
.5	9.90 061	076	092	107	123	138	154	169	185	200	216	.4	15-16
.6	216	232	247	263	278	294	309	325	340	356	371	.3	15-16
.7	371	387	403	418	434	449	465	480	496	511	527	.2	15-16
.8	527	542	558	573	589	604	620	635	651	666	682	.1	15-16
.9	682	697	713	728	744	759	775	790	806	821	837	51.0	15-16
39.0	837	852	868	883	899	914	930	945	961	976	992	.9	15-16
.1	992	007	023	038	054	069	085	100	116	131	147	.8	15-16
.2	9.91 147	162	178	193	209	224	239	255	270	286	301	.7	15-16
.3	301	317	332	348	363	379	394	410	425	441	456	.6	15-16
.4	456	471	487	502	518	533	549	564	580	595	610	.5	15-16
.5	610	626	641	657	672	688	703	719	734	749	765	.4	15-16
.6	765	780	796	811	827	842	857	873	888	904	919	.3	15-16
.7	919	935	950	965	981	996	012	027	042	058	073	.2	15-16
.8	9.92 073	089	104	120	135	150	166	181	197	212	227	.1	15-16
.9	227	243	258	274	289	304	320	335	351	366	381	50.0	15-16
	(10)	9	8	7	6	5	4	3	2	1	0	deg.	

LOG COT

LOG TAN

deg.	0	1	2	3	4	5	6	7	8	9	(10)	
40.0	9.92 381	397	412	428	443	458	474	489	504	520	535	.9
.1	535	551	566	581	597	612	628	643	658	674	689	.8
.2	689	704	720	735	751	766	781	797	812	827	843	.7
.3	843	858	873	889	904	920	935	950	966	981	996	.6
.4	996	012	027	042	058	073	088	104	119	135	150	.5
.5	9.93 150	165	181	196	211	227	242	257	273	288	303	.4
.6	303	319	334	349	365	380	395	411	426	441	457	.3
.7	457	472	487	503	518	533	549	564	579	595	610	.2
.8	610	625	641	656	671	687	702	717	733	748	763	.1
.9	763	778	794	809	824	840	855	870	886	901	916	49.0
41.0	916	932	947	962	978	993	008	023	039	054	069	.9
.1	9.94 069	085	100	115	131	146	161	176	192	207	222	.8
.2	222	238	253	268	284	299	314	329	345	360	375	.7
.3	375	391	406	421	436	452	467	482	498	513	528	.6
.4	528	543	559	574	589	604	620	635	650	666	681	.5
.5	681	696	711	727	742	757	772	788	803	818	834	.4
.6	834	849	864	879	895	910	925	940	956	971	986	.3
.7	986	001	017	032	047	062	078	093	108	124	139	.2
.8	9.95 139	154	169	185	200	215	230	246	261	276	291	.1
.9	291	307	322	337	352	368	383	398	413	429	444	48.0
42.0	444	459	474	489	505	520	535	550	566	581	596	.9
.1	596	611	627	642	657	672	688	703	718	733	748	.8
.2	748	764	779	794	809	825	840	855	870	886	901	.7
.3	901	916	931	946	962	977	992	007	023	038	053	.6
.4	9.96 053	068	083	099	114	129	144	160	175	190	205	.5 Diff.
.5	205	220	236	251	266	281	297	312	327	342	357	.4 15-16
.6	357	373	388	403	418	433	449	464	479	494	510	.3
.7	510	525	540	555	570	586	601	616	631	646	662	.2
.8	662	677	692	707	722	738	753	768	783	798	814	.1
.9	814	829	844	859	874	890	905	920	935	950	966	47.0
43.0	966	981	996	011	026	042	057	072	087	102	118	.9
.1	9.97 118	133	148	163	178	193	209	224	239	254	269	.8
.2	269	285	300	315	330	345	361	376	391	406	421	.7
.3	421	437	452	467	482	497	512	528	543	558	573	.6
.4	573	588	604	619	634	649	664	679	695	710	725	.5
.5	725	740	755	771	786	801	816	831	846	862	877	.4
.6	877	892	907	922	938	953	968	983	998	013	029	.3
.7	9.98 029	044	059	074	089	104	120	135	150	165	180	.2
.8	180	195	211	226	241	256	271	287	302	317	332	.1
.9	332	347	362	378	393	408	423	438	453	469	484	46.0
44.0	484	499	514	529	544	560	575	590	605	620	635	.9
.1	635	651	666	681	696	711	726	742	757	772	787	.8
.2	787	802	817	833	848	863	878	893	908	924	939	.7
.3	939	954	969	984	999	015	030	045	060	075	090	.6
.4	9.99 090	106	121	136	151	166	181	196	212	227	242	.5
.5	242	257	272	287	303	318	333	348	363	378	394	.4
.6	394	409	424	439	454	469	485	500	515	530	545	.3
.7	545	560	576	591	606	621	636	651	666	682	697	.2
.8	697	712	727	742	757	773	788	803	818	833	848	.1
.9	848	864	879	894	909	924	939	955	970	985	000	45.0 deg.
.00	(10)	9	8	7	6	5	4	3	2	1	0	

LOG COT

LOG TAN

deg.		0	1	2	3	4	5	6	7	8	9	(10)	
45.0	.00	000	015	030	045	061	076	091	106	121	136	152	.9
.1		152	167	182	197	212	227	243	258	273	288	303	.8
.2		303	318	334	349	364	379	394	409	424	440	455	.7
.3		455	470	485	500	515	531	546	561	576	591	606	.6
.4		606	622	637	652	667	682	697	713	728	743	758	.5
.5		758	773	788	804	819	834	849	864	879	894	910	.4
.6		910	925	940	955	970	985	001	016	031	046	061	.3
.7	.01	061	076	092	107	122	137	152	167	183	198	213	.2
.8		213	228	243	258	274	289	304	319	334	349	365	.1
.9		365	380	395	410	425	440	456	471	486	501	516	44.0
46.0		516	531	547	562	577	592	607	622	638	653	668	.9
.1		668	683	698	713	729	744	759	774	789	805	820	.8
.2		820	835	850	865	880	896	911	926	941	956	971	.7
.3		971	987	002	017	032	047	062	078	093	108	123	.6
.4	.02	123	138	154	169	184	199	214	229	245	260	275	.5
.5		275	290	305	321	336	351	366	381	396	412	427	.4
.6		427	442	457	472	488	503	518	533	548	563	579	.3
.7		579	594	609	624	639	655	670	685	700	715	731	.2
.8		731	746	761	776	791	807	822	837	852	867	882	.1
.9		882	898	913	928	943	958	974	989	004	019	034	43.0
47.0	.03	034	050	065	080	095	110	126	141	156	171	186	.9
.1		186	202	217	232	247	262	278	293	308	323	338	.8
.2		338	354	369	384	399	414	430	445	460	475	490	.7
.3		490	506	521	536	551	567	582	597	612	627	643	.6
.4		643	658	673	688	703	719	734	749	764	780	795	.5 Diff.
.5		795	810	825	840	856	871	886	901	917	932	947	.4 15-16
.6		947	962	977	993	008	023	038	054	069	084	099	.3
.7	.04	099	114	130	145	160	175	191	206	221	236	252	.2
.8		252	267	282	297	312	328	343	358	373	389	404	.1
.9		404	419	434	450	465	480	495	511	526	541	556	42.0
48.0		556	571	587	602	617	632	648	663	678	693	709	.9
.1		709	724	739	754	770	785	800	815	831	846	861	.8
.2		861	876	892	907	922	938	953	968	983	999	014	.7
.3	.05	014	029	044	060	075	090	105	121	136	151	166	.6
.4		166	182	197	212	228	243	258	273	289	304	319	.5
.5		319	334	350	365	380	396	411	426	441	457	472	.4
.6		472	487	502	518	533	548	564	579	594	609	625	.3
.7		625	640	655	671	686	701	716	732	747	762	778	.2
.8		778	793	808	824	839	854	869	885	900	915	931	.1
.9		931	946	961	977	992	007	022	038	053	068	084	41.0
49.0	.06	084	099	114	130	145	160	176	191	206	222	237	.9
.1		237	252	267	283	298	313	329	344	359	375	390	.8
.2		390	405	421	436	451	467	482	497	513	528	543	.7
.3		543	559	574	589	605	620	635	651	666	681	697	.6
.4		697	712	727	743	758	773	789	804	819	835	850	.5
.5		850	865	881	896	912	927	942	958	973	988	004	.4
.6	.07	004	019	034	050	065	080	096	111	127	142	157	.3
.7		157	173	188	203	219	234	249	265	280	296	311	.2
.8		311	326	342	357	372	388	403	419	434	449	465	.1
.9		465	480	496	511	526	542	557	572	588	603	619	40.0
													deg.
		(10)	9	8	7	6	5	4	3	2	1	0	

LOG COT

LOG TAN

deg.	0	1	2	3	4	5	6	7	8	9	(10)	Diff.
50.0	.07 619	634	649	665	680	696	711	726	742	757	773	.9
.1	773	788	803	819	834	850	865	880	896	911	927	.8
.2	927	942	958	973	988	004	019	035	050	065	081	.7
.3	.08 081	096	112	127	143	158	173	189	204	220	235	.6
.4	235	251	266	281	297	312	328	343	359	374	390	.5
.5	390	405	420	436	451	467	482	498	513	529	544	.4
.6	544	559	575	590	606	621	637	652	668	683	699	.3
.7	699	714	730	745	761	776	791	807	822	838	853	.2
.8	853	869	884	900	915	931	946	962	977	993	008	.1
.9	.09 008	024	039	055	070	086	101	117	132	148	163	39.0
51.0	163	179	194	210	225	241	256	272	287	303	318	.9 15-16
.1	318	334	349	365	380	396	411	427	442	458	473	.8
.2	473	489	504	520	535	551	566	582	597	613	629	.7
.3	629	644	660	675	691	706	722	737	753	768	784	.6
.4	784	800	815	831	846	862	877	893	908	924	939	.5
.5	939	955	971	986	002	017	033	048	064	080	095	.4
.6	.10 095	111	126	142	157	173	189	204	220	235	251	.3
.7	251	266	282	298	313	329	344	360	376	391	407	.2
.8	407	422	438	454	469	485	500	516	532	547	563	.1
.9	563	578	594	610	625	641	657	672	688	703	719	38.0
52.0	719	735	750	766	782	797	813	828	844	860	875	.9
.1	875	891	907	922	938	954	969	985	000	016	032	.8
.2	.11 032	047	063	079	094	110	126	141	157	173	188	.7
.3	188	204	220	235	251	267	282	298	314	329	345	.6
.4	345	361	376	392	408	423	439	455	471	486	502	.5
.5	502	518	533	549	565	580	596	612	628	643	659	.4
.6	659	675	690	706	722	738	753	769	785	800	816	.3
.7	816	832	848	863	879	895	911	926	942	958	973	.2
.8	973	989	005	021	036	052	068	084	099	115	131	.1
.9	.12 131	147	162	178	194	210	225	241	257	273	289	37.0
53.0	289	304	320	336	352	367	383	399	415	431	446	.9
.1	446	462	478	494	510	525	541	557	573	588	604	.8
.2	604	620	636	652	668	683	699	715	731	747	762	.7
.3	762	778	794	810	826	842	857	873	889	905	921	.6
.4	921	937	952	968	984	000	016	032	047	063	079	.5
.5	.13 079	095	111	127	143	158	174	190	206	222	238	.4
.6	238	254	269	285	301	317	333	349	365	381	397	.3
.7	397	412	428	444	460	476	492	508	524	540	555	.2
.8	555	571	587	603	619	635	651	667	683	699	715	.1
.9	715	731	746	762	778	794	810	826	842	858	874	36.0
54.0	874	890	906	922	938	954	970	986	001	017	033	.9
.1	.14 033	049	065	081	097	113	129	145	161	177	193	.8
.2	193	209	225	241	257	273	289	305	321	337	353	.7
.3	353	369	385	401	417	433	449	465	481	497	513	.6 16
.4	513	529	545	561	577	593	609	625	641	657	673	.5
.5	673	689	705	721	737	753	769	785	802	818	834	.4
.6	834	850	866	882	898	914	930	946	962	978	994	.3
.7	994	010	026	042	059	075	091	107	123	139	155	.2
.8	.15 155	171	187	203	219	236	252	268	284	300	316	.1
.9	316	332	348	364	381	397	413	429	445	461	477	35.0
												deg.
(10)	9	8	7	6	5	4	3	2	1	0		

LOG COT

LOG TAN

deg.	0	1	2	3	4	5	6	7	8	9	(10)	Diff.
55.0	.15 477	493	510	526	542	558	574	590	606	623	639	.9
.1	639	655	671	687	703	720	736	752	768	784	800	.8
.2	800	817	833	849	865	881	897	914	930	946	962	.7
.3	962	978	995	011	027	043	059	076	092	108	124	.6
.4	.16 124	141	157	173	189	205	222	238	254	270	287	.5
.5	287	303	319	335	352	368	384	400	417	433	449	.4
.6	449	465	482	498	514	530	547	563	579	595	612	.3
.7	612	628	644	661	677	693	710	726	742	758	775	.2
.8	775	791	807	824	840	856	873	889	905	922	938	.1
.9	938	954	971	987	003	020	036	052	069	085	101	34.0
56.0	.17 101	118	134	150	167	183	199	216	232	249	265	.9
.1	265	281	298	314	330	347	363	380	396	412	429	.8
.2	429	445	462	478	494	511	527	544	560	576	593	.7
.3	593	609	626	642	659	675	691	708	724	741	757	.6
.4	757	774	790	806	823	839	856	872	889	905	922	.5
.5	922	938	955	971	988	004	021	037	054	070	087	.4
.6	.18 087	103	120	136	153	169	186	202	219	235	252	.3 16-17
.7	252	268	285	301	318	334	351	367	384	400	417	.2
.8	417	433	450	467	483	500	516	533	549	566	582	.1
.9	582	599	616	632	649	665	682	698	715	732	748	33.0
57.0	748	765	781	798	815	831	848	864	881	898	914	.9
.1	914	931	948	964	981	997	014	031	047	064	081	.8
.2	.19 081	097	114	131	147	164	181	197	214	231	247	.7
.3	247	264	281	297	314	331	347	364	381	397	414	.6
.4	414	431	448	464	481	498	514	531	548	565	581	.5
.5	581	598	615	631	648	665	682	698	715	732	749	.4
.6	749	765	782	799	816	832	849	866	883	900	916	.3
.7	916	933	950	967	984	000	017	034	051	068	084	.2
.8	.20 084	101	118	135	152	168	185	202	219	236	253	.1
.9	253	269	286	303	320	337	354	370	387	404	421	32.0
58.0	421	438	455	472	489	505	522	539	556	573	590	.9
.1	590	607	624	641	657	674	691	708	725	742	759	.8
.2	759	776	793	810	827	844	861	878	894	911	928	.7
.3	928	945	962	979	996	013	030	047	064	081	098	.6
.4	.21 098	115	132	149	166	183	200	217	234	251	268	.5 17
.5	268	285	302	319	336	353	370	387	404	421	438	.4
.6	438	455	472	490	507	524	541	558	575	592	609	.3
.7	609	626	643	660	677	694	711	729	746	763	780	.2
.8	780	797	814	831	848	865	883	900	917	934	951	.1
.9	951	968	985	003	020	037	054	071	088	105	123	31.0
59.0	.22 123	140	157	174	191	209	226	243	260	277	294	.9
.1	294	312	329	346	363	381	398	415	432	449	467	.8
.2	467	484	501	518	536	553	570	587	605	622	639	.7
.3	639	656	674	691	708	726	743	760	777	795	812	.6
.4	812	829	847	864	881	899	916	933	950	968	985	.5
.5	985	002	020	037	055	072	089	107	124	141	159	.4
.6	.23 159	176	193	211	228	246	263	280	298	315	332	.3
.7	332	350	367	385	402	420	437	454	472	489	507	.2
.8	507	524	542	559	576	594	611	629	646	664	681	.1
.9	681	699	716	734	751	769	786	804	821	839	856	30.0 17-18
												deg.
	(10)	9	8	7	6	5	4	3	2	1	0	

LOG COT

LOG TAN

deg.	0	1	2	3	4	5	6	7	8	9	(10)	Diff.
60.0	.23 856	874	891	909	926	944	961	979	996	014̄	031̄	.9 17-18
.1	.24 031	049	066	084	101	119	137	154	172	189	207	.8
.2	207	224	242	260	277	295	312	330	348	365	383	.7
.3	383	400	418	436	453	471	489	506	524	541	559	.6
.4	559	577	594	612	630	647	665	683	700	718	736	.5
.5	736	753	771	789	807	824̲	842	860	877	895	913̲	.4
.6	913	931	948	966	984	002	019	037̄	055̄	073̄	090	.3
.7	.25 090	108	126	144	161	179	197	215	232	250	268	.2
.8	268	286	304	321	339	357	375	393	411	428	446	.1
.9	446	464	482	500	518	535	553	571	589	607	625	29.0
61.0	625	643	661	678	696	714	732	750	768	786	804	.9
.1	804	822̲	840̲	858	875	893	911	929	947	965	983	.8
.2	983	001	019	037̲	055̲	073̲	091	109̄	127̄	145̄	163̄	.7
.3	.26 163	181	199	217	235	253	271	289	307	325	343	.6 18
.4	343	361	379	397	415	433	451	469	487	505	524	.5
.5	524	542	560	578	596	614	632	650	668	686	705	.4
.6	705	723	741	759	777	795	813	831	850	868	886	.3
.7	886	904	922	940	959	977	995	013̄	031̄	050̄	068̄	.2
.8	.27 068	086	104	122	141	159	177	195	213	232	250	.1
.9	250	268	286	305	323	341	359	378	396	414	433	28.0
62.0	433	451	469	487	506	524	542	561	579	597	616	.9
.1	616	634	652	671	689	707	726	744	762	781	799	.8
.2	799	818̲	836̲	854̲	873̲	891̲	909̲	928̲	946̲	965̲	983̲	.7
.3	983	002	020	038̲	057̲	075̲	094	112̄	131̄	149̄	167̄	.6
.4	.28 167	186	204	223	241	260	278	297	315	334	352	.5 18-19
.5	352	371	389	408	426	445	463	482	501	519	538	.4
.6	538	556	575	593	612	630	649	668	686	705	723	.3
.7	723	742	761	779	798	816̲	835̲	854̲	872̲	891̲	910̲	.2
.8	910	928	947	966	984	003̄	022̄	040̄	059̄	078̄	096̄	.1
.9	.29 096	115	134	152	171	190	208	227	246	265	283	27.0
63.0	283	302	321	340	358	377	396	415	433	452	471	.9
.1	471	490	509	527	546	565	584	603	621	640	659	.8
.2	659	678	697	716	735	753	772	791	810	829̲	848̲	.7
.3	848	867	886	904	923	942	961	980	999	018̄	037̄	.6
.4	.30 037	056	075	094	113	132	150	169	188	207	226	.5
.5	226	245	264	283	302	321	340	359	378	397	416	.4 19
.6	416	435	455	474	493	512	531	550	569	588	607	.3
.7	607	626	645	664	683	702	722	741	760	779	798	.2
.8	798	817̲	836̲	856̲	875̲	894̲	913̲	932̲	951̲	971̲	990̲	.1
.9	990	009̄	028̄	047̄	066̄	086̄	105̄	124̄	143̄	163̄	182̄	26.0
64.0	.31 182	201	220	240	259	278	297	317	336	355	374	.9
.1	374	394	413	432	452	471	490	510	529	548	568	.8
.2	568	587	606	626	645	664	684	703	723	742	761	.7
.3	761	781	800	820	839	858	878	897	917	936	956	.6
.4	956	975	995	014̄	033̄	053̄	072̄	092̄	111̄	131̄	150̄	.5 19-20
.5	.32 150	170	189	209	228	248	268	287	307	326	346	.4
.6	346	365	385	404	424	444	463	483	502	522	542	.3
.7	542	561	581	601	620	640	659	679	699	718	738	.2
.8	738	758	777	797	817̲	837̲	856̲	876̲	896̲	915̲	935̲	.1
.9	935	955	975	994	014̄	034̄	054̄	073̄	093̄	113̄	133̄	25.0
.33												deg.
(10)	9	8	7	6	5	4	3	2	1	0		

LOG COT

LOG TAN

deg.	0	1	2	3	4	5	6	7	8	9	(10)	Diff.
65.0	.33 133	153	172	192	212	232	252	271	291	311	331	.9 19-20
.1	331	351	371	391	410	430	450	470	490	510	530	.8
.2	530	550	570	589	609	629	649	669	689	709	729	.7
.3	729	749	769	789	809	829	849	869	889	909	929	.6 20
.4	929	949	969	989	009	029	049	069	089	110	130	.5
.5	.34 130	150	170	190	210	230	250	270	290	311	331	.4
.6	331	351	371	391	411	432	452	472	492	512	533	.3
.7	533	553	573	593	613	634	654	674	694	715	735	.2
.8	735	755	776	796	816	836	857	877	897	918	938	.1
.9	938	958	979	999	019	040	060	081	101	121	142	24.0
66.0	.35 142	162	182	203	223	244	264	285	305	326	346	.9
.1	346	366	387	407	428	448	469	489	510	530	551	.8 20-21
.2	551	571	592	613	633	654	674	695	715	736	757	.7
.3	757	777	798	818	839	860	880	901	922	942	963	.6
.4	963	984	004	025	046	066	087	108	128	149	170	.5
.5	.36 170	191	211	232	253	274	294	315	336	357	377	.4
.6	377	398	419	440	461	481	502	523	544	565	586	.3
.7	586	607	627	648	669	690	711	732	753	774	795	.2
.8	795	816	837	858	879	899	920	941	962	983	004	.1 21
.9	.37 004	025	046	067	088	110	131	152	173	194	215	23.0
67.0	215	236	257	278	299	320	341	363	384	405	426	.9
.1	426	447	468	489	511	532	553	574	595	617	638	.8
.2	638	659	680	701	723	744	765	786	808	829	850	.7
.3	850	872	893	914	935	957	978	999	021	042	064	.6
.4	.38 064	085	106	128	149	170	192	213	235	256	278	.5
.5	278	299	320	342	363	385	406	428	449	471	492	.4 21-22
.6	492	514	535	557	578	600	622	643	665	686	708	.3
.7	708	729	751	773	794	816	838	859	881	902	924	.2
.8	924	946	967	989	011	033	054	076	098	119	141	.1
.9	.39 141	163	185	206	228	250	272	294	315	337	359	22.0
68.0	359	381	403	425	446	468	490	512	534	556	578	.9
.1	578	600	621	643	665	687	709	731	753	775	797	.8
.2	797	819	841	863	885	907	929	951	973	995	017	.7 22
.3	.40 017	039	061	084	106	128	150	172	194	216	238	.6
.4	238	261	283	305	327	349	371	394	416	438	460	.5
.5	460	482	505	527	549	571	594	616	638	661	683	.4
.6	683	705	728	750	772	795	817	839	862	884	906	.3
.7	906	929	951	974	996	019	041	063	086	108	131	.2
.8	.41 131	153	176	198	221	243	266	288	311	334	356	.1 22-23
.9	356	379	401	424	446	469	492	514	537	560	582	21.0
69.0	582	605	628	650	673	696	718	741	764	787	809	.9
.1	809	832	855	878	900	923	946	969	991	014	037	.8
.2	.42 037	060	083	106	129	151	174	197	220	243	266	.7
.3	266	289	312	335	358	381	404	427	450	473	496	.6 23
.4	496	519	542	565	588	611	634	657	680	703	726	.5
.5	726	749	772	796	819	842	865	888	911	935	958	.4
.6	958	981	004	027	051	074	097	120	144	167	190	.3
.7	.43 190	214	237	260	284	307	330	354	377	400	424	.2
.8	424	447	470	494	517	541	564	588	611	635	658	.1
.9	658	682	705	729	752	776	799	823	846	870	893	20.0 23-24
												deg.
(10)	9	8	7	6	5	4	3	2	1	0		

LOG COT

LOG TAN

deg.	0	1	2	3	4	5	6	7	8	9	(10)	Diff.
70.0	.43 893	917	941	964	988	011	035	059	082	106	130	.9
.1	.44 130	153	177	201	225	248	272	296	320	343	367	.8
.2	367	391	415	438	462	486	510	534	558	582	605	.7
.3	605	629	653	677	701	725	749	773	797	821	845	.6
.4	845	869	893	917	941	965	989	013	037	061	085	.5
.5	.45 085	109	133	157	182	206	230	254	278	302	327	.4
.6	327	351	375	399	423	448	472	496	520	545	569	.3
.7	569	593	618	642	666	691	715	739	764	788	813	.2
.8	813	837	861	886	910	935	959	984	008	033	057	.1
.9	.46 057	082	106	131	155	180	204	229	254	278	303	19.0
71.0	303	327	352	377	401	426	451	475	500	525	550	.9
.1	550	574	599	624	649	673	698	723	748	773	798	.8
.2	798	822	847	872	897	922	947	972	997	022	047	.7
.3	.47 047	071	096	121	146	171	196	222	247	272	297	.6
.4	297	322	347	372	397	422	447	472	498	523	548	.5
.5	548	573	598	624	649	674	699	725	750	775	800	.4
.6	800	826	851	876	902	927	953	978	003	029	054	.3
.7	.48 054	080	105	130	156	181	207	232	258	283	309	.2
.8	309	335	360	386	411	437	463	488	514	539	565	.1
.9	565	591	616	642	668	694	719	745	771	797	822	18.0
72.0	822	848	874	900	926	952	977	003	029	055	081	.9
.1	.49 081	107	133	159	185	211	237	263	289	315	341	.8
.2	341	367	393	419	445	471	497	523	549	576	602	.7
.3	602	628	654	680	707	733	759	785	812	838	864	.6
.4	864	890	917	943	969	996	022	049	075	101	128	.5
.5	.50 128	154	181	207	234	260	287	313	340	366	393	.4
.6	393	419	446	472	499	526	552	579	606	632	659	.3
.7	659	686	712	739	766	793	819	846	873	900	927	.2
.8	927	954	980	007	034	061	088	115	142	169	196	.1
.9	.51 196	223	250	277	304	331	358	385	412	439	466	17.0
73.0	466	493	520	547	575	602	629	656	683	711	738	.9
.1	738	765	792	820	847	874	902	929	956	984	011	.8
.2	.52 011	039	066	093	121	148	176	203	231	258	286	.7
.3	286	313	341	368	396	424	451	479	507	534	562	.6
.4	562	590	617	645	673	701	728	756	784	812	840	.5
.5	840	867	895	923	951	979	007	035	063	091	119	.4
.6	.53 119	147	175	203	231	259	287	315	343	371	399	.3
.7	399	427	456	484	512	540	568	597	625	653	681	.2
.8	681	710	738	766	795	823	851	880	908	937	965	.1
.9	965	994	022	050	079	108	136	165	193	222	250	16.0
74.0	.54 250	279	308	336	365	394	422	451	480	508	537	.9
.1	537	566	595	624	652	681	710	739	768	797	826	.8
.2	826	855	884	913	942	971	000	029	058	087	116	.7
.3	.55 116	145	174	203	232	262	291	320	349	378	408	.6
.4	408	437	466	496	525	554	584	613	642	672	701	.5
.5	701	731	760	790	819	849	878	908	937	967	996	.4
.6	996	026	056	085	115	145	174	204	234	264	293	.3
.7	.56 293	323	353	383	413	442	472	502	532	562	592	.2
.8	592	622	652	682	712	742	772	802	832	862	892	.1
.9	892	923	953	983	013	043	074	104	134	164	195	15.0
.57												deg.
	(10)	9	8	7	6	5	4	3	2	1	0	

Diff. column group values: 24, 25, 26, 27, 28, 29, 30

LOG COT

LOG TAN

deg.	0	1	2	3	4	5	6	7	8	9	(10)	Diff.	
75.0	.57 195	225	255	286	316	347	377	407	438	468	499	.9	
.1	499	529	560	590	621	652	682	713	744	774	805	.8	
.2	805	836	866	897	928	959	989	020	051	082	113	.7	
.3	.58 113	144	175	205	236	267	298	329	360	391	422	.6	31
.4	422	454	485	516	547	578	609	640	672	703	734	.5	
.5	734	765	797	828	859	891	922	954	985	016	048	.4	
.6	.59 048	079	111	142	174	205	237	269	300	332	364	.3	
.7	364	395	427	459	490	522	554	586	618	649	681	.2	
.8	681	713	745	777	809	841	873	905	937	969	001	.1	32
.9	.60 001	033	065	097	130	162	194	226	258	291	323	14.0	
76.0	323	355	388	420	452	485	517	549	582	614	647	.9	
.1	647	679	712	744	777	810	842	875	908	940	973	.8	
.2	973	006	038	071	104	137	170	203	235	268	301	.7	
.3	.61 301	334	367	400	433	466	499	532	566	599	632	.6	33
.4	632	665	698	731	765	798	831	865	898	931	965	.5	
.5	965	998	031	065	098	132	165	199	232	266	300	.4	
.6	.62 300	333	367	401	434	468	502	536	569	603	637	.3	
.7	637	671	705	739	773	807	841	875	909	943	977	.2	34
.8	977	011	045	079	113	148	182	216	250	285	319	.1	
.9	.63 319	353	388	422	457	491	525	560	594	629	664	13.0	
77.0	664	698	733	767	802	837	872	906	941	976	011	.9	
.1	.64 011	045	080	115	150	185	220	255	290	325	360	.8	35
.2	360	395	430	466	501	536	571	606	642	677	712	.7	
.3	712	748	783	819	854	889	925	960	996	032	067	.6	
.4	.65 067	103	138	174	210	245	281	317	353	389	424	.5	
.5	424	460	496	532	568	604	640	676	712	748	785	.4	36
.6	785	821	857	893	929	966	002	038	075	111	147	.3	
.7	.66 147	184	220	257	293	330	366	403	440	476	513	.2	
.8	513	550	586	623	660	697	734	770	807	844	881	.1	
.9	881	918	955	992	029	067	104	141	178	215	253	12.0	37
78.0	.67 253	290	327	364	402	439	477	514	552	589	627	.9	
.1	627	664	702	740	777	815	853	890	928	966	004	.8	
.2	.68 004	042	080	118	156	194	232	270	308	346	384	.7	38
.3	384	422	460	499	537	575	614	652	690	729	767	.6	
.4	767	806	844	883	922	960	999	037	076	115	154	.5	
.5	.69 154	193	231	270	309	348	387	426	465	504	543	.4	39
.6	543	582	622	661	700	739	779	818	857	897	936	.3	
.7	936	976	015	055	094	134	173	213	253	293	332	.2	
.8	.70 332	372	412	452	492	532	572	612	652	692	732	.1	40
.9	732	772	812	852	893	933	973	014	054	094	135	11.0	
79.0	.71 135	175	216	256	297	338	378	419	460	500	541	.9	
.1	541	582	623	664	705	746	787	828	869	910	951	.8	41
.2	951	992	034	075	116	158	199	240	282	323	365	.7	
.3	.72 365	406	448	490	531	573	615	657	698	740	782	.6	
.4	782	824	866	908	950	992	034	077	119	161	203	.5	42
.5	.73 203	246	288	330	373	415	458	500	543	586	628	.4	
.6	628	671	714	757	799	842	885	928	971	014	057	.3	43
.7	.74 057	100	143	187	230	273	316	360	403	447	490	.2	
.8	490	534	577	621	664	708	752	795	839	883	927	.1	
.9	927	971	015	059	103	147	191	235	280	324	368	10.0	44
.75												deg.	
	(10)	9	8	7	6	5	4	3	2	1	0		

LOG COT

LOG TAN

deg.	0	1	2	3	4	5	6	7	8	9	(10)		Diff.
80.0	.75 368	412	457	501	546	590	635	679	724	769	814	.9	44-45
.1	814	858	903	948	993	038	083	128	173	218	263	.8	44-45
.2	.76 263	308	354	399	444	490	535	581	626	672	717	.7	45-46
.3	717	763	809	854	900	946	992	038	084	130	176	.6	45-46
.4	.77 176	222	268	315	361	407	453	500	546	593	639	.5	46-47
.5	639	686	733	779	826	873	920	966	013	060	107	.4	46-47
.6	.78 107	154	202	249	296	343	390	438	485	533	580	.3	47-48
.7	580	628	675	723	771	818	866	914	962	010	058	.2	47-48
.8	.79 058	106	154	202	250	299	347	395	444	492	541	.1	48-49
.9	541	589	638	687	735	784	833	882	931	980	029	9.0	48-49
81.0	.80 029	078	127	176	225	275	324	373	423	472	522	.9	49-50
.1	522	572	621	671	721	771	821	870	920	971	021	.8	49-51
.2	.81 021	071	121	171	222	272	322	373	423	474	525	.7	50-51
.3	525	575	626	677	728	779	830	881	932	983	035	.6	50-52
.4	.82 035	086	137	189	240	292	343	395	447	498	550	.5	51-52
.5	550	602	654	706	758	810	862	915	967	019	072	.4	52-53
.6	.83 072	124	177	229	282	335	387	440	493	546	599	.3	52-53
.7	599	652	705	759	812	865	919	972	026	079	133	.2	53-54
.8	.84 133	187	240	294	348	402	456	510	565	619	673	.1	53-55
.9	673	727	782	836	891	946	000	055	110	165	220	8.0	54-55
82.0	.85 220	275	330	385	440	496	551	606	662	717	773	.9	55-56
.1	773	829	885	940	996	052	108	165	221	277	333	.8	55-57
.2	.86 333	390	446	503	559	616	673	730	787	844	901	.7	56-57
.3	901	958	015	072	130	187	244	302	360	417	475	.6	57-58
.4	.87 475	533	591	649	707	765	823	882	940	999	057	.5	58-59
.5	.88 057	116	174	233	292	351	410	469	528	587	647	.4	58-60
.6	647	706	766	825	885	944	004	064	124	184	244	.3	59-60
.7	.89 244	304	365	425	485	546	606	667	728	789	850	.2	60-61
.8	850	911	972	033	094	155	217	278	340	402	463	.1	61-62
.9	.90 463	525	587	649	711	773	836	898	960	023	086	7.0	62-63
83.0	.91 086	148	211	274	337	400	463	526	590	653	717	.9	62-64
.1	717	780	844	908	972	036	100	164	228	292	357	.8	63-65
.2	.92 357	421	486	551	615	680	745	810	876	941	006	.7	64-66
.3	.93 006	072	137	203	269	334	400	466	533	599	665	.6	65-67
.4	665	732	798	865	932	998	065	132	199	267	334	.5	66-68
.5	.94 334	401	469	537	604	672	740	808	876	945	013	.4	67-68
.6	.95 013	082	150	219	288	357	426	495	564	633	703	.3	68-70
.7	703	772	842	912	982	052	122	192	262	333	403	.2	69-71
.8	.96 403	474	545	615	686	758	829	900	972	043	115	.1	70-72
.9	.97 115	187	258	330	403	475	547	620	692	765	838	6.0	71-73
84.0	838	911	984	057	131	204	278	351	425	499	573	.9	73-74
.1	.98 573	647	722	796	871	945	020	095	170	245	321	.8	74-76
.2	.99 321	396	472	548	623	699	775	852	928	005	081	.7	75-77
.3	1.00 081	158	235	312	389	466	544	621	699	777	855	.6	77-78
.4	855	933	011	090	168	247	326	405	484	563	642	.5	78-79
.5	1.01 642	722	801	881	961	041	122	202	283	363	444	.4	79-81
.6	1.02 444	525	606	687	769	850	932	014	096	178	261	.3	81-83
.7	1.03 261	343	426	508	591	675	758	841	925	009	092	.2	82-84
.8	1.04 092	177	261	345	430	514	599	684	769	855	940	.1	84-86
.9	940	026	112	198	284	370	457	544	631	718	805	5.0	86-87
	1.05												deg.
	(10)	9	8	7	6	5	4	3	2	1	0		

LOG COT

LOG TAN

deg.	0	1	2	3	4	5	6	7	8	9	(10)	
85.0	1.05 805	892	980	068	155	244	332	420	509	598	687	.9
.1	1.06 687	776	865	955	044	134	224	315	405	496	586	.8
.2	1.07 586	677	769	860	951	043	135	227	320	412	505	.7
.3	1.08 505	598	691	784	878	971	065	159	254	348	443	.6
.4	1.09 443	538	633	728	824	920	016	112	208	305	402	.5
.5	1.10 402	499	596	693	791	889	987	085	184	283	382	.4
.6	1.11 382	481	580	680	780	880	980	081	181	283	384	.3
.7	1.12 384	485	587	689	791	894	996	099	202	306	409	.2
.8	1.13 409	513	617	722	827	931	037	142	248	354	460	.1
.9	1.14 460	566	673	780	887	994	102	210	318	427	536	4.0
86.0	1.15 536	645	754	864	974	084	194	305	416	527	639	.9
.1	1.16 639	751	863	975	088	201	314	428	542	656	770	.8
.2	1.17 770	885	000	115	231	347	463	580	697	814	932	.7
.3	1.18 932											
	1.19	050	168	286	405	524	644	763	884	004	125	.6
.4	1.20 125	246	367	489	611	734	857	980	103	227	351	.5
.5	1.21 351	476	601	726	852	978	104	231	358	486	613	.4
.6	1.22 613	742	870	999	129	258	388	519	650	781	913	.3
.7	1.23 913											
	1.24	045	177	310	444	577	711	846	981	116	252	.2
.8	1.25 252	388	525	662	799	937	076	215	354	494	634	.1
.9	1.26 634	774	915									
	1.27			057	199	341	484	627	771	916	060	3.0
87.0	1.28 060	206	351	498	644	792	939	088	236	386	535	.9
.1	1.29 535	686	836	988								
	1.30				140	292	445	598	752	907	062	.8
.2	1.31 062	217	374	530	688	846	004	163	323	483	644	.7
.3	1.32 644	805	967									
	1.33			130	293	457	621	786	952	118	285	.6
.4	1.34 285	453	621	790	959	130	300	472	644	817	991	.5
.5	1.35 991											
	1.36	165	340	516	692	869	047	226	405	585	766	.4
.6	1.37 766	947										
	1.38		130	313	496	681	867	053	240	428	616	.3
.7	1.39 616	806	996									
	1.40			187	379	572	765	960	155	351	549	.2
.8	1.41 549	747	946									
	1.42			146	346	548	751	954	159	364	571	.1
.9	1.43 571	778	987									
	1.44			196	407	618	831	044	259	475	692	2.0
	1.45											deg.
	(10)	9	8	7	6	5	4	3	2	1	0	

LOG COT

For 88° and 89° see the following two pages.

For a large table of logarithmic trigonometric functions of decimals of degrees, see "Zehnstellige Logarithmen der Trigonometrischen Funktionen von 0° bis 90° für jedes Tausendstel des Grades", by J. Peters.

DEG.	LOG TAN		DEG.	LOG TAN	
88.00	1.45 692	2.00	88.50	1.58 193	1.50
.01	1.45 909	1.99	.51	1.58 484	.49
.02	1.46 128	.98	.52	1.58 776	.48
.03	1.46 349	.97	.53	1.59 071	.47
.04	1.46 570	.96	.54	1.59 368	.46
.05	1.46 792	.95	.55	1.59 666	.45
.06	1.47 015	.94	.56	1.59 967	.44
.07	1.47 240	.93	.57	1.60 270	.43
.08	1.47 466	.92	.58	1.60 575	.42
.09	1.47 693	.91	.59	1.60 882	.41
88.10	1.47 921	1.90	88.60	1.61 191	1.40
.11	1.48 150	.89	.61	1.61 502	.39
.12	1.48 381	.88	.62	1.61 816	.38
.13	1.48 613	.87	.63	1.62 132	.37
.14	1.48 846	.86	.64	1.62 450	.36
.15	1.49 080	.85	.65	1.62 771	.35
.16	1.49 316	.84	.66	1.63 094	.34
.17	1.49 552	.83	.67	1.63 419	.33
.18	1.49 791	.82	.68	1.63 747	.32
.19	1.50 030	.81	.69	1.64 078	.31
88.20	1.50 271	1.80	88.70	1.64 410	1.30
.21	1.50 513	.79	.71	1.64 746	.29
.22	1.50 756	.78	.72	1.65 084	.28
.23	1.51 001	.77	.73	1.65 425	.27
.24	1.51 247	.76	.74	1.65 768	.26
.25	1.51 495	.75	.75	1.66 114	.25
.26	1.51 744	.74	.76	1.66 463	.24
.27	1.51 994	.73	.77	1.66 815	.23
.28	1.52 246	.72	.78	1.67 170	.22
.29	1.52 500	.71	.79	1.67 527	.21
88.30	1.52 755	1.70	88.80	1.67 888	1.20
.31	1.53 011	.69	.81	1.68 251	.19
.32	1.53 269	.68	.82	1.68 618	.18
.33	1.53 528	.67	.83	1.68 988	.17
.34	1.53 789	.66	.84	1.69 361	.16
.35	1.54 052	.65	.85	1.69 737	.15
.36	1.54 316	.64	.86	1.70 116	.14
.37	1.54 582	.63	.87	1.70 499	.13
.38	1.54 849	.62	.88	1.70 885	.12
.39	1.55 118	.61	.89	1.71 275	.11
88.40	1.55 389	1.60	88.90	1.71 668	1.10
.41	1.55 661	.59	.91	1.72 064	.09
.42	1.55 936	.58	.92	1.72 465	.08
.43	1.56 211	.57	.93	1.72 869	.07
.44	1.56 489	.56	.94	1.73 277	.06
.45	1.56 768	.55	.95	1.73 688	.05
.46	1.57 050	.54	.96	1.74 104	.04
.47	1.57 333	.53	.97	1.74 524	.03
.48	1.57 618	.52	.98	1.74 948	.02
.49	1.57 905	1.51	.99	1.75 376	1.01
	LOG COT	DEG.		LOG COT	DEG.

DEG.	LOG TAN		DEG.	LOG TAN	
89.00	1.75 808	1.00	89.50	2.05 914	0.50
.01	1.76 244	0.99	.51	2.06 792	.49
.02	1.76 685	.98	.52	2.07 687	.48
.03	1.77 131	.97	.53	2.08 602	.47
.04	1.77 581	.96	.54	2.09 536	.46
.05	1.78 036	.95	.55	2.10 490	.45
.06	1.78 496	.94	.56	2.11 466	.44
.07	1.78 960	.93	.57	2.12 465	.43
.08	1.79 430	.92	.58	2.13 487	.42
.09	1.79 904	.91	.59	2.14 533	.41
89.10	1.80 384	0.90	89.60	2.15 606	0.40
.11	1.80 870	.89	.61	2.16 705	.39
.12	1.81 361	.88	.62	2.17 833	.38
.13	1.81 857	.87	.63	2.18 991	.37
.14	1.82 359	.86	.64	2.20 181	.36
.15	1.82 867	.85	.65	2.21 405	.35
.16	1.83 381	.84	.66	2.22 664	.34
.17	1.83 901	.83	.67	2.23 960	.33
.18	1.84 428	.82	.68	2.25 297	.32
.19	1.84 961	.81	.69	2.26 676	.31
89.20	1.85 500	0.80	89.70	2.28 100	0.30
.21	1.86 047	.79	.71	2.29 572	.29
.22	1.86 600	.78	.72	2.31 096	.28
.23	1.87 161	.77	.73	2.32 676	.27
.24	1.87 728	.76	.74	2.34 315	.26
.25	1.88 304	.75	.75	2.36 018	.25
.26	1.88 887	.74	.76	2.37 791	.24
.27	1.89 478	.73	.77	2.39 639	.23
.28	1.90 077	.72	.78	2.41 570	.22
.29	1.90 684	.71	.79	2.43 590	.21
89.30	1.91 300	0.70	89.80	2.45 709	0.20
.31	1.91 925	.69	.81	2.47 937	.19
.32	1.92 559	.68	.82	2.50 285	.18
.33	1.93 203	.67	.83	2.52 767	.17
.34	1.93 856	.66	.84	2.55 400	.16
.35	1.94 519	.65	.85	2.58 203	.15
.36	1.95 192	.64	.86	2.61 199	.14
.37	1.95 876	.63	.87	2.64 418	.13
.38	1.96 571	.62	.88	2.67 894	.12
.39	1.97 278	.61	.89	2.71 673	.11
89.40	1.97 996	0.60	89.90	2.75 812	0.10
.41	1.98 726	.59	.91	2.80 388	.09
.42	1.99 468	.58	.92	2.85 503	.08
.43	2.00 223	.57	.93	2.91 302	.07
.44	2.00 992	.56	.94	2.97 997	.06
.45	2.01 775	.55	.95	3.05 915	.05
.46	2.02 572	.54	.96	3.15 606	.04
.47	2.03 383	.53	.97	3.28 100	.03
.48	2.04 211	.52	.98	3.45 709	.02
.49	2.05 054	0.51	.99	3.75 812	.01
			90.00	.....	0.00
	LOG COT	DEG.		LOG COT	DEG.

x	0	1	2	3	4	5	6	7	8	9	Diff.
1.00	.00 000	043	087	130	173	217	260	303	346	389	44-43
.01	432	475	518	561	604	647	689	732	775	817	43
.02	860	903	945	988	030	072	115	157	199	242	
.03	.01 284	326	368	410	452	494	536	578	620	662	42
.04	703	745	787	828	870	912	953	995	036	078	
.05	.02 119	160	202	243	284	325	366	407	449	490	41
.06	531	572	612	653	694	735	776	816	857	898	
.07	938	979	019	060	100	141	181	222	262	302	
.08	.03 342	383	423	463	503	543	583	623	663	703	40
.09	743	782	822	862	902	941	981	021	060	100	
1.10	.04 139	179	218	258	297	336	376	415	454	493	
.11	532	571	610	650	689	727	766	805	844	883	39
.12	922	961	999	038	077	115	154	192	231	269	
.13	.05 308	346	385	423	461	500	538	576	614	652	
.14	690	729	767	805	843	881	918	956	994	032	38
.15	.06 070	108	145	183	221	258	296	333	371	408	
.16	446	483	521	558	595	633	670	707	744	781	
.17	819	856	893	930	967	004	041	078	115	151	37
.18	.07 188	225	262	298	335	372	408	445	482	518	
.19	555	591	628	664	700	737	773	809	846	882	
1.20	918	954	990	027	063	099	135	171	207	243	36
.21	.08 279	314	350	386	422	458	493	529	565	600	
.22	636	672	707	743	778	814	849	884	920	955	
.23	991	026	061	096	132	167	202	237	272	307	
.24	.09 342	377	412	447	482	517	552	587	621	656	35
.25	691	726	760	795	830	864	899	934	968	003	
.26	.10 037	072	106	140	175	209	243	278	312	346	
.27	380	415	449	483	517	551	585	619	653	687	34
.28	721	755	789	823	857	890	924	958	992	025	
.29	.11 059	093	126	160	193	227	261	294	327	361	
1.30	394	428	461	494	528	561	594	628	661	694	
.31	727	760	793	826	860	893	926	959	992	024	33
.32	.12 057	090	123	156	189	222	254	287	320	352	
.33	385	418	450	483	516	548	581	613	646	678	
.34	710	743	775	808	840	872	905	937	969	001	
.35	.13 033	066	098	130	162	194	226	258	290	322	32
.36	354	386	418	450	481	513	545	577	609	640	
.37	672	704	735	767	799	830	862	893	925	956	
.38	988	019	051	082	114	145	176	208	239	270	
.39	.14 301	333	364	395	426	457	489	520	551	582	
1.40	613	644	675	706	737	768	799	829	860	891	31
.41	922	953	983	014	045	076	106	137	168	198	
.42	.15 229	259	290	320	351	381	412	442	473	503	
.43	534	564	594	625	655	685	715	746	776	806	
.44	836	866	897	927	957	987	017	047	077	107	30
.45	.16 137	167	197	227	256	286	316	346	376	406	
.46	435	465	495	524	554	584	613	643	673	702	
.47	732	761	791	820	850	879	909	938	967	997	
.48	.17 026	056	085	114	143	173	202	231	260	289	
.49	319	348	377	406	435	464	493	522	551	580	29

x	0	1	2	3	4	5	6	7	8	9	Diff.
1.50	.17 609	638	667	696	725	754	782	811	840	869	29
.51	898	926	955	984	013	041	070	099	127	156	
.52	.18 184	213	241	270	298	327	355	384	412	441	
.53	469	498	526	554	583	611	639	667	696	724	
.54	752	780	808	837	865	893	921	949	977	005	
.55	.19 033	061	089	117	145	173	201	229	257	285	28
.56	312	340	368	396	424	451	479	507	535	562	
.57	590	618	645	673	700	728	756	783	811	838	
.58	866	893	921	948	976	003	030	058	085	112	
.59	.20 140	167	194	222	249	276	303	330	358	385	
1.60	412	439	466	493	520	548	575	602	629	656	27
.61	683	710	737	763	790	817	844	871	898	925	
.62	952	978	005	032	059	085	112	139	165	192	
.63	.21 219	245	272	299	325	352	378	405	431	458	
.64	484	511	537	564	590	617	643	669	696	722	
.65	748	775	801	827	854	880	906	932	958	985	
.66	.22 011	037	063	089	115	141	167	194	220	246	
.67	272	298	324	350	376	401	427	453	479	505	26
.68	531	557	583	608	634	660	686	712	737	763	
.69	789	814	840	866	891	917	943	968	994	019	
1.70	.23 045	070	096	121	147	172	198	223	249	274	
.71	300	325	350	376	401	426	452	477	502	528	
.72	553	578	603	629	654	679	704	729	754	779	
.73	805	830	855	880	905	930	955	980	005	030	25
.74	.24 055	080	105	130	155	180	204	229	254	279	
.75	304	329	353	378	403	428	452	477	502	527	
.76	551	576	601	625	650	674	699	724	748	773	
.77	797	822	846	871	895	920	944	969	993	018	
.78	.25 042	066	091	115	139	164	188	212	237	261	
.79	285	310	334	358	382	406	431	455	479	503	
1.80	527	551	575	600	624	648	672	696	720	744	24
.81	768	792	816	840	864	888	912	935	959	983	
.82	.26 007	031	055	079	102	126	150	174	198	221	
.83	245	269	293	316	340	364	387	411	435	458	
.84	482	505	529	553	576	600	623	647	670	694	
.85	717	741	764	788	811	834	858	881	905	928	
.86	951	975	998	021	045	068	091	114	138	161	
.87	.27 184	207	231	254	277	300	323	346	370	393	
.88	416	439	462	485	508	531	554	577	600	623	23
.89	646	669	692	715	738	761	784	807	830	852	
1.90	875	898	921	944	967	989	012	035	058	081	
.91	.28 103	126	149	171	194	217	240	262	285	307	
.92	330	353	375	398	421	443	466	488	511	533	
.93	556	578	601	623	646	668	691	713	735	758	
.94	780	803	825	847	870	892	914	937	959	981	
.95	.29 003	026	048	070	092	115	137	159	181	203	
.96	226	248	270	292	314	336	358	380	403	425	
.97	447	469	491	513	535	557	579	601	623	645	22
.98	667	688	710	732	754	776	798	820	842	863	
.99	885	907	929	951	973	994	016	038	060	081	
.30											

x	0	1	2	3	4	5	6	7	8	9	Diff.
2.00	.30 103	125	146	168	190	211	233	255	276	298	
.01	320	341	363	384	406	428	449	471	492	514	22-21
.02	535	557	578	600	621	643	664	685	707	728	
.03	750	771	792	814	835	856	878	899	920	942	
.04	963	984	006	027	048	069	091	112	133	154	
.05	.31 175	197	218	239	260	281	302	323	345	366	
.06	387	408	429	450	471	492	513	534	555	576	21
.07	597	618	639	660	681	702	723	744	765	785	
.08	806	827	848	869	890	911	931	952	973	994	
.09	.32 015	035	056	077	098	118	139	160	181	201	
2.10	222	243	263	284	305	325	346	366	387	408	
.11	428	449	469	490	510	531	552	572	593	613	
.12	634	654	675	695	715	736	756	777	797	818	
.13	838	858	879	899	919	940	960	980	001	021	
.14	.33 041	062	082	102	122	143	163	183	203	224	
.15	244	264	284	304	325	345	365	385	405	425	
.16	445	465	486	506	526	546	566	586	606	626	
.17	646	666	686	706	726	746	766	786	806	826	20
.18	846	866	885	905	925	945	965	985	005	025	
.19	.34 044	064	084	104	124	143	163	183	203	223	
2.20	242	262	282	301	321	341	361	380	400	420	
.21	439	459	479	498	518	537	557	577	596	616	
.22	635	655	674	694	713	733	753	772	792	811	
.23	830	850	869	889	908	928	947	967	986	005	
.24	.35 025	044	064	083	102	122	141	160	180	199	
.25	218	238	257	276	295	315	334	353	372	392	
.26	411	430	449	468	488	507	526	545	564	583	
.27	603	622	641	660	679	698	717	736	755	774	
.28	795	813	832	851	870	889	908	927	946	965	
.29	984	003	021	040	059	078	097	116	135	154	19
2.30	.36 173	192	211	229	248	267	286	305	324	342	
.31	361	380	399	418	436	455	474	493	511	530	
.32	549	568	586	605	624	642	661	680	698	717	
.33	736	754	773	791	810	829	847	866	884	903	
.34	922	940	959	977	996	014	033	051	070	088	
.35	.37 107	125	144	162	181	199	218	236	254	273	
.36	291	310	328	346	365	383	401	420	438	457	
.37	475	493	511	530	548	566	585	603	621	639	
.38	658	676	694	712	731	749	767	785	803	822	
.39	840	858	876	894	912	931	949	967	985	003	
2.40	.38 021	039	057	075	093	112	130	148	166	184	
.41	202	220	238	256	274	292	310	328	346	364	18
.42	382	399	417	435	453	471	489	507	525	543	
.43	561	578	596	614	632	650	668	686	703	721	
.44	739	757	775	792	810	828	846	863	881	899	
.45	917	934	952	970	987	005	023	041	058	076	
.46	.39 094	111	129	146	164	182	199	217	235	252	
.47	270	287	305	322	340	358	375	393	410	428	
.48	445	463	480	498	515	533	550	568	585	602	18-17
.49	620	637	655	672	690	707	724	742	759	777	

x	0	1	2	3	4	5	6	7	8	9	Diff.
2.50	.39 794	811	829	846	863	881	898	915	933	950	18-17
.51	967	985	002	019	037	054	071	088	106	123	
.52	.40 140	157	175	192	209	226	243	261	278	295	
.53	312	329	346	364	381	398	415	432	449	466	
.54	483	500	518	535	552	569	586	603	620	637	
.55	654	671	688	705	722	739	756	773	790	807	
.56	824	841	858	875	892	909	926	943	960	976	17
.57	993	010	027	044	061	078	095	111	128	145	
.58	.41 162	179	196	212	229	246	263	280	296	313	
.59	330	347	363	380	397	414	430	447	464	481	
2.60	497	514	531	547	564	581	597	614	631	647	
.61	664	681	697	714	731	747	764	780	797	814	
.62	830	847	863	880	896	913	929	946	963	979	
.63	996	012	029	045	062	078	095	111	127	144	
.64	.42 160	177	193	210	226	243	259	275	292	308	
.65	325	341	357	374	390	406	423	439	455	472	
.66	488	504	521	537	553	570	586	602	619	635	
.67	651	667	684	700	716	732	749	765	781	797	
.68	813	830	846	862	878	894	911	927	943	959	
.69	975	991	008	024	040	056	072	088	104	120	
2.70	.43 136	152	169	185	201	217	233	249	265	281	
.71	297	313	329	345	361	377	393	409	425	441	
.72	457	473	489	505	521	537	553	569	584	600	16
.73	616	632	648	664	680	696	712	727	743	759	
.74	775	791	807	823	838	854	870	886	902	917	
.75	933	949	965	981	996	012	028	044	059	075	
.76	.44 091	107	122	138	154	170	185	201	217	232	
.77	248	264	279	295	311	326	342	358	373	389	
.78	404	420	436	451	467	483	498	514	529	545	
.79	560	576	592	607	623	638	654	669	685	700	
2.80	716	731	747	762	778	793	809	824	840	855	
.81	871	886	902	917	932	948	963	979	994	010	
.82	.45 025	040	056	071	086	102	117	133	148	163	
.83	179	194	209	225	240	255	271	286	301	317	
.84	332	347	362	378	393	408	423	439	454	469	
.85	484	500	515	530	545	561	576	591	606	621	
.86	637	652	667	682	697	712	728	743	758	773	
.87	788	803	818	834	849	864	879	894	909	924	
.88	939	954	969	984	000	015	030	045	060	075	
.89	.46 090	105	120	135	150	165	180	195	210	225	15
2.90	240	255	270	285	300	315	330	345	359	374	
.91	389	404	419	434	449	464	479	494	509	523	
.92	538	553	568	583	598	613	627	642	657	672	
.93	687	702	716	731	746	761	776	790	805	820	
.94	835	850	864	879	894	909	923	938	953	967	
.95	982	997	012	026	041	056	070	085	100	114	
.96	.47 129	144	159	173	188	202	217	232	246	261	
.97	276	290	305	319	334	349	363	378	392	407	
.98	422	436	451	465	480	494	509	524	538	553	
.99	567	582	596	611	625	640	654	669	683	698	15-14

x	0	1	2	3	4	5	6	7	8	9	Diff.
3.00	.47 712	727 741 756			770 784 799			813 828 842			15-14
.01	857	871 885 900			914 929 943			958 972 986			
.02	.48 001	015 029 044			058 073 087			101 116 130			
.03	144	159 173 187			202 216 230			244 259 273			
.04	287	302 316 330			344 359 373			387 401 416			
.05	430	444 458 473			487 501 515			530 544 558			
.06	572	586 601 615			629 643 657			671 686 700			
.07	714	728 742 756			770 785 799			813 827 841			
.08	855	869 883 897			911 926 940			954 968 982			
.09	996	0̅1̅0̅ 0̅2̅4̅ 0̅3̅8̅			0̅5̅2̅ 0̅6̅6̅ 0̅8̅0̅			0̅9̅4̅ 1̅0̅8̅ 1̅2̅2̅			
3.10	.49 136	150 164 178			192 206 220			234 248 262			14
.11	276	290 304 318			332 346 360			374 388 402			
.12	415	429 443 457			471 485 499			513 527 541			
.13	554	568 582 596			610 624 638			651 665 679			
.14	693	707 721 734			748 762 776			790 803 817			
.15	831	845 859 872			886 900 914			927 941 955			
.16	969	982 996 0̅1̅0̅			0̅2̅4̅ 0̅3̅7̅ 0̅5̅1̅			0̅6̅5̅ 0̅7̅9̅ 0̅9̅2̅			
.17	.50 106	120 133 147			161 174 188			202 215 229			
.18	243	256 270 284			297 311 325			338 352 365			
.19	379	393 406 420			433 447 461			474 488 501			
3.20	515	529 542 556			569 583 596			610 623 637			
.21	651	664 678 691			705 718 732			745 759 772			
.22	786	799 813 826			840 853 866			880 893 907			
.23	920	934 947 961			974 987 0̅0̅1̅			0̅1̅4̅ 0̅2̅8̅ 0̅4̅1̅			
.24	.51 055	068 081 095			108 121 135			148 162 175			
.25	188	202 215 228			242 255 268			282 295 308			
.26	322	335 348 362			375 388 402			415 428 441			
.27	455	468 481 495			508 521 534			548 561 574			
.28	587	601 614 627			640 654 667			680 693 706			
.29	720	733 746 759			772 786 799			812 825 838			
3.30	851	865 878 891			904 917 930			943 957 970			
.31	983	996 0̅0̅9̅ 0̅2̅2̅			0̅3̅5̅ 0̅4̅8̅ 0̅6̅1̅			0̅7̅5̅ 0̅8̅8̅ 1̅0̅1̅			
.32	.52 114	127 140 153			166 179 192			205 218 231			
.33	244	257 270 284			297 310 323			336 349 362			
.34	375	388 401 414			427 440 453			466 479 492			13
.35	504	517 530 543			556 569 582			595 608 621			
.36	634	647 660 673			686 699 711			724 737 750			
.37	763	776 789 802			815 827 840			853 866 879			
.38	892	905 917 930			943 956 969			982 994 0̅0̅7̅			
.39	.53 020	033 046 058			071 084 097			110 122 135			
3.40	148	161 173 186			199 212 224			237 250 263			
.41	275	288 301 314			326 339 352			364 377 390			
.42	403	415 428 441			453 466 479			491 504 517			
.43	529	542 555 567			580 593 605			618 631 643			
.44	656	668 681 694			706 719 732			744 757 769			
.45	782	794 807 820			832 845 857			870 882 895			
.46	908	920 933 945			958 970 983			995 0̅0̅8̅ 0̅2̅0̅			13-12
.47	.54 033	045 058 070			083 095 108			120 133 145			
.48	158	170 183 195			208 220 233			245 258 270			
.49	283	295 307 320			332 345 357			370 382 394			

x	0	1	2	3	4	5	6	7	8	9	Diff.
3.50	.54 407	419	432	444	456	469	481	494	506	518	13-12
.51	531	543	555	568	580	593	605	617	630	642	
.52	654	667	679	691	704	716	728	741	753	765	
.53	777	790	802	814	827	839	851	864	876	888	
.54	900	913	925	937	949	962	974	986	998	0̅1̅1̅	
.55	.55 023	035	047	060	072	084	096	108	121	133	
.56	145	157	169	182	194	206	218	230	242	255	
.57	267	279	291	303	315	328	340	352	364	376	
.58	388	400	413	425	437	449	461	473	485	497	
.59	509	522	534	546	558	570	582	594	606	618	
3.60	630	642	654	666	678	691	703	715	727	739	
.61	751	763	775	787	799	811	823	835	847	859	12
.62	871	883	895	907	919	931	943	955	967	979	
.63	991	0̅0̅3̅	0̅1̅5̅	0̅2̅7̅	0̅3̅8̅	0̅5̅0̅	0̅6̅2̅	0̅7̅4̅	0̅8̅6̅	0̅9̅8̅	
.64	.56 110	122	134	146	158	170	182	194	205	217	
.65	229	241	253	265	277	289	301	312	324	336	
.66	348	360	372	384	396	407	419	431	443	455	
.67	467	478	490	502	514	526	538	549	561	573	
.68	585	597	608	620	632	644	656	667	679	691	
.69	703	714	726	738	750	761	773	785	797	808	
3.70	820	832	844	855	867	879	891	902	914	926	
.71	937	949	961	972	984	996	0̅0̅8̅	0̅1̅9̅	0̅3̅1̅	0̅4̅3̅	
.72	.57 054	066	078	089	101	113	124	136	148	159	
.73	171	183	194	206	217	229	241	252	264	276	
.74	287	299	310	322	334	345	357	368	380	392	
.75	403	415	426	438	449	461	473	484	496	507	
.76	519	530	542	553	565	576	588	600	611	623	12-11
.77	634	646	657	669	680	692	703	715	726	738	
.78	749	761	772	784	795	807	818	830	841	852	
.79	864	875	887	898	910	921	933	944	955	967	
3.80	978	990	0̅0̅1̅	0̅1̅3̅	0̅2̅4̅	0̅3̅5̅	0̅4̅7̅	0̅5̅8̅	0̅7̅0̅	0̅8̅1̅	
.81	.58 092	104	115	127	138	149	161	172	184	195	
.82	206	218	229	240	252	263	274	286	297	309	
.83	320	331	343	354	365	377	388	399	410	422	
.84	433	444	456	467	478	490	501	512	524	535	
.85	546	557	569	580	591	602	614	625	636	647	
.86	659	670	681	692	704	715	726	737	749	760	
.87	771	782	794	805	816	827	838	850	861	872	
.88	883	894	906	917	928	939	950	961	973	984	
.89	995	0̅0̅6̅	0̅1̅7̅	0̅2̅8̅	0̅4̅0̅	0̅5̅1̅	0̅6̅2̅	0̅7̅3̅	0̅8̅4̅	0̅9̅5̅	
3.90	.59 106	118	129	140	151	162	173	184	195	207	
.91	218	229	240	251	262	273	284	295	306	318	
.92	329	340	351	362	373	384	395	406	417	428	
.93	439	450	461	472	483	494	506	517	528	539	
.94	550	561	572	583	594	605	616	627	638	649	11
.95	660	671	682	693	704	715	726	737	748	759	
.96	770	780	791	802	813	824	835	846	857	868	
.97	879	890	901	912	923	934	945	956	966	977	
.98	988	999	0̅1̅0̅	0̅2̅1̅	0̅3̅2̅	0̅4̅3̅	0̅5̅4̅	0̅6̅5̅	0̅7̅6̅	0̅8̅6̅	
.99	.60 097	108	119	130	141	152	163	173	184	195	

5-PLACE COMMON LOGARITHMS OF NUMBERS Log_{10} x

x	0	1	2	3	4	5	6	7	8	9	Diff.
4.00	.60 206	217	228	239	249	260	271	282	293	304	
.01	314	325	336	347	358	369	379	390	401	412	
.02	423	433	444	455	466	477	487	498	509	520	
.03	531	541	552	563	574	584	595	606	617	627	
.04	638	649	660	670	681	692	703	713	724	735	
.05	746	756	767	778	788	799	810	821	831	842	
.06	853	863	874	885	895	906	917	927	938	949	
.07	959	970	981	991	002	013	023	034	045	055	
.08	.61 066	077	087	098	109	119	130	140	151	162	
.09	172	183	194	204	215	225	236	247	257	268	
4.10	278	289	300	310	321	331	342	352	363	374	
.11	384	395	405	416	426	437	448	458	469	479	
.12	490	500	511	521	532	542	553	563	574	584	
.13	595	606	616	627	637	648	658	669	679	690	11-10
.14	700	711	721	731	742	752	763	773	784	794	
.15	805	815	826	836	847	857	868	878	888	899	
.16	909	920	930	941	951	962	972	982	993	003	
.17	.62 014	024	034	045	055	066	076	086	097	107	
.18	118	128	138	149	159	170	180	190	201	211	
.19	221	232	242	252	263	273	284	294	304	315	
4.20	325	335	346	356	366	377	387	397	408	418	
.21	428	439	449	459	469	480	490	500	511	521	
.22	531	542	552	562	572	583	593	603	613	624	
.23	634	644	655	665	675	685	696	706	716	726	
.24	737	747	757	767	778	788	798	808	818	829	
.25	839	849	859	870	880	890	900	910	921	931	
.26	941	951	961	972	982	992	002	012	022	033	
.27	.63 043	053	063	073	083	094	104	114	124	134	
.28	144	155	165	175	185	195	205	215	225	236	
.29	246	256	266	276	286	296	306	317	327	337	
4.30	347	357	367	377	387	397	407	417	428	438	
.31	448	458	468	478	488	498	508	518	528	538	
.32	548	558	568	579	589	599	609	619	629	639	
.33	649	659	669	679	689	699	709	719	729	739	
.34	749	759	769	779	789	799	809	819	829	839	10
.35	849	859	869	879	889	899	909	919	929	939	
.36	949	959	969	979	988	998	008	018	028	038	
.37	.64 048	058	068	078	088	098	108	118	128	137	
.38	147	157	167	177	187	197	207	217	227	237	
.39	246	256	266	276	286	296	306	316	326	335	
4.40	345	355	365	375	385	395	404	414	424	434	
.41	444	454	464	473	483	493	503	513	523	532	
.42	542	552	562	572	582	591	601	611	621	631	
.43	640	650	660	670	680	689	699	709	719	729	
.44	738	748	758	768	777	787	797	807	816	826	
.45	836	846	856	865	875	885	895	904	914	924	
.46	933	943	953	963	972	982	992	002	011	021	
.47	.65 031	040	050	060	070	079	089	099	108	118	
.48	128	137	147	157	167	176	186	196	205	215	
.49	225	234	244	254	263	273	283	292	302	312	

x	0	1	2	3	4	5	6	7	8	9	Diff.
4.50	.65 321	331	341	350	360	369	379	389	398	408	
.51	418	427	437	447	456	466	475	485	495	504	
.52	514	523	533	543	552	562	571	581	591	600	
.53	610	619	629	639	648	658	667	677	686	696	
.54	706	715	725	734	744	753	763	772	782	792	
.55	801	811	820	830	839	849	858	868	877	887	
.56	896	906	916	925	935	944	954	963	973	982	
.57	992	0̄01	0̄11	0̄20	0̄30	0̄39	0̄49	0̄58	0̄68	0̄77	10-9
.58	.66 087	096	106	115	124	134	143	153	162	172	
.59	181	191	200	210	219	229	238	247	257	266	
4.60	276	285	295	304	314	323	332	342	351	361	
.61	370	380	389	398	408	417	427	436	445	455	
.62	464	474	483	492	502	511	521	530	539	549	
.63	558	567	577	586	596	605	614	624	633	642	
.64	652	661	671	680	689	699	708	717	727	736	
.65	745	755	764	773	783	792	801	811	820	829	
.66	839	848	857	867	876	885	894	904	913	922	
.67	932	941	950	960	969	978	987	997	0̄06	0̄15	
.68	.67 025	034	043	052	062	071	080	089	099	108	
.69	117	127	136	145	154	164	173	182	191	201	
4.70	210	219	228	237	247	256	265	274	284	293	
.71	302	311	321	330	339	348	357	367	376	385	
.72	394	403	413	422	431	440	449	459	468	477	
.73	486	495	504	514	523	532	541	550	560	569	
.74	578	587	596	605	614	624	633	642	651	660	
.75	669	679	688	697	706	715	724	733	742	752	
.76	761	770	779	788	797	806	815	825	834	843	
.77	852	861	870	879	888	897	906	916	925	934	
.78	943	952	961	970	979	988	997	0̄06	0̄15	0̄24	
.79	.68 034	043	052	061	070	079	088	097	106	115	
4.80	124	133	142	151	160	169	178	187	196	205	
.81	215	224	233	242	251	260	269	278	287	296	
.82	305	314	323	332	341	350	359	368	377	386	9
.83	395	404	413	422	431	440	449	458	467	476	
.84	485	494	502	511	520	529	538	547	556	565	
.85	574	583	592	601	610	619	628	637	646	655	
.86	664	673	681	690	699	708	717	726	735	744	
.87	753	762	771	780	789	797	806	815	824	833	
.88	842	851	860	869	878	886	895	904	913	922	
.89	931	940	949	958	966	975	984	993	0̄02	0̄11	
4.90	.69 020	028	037	046	055	064	073	082	090	099	
.91	108	117	126	135	144	152	161	170	179	188	
.92	197	205	214	223	232	241	249	258	267	276	
.93	285	294	302	311	320	329	338	346	355	364	
.94	373	381	390	399	408	417	425	434	443	452	
.95	461	469	478	487	496	504	513	522	531	539	
.96	548	557	566	574	583	592	601	609	618	627	
.97	636	644	653	662	671	679	688	697	705	714	
.98	723	732	740	749	758	767	775	784	793	801	
.99	810	819	827	836	845	854	862	871	880	888	9-8

x	0	1	2	3	4	5	6	7	8	9	Diff.
5.00	.69 897	906	914	923	932	940	949	958	966	975	
.01	984	992	001	010	018	027	036	044	053	062	
.02	.70 070	079	088	096	105	114	122	131	140	148	
.03	157	165	174	183	191	200	209	217	226	234	
.04	243	252	260	269	278	286	295	303	312	321	
.05	329	338	346	355	364	372	381	389	398	406	
.06	415	424	432	441	449	458	467	475	484	492	
.07	501	509	518	526	535	544	552	561	569	578	
.08	586	595	603	612	621	629	638	646	655	663	
.09	672	680	689	697	706	714	723	731	740	749	
5.10	757	766	774	783	791	800	808	817	825	834	9-8
.11	842	851	859	868	876	885	893	902	910	919	
.12	927	935	944	952	961	969	978	986	995	003	
.13	.71 012	020	029	037	046	054	063	071	079	088	
.14	096	105	113	122	130	139	147	155	164	172	
.15	181	189	198	206	214	223	231	240	248	257	
.16	265	273	282	290	299	307	315	324	332	341	
.17	349	357	366	374	383	391	399	408	416	425	
.18	433	441	450	458	466	475	483	492	500	508	
.19	517	525	533	542	550	559	567	575	584	592	
5.20	600	609	617	625	634	642	650	659	667	675	
.21	684	692	700	709	717	725	734	742	750	759	
.22	767	775	784	792	800	809	817	825	834	842	
.23	850	858	867	875	883	892	900	908	917	925	
.24	933	941	950	958	966	975	983	991	999	008	
.25	.72 016	024	032	041	049	057	066	074	082	090	
.26	099	107	115	123	132	140	148	156	165	173	
.27	181	189	198	206	214	222	230	239	247	255	
.28	263	272	280	288	296	304	313	321	329	337	
.29	346	354	362	370	378	387	395	403	411	419	
5.30	428	436	444	452	460	469	477	485	493	501	
.31	509	518	526	534	542	550	558	567	575	583	
.32	591	599	607	616	624	632	640	648	656	665	
.33	673	681	689	697	705	713	722	730	738	746	
.34	754	762	770	779	787	795	803	811	819	827	
.35	835	843	852	860	868	876	884	892	900	908	
.36	916	925	933	941	949	957	965	973	981	989	
.37	997	006	014	022	030	038	046	054	062	070	
.38	.73 078	086	094	102	111	119	127	135	143	151	
.39	159	167	175	183	191	199	207	215	223	231	
5.40	239	247	255	263	272	280	288	296	304	312	
.41	320	328	336	344	352	360	368	376	384	392	
.42	400	408	416	424	432	440	448	456	464	472	8
.43	480	488	496	504	512	520	528	536	544	552	
.44	560	568	576	584	592	600	608	616	624	632	
.45	640	648	656	664	672	679	687	695	703	711	
.46	719	727	735	743	751	759	767	775	783	791	
.47	799	807	815	823	830	838	846	854	862	870	
.48	878	886	894	902	910	918	926	933	941	949	
.49	957	965	973	981	989	997	005	013	020	028	
.74											

x	0	1	2	3	4	5	6	7	8	9	Diff.
5.50	.74 036	044 052 060			068 076 084			092 099 107			8
.51	115	123 131 139			147 155 162			170 178 186			
.52	194	202 210 218			225 233 241			249 257 265			
.53	273	280 288 296			304 312 320			327 335 343			
.54	351	359 367 374			382 390 398			406 414 421			
.55	429	437 445 453			461 468 476			484 492 500			
.56	507	515 523 531			539 547 554			562 570 578			
.57	586	593 601 609			617 624 632			640 648 656			
.58	663	671 679 687			695 702 710			718 726 733			
.59	741	749 757 764			772 780 788			796 803 811			
5.60	819	827 834 842			850 858 865			873 881 889			
.61	896	904 912 920			927 935 943			950 958 966			
.62	974	981 989 997			005 012 020			028 035 043			
.63	.75 051	059 066 074			082 089 097			105 113 120			
.64	128	136 143 151			159 166 174			182 189 197			
.65	205	213 220 228			236 243 251			259 266 274			
.66	282	289 297 305			312 320 328			335 343 351			
.67	358	366 374 381			389 397 404			412 420 427			
.68	435	442 450 458			465 473 481			488 496 504			
.69	511	519 526 534			542 549 557			565 572 580			
5.70	587	595 603 610			618 626 633			641 648 656			
.71	664	671 679 686			694 702 709			717 724 732			
.72	740	747 755 762			770 778 785			793 800 808			
.73	815	823 831 838			846 853 861			868 876 884			
.74	891	899 906 914			921 929 937			944 952 959			
.75	967	974 982 989			997 005 012			020 027 035			
.76	.76 042	050 057 065			072 080 087			095 103 110			
.77	118	125 133 140			148 155 163			170 178 185			
.78	193	200 208 215			223 230 238			245 253 260			8-7
.79	268	275 283 290			298 305 313			320 328 335			
5.80	343	350 358 365			373 380 388			395 403 410			
.81	418	425 433 440			448 455 462			470 477 485			
.82	492	500 507 515			522 530 537			545 552 559			
.83	567	574 582 589			597 604 612			619 626 634			
.84	641	649 656 664			671 678 686			693 701 708			
.85	716	723 730 738			745 753 760			768 775 782			
.86	790	797 805 812			819 827 834			842 849 856			
.87	864	871 879 886			893 901 908			916 923 930			
.88	938	945 953 960			967 975 982			989 997 004			
.89	.77 012	019 026 034			041 048 056			063 070 078			
5.90	085	093 100 107			115 122 129			137 144 151			
.91	159	166 173 181			188 195 203			210 217 225			
.92	232	240 247 254			262 269 276			283 291 298			
.93	305	313 320 327			335 342 349			357 364 371			
.94	379	386 393 401			408 415 422			430 437 444			
.95	452	459 466 474			481 488 495			503 510 517			
.96	525	532 539 546			554 561 568			576 583 590			
.97	597	605 612 619			627 634 641			648 656 663			
.98	670	677 685 692			699 706 714			721 728 735			
.99	743	750 757 764			772 779 786			793 801 808			7

x	0	1	2	3	4	5	6	7	8	9	Diff.
6.00	.77 815	822	830	837	844	851	859	866	873	880	
.01	887	895	902	909	916	924	931	938	945	952	
.02	960	967	974	981	988	996	003	010	017	025	
.03	.78 032	039	046	053	061	068	075	082	089	097	
.04	104	111	118	125	132	140	147	154	161	168	
.05	176	183	190	197	204	211	219	226	233	240	
.06	247	254	262	269	276	283	290	297	305	312	
.07	319	326	333	340	347	355	362	369	376	383	
.08	390	398	405	412	419	426	433	440	447	455	
.09	462	469	476	483	490	497	504	512	519	526	
6.10	533	540	547	554	561	569	576	583	590	597	
.11	604	611	618	625	633	640	647	654	661	668	
.12	675	682	689	696	704	711	718	725	732	739	
.13	746	753	760	767	774	781	789	796	803	810	
.14	817	824	831	838	845	852	859	866	873	880	
.15	888	895	902	909	916	923	930	937	944	951	
.16	958	965	972	979	986	993	000	007	014	021	
.17	.79 029	036	043	050	057	064	071	078	085	092	
.18	099	106	113	120	127	134	141	148	155	162	
.19	169	176	183	190	197	204	211	218	225	232	
6.20	239	246	253	260	267	274	281	288	295	302	7
.21	309	316	323	330	337	344	351	358	365	372	
.22	379	386	393	400	407	414	421	428	435	442	
.23	449	456	463	470	477	484	491	498	505	511	
.24	518	525	532	539	546	553	560	567	574	581	
.25	588	595	602	609	616	623	630	637	644	650	
.26	657	664	671	678	685	692	699	706	713	720	
.27	727	734	741	748	754	761	768	775	782	789	
.28	796	803	810	817	824	831	837	844	851	858	
.29	865	872	879	886	893	900	906	913	920	927	
6.30	934	941	948	955	962	969	975	982	989	996	
.31	.80 003	010	017	024	030	037	044	051	058	065	
.32	072	079	085	092	099	106	113	120	127	134	
.33	140	147	154	161	168	175	182	188	195	202	
.34	209	216	223	229	236	243	250	257	264	271	
.35	277	284	291	298	305	312	318	325	332	339	
.36	346	353	359	366	373	380	387	393	400	407	
.37	414	421	428	434	441	448	455	462	468	475	
.38	482	489	496	502	509	516	523	530	536	543	
.39	550	557	564	570	577	584	591	598	604	611	
6.40	618	625	632	638	645	652	659	665	672	679	
.41	686	693	699	706	713	720	726	733	740	747	
.42	754	760	767	774	781	787	794	801	808	814	
.43	821	828	835	841	848	855	862	868	875	882	
.44	889	895	902	909	916	922	929	936	943	949	
.45	956	963	969	976	983	990	996	003	010	017	
.46	.81 023	030	037	043	050	057	064	070	077	084	
.47	090	097	104	111	117	124	131	137	144	151	
.48	158	164	171	178	184	191	198	204	211	218	
.49	224	231	238	245	251	258	265	271	278	285	

x	0	1	2	3	4	5	6	7	8	9	Diff.
6.50	.81 291	298	305	311	318	325	331	338	345	351	
.51	358	365	371	378	385	391	398	405	411	418	
.52	425	431	438	445	451	458	465	471	478	485	
.53	491	498	505	511	518	525	531	538	544	551	
.54	558	564	571	578	584	591	598	604	611	617	
.55	624	631	637	644	651	657	664	671	677	684	
.56	690	697	704	710	717	723	730	737	743	750	
.57	757	763	770	776	783	790	796	803	809	816	
.58	823	829	836	842	849	856	862	869	875	882	
.59	889	895	902	908	915	921	928	935	941	948	
6.60	954	961	968	974	981	987	994	000	007	014	
.61	.82 020	027	033	040	046	053	060	066	073	079	
.62	086	092	099	105	112	119	125	132	138	145	
.63	151	158	164	171	178	184	191	197	204	210	
.64	217	223	230	236	243	249	256	263	269	276	
.65	282	289	295	302	308	315	321	328	334	341	
.66	347	354	360	367	373	380	387	393	400	406	
.67	413	419	426	432	439	445	452	458	465	471	
.68	478	484	491	497	504	510	517	523	530	536	7-6
.69	543	549	556	562	569	575	582	588	595	601	
6.70	607	614	620	627	633	640	646	653	659	666	
.71	672	679	685	692	698	705	711	718	724	730	
.72	737	743	750	756	763	769	776	782	789	795	
.73	802	808	814	821	827	834	840	847	853	860	
.74	866	872	879	885	892	898	905	911	918	924	
.75	930	937	943	950	956	963	969	975	982	988	
.76	995	001	008	014	020	027	033	040	046	052	
.77	.83 059	065	072	078	085	091	097	104	110	117	
.78	123	129	136	142	149	155	161	168	174	181	
.79	187	193	200	206	213	219	225	232	238	245	
6.80	251	257	264	270	276	283	289	296	302	308	
.81	315	321	327	334	340	347	353	359	366	372	
.82	378	385	391	398	404	410	417	423	429	436	
.83	442	448	455	461	467	474	480	487	493	499	
.84	506	512	518	525	531	537	544	550	556	563	
.85	569	575	582	588	594	601	607	613	620	626	
.86	632	639	645	651	658	664	670	677	683	689	
.87	696	702	708	715	721	727	734	740	746	753	
.88	759	765	771	778	784	790	797	803	809	816	
.89	822	828	835	841	847	853	860	866	872	879	
6.90	885	891	897	904	910	916	923	929	935	942	
.91	948	954	960	967	973	979	985	992	998	004	
.92	.84 011	017	023	029	036	042	048	055	061	067	
.93	073	080	086	092	098	105	111	117	123	130	
.94	136	142	148	155	161	167	173	180	186	192	
.95	198	205	211	217	223	230	236	242	248	255	
.96	261	267	273	280	286	292	298	305	311	317	
.97	323	330	336	342	348	354	361	367	373	379	
.98	386	392	398	404	410	417	423	429	435	442	
.99	448	454	460	466	473	479	485	491	497	504	

5-PLACE COMMON LOGARITHMS OF NUMBERS Log₁₀ x

x	0	1	2	3	4	5	6	7	8	9	Diff.
7.00	.84 510	516	522	528	535	541	547	553	559	566	
.01	572	578	584	590	597	603	609	615	621	628	
.02	634	640	646	652	658	665	671	677	683	689	
.03	696	702	708	714	720	726	733	739	745	751	
.04	757	763	770	776	782	788	794	800	807	813	
.05	819	825	831	837	844	850	856	862	868	874	
.06	880	887	893	899	905	911	917	924	930	936	
.07	942	948	954	960	967	973	979	985	991	997	
.08	.85 003	009	016	022	028	034	040	046	052	058	
.09	065	071	077	083	089	095	101	107	114	120	
7.10	126	132	138	144	150	156	163	169	175	181	
.11	187	193	199	205	211	217	224	230	236	242	
.12	248	254	260	266	272	278	285	291	297	303	
.13	309	315	321	327	333	339	345	352	358	364	
.14	370	376	382	388	394	400	406	412	418	425	
.15	431	437	443	449	455	461	467	473	479	485	
.16	491	497	503	509	516	522	528	534	540	546	
.17	552	558	564	570	576	582	588	594	600	606	
.18	612	618	625	631	637	643	649	655	661	667	
.19	673	679	685	691	697	703	709	715	721	727	
7.20	733	739	745	751	757	763	769	775	781	788	
.21	794	800	806	812	818	824	830	836	842	848	
.22	854	860	866	872	878	884	890	896	902	908	
.23	914	920	926	932	938	944	950	956	962	968	6
.24	974	980	986	992	998	0̄0̄4̄	0̄1̄0̄	0̄1̄6̄	0̄2̄2̄	0̄2̄8̄	
.25	.86 034	040	046	052	058	064	070	076	082	088	
.26	094	100	106	112	118	124	130	136	141	147	
.27	153	159	165	171	177	183	189	195	201	207	
.28	213	219	225	231	237	243	249	255	261	267	
.29	273	279	285	291	297	303	308	314	320	326	
7.30	332	338	344	350	356	362	368	374	380	386	
.31	392	398	404	410	415	421	427	433	439	445	
.32	451	457	463	469	475	481	487	493	499	504	
.33	510	516	522	528	534	540	546	552	558	564	
.34	570	576	581	587	593	599	605	611	617	623	
.35	629	635	641	646	652	658	664	670	676	682	
.36	688	694	700	705	711	717	723	729	735	741	
.37	747	753	759	764	770	776	782	788	794	800	
.38	806	812	817	823	829	835	841	847	853	859	
.39	864	870	876	882	888	894	900	906	911	917	
7.40	923	929	935	941	947	953	958	964	970	976	
.41	982	988	994	999	0̄0̄5̄	0̄1̄1̄	0̄1̄7̄	0̄2̄3̄	0̄2̄9̄	0̄3̄5̄	
.42	.87 040	046	052	058	064	070	075	081	087	093	
.43	099	105	111	116	122	128	134	140	146	151	
.44	157	163	169	175	181	186	192	198	204	210	
.45	216	221	227	233	239	245	251	256	262	268	
.46	274	280	286	291	297	303	309	315	320	326	
.47	332	338	344	349	355	361	367	373	379	384	
.48	390	396	402	408	413	419	425	431	437	442	
.49	448	454	460	466	471	477	483	489	495	500	

x	0	1	2	3	4	5	6	7	8	9	Diff.
7.50	.87 506	512	518	523	529	535	541	547	552	558	6-5
.51	564	570	576	581	587	593	599	604	610	616	
.52	622	628	633	639	645	651	656	662	668	674	
.53	679	685	691	697	703	708	714	720	726	731	
.54	737	743	749	754	760	766	772	777	783	789	
.55	795	800	806	812	818	823	829	835	841	846	
.56	852	858	864	869	875	881	887	892	898	904	
.57	910	915	921	927	933	938	944	950	955	961	
.58	967	973	978	984	990	996	001	007	013	018	
.59	.88 024	030	036	041	047	053	058	064	070	076	
7.60	081	087	093	098	104	110	116	121	127	133	
.61	138	144	150	156	161	167	173	178	184	190	
.62	195	201	207	213	218	224	230	235	241	247	
.63	252	258	264	270	275	281	287	292	298	304	
.64	309	315	321	326	332	338	343	349	355	360	
.65	366	372	377	383	389	395	400	406	412	417	
.66	423	429	434	440	446	451	457	463	468	474	
.67	480	485	491	497	502	508	513	519	525	530	
.68	536	542	547	553	559	564	570	576	581	587	
.69	593	598	604	610	615	621	627	632	638	643	
7.70	649	655	660	666	672	677	683	689	694	700	
.71	705	711	717	722	728	734	739	745	750	756	
.72	762	767	773	779	784	790	795	801	807	812	
.73	818	824	829	835	840	846	852	857	863	868	
.74	874	880	885	891	897	902	908	913	919	925	
.75	930	936	941	947	953	958	964	969	975	981	
.76	986	992	997	003	009	014	020	025	031	037	
.77	.89 042	048	053	059	064	070	076	081	087	092	
.78	098	104	109	115	120	126	131	137	143	148	
.79	154	159	165	170	176	182	187	193	198	204	
7.80	209	215	221	226	232	237	243	248	254	260	
.81	265	271	276	282	287	293	298	304	310	315	
.82	321	326	332	337	343	348	354	360	365	371	
.83	376	382	387	393	398	404	409	415	421	426	
.84	432	437	443	448	454	459	465	470	476	481	
.85	487	492	498	504	509	515	520	526	531	537	
.86	542	548	553	559	564	570	575	581	586	592	
.87	597	603	609	614	620	625	631	636	642	647	
.88	653	658	664	669	675	680	686	691	697	702	
.89	708	713	719	724	730	735	741	746	752	757	6-5
7.90	763	768	774	779	785	790	796	801	807	812	
.91	818	823	829	834	840	845	851	856	862	867	
.92	873	878	883	889	894	900	905	911	916	922	
.93	927	933	938	944	949	955	960	966	971	977	
.94	982	988	993	998	004	009	015	020	026	031	
.95	.90 037	042	048	053	059	064	069	075	080	086	
.96	091	097	102	108	113	119	124	129	135	140	
.97	146	151	157	162	168	173	179	184	189	195	
.98	200	206	211	217	222	227	233	238	244	249	
.99	255	260	266	271	276	282	287	293	298	304	

5-PLACE COMMON LOGARITHMS OF NUMBERS Log$_{10}$ x

x	0	1	2	3	4	5	6	7	8	9	Diff.
8.00	.90 309	314	320	325	331	336	342	347	352	358	
.01	363	369	374	380	385	390	396	401	407	412	
.02	417	423	428	434	439	445	450	455	461	466	
.03	472	477	482	488	493	499	504	509	515	520	
.04	526	531	536	542	547	553	558	563	569	574	
.05	580	585	590	596	601	607	612	617	623	628	
.06	634	639	644	650	655	660	666	671	677	682	
.07	687	693	698	703	709	714	720	725	730	736	
.08	741	747	752	757	763	768	773	779	784	789	
.09	795	800	806	811	816	822	827	832	838	843	
8.10	849	854	859	865	870	875	881	886	891	897	
.11	902	907	913	918	924	929	934	940	945	950	
.12	956	961	966	972	977	982	988	993	998	$\overline{004}$	
.13	.91 009	014	020	025	030	036	041	046	052	057	
.14	062	068	073	078	084	089	094	100	105	110	
.15	116	121	126	132	137	142	148	153	158	164	
.16	169	174	180	185	190	196	201	206	212	217	
.17	222	228	233	238	243	249	254	259	265	270	
.18	275	281	286	291	297	302	307	312	318	323	
.19	328	334	339	344	350	355	360	365	371	376	
8.20	381	387	392	397	403	408	413	418	424	429	
.21	434	440	445	450	455	461	466	471	477	482	
.22	487	492	498	503	508	514	519	524	529	535	
.23	540	545	551	556	561	566	572	577	582	587	
.24	593	598	603	609	614	619	624	630	635	640	
.25	645	651	656	661	666	672	677	682	687	693	6-5
.26	698	703	709	714	719	724	730	735	740	745	
.27	751	756	761	766	772	777	782	787	793	798	
.28	803	808	814	819	824	829	834	840	845	850	
.29	855	861	866	871	876	882	887	892	897	903	
8.30	908	913	918	924	929	934	939	944	950	955	
.31	960	965	971	976	981	986	991	997	$\overline{002}$	$\overline{007}$	
.32	.92 012	018	023	028	033	038	044	049	054	059	
.33	065	070	075	080	085	091	096	101	106	111	
.34	117	122	127	132	137	143	148	153	158	163	
.35	169	174	179	184	189	195	200	205	210	215	
.36	221	226	231	236	241	247	252	257	262	267	
.37	273	278	283	288	293	298	304	309	314	319	
.38	324	330	335	340	345	350	355	361	366	371	
.39	376	381	387	392	397	402	407	412	418	423	
8.40	428	433	438	443	449	454	459	464	469	474	
.41	480	485	490	495	500	505	511	516	521	526	
.42	531	536	542	547	552	557	562	567	572	578	
.43	583	588	593	598	603	609	614	619	624	629	
.44	634	639	645	650	655	660	665	670	675	681	
.45	686	691	696	701	706	711	716	722	727	732	
.46	737	742	747	752	758	763	768	773	778	783	
.47	788	793	799	804	809	814	819	824	829	834	
.48	840	845	850	855	860	865	870	875	881	886	
.49	891	896	901	906	911	916	921	927	932	937	

x	0	1	2	3	4	5	6	7	8	9	Diff.
8.50	.92 942	947	952	957	962	967	973	978	983	988	
.51	993	998	003	008	013	018	024	029	034	039	
.52	.93 044	049	054	059	064	069	075	080	085	090	
.53	095	100	105	110	115	120	125	131	136	141	
.54	146	151	156	161	166	171	176	181	186	192	
.55	197	202	207	212	217	222	227	232	237	242	
.56	247	252	258	263	268	273	278	283	288	293	
.57	298	303	308	313	318	323	328	334	339	344	
.58	349	354	359	364	369	374	379	384	389	394	
.59	399	404	409	414	420	425	430	435	440	445	
8.60	450	455	460	465	470	475	480	485	490	495	
.61	500	505	510	515	520	526	531	536	541	546	
.62	551	556	561	566	571	576	581	586	591	596	
.63	601	606	611	616	621	626	631	636	641	646	
.64	651	656	661	666	671	676	682	687	692	697	
.65	702	707	712	717	722	727	732	737	742	747	
.66	752	757	762	767	772	777	782	787	792	797	
.67	802	807	812	817	822	827	832	837	842	847	
.68	852	857	862	867	872	877	882	887	892	897	5
.69	902	907	912	917	922	927	932	937	942	947	
8.70	952	957	962	967	972	977	982	987	992	997	
.71	.94 002	007	012	017	022	027	032	037	042	047	
.72	052	057	062	067	072	077	082	086	091	096	
.73	101	106	111	116	121	126	131	136	141	146	
.74	151	156	161	166	171	176	181	186	191	196	
.75	201	206	211	216	221	226	231	236	240	245	
.76	250	255	260	265	270	275	280	285	290	295	
.77	300	305	310	315	320	325	330	335	340	345	
.78	349	354	359	364	369	374	379	384	389	394	
.79	399	404	409	414	419	424	429	433	438	443	
8.80	448	453	458	463	468	473	478	483	488	493	
.81	498	503	507	512	517	522	527	532	537	542	
.82	547	552	557	562	567	571	576	581	586	591	
.83	596	601	606	611	616	621	626	630	635	640	
.84	645	650	655	660	665	670	675	680	685	689	
.85	694	699	704	709	714	719	724	729	734	738	
.86	743	748	753	758	763	768	773	778	783	787	
.87	792	797	802	807	812	817	822	827	832	836	
.88	841	846	851	856	861	866	871	876	880	885	
.89	890	895	900	905	910	915	919	924	929	934	
8.90	939	944	949	954	959	963	968	973	978	983	
.91	988	993	998	002	007	012	017	022	027	032	
.92	.95 036	041	046	051	056	061	066	071	075	080	
.93	085	090	095	100	105	109	114	119	124	129	
.94	134	139	143	148	153	158	163	168	173	177	
.95	182	187	192	197	202	207	211	216	221	226	
.96	231	236	240	245	250	255	260	265	270	274	
.97	279	284	289	294	299	303	308	313	318	323	
.98	328	332	337	342	347	352	357	361	366	371	
.99	376	381	386	390	395	400	405	410	415	419	

5-PLACE COMMON LOGARITHMS OF NUMBERS $\text{Log}_{10}\ x$

x	0	1	2	3	4	5	6	7	8	9	Diff.
9.00	.95 424	429	434	439	444	448	453	458	463	468	
.01	472	477	482	487	492	497	501	506	511	516	
.02	521	525	530	535	540	545	550	554	559	564	
.03	569	574	578	583	588	593	598	602	607	612	
.04	617	622	626	631	636	641	646	650	655	660	
.05	665	670	674	679	684	689	694	698	703	708	
.06	713	718	722	727	732	737	742	746	751	756	
.07	761	766	770	775	780	785	789	794	799	804	
.08	809	813	818	823	828	832	837	842	847	852	
.09	856	861	866	871	875	880	885	890	895	899	
9.10	904	909	914	918	923	928	933	938	942	947	
.11	952	957	961	966	971	976	980	985	990	995	
.12	999	004	009	014	019	023	028	033	038	042	
.13	.96 047	052	057	061	066	071	076	080	085	090	
.14	095	099	104	109	114	118	123	128	133	137	
.15	142	147	152	156	161	166	171	175	180	185	
.16	190	194	199	204	209	213	218	223	227	232	
.17	237	242	246	251	256	261	265	270	275	280	
.18	284	289	294	298	303	308	313	317	322	327	
.19	332	336	341	346	350	355	360	365	369	374	
9.20	379	384	388	393	398	402	407	412	417	421	
.21	426	431	435	440	445	450	454	459	464	468	
.22	473	478	483	487	492	497	501	506	511	515	
.23	520	525	530	534	539	544	548	553	558	562	
.24	567	572	577	581	586	591	595	600	605	609	
.25	614	619	624	628	633	638	642	647	652	656	5-4
.26	661	666	670	675	680	685	689	694	699	703	
.27	708	713	717	722	727	731	736	741	745	750	
.28	755	759	764	769	774	778	783	788	792	797	
.29	802	806	811	816	820	825	830	834	839	844	
9.30	848	853	858	862	867	872	876	881	886	890	
.31	895	900	904	909	914	918	923	928	932	937	
.32	942	946	951	956	960	965	970	974	979	984	
.33	988	993	997	002	007	011	016	021	025	030	
.34	.97 035	039	044	049	053	058	063	067	072	077	
.35	081	086	090	095	100	104	109	114	118	123	
.36	128	132	137	142	146	151	155	160	165	169	
.37	174	179	183	188	192	197	202	206	211	216	
.38	220	225	230	234	239	243	248	253	257	262	
.39	267	271	276	280	285	290	294	299	304	308	
9.40	313	317	322	327	331	336	340	345	350	354	
.41	359	364	368	373	377	382	387	391	396	400	
.42	405	410	414	419	424	428	433	437	442	447	
.43	451	456	460	465	470	474	479	483	488	493	
.44	497	502	506	511	516	520	525	529	534	539	
.45	543	548	552	557	562	566	571	575	580	585	
.46	589	594	598	603	607	612	617	621	626	630	
.47	635	640	644	649	653	658	663	667	672	676	
.48	681	685	690	695	699	704	708	713	717	722	
.49	727	731	736	740	745	749	754	759	763	768	

x	0	1	2	3	4	5	6	7	8	9	Diff.
9.50	.97 772	777 782 786			791 795 800			804 809 813			
.51	818	823 827 832			836 841 845			850 855 859			
.52	864	868 873 877			882 886 891			896 900 905			
.53	909	914 918 923			928 932 937			941 946 950			
.54	955	959 964 968			973 978 982			987 991 996			
.55	.98 000	005 009 014			019 023 028			032 037 041			
.56	046	050 055 059			064 068 073			078 082 087			
.57	091	096 100 105			109 114 118			123 127 132			
.58	137	141 146 150			155 159 164			168 173 177			
.59	182	186 191 195			200 204 209			214 218 223			
9.60	227	232 236 241			245 250 254			259 263 268			
.61	272	277 281 286			290 295 299			304 308 313			
.62	318	322 327 331			336 340 345			349 354 358			
.63	363	367 372 376			381 385 390			394 399 403			
.64	408	412 417 421			426 430 435			439 444 448			
.65	453	457 462 466			471 475 480			484 489 493			
.66	498	502 507 511			516 520 525			529 534 538			
.67	543	547 552 556			561 565 570			574 579 583			
.68	588	592 597 601			605 610 614			619 623 628			
.69	632	637 641 646			650 655 659			664 668 673			
9.70	677	682 686 691			695 700 704			709 713 717			
.71	722	726 731 735			740 744 749			753 758 762			
.72	767	771 776 780			784 789 793			798 802 807			
.73	811	816 820 825			829 834 838			843 847 851			
.74	856	860 865 869			874 878 883			887 892 896			
.75	900	905 909 914			918 923 927			932 936 941			5-4
.76	945	949 954 958			963 967 972			976 981 985			
.77	989	994 998 003			007 012 016			021 025 029			
.78	.99 034	038 043 047			052 056 061			065 069 074			
.79	078	083 087 092			096 100 105			109 114 118			
9.80	123	127 131 136			140 145 149			154 158 162			
.81	167	171 176 180			185 189 193			198 202 207			
.82	211	216 220 224			229 233 238			242 247 251			
.83	255	260 264 269			273 277 282			286 291 295			
.84	300	304 308 313			317 322 326			330 335 339			
.85	344	348 352 357			361 366 370			374 379 383			
.86	388	392 396 401			405 410 414			419 423 427			
.87	432	436 441 445			449 454 458			463 467 471			
.88	476	480 484 489			493 498 502			506 511 515			
.89	520	524 528 533			537 542 546			550 555 559			
9.90	564	568 572 577			581 585 590			594 599 603			
.91	607	612 616 621			625 629 634			638 642 647			
.92	651	656 660 664			669 673 677			682 686 691			
.93	695	699 704 708			712 717 721			726 730 734			
.94	739	743 747 752			756 760 765			769 774 778			
.95	782	787 791 795			800 804 808			813 817 822			
.96	826	830 835 839			843 848 852			856 861 865			
.97	870	874 878 883			887 891 896			900 904 909			
.98	913	917 922 926			930 935 939			944 948 952			
.99	957	961 965 970			974 978 983			987 991 996			
10.00	1.00 000										

COMMON LOGARITHMS $LOG_{10}X$

x	0	1	2	3	4	5	6	7	8	9	Diff.
1.0	0000	0043	0086	0128	0170	0212	0253	0294	0334	0374	43-40
1.1	0414	0453	0492	0531	0569	0607	0645	0682	0719	0755	39-36
1.2	0792	0828	0864	0899	0934	0969	1004	1038	1072	1106	36-33
1.3	1139	1173	1206	1239	1271	1303	1335	1367	1399	1430	34-31
1.4	1461	1492	1523	1553	1584	1614	1644	1673	1703	1732	31-29
1.5	1761	1790	1818	1847	1875	1903	1931	1959	1987	2014	29-27
1.6	2041	2068	2095	2122	2148	2175	2201	2227	2253	2279	27-25
1.7	2304	2330	2355	2380	2405	2430	2455	2480	2504	2529	26-24
1.8	2553	2577	2601	2625	2648	2672	2695	2718	2742	2765	24-23
1.9	2788	2810	2833	2856	2878	2900	2923	2945	2967	2989	23-21
2.0	3010	3032	3054	3075	3096	3118	3139	3160	3181	3201	22-20
2.1	3222	3243	3263	3284	3304	3324	3345	3365	3385	3404	21-20
2.2	3424	3444	3464	3483	3502	3522	3541	3560	3579	3598	20-19
2.3	3617	3636	3655	3674	3692	3711	3729	3747	3766	3784	19-18
2.4	3802	3820	3838	3856	3874	3892	3909	3927	3945	3962	18-17
2.5	3979	3997	4014	4031	4048	4065	4082	4099	4116	4133	18-17
2.6	4150	4166	4183	4200	4216	4232	4249	4265	4281	4298	17-16
2.7	4314	4330	4346	4362	4378	4393	4409	4425	4440	4456	16-15
2.8	4472	4487	4502	4518	4533	4548	4564	4579	4594	4609	16-15
2.9	4624	4639	4654	4669	4683	4698	4713	4728	4742	4757	15-14
3.0	4771	4786	4800	4814	4829	4843	4857	4871	4886	4900	15-14
3.1	4914	4928	4942	4955	4969	4983	4997	5011	5024	5038	14-13
3.2	5051	5065	5079	5092	5105	5119	5132	5145	5159	5172	14-13
3.3	5185	5198	5211	5224	5237	5250	5263	5276	5289	5302	13
3.4	5315	5328	5340	5353	5366	5378	5391	5403	5416	5428	13-12
3.5	5441	5453	5465	5478	5490	5502	5514	5527	5539	5551	13-12
3.6	5563	5575	5587	5599	5611	5623	5635	5647	5658	5670	12-11
3.7	5682	5694	5705	5717	5729	5740	5752	5763	5775	5786	12-11
3.8	5798	5809	5821	5832	5843	5855	5866	5877	5888	5899	12-11
3.9	5911	5922	5933	5944	5955	5966	5977	5988	5999	6010	11
4.0	6021	6031	6042	6053	6064	6075	6085	6096	6107	6117	11-10
4.1	6128	6138	6149	6160	6170	6180	6191	6201	6212	6222	11-10
4.2	6232	6243	6253	6263	6274	6284	6294	6304	6314	6325	11-10
4.3	6335	6345	6355	6365	6375	6385	6395	6405	6415	6425	10
4.4	6435	6444	6454	6464	6474	6484	6493	6503	6513	6522	10-9
4.5	6532	6542	6551	6561	6571	6580	6590	6599	6609	6618	10-9
4.6	6628	6637	6646	6656	6665	6675	6684	6693	6702	6712	10-9
4.7	6721	6730	6739	6749	6758	6767	6776	6785	6794	6803	10-9
4.8	6812	6821	6830	6839	6848	6857	6866	6875	6884	6893	9
4.9	6902	6911	6920	6928	6937	6946	6955	6964	6972	6981	9-8
5.0	6990	6998	7007	7016	7024	7033	7042	7050	7059	7067	9-8
5.1	7076	7084	7093	7101	7110	7118	7126	7135	7143	7152	9-8
5.2	7160	7168	7177	7185	7193	7202	7210	7218	7226	7235	9-8
5.3	7243	7251	7259	7267	7275	7284	7292	7300	7308	7316	9-8
5.4	7324	7332	7340	7348	7356	7364	7372	7380	7388	7396	8
5.5	7404	7412	7419	7427	7435	7443	7451	7459	7466	7474	8-7
5.6	7482	7490	7497	7505	7513	7520	7528	7536	7543	7551	8-7
5.7	7559	7566	7574	7582	7589	7597	7604	7612	7619	7627	8-7
5.8	7634	7642	7649	7657	7664	7672	7679	7686	7694	7701	8-7
5.9	7709	7716	7723	7731	7738	7745	7752	7760	7767	7774	8-7

x	0	1	2	3	4	5	6	7	8	9	Diff.
6.0	7782	7789	7796	7803	7810	7818	7825	7832	7839	7846	
6.1	7853	7860	7868	7875	7882	7889	7896	7903	7910	7917	
6.2	7924	7931	7938	7945	7952	7959	7966	7973	7980	7987	7
6.3	7993	8000	8007	8014	8021	8028	8035	8041	8048	8055	
6.4	8062	8069	8075	8082	8089	8096	8102	8109	8116	8122	
6.5	8129	8136	8142	8149	8156	8162	8169	8176	8182	8189	
6.6	8195	8202	8209	8215	8222	8228	8235	8241	8248	8254	
6.7	8261	8267	8274	8280	8287	8293	8299	8306	8312	8319	
6.8	8325	8331	8338	8344	8351	8357	8363	8370	8376	8382	
6.9	8388	8395	8401	8407	8414	8420	8426	8432	8439	8445	
7.0	8451	8457	8463	8470	8476	8482	8488	8494	8500	8506	
7.1	8513	8519	8525	8531	8537	8543	8549	8555	8561	8567	6
7.2	8573	8579	8585	8591	8597	8603	8609	8615	8621	8627	
7.3	8633	8639	8645	8651	8657	8663	8669	8675	8681	8686	
7.4	8692	8698	8704	8710	8716	8722	8727	8733	8739	8745	
7.5	8751	8756	8762	8768	8774	8779	8785	8791	8797	8802	
7.6	8808	8814	8820	8825	8831	8837	8842	8848	8854	8859	
7.7	8865	8871	8876	8882	8887	8893	8899	8904	8910	8915	
7.8	8921	8927	8932	8938	8943	8949	8954	8960	8965	8971	
7.9	8976	8982	8987	8993	8998	9004	9009	9015	9020	9025	
8.0	9031	9036	9042	9047	9053	9058	9063	9069	9074	9079	
8.1	9085	9090	9096	9101	9106	9112	9117	9122	9128	9133	
8.2	9138	9143	9149	9154	9159	9165	9170	9175	9180	9186	
8.3	9191	9196	9201	9206	9212	9217	9222	9227	9232	9238	
8.4	9243	9248	9253	9258	9263	9269	9274	9279	9284	9289	
8.5	9294	9299	9304	9309	9315	9320	9325	9330	9335	9340	
8.6	9345	9350	9355	9360	9365	9370	9375	9380	9385	9390	5
8.7	9395	9400	9405	9410	9415	9420	9425	9430	9435	9440	
8.8	9445	9450	9455	9460	9465	9469	9474	9479	9484	9489	
8.9	9494	9499	9504	9509	9513	9518	9523	9528	9533	9538	
9.0	9542	9547	9552	9557	9562	9566	9571	9576	9581	9586	
9.1	9590	9595	9600	9605	9609	9614	9619	9624	9628	9633	
9.2	9638	9643	9647	9652	9657	9661	9666	9671	9675	9680	
9.3	9685	9689	9694	9699	9703	9708	9713	9717	9722	9727	
9.4	9731	9736	9741	9745	9750	9754	9759	9763	9768	9773	
9.5	9777	9782	9786	9791	9795	9800	9805	9809	9814	9818	
9.6	9823	9827	9832	9836	9841	9845	9850	9854	9859	9863	
9.7	9868	9872	9877	9881	9886	9890	9894	9899	9903	9908	
9.8	9912	9917	9921	9926	9930	9934	9939	9943	9948	9952	
9.9	9956	9961	9965	9969	9974	9978	9983	9987	9991	9996	5-4

A decimal point is understood before each number.

INDEX

Index

CATALOGUE OF DOVER BOOKS

BOOKS EXPLAINING SCIENCE AND MATHEMATICS

General

WHAT IS SCIENCE?, Norman Campbell. This excellent introduction explains scientific method, role of mathematics, types of scientific laws. Contents: 2 aspects of science, science & nature, laws of science, discovery of laws, explanation of laws, measurement & numerical laws, applications of science. 192pp. 5⅜ x 8. S43 Paperbound **$1.25**

THE COMMON SENSE OF THE EXACT SCIENCES, W. K. Clifford. Introduction by James Newman, edited by Karl Pearson. For 70 years this has been a guide to classical scientific and mathematical thought. Explains with unusual clarity basic concepts, such as extension of meaning of symbols, characteristics of surface boundaries, properties of plane figures, vectors, Cartesian method of determining position, etc. Long preface by Bertrand Russell. Bibliography of Clifford. Corrected, 130 diagrams redrawn. 249pp. 5⅜ x 8.
T61 Paperbound **$1.60**

SCIENCE THEORY AND MAN, Erwin Schrödinger. This is a complete and unabridged reissue of SCIENCE AND THE HUMAN TEMPERAMENT plus an additional essay: "What is an Elementary Particle?" Nobel laureate Schrödinger discusses such topics as nature of scientific method, the nature of science, chance and determinism, science and society, conceptual models for physical entities, elementary particles and wave mechanics. Presentation is popular and may be followed by most people with little or no scientific training. "Fine practical preparation for a time when laws of nature, human institutions . . . are undergoing a critical examination without parallel," Waldemar Kaempffert, N. Y. TIMES. 192pp. 5⅜ x 8.
T428 Paperbound **$1.35**

FADS AND FALLACIES IN THE NAME OF SCIENCE, Martin Gardner. Examines various cults, quack systems, frauds, delusions which at various times have masqueraded as science. Accounts of hollow-earth fanatics like Symmes; Velikovsky and wandering planets; Hoerbiger; Bellamy and the theory of multiple moons; Charles Fort; dowsing, pseudoscientific methods for finding water, ores, oil. Sections on naturopathy, iridiagnosis, zone therapy, food fads, etc. Analytical accounts of Wilhelm Reich and orgone sex energy; L. Ron Hubbard and Dianetics; A. Korzybski and General Semantics; many others. Brought up to date to include Bridey Murphy, others. Not just a collection of anecdotes, but a fair, reasoned appraisal of eccentric theory. Formerly titled IN THE NAME OF SCIENCE. Preface. Index. x + 384pp. 5⅜ x 8. T394 Paperbound **$1.75**

A DOVER SCIENCE SAMPLER, edited by George Barkin. 64-page book, sturdily bound, containing excerpts from over 20 Dover books, explaining science. Edwin Hubble, George Sarton, Ernst Mach, A. d'Abro, Galileo, Newton, others, discussing island-universes, scientific truth, biological phenomena, stability in bridges, etc. Copies limited; no more than 1 to a customer,
FREE

POPULAR SCIENTIFIC LECTURES, Hermann von Helmholtz. Helmholtz was a superb expositor as well as a scientist of genius in many areas. The seven essays in this volume are models of clarity, and even today they rank among the best general descriptions of their subjects ever written. "The Physiological Causes of Harmony in Music" was the first significant physiological explanation of musical consonance and dissonance. Two essays, "On the Interaction of Natural Forces" and "On the Conservation of Force," were of great importance in the history of science, for they firmly established the principle of the conservation of energy. Other lectures include "On the Relation of Optics to Painting," "On Recent Progress in the Theory of Vision," "On Goethe's Scientific Researches," and "On the Origin and Significance of Geometrical Axioms." Selected and edited with an introduction by Professor Morris Kline. xii + 286pp. 5⅜ x 8½. T799 Paperbound **$1.45**

BOOKS EXPLAINING SCIENCE AND MATHEMATICS

Physics

CONCERNING THE NATURE OF THINGS, Sir William Bragg. Christmas lectures delivered at the Royal Society by Nobel laureate. Why a spinning ball travels in a curved track; how uranium is transmuted to lead, etc. Partial contents: atoms, gases, liquids, crystals, metals, etc. No scientific background needed; wonderful for intelligent child. 32pp. of photos, 57 figures. xii + 232pp. 5⅜ x 8. T31 Paperbound **$1.50**

THE RESTLESS UNIVERSE, Max Born. New enlarged version of this remarkably readable account by a Nobel laureate. Moving from sub-atomic particles to universe, the author explains in very simple terms the latest theories of wave mechanics. Partial contents: air and its relatives, electrons & ions, waves & particles, electronic structure of the atom, nuclear physics. Nearly 1000 illustrations, including 7 animated sequences. 325pp. 6 x 9. T412 Paperbound **$2.00**

FROM EUCLID TO EDDINGTON: A STUDY OF THE CONCEPTIONS OF THE EXTERNAL WORLD, Sir Edmund Whittaker. A foremost British scientist traces the development of theories of natural philosophy from the western rediscovery of Euclid to Eddington, Einstein, Dirac, etc. The inadequacy of classical physics is contrasted with present day attempts to understand the physical world through relativity, non-Euclidean geometry, space curvature, wave mechanics, etc. 5 major divisions of examination: Space; Time and Movement; the Concepts of Classical Physics; the Concepts of Quantum Mechanics; the Eddington Universe. 212pp. 5⅜ x 8.   T491 Paperbound **$1.35**

PHYSICS, THE PIONEER SCIENCE, L. W. Taylor. First thorough text to place all important physical phenomena in cultural-historical framework; remains best work of its kind. Exposition of physical laws, theories- developed chronologically, with great historical, illustrative experiments diagrammed, described, worked out mathematically. Excellent physics text for self-study as well as class work. Vol. 1: Heat, Sound: motion, acceleration, gravitation, conservation of energy, heat engines, rotation, heat, mechanical energy, etc. 211 illus. 407pp. 5⅜ x 8. Vol. 2: Light, Electricity: images, lenses, prisms, magnetism, Ohm's law, dynamos, telegraph, quantum theory, decline of mechanical view of nature, etc. Bibliography. 13 table appendix. Index. 551 illus. 2 color plates. 508pp. 5⅜ x 8.

Vol. 1 S565 Paperbound **$2.25**
Vol. 2 S566 Paperbound **$2.25**
The set **$4.50**

A SURVEY OF PHYSICAL THEORY, Max Planck. One of the greatest scientists of all time, creator of the quantum revolution in physics, writes in non-technical terms of his own discoveries and those of other outstanding creators of modern physics. Planck wrote this book when science had just crossed the threshold of the new physics, and he communicates the excitement felt then as he discusses electromagnetic theories, statistical methods, evolution of the concept of light, a step-by-step description of how he developed his own momentous theory, and many more of the basic ideas behind modern physics. Formerly "A Survey of Physics." Bibliography. Index. 128pp. 5⅜ x 8.   S650 Paperbound **$1.15**

THE ATOMIC NUCLEUS, M. Korsunsky. The only non-technical comprehensive account of the atomic nucleus in English. For college physics students, etc. Chapters cover: Radioactivity, the Nuclear Model of the Atom, the Mass of Atomic Nuclei, the Disintegration of Atomic Nuclei, the Discovery of the Positron, the Artificial Transformation of Atomic Nuclei, Artificial Radioactivity, Mesons, the Neutrino, the Structure of Atomic Nuclei and Forces Acting Between Nuclear Particles, Nuclear Fission, Chain Reaction, Peaceful Uses, Thermonuclear Reactions. Slightly abridged edition. Translated by G. Yankovsky. 65 figures. Appendix includes 45 photographic illustrations. 413 pp. 5⅜ x 8.   S1052 Paperbound **$2.00**

PRINCIPLES OF MECHANICS SIMPLY EXPLAINED, Morton Mott-Smith. Excellent, highly readable introduction to the theories and discoveries of classical physics. Ideal for the layman who desires a foundation which will enable him to understand and appreciate contemporary developments in the physical sciences. Discusses: Density, The Law of Gravitation, Mass and Weight, Action and Reaction, Kinetic and Potential Energy, The Law of Inertia, Effects of Acceleration, The Independence of Motions, Galileo and the New Science of Dynamics, Newton and the New Cosmos, The Conservation of Momentum, and other topics. Revised edition of "This Mechanical World." Illustrated by E. Kosa, Jr. Bibliography and Chronology. Index. xiv + 171pp. 5⅜ x 8½.   T1067 Paperbound **$1.35**

THE CONCEPT OF ENERGY SIMPLY EXPLAINED, Morton Mott-Smith. Elementary, non-technical exposition which traces the story of man's conquest of energy, with particular emphasis on the developments during the nineteenth century and the first three decades of our own century. Discusses man's earlier efforts to harness energy, more recent experiments and discoveries relating to the steam engine, the engine indicator, the motive power of heat, the principle of excluded perpetual motion, the bases of the conservation of energy, the concept of entropy, the internal combustion engine, mechanical refrigeration, and many other related topics. Also much biographical material. Index. Bibliography. 33 illustrations. ix + 215pp. 5⅜ x 8½.   T1071 Paperbound **$1.25**

HEAT AND ITS WORKINGS, Morton Mott-Smith. One of the best elementary introductions to the theory and attributes of heat, covering such matters as the laws governing the effect of heat on solids, liquids and gases, the methods by which heat is measured, the conversion of a substance from one form to another through heating and cooling, evaporation, the effects of pressure on boiling and freezing points, and the three ways in which heat is transmitted (conduction, convection, radiation). Also brief notes on major experiments and discoveries. Concise, but complete, it presents all the essential facts about the subject in readable style. Will give the layman and beginning student a first-rate background in this major topic in physics. Index. Bibliography. 50 illustrations. x + 165pp. 5⅜ x 8½. T978 Paperbound **$1.15**

THE STORY OF ATOMIC THEORY AND ATOMIC ENERGY, J. G. Feinberg. Wider range of facts on physical theory, cultural implications, than any other similar source. Completely non-technical. Begins with first atomic theory, 600 B.C., goes through A-bomb, developments to 1959. Avogadro, Rutherford, Bohr, Einstein, radioactive decay, binding energy, radiation danger, future benefits of nuclear power, dozens of other topics, told in lively, related, informal manner. Particular stress on European atomic research. "Deserves special mention . . . authoritative," Saturday Review. Formerly "The Atom Story." New chapter to 1959. Index. 34 illustrations. 251pp. 5⅜ x 8.   T625 Paperbound **$1.60**

THE STRANGE STORY OF THE QUANTUM, AN ACCOUNT FOR THE GENERAL READER OF THE GROWTH OF IDEAS UNDERLYING OUR PRESENT ATOMIC KNOWLEDGE, B. Hoffmann. Presents lucidly and expertly, with barest amount of mathematics, the problems and theories which led to modern quantum physics. Dr. Hoffmann begins with the closing years of the 19th century, when certain trifling discrepancies were noticed, and with illuminating analogies and examples takes you through the brilliant concepts of Planck, Einstein, Pauli, de Broglie, Bohr, Schroedinger, Heisenberg, Dirac, Sommerfeld, Feynman, etc. This edition includes a new, long postscript carrying the story through 1958. "Of the books attempting an account of the history and contents of our modern atomic physics which have come to my attention, this is the best," H. Margenau, Yale University, in "American Journal of Physics." 32 tables and line illustrations. Index. 275pp. 5⅜ x 8.   T518 Paperbound **$1.75**

THE EVOLUTION OF SCIENTIFIC THOUGHT FROM NEWTON TO EINSTEIN, A. d'Abro. Einstein's special and general theories of relativity, with their historical implications, are analyzed in non-technical terms. Excellent accounts of the contributions of Newton, Riemann, Weyl, Planck, Eddington, Maxwell, Lorentz and others are treated in terms of space and time, equations of electromagnetics, finiteness of the universe, methodology of science. 21 diagrams. 482pp. 5⅜ x 8.   T2 Paperound **$2.25**

THE RISE OF THE NEW PHYSICS, A. d'Abro. A half-million word exposition, formerly titled THE DECLINE OF MECHANISM, for readers not versed in higher mathematics. The only thorough explanation, in everyday language, of the central core of modern mathematical physical theory, treating both classical and modern theoretical physics, and presenting in terms almost anyone can understand the equivalent of 5 years of study of mathematical physics. Scientifically impeccable coverage of mathematical-physical thought from the Newtonian system up through the electronic theories of Dirac and Heisenberg and Fermi's statistics. Combines both history and exposition; provides a broad yet unified and detailed view, with constant comparison of classical and modern views on phenomena and theories. "A must for anyone doing serious study in the physical sciences," JOURNAL OF THE FRANKLIN INSTITUTE. "Extraordinary faculty . . . to explain ideas and theories of theoretical physics in the language of daily life," ISIS. First part of set covers philosophy of science, drawing upon the practice of Newton, Maxwell, Poincaré, Einstein, others, discussing modes of thought; experiment, interpretations of causality, etc. In the second part, 100 pages explain grammar and vocabulary of mathematics, with discussions of functions, groups, series, Fourier series, etc. The remainder is devoted to concrete, detailed coverage of both classical and quantum physics, explaining such topics as analytic mechanics, Hamilton's principle, wave theory of light, electromagnetic waves, groups of transformations, thermodynamics, phase rule, Brownian movement, kinetics, special relativity, Planck's original quantum theory, Bohr's atom, Zeeman effect, Broglie's wave mechanics, Heisenberg's uncertainty, Eigen-values, matrices, scores of other important topics. Discoveries and theories are covered for such men as Alembert, Born, Cantor, Debye, Euler, Foucault, Galois, Gauss, Hadamard, Kelvin, Kepler, Laplace, Maxwell, Pauli, Rayleigh, Volterra, Weyl, Young, more than 180 others. Indexed. 97 illustrations. ix + 982pp. 5⅜ x 8.   T3 Volume 1, Paperbound **$2.25**
T4 Volume 2, Paperbound **$2.25**

SPINNING TOPS AND GYROSCOPIC MOTION, John Perry. Well-known classic of science still unsurpassed for lucid, accurate, delightful exposition. How quasi-rigidity is induced in flexible and fluid bodies by rapid motions; why gyrostat falls, top rises; nature and effect on climatic conditions of earth's precessional movement; effect of internal fluidity on rotating bodies, etc. Appendixes describe practical uses to which gyroscopes have been put in ships, compasses, monorail transportation. 62 figures. 128pp. 5⅜ x 8.   T416 Paperbound **$1.25**

THE UNIVERSE OF LIGHT, Sir William Bragg. No scientific training needed to read Nobel Prize winner's expansion of his Royal Institute Christmas Lectures. Insight into nature of light, methods and philosophy of science. Explains lenses, reflection, color, resonance, polarization, x-rays, the spectrum, Newton's work with prisms, Huygens' with polarization, Crookes' with cathode ray, etc. Leads into clear statement of 2 major historical theories of light, corpuscle and wave. Dozens of experiments you can do. 199 illus., including 2 full-page color plates. 293pp. 5⅜ x 8.   S538 Paperbound **$1.85**

THE STORY OF X-RAYS FROM RÖNTGEN TO ISOTOPES, A. R. Bleich. Non-technical history of x-rays, their scientific explanation, their applications in medicine, industry, research, and art, and their effect on the individual and his descendants. Includes amusing early reactions to Röntgen's discovery, cancer therapy, detections of art and stamp forgeries, potential risks to patient and operator, etc. Illustrations show x-rays of flower structure, the gall bladder, gears with hidden defects, etc. Original Dover publication. Glossary. Bibliography. Index. 55 photos and figures. xiv + 186pp. 5⅜ x 8.   T662 Paperbound **$1.50**

ELECTRONS, ATOMS, METALS AND ALLOYS, Wm. Hume-Rothery. An introductory-level explanation of the application of the electronic theory to the structure and properties ot metals and alloys, taking into account the new theoretical work done by mathematical physicists. Material presented in dialogue-form between an "Old Metallurgist" and a "Young Scientist." Their discussion falls into 4 main parts: the nature of an atom, the nature of a metal, the nature of an alloy, and the structure of the nucleus. They cover such topics as the hydrogen atom, electron waves, wave mechanics, Brillouin zones, co-valent bonds, radioactivity and natural disintegration, fundamental particles, structure and fission of the nucleus, etc. Revised, enlarged edition. 177 illustrations. Subject and name indexes. 407pp. 5⅜ x 8½.   S1046 Paperbound **$2.25**

OUT OF THE SKY, H. H. Nininger. A non-technical but comprehensive introduction to "meteoritics", the young science concerned with all aspects of the arrival of matter from outer space. Written by one of the world's experts on meteorites, this work shows how, despite difficulties of observation and sparseness of data, a considerable body of knowledge has arisen. It defines meteors and meteorites; studies fireball clusters and processions, meteorite composition, size, distribution, showers, explosions, origins, craters, and much more. A true connecting link between astronomy and geology. More than 175 photos, 22 other illustrations. References. Bibliography of author's publications on meteorites. Index. viii + 336pp. 5⅜ x 8. T519 Paperbound **$1.85**

SATELLITES AND SCIENTIFIC RESEARCH, D. King-Hele. Non-technical account of the manmade satellites and the discoveries they have yielded up to the autumn of 1961. Brings together information hitherto published only in hard-to-get scientific journals. Includes the life history of a typical satellite, methods of tracking, new information on the shape of the earth, zones of radiation, etc. Over 60 diagrams and 6 photographs. Mathematical appendix. Bibliography of over 100 items. Index. xii + 180pp. 5⅜ x 8½. T703 Paperbound **$2.00**

BOOKS EXPLAINING SCIENCE AND MATHEMATICS

Mathematics

CHANCE, LUCK AND STATISTICS: THE SCIENCE OF CHANCE, Horace C. Levinson. Theory of probability and science of statistics in simple, non-technical language. Part I deals with theory of probability, covering odd superstitions in regard to "luck," the meaning of betting odds, the law of mathematical expectation, gambling, and applications in poker, roulette, lotteries, dice, bridge, and other games of chance. Part II discusses the misuse of statistics, the concept of statistical probabilities, normal and skew frequency distributions, and statistics applied to various fields—birth rates, stock speculation, insurance rates, advertising, etc. "Presented in an easy humorous style which I consider the best kind of expository writing," Prof. A. C. Cohen, Industry Quality Control. Enlarged revised edition. Formerly titled "The Science of Chance." Preface and two new appendices by the author. Index. xiv + 365pp. 5⅜ x 8. T1007 Paperbound **$1.85**

PROBABILITIES AND LIFE, Emile Borel. Translated by M. Baudin. Non-technical, highly readable introduction to the results of probability as applied to everyday situations. Partial contents: Fallacies About Probabilities Concerning Life After Death; Negligible Probabilities and the Probabilities of Everyday Life; Events of Small Probability; Application of Probabilities to Certain Problems of Heredity; Probabilities of Deaths, Diseases, and Accidents; On Poisson's Formula. Index. 3 Appendices of statistical studies and tables. vi + 87pp. 5⅜ x 8½. T121 Paperbound **$1.00**

GREAT IDEAS OF MODERN MATHEMATICS: THEIR NATURE AND USE, Jagjit Singh. Reader with only high school math will understand main mathematical ideas of modern physics, astronomy, genetics, psychology, evolution, etc., better than many who use them as tools, but comprehend little of their basic structure. Author uses his wide knowledge of non-mathematical fields in brilliant exposition of differential equations, matrices, group theory, logic, statistics, problems of mathematical foundations, imaginary numbers, vectors, etc. Original publication. 2 appendices. 2 indexes. 65 illustr. 322pp. 5⅜ x 8. S587 Paperbound **$2.00**

MATHEMATICS IN ACTION, O. G. Sutton. Everyone with a command of high school algebra will find this book one of the finest possible introductions to the application of mathematics to physical theory. Ballistics, numerical analysis, waves and wavelike phenomena, Fourier series, group concepts, fluid flow and aerodynamics, statistical measures, and meteorology are discussed with unusual clarity. Some calculus and differential equations theory is developed by the author for the reader's help in the more difficult sections. 88 figures. Index. viii + 236pp. 5⅜ x 8. T440 Clothbound **$3.50**

THE FOURTH DIMENSION SIMPLY EXPLAINED, edited by H. P. Manning. 22 essays, originally Scientific American contest entries, that use a minimum of mathematics to explain aspects of 4-dimensional geometry: analogues to 3-dimensional space, 4-dimensional absurdities and curiosities (such as removing the contents of an egg without puncturing its shell), possible measurements and forms, etc. Introduction by the editor. Only book of its sort on a truly elementary level, excellent introduction to advanced works. 82 figures. 251pp. 5⅜ x 8. T711 Paperbound **$1.50**

MATHEMATICS—INTERMEDIATE TO ADVANCED

General

INTRODUCTION TO APPLIED MATHEMATICS, Francis D. Murnaghan. A practical and thoroughly sound introduction to a number of advanced branches of higher mathematics. Among the selected topics covered in detail are: vector and matrix analysis, partial and differential equations, integral equations, calculus of variations, Laplace transform theory, the vector triple product, linear vector functions, quadratic and bilinear forms, Fourier series, spherical harmonics, Bessel functions, the Heaviside expansion formula, and many others. Extremely useful book for graduate students in physics, engineering, chemistry, and mathematics. Index. 111 study exercises with answers. 41 illustrations. ix + 389pp. 5⅜ x 8½.
S1042 Paperbound **$2.25**

OPERATIONAL METHODS IN APPLIED MATHEMATICS, H. S. Carslaw and J. C. Jaeger. Explanation of the application of the Laplace Transformation to differential equations, a simple and effective substitute for more difficult and obscure operational methods. Of great practical value to engineers and to all workers in applied mathematics. Chapters on: Ordinary Linear Differential Equations with Constant Coefficients;; Electric Circuit Theory; Dynamical Applications; The Inversion Theorem for the Laplace Transformation; Conduction of Heat; Vibrations of Continuous Mechanical Systems; Hydrodynamics; Impulsive Functions; Chains of Differential Equations; and other related matters. 3 appendices. 153 problems, many with answers. 22 figures. xvi + 359pp. 5⅜ x 8½.
S1011 Paperbound **$2.25**

APPLIED MATHEMATICS FOR RADIO AND COMMUNICATIONS ENGINEERS, C. E. Smith. No extraneous material here!—only the theories, equations, and operations essential and immediately useful for radio work. Can be used as refresher, as handbook of applications and tables, or as full home-study course. Ranges from simplest arithmetic through calculus, series, and wave forms, hyperbolic trigonometry, simultaneous equations in mesh circuits, etc. Supplies applications right along with each math topic discussed. 22 useful tables of functions, formulas, logs, etc. Index. 166 exercises, 140 examples, all with answers. 95 diagrams. Bibliography. x + 336pp. 5⅜ x 8.
S141 Paperbound **$1.75**

Algebra, group theory, determinants, sets, matrix theory

ALGEBRAS AND THEIR ARITHMETICS, L. E. Dickson. Provides the foundation and background necessary to any advanced undergraduate or graduate student studying abstract algebra. Begins with elementary introduction to linear transformations, matrices, field of complex numbers; proceeds to order, basal units, modulus, quaternions, etc.; develops calculus of linears sets, describes various examples of algebras including invariant, difference, nilpotent, semi-simple. "Makes the reader marvel at his genius for clear and profound analysis," Amer. Mathematical Monthly. Index. xii + 241pp. 5⅜ x 8.
S616 Paperbound **$1.50**

THE THEORY OF EQUATIONS WITH AN INTRODUCTION TO THE THEORY OF BINARY ALGEBRAIC FORMS, W. S. Burnside and A. W. Panton. Extremely thorough and concrete discussion of the theory of equations, with extensive detailed treatment of many topics curtailed in later texts. Covers theory of algebraic equations, properties of polynomials, symmetric functions, derived functions, Horner's process, complex numbers and the complex variable, determinants and methods of elimination, invariant theory (nearly 100 pages), transformations, introduction to Galois theory, Abelian equations, and much more. Invaluable supplementary work for modern students and teachers. 759 examples and exercises. Index in each volume. Two volume set. Total of xxiv + 604pp. 5⅜ x 8.
S714 Vol I Paperbound **$1.85**
S715 Vol II Paperbound **$1.85**
The set **$3.70**

COMPUTATIONAL METHODS OF LINEAR ALGEBRA, V. N. Faddeeva, translated by **C. D. Benster.** First English translation of a unique and valuable work, the only work in English presenting a systematic exposition of the most important methods of linear algebra—classical and contemporary. Shows in detail how to derive numerical solutions of problems in mathematical physics which are frequently connected with those of linear algebra. Theory as well as individual practice. Part I surveys the mathematical background that is indispensable to what follows. Parts II and III, the conclusion, set forth the most important methods of solution, for both exact and iterative groups. One of the most outstanding and valuable features of this work is the 23 tables, double and triple checked for accuracy. These tables will not be found elsewhere. Author's preface. Translator's note. New bibliography and index. x + 252pp. 5⅜ x 8.
S424 Paperbound **$2.00**

ALGEBRAIC EQUATIONS, E. Dehn. Careful and complete presentation of Galois' theory of algebraic equations; theories of Lagrange and Galois developed in logical rather than historical form, with a more thorough exposition than in most modern texts. Many concrete applications and fully-worked-out examples. Discusses basic theory (very clear exposition of the symmetric group); isomorphic, transitive, and Abelian groups; applications of Lagrange's and Galois' theories; and much more. Newly revised by the author. Index. List of Theorems. xi + 208pp. 5⅜ x 8.
S697 Paperbound **$1.45**

Differential equations, ordinary and partial; integral equations

INTRODUCTION TO THE DIFFERENTIAL EQUATIONS OF PHYSICS, L. Hopf. Especially valuable to the engineer with no math beyond elementary calculus. Emphasizing intuitive rather than formal aspects of concepts, the author covers an extensive territory. Partial contents: Law of causality, energy theorem, damped oscillations, coupling by friction, cylindrical and spherical coordinates, heat source, etc. Index. 48 figures. 160pp. 5⅜ x 8.
S120 Paperbound **$1.35**

INTRODUCTION TO THE THEORY OF LINEAR DIFFERENTIAL EQUATIONS, E. G. Poole. Authoritative discussions of important topics, with methods of solution more detailed than usual, for students with background of elementary course in differential equations. Studies existence theorems, linearly independent solutions; equations with constant coefficients; with uniform analytic coefficients; regular singularities; the hypergeometric equation; conformal representation; etc. Exercises. Index. 210pp. 5⅜ x 8.
S629 Paperbound **$1.65**

DIFFERENTIAL EQUATIONS FOR ENGINEERS, P. Franklin. Outgrowth of a course given 10 years at M. I. T. Makes most useful branch of pure math accessible for practical work. Theoretical basis of D.E.'s; solution of ordinary D.E.'s and partial derivatives arising from heat flow, steady-state temperature of a plate, wave equations; analytic functions; convergence of Fourier Series. 400 problems on electricity, vibratory systems, other topics. Formerly "Differential Equations for Electrical Engineers." Index 41 illus. 307pp. 5⅜ x 8.
S601 Paperbound **$2.00**

DIFFERENTIAL EQUATIONS, F. R. Moulton. A detailed, rigorous exposition of all the non-elementary processes of solving ordinary differential equations. Several chapters devoted to the treatment of practical problems, especially those of a physical nature, which are far more advanced than problems usually given as illustrations. Includes analytic differential equations; variations of a parameter; integrals of differential equations; analytic implicit functions; problems of elliptic motion; sine-amplitude functions; deviation of formal bodies; Cauchy-Lipschitz process; linear differential equations with periodic coefficients; differential equations in infinitely many variations; much more. Historical notes. 10 figures. 222 problems. Index. xv + 395pp. 5⅜ x 8.
S451 Paperbound **$2.00**

DIFFERENTIAL AND INTEGRAL EQUATIONS OF MECHANICS AND PHYSICS (DIE DIFFERENTIAL-UND INTEGRALGLEICHUNGEN DER MECHANIK UND PHYSIK), edited by P. Frank and R. von Mises. Most comprehensive and authoritative work on the mathematics of mathematical physics available today in the United States: the standard, definitive reference for teachers, physicists, engineers, and mathematicians—now published (in the original German) at a relatively inexpensive price for the first time! Every chapter in this 2,000-page set is by an expert in his field: Carathéodory, Courant, Frank, Mises, and a dozen others. Vol I, on mathematics, gives concise but complete coverages of advanced calculus, differential equations, integral equations, and potential, and partial differential equations. Index. xxiii + 916pp. Vol. II (physics): classical mechanics, optics, continuous mechanics, heat conduction and diffusion, the stationary and quasi-stationary electromagnetic field, electromagnetic oscillations, and wave mechanics. Index. xxiv + 1106pp. Two volume set. Each volume available separately. 5⅝ x 8⅜.
S787 Vol I Clothbound **$7.50**
S788 Vol II Clothbound **$7.50**
The set **$15.00**

LECTURES ON CAUCHY'S PROBLEM, J. Hadamard. Based on lectures given at Columbia, Rome, this discusses work of Riemann, Kirchhoff, Volterra, and the author's own research on the hyperbolic case in linear partial differential equations. It extends spherical and cylindrical waves to apply to all (normal) hyperbolic equations. Partial contents: Cauchy's problem, fundamental formula, equations with odd number, with even number of independent variables; method of descent. 32 figures. Index. iii + 316pp. 5⅜ x 8. S105 Paperbound **$1.75**

THEORY OF DIFFERENTIAL EQUATIONS, A. R. Forsyth. Out of print for over a decade, the complete 6 volumes (now bound as 3) of this monumental work represent the most comprehensive treatment of differential equations ever written. Historical presentation includes in 2500 pages every substantial development. Vol. 1, 2: EXACT EQUATIONS, PFAFF'S PROBLEM; ORDINARY EQUATIONS, NOT LINEAR: methods of Grassmann, Clebsch, Lie, Darboux; Cauchy's theorem; branch points; etc. Vol. 3, 4: ORDINARY EQUATIONS, NOT LINEAR; ORDINARY LINEAR EQUATIONS: Zeta Fuchsian functions, general theorems on algebraic integrals, Brun's theorem, equations with uniform periodic coffiecients, etc. Vol. 4, 5: PARTIAL DIFFERENTIAL EQUATIONS: 2 existence-theorems, equations of theoretical dynamics, Laplace transformations, general transformation of equations of the 2nd order, much more. Indexes. Total of 2766pp. 5⅜ x 8.
S576-7-8 Clothbound: the set **$15.00**

PARTIAL DIFFERENTIAL EQUATIONS OF MATHEMATICAL PHYSICS, A. G. Webster. A keystone work in the library of every mature physicist, engineer, researcher. Valuable sections on elasticity, compression theory, potential theory, theory of sound, heat conduction, wave propagation, vibration theory. Contents include: deduction of differential equations, vibrations, normal functions, Fourier's series, Cauchy's method, boundary problems, method of Riemann-Volterra. Spherical, cylindrical, ellipsoidal harmonics, applications, etc. 97 figures. vii + 440pp. 5⅜ x 8.
S263 Paperbound **$2.25**

CATALOGUE OF DOVER BOOKS

ELEMENTARY CONCEPTS OF TOPOLOGY, P. Alexandroff. First English translation of the famous brief introduction to topology for the beginner or for the mathematician not undertaking extensive study. This unusually useful intuitive approach deals primarily with the concepts of complex, cycle, and homology, and is wholly consistent with current investigations. Ranges from basic concepts of set-theoretic topology to the concept of Betti groups. "Glowing example of harmony between intuition and thought," David Hilbert. Translated by A. E. Farley. Introduction by D. Hilbert. Index. 25 figures. 73pp. 5⅜ x 8. S747 Paperbound **$1.00**

Number theory

INTRODUCTION TO THE THEORY OF NUMBERS, L. E. Dickson. Thorough, comprehensive approach with adequate coverage of classical literature, an introductory volume beginners can follow. Chapters on divisibility, congruences, quadratic residues & reciprocity, Diophantine equations, etc. Full treatment of binary quadratic forms without usual restriction to integral coefficients. Covers infinitude of primes, least residues, Fermat's theorem, Euler's phi function, Legendre's symbol, Gauss's lemma, automorphs, reduced forms, recent theorems of Thue & Siegel, many more. Much material not readily available elsewhere. 239 problems. Index. I figure. viii + 183pp. 5⅜ x 8. S342 Paperbound **$1.75**

ELEMENTS OF NUMBER THEORY, I. M. Vinogradov. Detailed 1st course for persons without advanced mathematics; 95% of this book can be understood by readers who have gone no farther than high school algebra. Partial contents: divisibility theory, important number theoretical functions, congruences, primitive roots and indices, etc. Solutions to both problems and exercises. Tables of primes, indices, etc. Covers almost every essential formula in elementary number theory! Translated from Russian. 233 problems, 104 exercises. viii + 227pp. 5⅜ x 8. S259 Paperbound **$1.75**

THEORY OF NUMBERS and DIOPHANTINE ANALYSIS, R. D. Carmichael. These two complete works in one volume form one of the most lucid introductions to number theory, requiring only a firm foundation in high school mathematics. "Theory of Numbers," partial contents: Eratosthenes' sieve, Euclid's fundamental theorem, G.C.F. and L.C.M. of two or more integers, linear congruences, etc "Diophantine Analysis": rational triangles, Pythagorean triangles, equations of third, fourth, higher degrees, method of functional equations, much more. "Theory of Numbers": 76 problems. Index. 94pp. "Diophantine Analysis": 222 problems. Index. 118pp. 5⅜ x 8. S529 Paperbound **$1.35**

Numerical analysis, tables

MATHEMATICAL TABLES AND FORMULAS, Compiled by Robert D. Carmichael and Edwin R. Smith. Valuable collection for students, etc. Contains all tables necessary in college algebra and trigonometry, such as five-place common logarithms, logarithmic sines and tangents of small angles, logarithmic trigonometric functions, natural trigonometric functions, four-place antilogarithms, tables for changing from sexagesimal to circular and from circular to sexagesimal measure of angles, etc. Also many tables and formulas not ordinarily accessible, including powers, roots, and reciprocals, exponential and hyperbolic functions, ten-place logarithms of prime numbers, and formulas and theorems from analytical and elementary geometry and from calculus. Explanatory introduction. viii + 269pp. 5⅜ x 8½. S111 Paperbound **$1.25**

MATHEMATICAL TABLES, H. B. Dwight. Unique for its coverage in one volume of almost every function of importance in applied mathematics, engineering, and the physical sciences. Three extremely fine tables of the three trig functions and their inverse functions to thousandths of radians; natural and common logarithms; squares; cubes; hyperbolic functions and the inverse hyperbolic functions; $(a^2 + b^2)$ exp. ½a; complete elliptic integrals of the 1st and 2nd kind; sine and cosine integrals; exponential integrals Ei(x) and Ei(— x); binomial coefficients; factorials to 250; surface zonal harmonics and first derivatives; Bernoulli and Euler numbers and their logs to base of 10; Gamma function; normal probability integral; over 60 pages of Bessel functions; the Riemann Zeta function. Each table with formulae generally used, sources of more extensive tables, interpolation data, etc. Over half have columns of differences, to facilitate interpolation. Introduction. Index. viii + 231pp. 5⅜ x 8. S445 Paperbound **$2.00**

TABLES OF FUNCTIONS WITH FORMULAE AND CURVES, E. Jahnke & F. Emde. The world's most comprehensive 1-volume English-text collection of tables, formulae, curves of transcendent functions. 4th corrected edition, new 76-page section giving tables, formulae for elementary functions—not in other English editions. Partial contents: sine, cosine, logarithmic integral; factorial function; error integral; theta functions; elliptic integrals, functions; Legendre, Bessel, Riemann, Mathieu, hypergeometric functions, etc. Supplementary books. Bibliography. Indexed. "Out of the way functions for which we know no other source," SCIENTIFIC COMPUTING SERVICE, Ltd. 212 figures. 400pp. 5⅜ x 8. S133 Paperbound **$2.00**

CHEMISTRY AND PHYSICAL CHEMISTRY

ORGANIC CHEMISTRY, F. C. Whitmore. The entire subject of organic chemistry for the practicing chemist and the advanced student. Storehouse of facts, theories, processes found elsewhere only in specialized journals. Covers aliphatic compounds (500 pages on the properties and synthetic preparation of hydrocarbons, halides, proteins, ketones, etc.), alicyclic compounds, aromatic compounds, heterocyclic compounds, organophosphorus and organometallic compounds. Methods of synthetic preparation analyzed critically throughout. Includes much of biochemical interest. "The scope of this volume is astonishing," INDUSTRIAL AND ENGINEERING CHEMISTRY. 12,000-reference index. 2387-item bibliography. Total of x + 1005pp. 5⅜ x 8. Two volume set.

S700 Vol I Paperbound **$2.25**
S701 Vol II Paperbound **$2.25**
The set **$4.50**

THE MODERN THEORY OF MOLECULAR STRUCTURE, Bernard Pullman. A reasonably popular account of recent developments in atomic and molecular theory. Contents: The Wave Function and Wave Equations (history and bases of present theories of molecular structure); The Electronic Structure of Atoms (Description and classification of atomic wave functions, etc.); Diatomic Molecules; Non-Conjugated Polyatomic Molecules; Conjugated Polyatomic Molecules; The Structure of Complexes. Minimum of mathematical background needed. New translation by David Antin of "La Structure Moleculaire." Index. Bibliography. vii + 87pp. 5⅜ x 8½.

S987 Paperbound **$1.00**

CATALYSIS AND CATALYSTS, Marcel Prettre, Director, Research Institute on Catalysis. This brief book, translated into English for the first time, is the finest summary of the principal modern concepts, methods, and results of catalysis. Ideal introduction for beginning chemistry and physics students. Chapters: Basic Definitions of Catalysis (true catalysis and generalization of the concept of catalysis); The Scientific Bases of Catalysis (Catalysis and chemical thermodynamics, catalysis and chemical kinetics); Homogeneous Catalysis (acid-base catalysis, etc.); Chain Reactions; Contact Masses; Heterogeneous Catalysis (Mechanisms of contact catalyses, etc.); and Industrial Applications (acids and fertilizers, petroleum and petroleum chemistry, rubber, plastics, synthetic resins, and fibers). Translated by David Antin. Index. vi + 88pp. 5⅜ x 8½.

S998 Paperbound **$1.00**

POLAR MOLECULES, Pieter Debye. This work by Nobel laureate Debye offers a complete guide to fundamental electrostatic field relations, polarizability, molecular structure. Partial contents: electric intensity, displacement and force, polarization by orientation, molar polarization and molar refraction, halogen-hydrides, polar liquids, ionic saturation, dielectric constant, etc. Special chapter considers quantum theory. Indexed. 172pp. 5⅜ x 8.

S64 Paperbound **$1.65**

THE ELECTRONIC THEORY OF ACIDS AND BASES, W. F. Luder and Saverio Zuffanti. The first full systematic presentation of the electronic theory of acids and bases—treating the theory and its ramifications in an uncomplicated manner. Chapters: Historical Background; Atomic Orbitals and Valence; The Electronic Theory of Acids and Bases; Electrophilic and Electrodotic Reagents; Acidic and Basic Radicals; Neutralization; Titrations with Indicators; Displacement; Catalysis; Acid Catalysis; Base Catalysis; Alkoxides and Catalysts; Conclusion. Required reading for all chemists. Second revised (1961) edition, with additional examples and references. 3 figures. 9 tables. Index. Bibliography xii + 165pp. 5⅜ x 8.

S201 Paperbound **$1.50**

KINETIC THEORY OF LIQUIDS, J. Frenkel. Regarding the kinetic theory of liquids as a generalization and extension of the theory of solid bodies, this volume covers all types of arrangements of solids, thermal displacements of atoms, interstitial atoms and ions, orientational and rotational motion of molecules, and transition between states of matter. Mathematical theory is developed close to the physical subject matter. 216 bibliographical footnotes. 55 figures. xi + 485pp. 5⅜ x 8.

S95 Paperbound **$2.55**

THE PRINCIPLES OF ELECTROCHEMISTRY, D. A. MacInnes. Basic equations for almost every subfield of electrochemistry from first principles, referring at all times to the soundest and most recent theories and results; unusually useful as text or as reference. Covers coulometers and Faraday's Law, electrolytic conductance, the Debye-Hueckel method for the theoretical calculation of activity coefficients, concentration cells, standard electrode potentials, thermodynamic ionization constants, pH, potentiometric titrations, irreversible phenomena, Planck's equation, and much more. "Excellent treatise," AMERICAN CHEMICAL SOCIETY JOURNAL. "Highly recommended," CHEMICAL AND METALLURGICAL ENGINEERING. 2 Indices. Appendix. 585-item bibliography. 137 figures. 94 tables. ii + 478pp. 5⅝ x 8⅜.

S52 Paperbound **$2.75**

THE PHASE RULE AND ITS APPLICATION, Alexander Findlay. Covering chemical phenomena of 1, 2, 3, 4, and multiple component systems, this "standard work on the subject" (NATURE, London) has been completely revised and brought up to date by A. N. Campbell and N. O. Smith. Brand new material has been added on such matters as binary, tertiary liquid equilibria, solid solutions in ternary systems, quinary systems of salts and water. Completely revised to triangular coordinates in ternary systems, clarified graphic representation, solid models, etc. 9th revised edition. Author, subject indexes. 236 figures. 505 footnotes, mostly bibliographic. xii + 494pp. 5⅜ x 8.

S91 Paperbound **$2.50**

PHYSICS

General physics

FOUNDATIONS OF PHYSICS, R. B. Lindsay & H. Margenau. Excellent bridge between semi-popular works & technical treatises. A discussion of methods of physical description, construction of theory; valuable for physicist with elementary calculus who is interested in ideas that give meaning to data, tools of modern physics. Contents include symbolism, mathematical equations; space & time foundations of mechanics; probability; physics & continua; electron theory; special & general relativity; quantum mechanics; causality. "Thorough and yet not overdetailed. Unreservedly recommended," NATURE (London). Unabridged, corrected edition. List of recommended readings. 35 illustrations. xi + 537pp. 5⅜ x 8.
S377 Paperbound **$3.00**

FUNDAMENTAL FORMULAS OF PHYSICS, ed. by D. H. Menzel. Highly useful, fully inexpensive reference and study text, ranging from simple to highly sophisticated operations. Mathematics integrated into text—each chapter stands as short textbook of field represented. Vol. 1: Statistics, Physical Constants, Special Theory of Relativity, Hydrodynamics, Aerodynamics, Boundary Value Problems in Math. Physics; Viscosity, Electromagnetic Theory, etc. Vol. 2: Sound, Acoustics, Geometrical Optics, Electron Optics, High-Energy Phenomena, Magnetism, Biophysics, much more. Index. Total of 800pp. 5⅜ x 8.
Vol. 1 S595 Paperbound **$2.25**
Vol. 2 S596 Paperbound **$2.25**

MATHEMATICAL PHYSICS, D. H. Menzel. Thorough one-volume treatment of the mathematical techniques vital for classic mechanics, electromagnetic theory, quantum theory, and relativity. Written by the Harvard Professor of Astrophysics for junior, senior, and graduate courses, it gives clear explanations of all those aspects of function theory, vectors, matrices, dyadics, tensors, partial differential equations, etc., necessary for the understanding of the various physical theories. Electron theory, relativity, and other topics seldom presented appear here in considerable detail. Scores of definitions, conversion factors, dimensional constants, etc. "More detailed than normal for an advanced text . . . excellent set of sections on Dyadics, Matrices, and Tensors," JOURNAL OF THE FRANKLIN INSTITUTE. Index. 193 problems, with answers. x + 412pp. 5⅜ x 8.
S56 Paperbound **$2.50**

THE SCIENTIFIC PAPERS OF J. WILLARD GIBBS. All the published papers of America's outstanding theoretical scientist (except for "Statistical Mechanics" and "Vector Analysis"). Vol I (thermodynamics) contains one of the most brilliant of all 19th-century scientific papers—the 300-page "On the Equilibrium of Heterogeneous Substances," which founded the science of physical chemistry, and clearly stated a number of highly important natural laws for the first time; 8 other papers complete the first volume. Vol II includes 2 papers on dynamics, 8 on vector analysis and multiple algebra, 5 on the electromagnetic theory of light, and 6 miscellaneous papers. Biographical sketch by H. A. Bumstead. Total of xxxvi + 718pp. 5⅝ x 8⅜.
S721 Vol I Paperbound **$2.50**
S722 Vol II Paperbound **$2.25**
The set **$4.75**

BASIC THEORIES OF PHYSICS, Peter Gabriel Bergmann. Two-volume set which presents a critical examination of important topics in the major subdivisions of classical and modern physics. The first volume is concerned with classical mechanics and electrodynamics: mechanics of mass points, analytical mechanics, matter in bulk, electrostatics and magnetostatics, electromagnetic interaction, the field waves, special relativity, and waves. The second volume (Heat and Quanta) contains discussions of the kinetic hypothesis, physics and statistics, stationary ensembles, laws of thermodynamics, early quantum theories, atomic spectra, probability waves, quantization in wave mechanics, approximation methods, and abstract quantum theory. A valuable supplement to any thorough course or text.
Heat and Quanta: Index. 8 figures. x + 300pp. 5⅜ x 8½.
S968 Paperbound **$2.00**
Mechanics and Electrodynamics: Index. 14 figures. vii + 280pp. 5⅜ x 8½.
S969 Paperbound **$1.85**

THEORETICAL PHYSICS, A. S. Kompaneyets. One of the very few thorough studies of the subject in this price range. Provides advanced students with a comprehensive theoretical background. Especially strong on recent experimentation and developments in quantum theory. Contents: Mechanics (Generalized Coordinates, Lagrange's Equation, Collision of Particles, etc.), Electrodynamics (Vector Analysis, Maxwell's equations, Transmission of Signals, Theory of Relativity, etc.), Quantum Mechanics (the Inadequacy of Classical Mechanics, the Wave Equation, Motion in a Central Field, Quantum Theory of Radiation, Quantum Theories of Dispersion and Scattering, etc.), and Statistical Physics (Equilibrium Distribution of Molecules in an Ideal Gas, Boltzmann statistics, Bose and Fermi Distribution, Thermodynamic Quantities, etc.). Revised to 1961. Translated by George Yankovsky, authorized by Kompaneyets. 137 exercises. 56 figures. 529pp. 5⅜ x 8½. S972 Paperbound **$2.50**

ANALYTICAL AND CANONICAL FORMALISM IN PHYSICS, André Mercier. A survey, in one volume, of the variational principles (the key principles—in mathematical form—from which the basic laws of any one branch of physics can be derived) of the several branches of physical theory, together with an examination of the relationships among them. Contents: the Lagrangian Formalism, Lagrangian Densities, Canonical Formalism, Canonical Form of Electrodynamics, Hamiltonian Densities, Transformations, and Canonical Form with Vanishing Jacobian Determinant. Numerous examples and exercises. For advanced students, teachers, etc. 6 figures. Index. viii + 222pp. 5⅜ x 8½.
S1077 Paperbound **$1.75**

MATHEMATICAL PUZZLES AND RECREATIONS

AMUSEMENTS IN MATHEMATICS, Henry Ernest Dudeney. The foremost British originator of mathematical puzzles is always intriguing, witty, and paradoxical in this classic, one of the largest collections of mathematical amusements. More than 430 puzzles, problems, and paradoxes. Mazes and games, problems on number manipulation, unicursal and other route problems, puzzles on measuring, weighing, packing, age, kinship, chessboards, joining, crossing river, plane figure dissection, and many others. Solutions. More than 450 illustrations. vii + 258pp. 5⅜ x 8.　　　　　　　　　　　　　　　　　　　T473 Paperbound **$1.25**

SYMBOLIC LOGIC and THE GAME OF LOGIC, Lewis Carroll. "Symbolic Logic" is not concerned with modern symbolic logic, but is instead a collection of over 380 problems posed with charm and imagination, using the syllogism, and a fascinating diagrammatic method of drawing conclusions. In "The Game of Logic," Carroll's whimsical imagination devises a logical game played with 2 diagrams and counters (included) to manipulate hundreds of tricky syllogisms. The final section, "Hit or Miss" is a lagniappe-of 101 additional puzzles in the delightful Carroll manner. Until this reprint edition, both of these books were rarities costing up to $15 each. Symbolic Logic: Index, xxxi + 199pp. The Game of Logic: 96pp. Two vols. bound as one. 5⅜ x 8.　　　　　　　　　　　　　　　　　　　T492 Paperbound **$1.75**

MAZES AND LABYRINTHS: A BOOK OF PUZZLES, W. Shepherd. Mazes, formerly associated with mystery and ritual, are still among the most intriguing of intellectual puzzles. This is a novel and different collection of 50 amusements that embody the principle of the maze: mazes in the classical tradition; 3-dimensional, ribbon, and Möbius-strip mazes; hidden messages; spatial arrangements; etc.—almost all built on amusing story situations. 84 illustrations. Essay on maze psychology. Solutions. xv + 122pp. 5⅜ x 8.　　　T731 Paperbound **$1.00**

MATHEMATICAL RECREATIONS, M. Kraitchik. Some 250 puzzles, problems, demonstrations of recreational mathematics for beginners & advanced mathematicians. Unusual historical problems from Greek, Medieval, Arabic, Hindu sources: modern problems based on "mathematics without numbers," geometry, topology, arithmetic, etc. Pastimes derived from figurative numbers, Mersenne numbers, Fermat numbers; fairy chess, latruncles, reversi, many topics. Full solutions. Excellent for insights into special fields of math. 181 illustrations. 330pp. 5⅜ x 8.　　　　　　　　　　　　　　　　　　　　　　　　　　T163 Paperbound **$1.75**

MATHEMATICAL PUZZLES OF SAM LOYD, Vol. I, selected and edited by M. Gardner. Puzzles by the greatest puzzle creator and innovator. Selected from his famous "Cyclopedia of Puzzles," they retain the unique style and historical flavor of the originals. There are posers based on arithmetic, algebra, probability, game theory, route tracing, topology, counter, sliding block, operations research, geometrical dissection. Includes his famous "14-15" puzzle which was a national craze, and his "Horse of a Different Color" which sold millions of copies. 117 of his most ingenious puzzles in all, 120 line drawings and diagrams. Solutions. Selected references. xx + 167pp. 5⅜ x 8.　　　　　　　T498 Paperbound **$1.00**

MY BEST PUZZLES IN MATHEMATICS, Hubert Phillips ("Caliban"). Caliban is generally considered the best of the modern problemists. Here are 100 of his best and wittiest puzzles, selected by the author himself from such publications as the London Daily Telegraph, and each puzzle is guaranteed to put even the sharpest puzzle detective through his paces. Perfect for the development of clear thinking and a logical mind. Complete solutions are provided for every puzzle. x + 107pp. 5⅜ x 8½.　　　　　　　　T91 Paperbound **$1.00**

MY BEST PUZZLES IN LOGIC AND REASONING, H. Phillips ("Caliban"). 100 choice, hitherto unavailable puzzles by England's best-known problemist. No special knowledge needed to solve these logical or inferential problems, just an unclouded mind, nerves of steel, and fast reflexes. Data presented are both necessary and just sufficient to allow one unambiguous answer. More than 30 different types of puzzles, all ingenious and varied, many one of a kind, that will challenge the expert, please the beginner. Original publication. 100 puzzles, full solutions. x + 107pp. 5⅜ x 8½.　　　　　　　　　　　　T119 Paperbound **$1.00**

MATHEMATICAL PUZZLES FOR BEGINNERS AND ENTHUSIASTS, G. Mott-Smith. 188 mathematical puzzles to test mental agility. Inference, interpretation, algebra, dissection of plane figures, geometry, properties of numbers, decimation, permutations, probability, all enter these delightful problems. Puzzles like the Odic Force, How to Draw an Ellipse, Spider's Cousin, more than 180 others. Detailed solutions. Appendix with square roots, triangular numbers, primes, etc. 135 illustrations. 2nd revised edition. 248pp. 5⅜ x 8.　　T198 Paperbound **$1.25**

MATHEMATICS, MAGIC AND MYSTERY, Martin Gardner. Card tricks, feats of mental mathematics, stage mind-reading, other "magic" explained as applications of probability, sets, theory of numbers, topology, various branches of mathematics. Creative examination of laws and their applications with scores of new tricks and insights. 115 sections discuss tricks wtih cards, dice, coins; geometrical vanishing tricks, dozens of others. No sleight of hand needed; mathematics guarantees success. 115 illustrations. xii + 174pp. 5⅜ x 8.　　　　　　　　　　　　　　　　　　　　　　　　　　T335 Paperbound **$1.00**

RECREATIONS IN THE THEORY OF NUMBERS: THE QUEEN OF MATHEMATICS ENTERTAINS, Albert H. Beiler. The theory of numbers is often referred to as the "Queen of Mathematics." In this book Mr. Beiler has compiled the first English volume to deal exclusively with the recreational aspects of number theory, an inherently recreational branch of mathematics. The author's clear style makes for enjoyable reading as he deals with such topics as: perfect numbers, amicable numbers, Fermat's theorem, Wilson's theorem, interesting properties of digits, methods of factoring, primitive roots, Euler's function, polygonal and figurate numbers, Mersenne numbers, congruence, repeating decimals, etc. Countless puzzle problems, with full answers and explanations. For mathematicians and mathematically-inclined laymen, etc. New publication. 28 figures. 9 illustrations. 103 tables. Bibliography at chapter ends. vi + 247pp. 5⅜ x 8½.
T1096 Paperbound **$2.00**

PAPER FOLDING FOR BEGINNERS, W. D. Murray and F. J. Rigney. A delightful introduction to the varied and entertaining Japanese art of origami (paper folding), with a full crystal-clear text that anticipates every difficulty; over 275 clearly labeled diagrams of all important stages in creation. You get results at each stage, since complex figures are logically developed from simpler ones. 43 different pieces are explained: place mats, drinking cups, bonbon boxes, sailboats, frogs, roosters, etc. 6 photographic plates. 279 diagrams. 95pp. 5⅝ x 8⅜.
T713 Paperbound **$1.00**

1800 RIDDLES, ENIGMAS AND CONUNDRUMS, Darwin A. Hindman. Entertaining collection ranging from hilarious gags to outrageous puns to sheer nonsense—a welcome respite from sophisticated humor. Children, toastmasters, and practically anyone with a funny bone will find these zany riddles tickling and eminently repeatable. Sample: "Why does Santa Claus always go down the chimney?" "Because it soots him." Some old, some new—covering a wide variety of subjects. New publication. iii + 154pp. 5⅜ x 8½. T1059 Paperbound **$1.00**

EASY-TO-DO ENTERTAINMENTS AND DIVERSIONS WITH CARDS, STRING, COINS, PAPER AND MATCHES, R. M. Abraham. Over 300 entertaining games, tricks, puzzles, and pastimes for children and adults. Invaluable to anyone in charge of groups of youngsters, for party givers, etc. Contains sections on card tricks and games, making things by paperfolding—toys, decorations, and the like; tricks with coins, matches, and pieces of string; descriptions of games; toys that can be made from common household objects; mathematical recreations; word games; and 50 miscellaneous entertainments. Formerly "Winter Nights Entertainments." Introduction by Lord Baden Powell. 329 illustrations. v + 186pp. 5⅜ x 8.
T921 Paperbound **$1.00**

DIVERSIONS AND PASTIMES WITH CARDS, STRING, PAPER AND MATCHES, R. M. Abraham. Another collection of amusements and diversion for game and puzzle fans of all ages. Many new paperfolding ideas and tricks, an extensive section on amusements with knots and splices, two chapters of easy and not-so-easy problems, coin and match tricks, and lots of other parlor pastimes from the agile mind of the late British problemist and gamester. Corrected and revised version. Illustrations. 160pp. 5⅜ x 8½. T1127 Paperbound **$1.00**

STRING FIGURES AND HOW TO MAKE THEM: A STUDY OF CAT'S-CRADLE IN MANY LANDS, Caroline Furness Jayne. In a simple and easy-to-follow manner, this book describes how to make 107 different string figures. Not only is looping and crossing string between the fingers a common youthful diversion, but it is an ancient form of amusement practiced in all parts of the globe, especially popular among primitive tribes. These games are fun for all ages and offer an excellent means for developing manual dexterity and coordination. Much insight also for the anthropological observer on games and diversions in many different cultures. Index. Bibliography. Introduction by A. C. Haddon, Cambridge University. 17 full-page plates. 950 illustrations. xxiii + 407pp. 5⅜ x 8½. T152 Paperbound **$2.00**

CRYPTANALYSIS, Helen F. Gaines. (Formerly ELEMENTARY CRYPTANALYSIS.) A standard elementary and intermediate text for serious students. It does not confine itself to old material, but contains much that is not generally known, except to experts. Concealment, Transposition, Substitution ciphers; Vigenère, Kasiski, Playfair, multafid, dozens of other techniques. Appendix with sequence charts, letter frequencies in English, 5 other languages, English word frequencies. Bibliography. 167 codes. New to this edition: solution to codes. vi + 230pp. 5⅜ x 8. T97 Paperbound **$2.25**

MAGIC SQUARES AND CUBES, W. S. Andrews. Only book-length treatment in English, a thorough non-technical description and analysis. Here are nasik, overlapping, pandiagonal, serrated squares; magic circles, cubes, spheres, rhombuses. Try your hand at 4-dimensional magical figures! Much unusual folklore and tradition included. High school algebra is sufficient. 754 diagrams and illustrations. viii + 419pp. 5⅜ x 8. T658 Paperbound **$1.85**

CALIBAN'S PROBLEM BOOK: MATHEMATICAL, INFERENTIAL, AND CRYPTOGRAPHIC PUZZLES, H. Phillips ("Caliban"), S. T. Shovelton, G. S. Marshall. 105 ingenious problems by the greatest living creator of puzzles based on logic and inference. Rigorous, modern, piquant, and reflecting their author's unusual personality, these intermediate and advanced puzzles all involve the ability to reason clearly through complex situations; some call for mathematical knowledge, ranging from algebra to number theory. Solutions. xi + 180pp. 5⅜ x 8.
T736 Paperbound **$1.25**

FICTION

THE LAND THAT TIME FORGOT and THE MOON MAID, Edgar Rice Burrougns. In the opinion of many, Burroughs' best work. The first concerns a strange island where evolution is individual rather than phylogenetic. Speechless anthropoids develop into intelligent human beings within a single generation. The second projects the reader far into the future and describes the first voyage to the Moon (in the year 2025), the conquest of the Earth by the Moon, and years of violence and adventure as the enslaved Earthmen try to regain possession of their planet. "An imaginative tour de force that keeps the reader keyed up and expectant," NEW YORK TIMES. Complete, unabridged text of the original two novels (three parts in each). 5 illustrations by J. Allen St. John. vi + 552pp. 5⅜ x 8½.
T1020 Clothbound **$3.75**
T358 Paperbound **$2.00**

AT THE EARTH'S CORE, PELLUCIDAR, TANAR OF PELLUCIDAR: THREE SCIENCE FICTION NOVELS BY EDGAR RICE BURROUGHS. Complete, unabridged texts of the first three Pellucidar novels. Tales of derring-do by the famous master of science fiction. The locale for these three related stories is the inner surface of the hollow Earth where we discover the world of Pellucidar, complete with all types of bizarre, menacing creatures, strange peoples, and alluring maidens—guaranteed to delight all Burroughs fans and a wide circle of adventure lovers. Illustrated by J. Allen St. John and P. F. Berdanier. vi + 433pp. 5⅜ x 8½.
T1051 Paperbound **$2.00**

THE PIRATES OF VENUS and LOST ON VENUS: TWO VENUS NOVELS BY EDGAR RICE BURROUGHS. Two related novels, complete and unabridged. Exciting adventure on the planet Venus with Earthman Carson Napier broken-field running through one dangerous episode after another. All lovers of swashbuckling science fiction will enjoy these two stories set in a world of fascinating societies, fierce beasts, 5000-ft. trees, lush vegetation, and wide seas. Illustrations by Fortunino Matania. Total of vi + 340pp. 5⅜ x 8½.
T1053 Paperbound **$1.75**

A PRINCESS OF MARS and A FIGHTING MAN OF MARS: TWO MARTIAN NOVELS BY EDGAR RICE BURROUGHS. "Princess of Mars" is the very first of the great Martian novels written by Burroughs, and it is probably the best of them all; it set the pattern for all of his later fantasy novels and contains a thrilling cast of strange peoples and creatures and the formula of Olympian heroism amidst ever-fluctuating fortunes which Burroughs carries off so successfully. "Fighting Man" returns to the same scenes and cities—many years later. A mad scientist, a degenerate dictator, and an indomitable defender of the right clash—with the fate of the Red Planet at stake! Complete, unabridged reprinting of original editions. Illustrations by F. E. Schoonover and Hugh Hutton. v + 356pp. 5⅜ x 8½.
T1140 Paperbound **$1.75**

THREE MARTIAN NOVELS, Edgar Rice Burroughs. Contains: Thuvia, Maid of Mars; The Chessmen of Mars; and The Master Mind of Mars. High adventure set in an imaginative and intricate conception of the Red Planet. Mars is peopled with an intelligent, heroic human race which lives in densely populated cities and with fierce barbarians who inhabit dead sea bottoms. Other exciting creatures abound amidst an inventive framework of Martian history and geography. Complete unabridged reprintings of the first edition. 16 illustrations by J. Allen St. John. vi + 499pp. 5⅜ x 8½.
T39 Paperbound **$1.85**

THREE PROPHETIC NOVELS BY H. G. WELLS, edited by E. F. Bleiler. Complete texts of "When the Sleeper Wakes" (1st book printing in 50 years), "A Story of the Days to Come," "The Time Machine" (1st complete printing in book form). Exciting adventures in the future are as enjoyable today as 50 years ago when first printed. Predict TV, movies, intercontinental airplanes, prefabricated houses, air-conditioned cities, etc. First important author to foresee problems of mind control, technological dictatorships. "Absolute best of imaginative fiction," N. Y. Times. Introduction. 335pp. 5⅜ x 8.
T605 Paperbound **$1.50**

28 SCIENCE FICTION STORIES OF H. G. WELLS. Two full unabridged novels, MEN LIKE GODS and STAR BEGOTTEN, plus 26 short stories by the master science-fiction writer of all time. Stories of space, time, invention, exploration, future adventure—an indispensable part of the library of everyone interested in science and adventure. PARTIAL CONTENTS: Men Like Gods, The Country of the Blind, In the Abyss, The Crystal Egg, The Man Who Could Work Miracles, A Story of the Days to Come, The Valley of Spiders, and 21 more! 928pp. 5⅜ x 8.
T265 Clothbound **$4.50**

THE WAR IN THE AIR, IN THE DAYS OF THE COMET, THE FOOD OF THE GODS: THREE SCIENCE FICTION NOVELS BY H. G. WELLS. Three exciting Wells offerings bearing on vital social and philosophical issues of his and our own day. Here are tales of air power, strategic bombing,,East vs. West, the potential miracles of science, the potential disasters from outer space, the relationship between scientific advancement and moral progress, etc. First reprinting of "War in the Air" in almost 50 years. An excellent sampling of Wells at his storytelling best. Complete, unabridged reprintings. 16 illustrations. 645pp. 5⅜ x 8½.
T1135 Paperbound **$2.00**

SEVEN SCIENCE FICTION NOVELS, H. G. Wells. Full unabridged texts of 7 science-fiction novels of the master. Ranging from biology, physics, chemistry, astronomy to sociology and other studies, Mr. Wells extrapolates whole worlds of strange and intriguing character. "One will have to go far to match this for entertainment, excitement, and sheer pleasure . . .," NEW YORK TIMES. Contents: The Time Machine, The Island of Dr. Moreau, First Men in the Moon, The Invisible Man, The War of the Worlds, The Food of the Gods, In the Days of the Comet. 1015pp. 5⅜ x 8. **T264 Clothbound $4.50**

BEST GHOST STORIES OF J. S. LE FANU, Selected and introduced by E. F. Bleiler. LeFanu is deemed the greatest name in Victorian supernatural fiction. Here are 16 of his best horror stories, including 2 nouvelles: "Carmilla," a classic vampire tale couched in a perverse eroticism, and "The Haunted Baronet." Also: "Sir Toby's Will," "Green Tea," "Schalken the Painter," "Ultor de Lacy," "The Familiar," etc. The first American publication of about half of this material: a long-overdue opportunity to get a choice sampling of LeFanu's work. New selection (1964). 8 illustrations. 5⅜ x 8⅜. **T415 Paperbound $1.85**

THE WONDERFUL WIZARD OF OZ, L. F. Baum. Only edition in print with all the original W. W. Denslow illustrations in full color—as much a part of "The Wizard" as Tenniel's drawings are for "Alice in Wonderland." "The Wizard" is still America's best-loved fairy tale, in which, as the author expresses it, "The wonderment and joy are retained and the heartaches and nightmares left out." Now today's young readers can enjoy every word and wonderful picture of the original book. New introduction by Martin Gardner. A Baum bibliography. 23 full-page color plates. viii + 268pp. 5⅜ x 8. **T691 Paperbound $1.50**

GHOST AND HORROR STORIES OF AMBROSE BIERCE, Selected and introduced by E. F. Bleiler. 24 morbid, eerie tales—the cream of Bierce's fiction output. Contains such memorable pieces as "The Moonlit Road," "The Damned Thing," "An Inhabitant of Carcosa," "The Eyes of the Panther," "The Famous Gilson Bequest," "The Middle Toe of the Right Foot," and other chilling stories, plus the essay, "Visions of the Night" in which Bierce gives us a kind of rationale for his aesthetic of horror. New collection (1964). xxii + 199pp. 5⅜ x 8⅜. **T767 Paperbound $1.00**

HUMOR

MR. DOOLEY ON IVRYTHING AND IVRYBODY, Finley Peter Dunne. Since the time of his appearance in 1893, "Mr. Dooley," the fictitious Chicago bartender, has been recognized as America's most humorous social and political commentator. Collected in this volume are 102 of the best Dooley pieces—all written around the turn of the century, the height of his popularity. Mr. Dooley's Irish brogue is employed wittily and penetratingly on subjects which are just as fresh and relevant today as they were then: corruption and hypocrisy of politicans, war preparations and chauvinism, automation, Latin American affairs, superbombs, etc. Other articles range from Rudyard Kipling to football. Selected with an introduction by Robert Hutchinson. xii + 244pp. 5⅜ x 8½. **T626 Paperbound $1.00**

RUTHLESS RHYMES FOR HEARTLESS HOMES and MORE RUTHLESS RHYMES FOR HEARTLESS HOMES, Harry Graham ("Col. D. Streamer"). A collection of Little Willy and 48 other poetic "disasters." Graham's funniest and most disrespectful verse, accompanied by original illustrations. Nonsensical, wry humor which employs stern parents, careless nurses, uninhibited children, practical jokers, single-minded golfers, Scottish lairds, etc. in the leading roles. A precursor of the "sick joke" school of today. This volume contains, bound together for the first time, two of the most perennially popular books of humor in England and America. Index. vi + 69pp. 5⅜ x 8. **T930 Paperbound 75¢**

A WHIMSEY ANTHOLOGY, Collected by Carolyn Wells. 250 of the most amusing rhymes ever written. Acrostics, anagrams, palindromes, alphabetical jingles, tongue twisters, echo verses, alliterative verses, riddles, mnemonic rhymes, interior rhymes, over 40 limericks, etc. by Lewis Carroll, Edward Lear, Joseph Addison, W. S. Gilbert, Christina Rossetti, Chas. Lamb, James Boswell, Hood, Dickens, Swinburne, Leigh Hunt, Harry Graham, Poe, Eugene Field, and many others. xiv + 221pp. 5⅜ x 8½. **T195 Paperbound $1.25**

MY PIOUS FRIENDS AND DRUNKEN COMPANIONS and MORE PIOUS FRIENDS AND DRUNKEN COMPANIONS, Songs and ballads of Conviviality Collected by Frank Shay. Magnificently illuminated by John Held, Jr. 132 ballads, blues, vaudeville numbers, drinking songs, cowboy songs, sea chanties, comedy songs, etc. of the Naughty Nineties and early 20th century. Over a third are reprinted with music. Many perennial favorites such as: The Band Played On, Frankie and Johnnie, The Old Grey Mare, The Face on the Bar-room Floor, etc. Many others unlocatable elsewhere: The Dog-Catcher's Child, The Cannibal Maiden, Don't Go in the Lion's Cage Tonight, Mother, etc. Complete verses and introductions to songs. Unabridged republication of first editions, 2 Indexes (song titles and first lines and choruses). Introduction by Frank Shay. 2 volumes bounds as 1. Total of xvi + 235pp. 5⅜ x 8½. **T946 Paperbound $1.25**

CATALOGUE OF DOVER BOOKS

MAX AND MORITZ, Wilhelm Busch. Edited and annotated by H. Arthur Klein. Translated by H. Arthur Klein, M. C. Klein, and others. The mischievous high jinks of Max and Moritz, Peter and Paul, Ker and Plunk, etc. are delightfully captured in sketch and rhyme. (Companion volume to "Hypocritical Helena.") In addition to the title piece, it contians: Ker and Plunk; Two Dogs and Two Boys; The Egghead and the Two Cut-ups of Corinth; Deceitful Henry; The Boys and the Pipe; Cat and Mouse; and others. (Original German text with accompanying English translations.) Afterword by H. A. Klein. vi + 216pp. 5⅜ x 8½.
T181 Paperbound **$1.15**

THROUGH THE ALIMENTARY CANAL WITH GUN AND CAMERA: A FASCINATING TRIP TO THE INTERIOR, Personally Conducted by George S. Chappell. In mock-travelogue style, the amusing account of an imaginative journey down the alimentary canal. The "explorers" enter the esophagus, round the Adam's Apple, narrowly escape from a fierce Amoeba, struggle through the impenetrable Nerve Forests of the Lumbar Region, etc. Illustrated by the famous cartoonist, Otto Soglow, the book is as much a brilliant satire of academic pomposity and professional travel literature as it is a clever use of the facts of physiology for supremely comic purposes. Preface by Robert Benchley. Author's Foreword. 1 Photograph. 17 illustrations by O. Soglow. xii + 114pp. 5⅜ x 8½.
T376 Paperbound **$1.00**

THE BAD CHILD'S BOOK OF BEASTS, MORE BEASTS FOR WORSE CHILDREN, and A MORAL ALPHABET, H. Belloc. Hardly an anthology of humorous verse has appeared in the last 50 years without at least a couple of these famous nonsense verses. But one must see the entire volumes—with all the delightful original illustrations by Sir Basil Blackwood—to appreciate fully Belloc's charming and witty verses that play so subacidly on the platitudes of life and morals that beset his day—and ours. A great humor classic. Three books in one. Total of 157pp. 5⅜ x 8.
T749 Paperbound **$1.00**

THE DEVIL'S DICTIONARY, Ambrose Bierce. Sardonic and irreverent barbs puncturing the pomposities and absurdities of American politics, business, religion, literature, and arts, by the country's greatest satirist in the classic tradition. Epigrammatic as Shaw, piercing as Swift, American as Mark Twain, Will Rogers, and Fred Allen. Bierce will always remain the favorite of a small coterie of enthusiasts, and of writers and speakers whom he supplies with "some of the most gorgeous witticisms of the English language." (H. L. Mencken) Over 1000 entries in alphabetical order. 144pp. 5⅜ x 8.
T487 Paperbound **$1.00**

THE COMPLETE NONSENSE OF EDWARD LEAR. This is the only complete edition of this master of gentle madness available at a popular price. A BOOK OF NONSENSE, NONSENSE SONGS, MORE NONSENSE SONGS AND STORIES in their entirety with all the old favorites that have delighted children and adults for years. The Dong With A Luminous Nose, The Jumblies, The Owl and the Pussycat, and hundreds of other bits of wonderful nonsense. 214 limericks, 3 sets of Nonsense Botany, 5 Nonsense Alphabets. 546 drawings by Lear himself, and much more. 320pp. 5⅜ x 8.
T167 Paperbound **$1.00**

SINGULAR TRAVELS, CAMPAIGNS, AND ADVENTURES OF BARON MUNCHAUSEN, R. E. Raspe, with 90 illustrations by Gustave Doré. The first edition in over 150 years to reestablish the deeds of the Prince of Liars exactly as Raspe first recorded them in 1785—the genuine Baron Munchausen, one of the most popular personalities in English literature. Included also are the best of the many sequels, written by other hands. Introduction on Raspe by J. Carswell. Bibliography of early editions. xliv + 192pp. 5⅜ x 8.
T698 Paperbound **$1.00**

HOW TO TELL THE BIRDS FROM THE FLOWERS, R. W. Wood. How not to confuse a carrot with a parrot, a grape with an ape, a puffin with nuffin. Delightful drawings, clever puns, absurd little poems point out farfetched resemblances in nature. The author was a leading physicist. Introduction by Margaret Wood White. 106 illus. 60pp. 5⅜ x 8.
T523 Paperbound **75¢**

JOE MILLER'S JESTS OR, THE WITS VADE-MECUM. The original Joe Miller jest book. Gives a keen and pungent impression of life in 18th-century England. Many are somewhat on the bawdy side and they are still capable of provoking amusement and good fun. This volume is a facsimile of the original "Joe Miller" first published in 1739. It remains the most popular and influential humor book of all time. New introduction by Robert Hutchinson. xxi + 70pp. 5⅜ x 8½.
T423 Paperbound **$1.00**

Prices subject to change without notice.

Dover publishes books on art, music, philosophy, literature, languages, history, social sciences, psychology, handcrafts, orientalia, puzzles and entertainments, chess, pets and gardens, books explaining science, intermediate and higher mathematics, mathematical physics, engineering, biological sciences, earth sciences, classics of science, etc. Write to:

Dept. catrr.
Dover Publications, Inc.
180 Varick Street, N.Y. 14, N.Y.